ATOMIC AND NUCLEAR PHYSICS

A Blaisdell Book in the Pure and Applied Sciences

CONSULTING EDITORS

Brenton F. Stearns, *Tufts University*
Aaron Lemonick, *Princeton University*

ATOMIC AND
NUCLEAR PHYSICS

DEREK L. LIVESEY

The University of British Columbia

BLAISDELL PUBLISHING COMPANY

A Division of Ginn and Company

WALTHAM, MASSACHUSETTS· TORONTO· LONDON

To Lois

PREFACE

The study of atomic and nuclear structure forms an essential part of the training of any physicist. Current undergraduate programs in physics introduce atoms and nuclei at an early stage, but the detailed consideration of quantum-mechanical methods is usually deferred for mathematical reasons. As a result, senior undergraduates must undertake extensive study of a formidably complex subject if they are to prepare themselves for research in physics. It follows that the selection of subject matter for a senior course in atomic physics is both important and difficult.

This book attempts to present a balanced account of atoms, nuclei, and high-energy particles at a level suitable for undergraduate study. It is assumed that the student will take separate courses in thermodynamics, electromagnetic theory, and relativity, although all these topics are important at one stage or another in this course. Mathematical developments have been kept relatively simple in the early chapters, where some emphasis is laid on historical events and classic experiments. The later chapters are more systematic, but the development of experimental techniques has been stressed, notably in the chapter on nuclear physics. In the chapter on quantum mechanics the details of the solution of Schrödinger's equation in simple cases have been given and elementary work with matrices is introduced. Strong emphasis is laid on statistical methods at several places throughout the book, including an approach to the quantum theory of the solid state. In every chapter the material has been condensed by the omission of topics set as problems, which therefore form an integral part of the course.

A limited number of footnote references has been supplied to direct the student's attention to classic papers or clear expositions of specific details. At the end of each chapter a selected list of reading materials is provided so that the student can pursue major topics in greater depth. The advent of paperback editions of original papers and monographs means that all serious students have access to the main current of scientific literature: in addition there are the review journals, which should be consulted regularly.

A book of this kind cannot be written without a great deal of help, which is not easily acknowledged, from other authors in the field. I am even more conscious of the great debt I owe to my colleagues in several institutions of learning for their enlightening discussions and occasional encouragement. I am very grateful to my present and former students for their patience and help and the examination papers they have written. Finally I must thank my wife for her continued forbearance and encouragement of an author in the house.

D.L.L.

CONTENTS

ATOMIC AND NUCLEAR PHYSICS

≫-≫-≫-≫-≫-≫-≫-≫-≫-≫-≫-≫-≫-≫-≫-≫-≫-≫-≫ ≫-≫-≫-≫-≫-≫-≫-≫-≫-≫-≫-≫-≫-≫-≫

CHAPTER I

THE ATOMIC THEORY
OF MATTER

During the twentieth century the detailed study of atomic and nuclear structure has developed into a subject of immense scope and forbidding complexity. But the atomic theory of matter is over two thousand years old, having originated in the philosophy of the ancient Greeks. For centuries the idea that matter consists of indivisible atoms was a commonplace of speculative thought, but the concept became valuable only when it could be applied quantitatively—to an explanation of the gas laws (commencing in the eighteenth century) and the laws of chemical combination (in the early nineteenth century). Even in the early 1900's scientists as eminent as Mach and Ostwald could still regard the existence of atoms as a hypothesis with little experimental support. In the same period, however, a series of brilliant discoveries opened the way to atomic investigations of many kinds: the atom was established as the smallest unit of a chemical element, but it could no longer be thought of as indivisible.

This preliminary chapter is concerned with the historical aspects of atomic theory and the contributions made by chemistry and philosophy to its development. It is important to recognize that the existence of particles in the physical world raises complex problems when we try to describe their behavior mathematically. For example, relativity theory is framed in terms of point-particles, but a charged point-particle should have infinite self-energy if its electromagnetic field is taken into account. Moreover, the entire question of interaction between different particles requires elaborate treatment in the context of any field theory. Rather than dwell on the mathematical problem of interactions, we shall commence with a brief discussion of the relations between the atom and the continuum.

1.1 The Atom and the Continuum

The atomic theory of matter originated in the speculations of Leucippus and Democritus, who lived in Greece during the fifth century B.C. Nowadays we may wonder why these philosophers should have adopted so bold a theory without possessing any experimental evidence on the subject. The answer may lie in the difficult logical questions raised by the Eleatics, an earlier school of philosophers headed by Parmenides. The Eleatic thinkers became famous for their use of uncompromising logic in analyzing the nature of matter and motion, and they certainly reached some astonishing conclusions.

As an example of Parmenides' arguments we may consider his contention that all space is filled with matter, that is, a vacuum cannot occur. The statement was based on the proposition "That which does not exist does not exist." If we accept this and the additional hypothesis that no two bodies can occupy the same place, it follows that motion is impossible, or at best illusory.* This conclusion was supported by Zeno, a disciple of Parmenides, in four famous "paradoxes" concerning the concepts of time and space. Possibly the most significant paradox concerns a flying arrow. The arrow is imagined to be at rest at any given instant of time; but, if it is stationary at all possible instants, how can it ever move from place to place? Of course the validity of such a result depends on the assumptions granted—in this case, the idea of an "instant" is essential to the analysis. In their historical context, Zeno's paradoxes were powerful arguments for treating space and time as intrinsically continuous, whatever the nature of matter may be.

The work of the Eleatics caused a crisis in Greek thought and out of this crisis new theories of matter arose. Leucippus and Democritus daringly postulated the existence of a vacuum separating the indivisible atoms of matter. In this way they were able to account for the compression and rarefaction of gases, also to explain the properties of different substances as being due to different atomic species. Democritus clearly enunciated the principle of conservation of matter, based on the indestructibility of atoms. Later the ideas of the atomists were revived by Epicurus and they found remarkable expression in Lucretius' poem *De Rerum Natura*, which includes a sustained panegyric on the beauties of atomic theory.

However, several philosophers, including the great Aristotle, argued in favor of a continuous theory of matter, partly on the grounds that atoms separated by a vacuum cannot conceivably interact except at contact. In the third century B.C. the Stoic philosophers observed waves spreading on the surface of water and supposed that sound travels in a similar way through air. By considering the propagation of waves in a medium, they were led to postulate the existence of a rarefied continuum, later called "the aether," pervading all space and linking material bodies together in some way. Ideas based on the properties of a continuum were not easily reconciled with the tenets of atomic theory.

This kind of difficulty persists in modern physics, where we have, on the one hand, field theories of phenomena (such as Maxwell's electromagnetic theory) and, on the other, clear evidence of particles interacting with each other. Despite the many successes of quantum mechanics and of quantum electrodynamics, the interactions of a particle with a field and, via the field, with other particles are not described satisfactorily in mathematical terms. The philosophical problems raised by Zeno still require consideration, although the purely mathematical difficulties of the paradoxes have been resolved. Whitehead† has argued that, in our range of experience, all actual events are atomic or discrete in nature, but potential occurrences must be described in terms of continuity. Thus a particle is regarded in quantum mechanics as potentially occurring anywhere in the universe, yet its existence is recognized experimentally only by discrete events located in space-time. Some kind of reconciliation between the two types of theory is necessary for any understanding of present-day physics; needless to say, the last paper on the subject has not been written.

---

* According to some authorities, Parmenides refused to recognize "motion" in the absolute sense of the word, but allowed the possibility of rotational motion and of relative motion between material objects.
† A. N. Whitehead, *Process and Reality* (Harper Torchbooks, Harper & Row, New York, 1960), Part II, Chap. II.

1.2 The Chemical Elements

The concept of atoms was familiar to Boyle, who laid the foundations of modern chemistry in the seventeenth century, and it may have assisted him in his attempts to classify all substances into elements, compounds, and mixtures. However, the full importance of the atomic theory in chemistry was not realized until Dalton used it to expound the laws of chemical combination in 1803. Since the chemical elements react with each other in fixed proportions by weight, it appears that atoms of the different elements are combining to form "compound atoms" or *molecules*. The success of this idea led to the introduction of chemical formulae for the simpler compounds, each formula indicating the atoms present in a single molecule of the compound.

An important development in nineteenth-century chemistry was the use of the *valence number*, which is, ideally, the number of hydrogen atoms combining with one atom of the element considered. Elements like carbon and oxygen form, with hydrogen, many compounds in which carbon has a valence of 4 and oxygen a valence of 2. Through the introduction of single, double, and triple bonds of the "covalent" type, the greater part of organic chemistry can be brought into one scheme. Again, there is great value in the theory of "electrovalence," according to which inorganic salts, such as sodium chloride (NaCl), consist of charged ions of fixed character (like Na^+ and Cl^-). At the same time, there are many elements like nitrogen and sulfur which do not form ions and which exhibit variable valence; thus a single valence is not appropriate for many atoms. It is clearly important that atomic theory should be able to account for these differences in the chemical behavior of the elements.

Amid the confusion of chemical ideas which prevailed in the middle years of the nineteenth century, a major development was Mendeleev's periodic classification of the elements in 1869. Based on the atomic weights known at that time, Mendeleev's table grouped similar elements with similar valence properties in vertical columns, numbered from I to VIII (Figure 1.1). The chemical resemblances of the first two rows or "octaves" (lithium to fluorine and sodium to chlorine) had been recognized for some time. Mendeleev's highly original contribution lay in his acceptance of gaps in the list of elements and in his predictions of the properties of the missing elements. Although the scheme was received at first with scepticism, its essential correctness was demonstrated eventually by the discovery of the inert gases (helium, neon, argon, krypton, and xenon), which provided a completely new column in the table.

In its modern form (Appendix II) the periodic table is based on the *atomic numbers* (Z) of the elements, where Z is the number of electrons accommodated outside the nucleus of an atom. The rather strained analogies which Mendeleev and his successors introduced to justify the occurrence of metals beneath nonmetals (in column IV and to the right of it in Figure 1.1) are eliminated by inserting three series of *transition metals*. Another insertion is the group of 14 *rare earths* or "lanthanides," which resemble each other very closely. The final row of elements, starting with the radioactive element francium, is still far from complete, although the group of 14 "actinides" has been filled with new elements produced artificially by nuclear transmutation.

Obviously the periodic classification of the elements is a rich source of material for any detailed theory of atomic structure: it shows immediately that the electrons in an atom

GROUP	I	II	III	IV	V	VI	VII	VIII		
Series										
1	H 1									
2	Li 7	Be 9.4	B 11	C 12	N 14	O 16	Fl 19			
3	Na 23	Mg 24	Al 27.3	Si 28	P 31	S 32	Cl 35.5			
4	K 39	Ca 40	( )	Ti 48	V 51	Cr 52	Mn 55	Fe 56	Co 59	Ni 59
5	Cu 63	Zn 65	( )	( )	As 75	Se 78	Br 80			
6	Rb 85	Sr 87	Y 88	Zr 90	Nb 94	Mo 96	( )	Ru 103	Rh 104	Pd 106
7	Ag 108	Cd 112	In 113	Sn 118	Sb 122	Te 125	I 127			
8	Cs 135	Ba 137	(Rare Earths. . .)							
9		. . .	. . .		Ta 182	W 184	( )	Os 195	Ir 197	Pt 198
10	Au 199	Hg 200	Tl 204	Pb 207	Bi 208	. . .				

FIGURE 1.1.   *Periodic table of the chemical elements arranged by Mendeleev on the basis of atomic weights. Many elements were subsequently found to fill the gaps (compare the modern form of the table in Appendix II).*

possess some kind of *shell structure*, reflected in the completed rows of 2, 8, 8, 18, 18, and 32 elements. The chemical behavior of an atom is largely determined by the number of electrons in its outer shell, the "valence electrons." Frequently the effects of incomplete inner shells are physically important, especially in the first series of transition elements, which include the ferromagnetic metals—iron, cobalt, and nickel. Metals, occurring in the transition series and in the left-hand columns of the periodic table, form an important class of solids with the special properties of high electrical and thermal conductivity. Electronic shell structure in the atom is nowhere more significant than in its bearing on the properties of metals in the solid state.

1.3   The Development of Atomic Physics

In succeeding chapters the evolution of ideas about atomic and nuclear structure is described in a broadly historical framework, with frequent reference to statistical mechanics, which deals with the equilibrium properties of assemblies containing large numbers of particles. The failure of classical statistics to account for the thermal properties of gases and solids first illustrated the need for new principles in treating atomic systems. Moreover, the classical theory could not explain the properties of blackbody radiation, and this failure led to the introduction of the quantum concept by Planck in 1900. Planck based his successful theory of radiation on the assumption that radiant energy is *quantized* in amounts of magnitude

$$E = h\nu, \qquad [1.1]$$

where E is the energy absorbed or emitted by an atom,

ν is the frequency of the radiation,

h is Planck's constant.

Although the quantum hypothesis was first introduced in a statistical context, it explained other phenomena where atoms interact with radiation, such as the photoelectric effect and the emission of characteristic spectral lines by chemical elements. In 1911 Rutherford developed a nuclear model for the atom and Bohr combined this model with the quantum rules to formulate the first successful theory of the hydrogen atom in 1913. However, it was soon found that Bohr's semiclassical methods could not account for the detailed structure of complex atoms and it became necessary to reexamine the entire basis of mechanics as applied to microscopic systems. Experiments showed that a beam of electrons or atoms displays distinct wavelike properties; while electromagnetic radiation, formerly regarded as a wave phenomenon, can behave like a stream of particlelike *photons*, each with definite energy and momentum. It is therefore no longer possible to make clear distinctions between matter and radiation, both being described by the relativistic mechanics of Einstein and both being essentially forms of energy.

The new quantum mechanics was first developed by Heisenberg, Born, and Schrödinger, and it was highly successful when applied to atomic problems, where interactions between the particles are not too strong. However, this condition does not obtain for nuclear particles, which act on each other with powerful short-range forces, the details of which are not yet clear. For this reason the study of complex nuclei requires the use of models which are based on the general behavior of nuclear forces rather than on their precise form. When experiments on particle interactions are extended into the high-energy region, numerous unstable particles (the "mesons" and "hyperons") appear and their relations with each other and with nuclear particles are extremely complicated. Evidently these particles play important roles in nuclear interactions but the mathematical difficulties of dealing with strong interactions are so formidable that no complete theory has yet been formulated. Instead, attention has been directed to formal properties, such as the conservation rules obeyed by particles in their various transformations and reactions; this approach has been successful in establishing limits within which the basic conservation rules apply and to this extent many aspects of particle behavior can be understood.

Although much of this book is concerned with theories and the mathematical expression of theoretical ideas, several crucial experiments are described and the vital importance of experiments in the evolution of the subject must be stressed. In practice neither the experimental physicists nor the theorists enjoy a monopoly in the means of making progress. Very often a new experimental technique has removed previous difficulties at a stroke or has opened up entirely new lines of investigation. On the other hand, there have been periods when quantities of accurate experimental data existed before the theory was able to correlate the evidence. Ideally there should always be close communication between experimenters and theorists working in the same field, and even in fields which do not appear to be related; cooperation can be effective only if each group is fully aware of the methods and limitations of other research groups. It is hoped that the theoretical developments described here will serve to clarify the physical principles involved and that these principles are not obscured by the wealth of data available in the fields of atomic and nuclear physics.

FOR FURTHER READING

Greek philosophy:
    W. K. C. GUTHRIE, *The Greek Philosophers, from Thales to Aristotle* (Harper Torchbooks, Harper & Row, New York, 1960).
Greek science:
    S. SAMBURSKY, *The Physical World of the Greeks*, translator, M. Dagut (Collier Books, New York, 1962).
Atoms in verse (translated into prose):
    LUCRETIUS, *The Nature of the Universe*, translator, R. E. Latham (Penguin Books, Baltimore, 1951).
History of science:
    H. T. PLEDGE, *Science since 1500* (Harper Torchbooks, Harper & Row, New York, 1959).
Chemistry:
    L. PAULING, *General Chemistry* (Freeman & Co., San Francisco, 1958) 2nd ed.

CHAPTER II

꙾ꙌꙌꙌꙌꙌꙌꙌꙌꙌꙌꙌꙌꙌꙌꙌꙌꙌꙌꙌꙌꙌꙌꙌꙌꙌꙌ

THE KINETIC THEORY

The atomic theory of matter was proposed by Dalton as a basis for quantitative chemistry, but it also became important in physics as part of the theory of heat. In 1798 Rumford claimed that any amount of heat can be obtained if enough mechanical work is done. However, it was not until 1842 that Mayer stated clearly the first law of thermodynamics, which was amplified later by Helmholtz to form the basic physical principle of conservation of energy. In 1850 Clausius formulated the second law of thermodynamics, which was used by Kelvin to define an absolute thermodynamic scale of temperature with an origin (written $0°K$) at the absolute zero.

During the same period the kinetic theory of gases, which had been outlined by Daniel Bernoulli in 1738, was revived by Waterston, Maxwell, and others. Maxwell's success in deriving many of the thermal properties of matter from kinetic theory made it evident that the detailed relations between this theory and thermodynamics required clarification. In particular, the behavior of assemblies of molecules in large numbers needed elaborate statistical treatment. Boltzmann spent many years of research on the basic problems of statistical mechanics, which received full expression in the work of Gibbs (1901) and Einstein (1902). In this way the theoretical treatment of matter in bulk was placed on a foundation which is essentially the same as that used at present, although the modern theory is based on the quantum mechanics of atomic systems.

Another aspect of kinetic theory requiring investigation was the problem of determining the numbers and sizes of molecules from the known properties of gases, liquids, and solids. In 1865 Loschmidt obtained estimates of molecular diameters from measurements of liquid density and gaseous viscosity, a method which is now of historical interest only. In the early years of the twentieth century, measurements of Avogadro's number (the number of molecules in one *mole* or gram-molecular weight of any substance) were carried out by Perrin, who studied the Brownian motion and sedimentation of colloidal particles in a liquid. Perrin's results agreed sufficiently well with more accurate figures based on electrical research to provide quantitative accord between molecular physics, based on the kinetic theory, and the detailed theories of atomic structure developed later.

A recurring problem concerns the nature of intermolecular interactions. Polar molecules exert electrostatic forces on each other and even neutral molecules attract each other by virtue of the *Van der Waals forces*, which are electrical in origin. However in phenomenological treatments of molecular interaction, it is necessary to superimpose on the attractive forces a short-range repulsive force, which is not precisely explained but is invoked to maintain molecular identity.

7

2.1 The Ideal Gas

(*a*) *Basic relations*

The kinetic theory of gases is based on the supposition that the pressure (*P*) exerted by an ideal gas on the walls of an enclosure (of volume *V*) is due to elastic collisions of the molecules with the walls, the mean molecular speed (*v*) depending only on the temperature (*T*) for a given gas. A straightforward calculation of the pressure yields the expression

$$PV = \frac{Nmv^2}{3},$$

[2.1.1]

where *N* is the number of molecules present, and *m* is the mass of each molecule. Alternatively, we may introduce the gas density (ρ)

$$\rho = \frac{Nm}{V}$$

and obtain

$$P = \frac{\rho v^2}{3}.$$

[2.1.2]

This relation enables us to calculate mean molecular velocities for gases of known pressure and density and the results usually lie in the region of 10^2 to 10^3 m/sec.

In order to relate these theoretical results to experimental data on actual gases, it is necessary to define an appropriate scale of temperature (*T*). In practice the absolute gas scale is specified in such a way that the product *PV* is proportional to *T* (in degrees Kelvin) and the scale is realized by the use of gas thermometers under carefully prescribed conditions. Then for 1 *kmole* (the molecular weight in kilograms) of any gas under ideal conditions we write

$$PV = \frac{N^*mv^2}{3} = RT,$$

[2.1.3]

where N^* is the number of molecules per kilomole and *R* is the ideal gas constant. According to present estimates, based on the C^{12} scale of atomic weights, N^* and *R* take the values

$$N^* = 6.023 \times 10^{26},$$

$$R = 8.314 \times 10^3 \text{ J/kmole } ^\circ\text{K}.$$

This means that the average kinetic energy per molecule is

$$\tfrac{1}{2}mv^2 = \frac{3RT}{2N^*} = \frac{3kT}{2},$$

[2.1.4]

where $k = \dfrac{R}{N^*} = 1.381 \times 10^{-23}$ J/molecule $^\circ$K and is known as Boltzmann's constant.

(*b*) *Experimental observations*

Although the above relations are well established in classical physics, it is necessary to examine certain experimental data before full reliance can be placed on the kinetic theory of gases. One outstanding piece of evidence was the discovery of Brown in 1827 that submicroscopic particles suspended in a fluid exhibit continual agitation. This *Brownian motion*

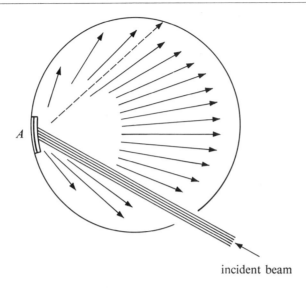

incident beam

FIGURE 2.1 *Knudsen's experiment on molecular collisions with the wall of an enclosure; the incident beam strikes the wall at A and the dotted line shows the expected direction of rebound if the collisions are elastic. In fact molecules reach all parts of the enclosure.*

is due to statistical fluctuations in molecular impacts on the observed particles, which are, of course, much more massive than the molecules themselves. The study of these fluctuations led eventually to estimates of the number N^*, based on the work of Einstein and Smoluchowski (1905). Such results are necessarily approximate, but they agree well enough with other determinations of N^* to corroborate the kinetic explanation of Brownian motion.

In the simple theory it is assumed that molecular collisions with the walls of the enclosure are perfectly elastic. It is clear that if the collisions were to some extent inelastic the pressure exerted would be less than that expressed by Equation (2.1.1). On the other hand, it is necessary that the average kinetic energy of molecules leaving the walls should be equal to the average energy of the molecules arriving, otherwise there could not be thermal equilibrium between the gas and its enclosure.

In 1915 Knudsen reported the results of an experiment designed to test the assumption that molecules make truly elastic collisions with solid surfaces. A beam of molecules was directed against a limited area A of a spherical enclosure (Figure 2.1). The part A was kept at room temperature while the rest of the enclosure was cooled in liquid air. The gas pressure was so low that molecules were expected to strike A directly and any rebounding from A would travel to the walls, where they should be condensed immediately. It was found that the condensed material did not appear in a limited area, as would be expected if the molecules rebounded elastically at A, but was distributed all over the inner surface. The result indicated that gas molecules spend some little time in contact with the wall before they leave and that the direction of departure is not related to the direction of arrival.

Knudsen's results throw some light on the action of a simple device known as Crookes' radiometer (Figure 2.2). Four equal vanes are held in the form of a cross which is balanced delicately on a pivot and the vanes are enclosed in a glass bulb which contains residual gas at a fairly low pressure [about 10^{-7} atmosphere (atm)]. When visible light or infrared radiation falls on the bulb, the vanes revolve rapidly with the shiny surfaces leading. Any

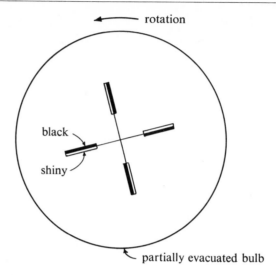

rotation

black

shiny

partially evacuated bulb

FIGURE 2.2   *Crookes' radiometer (in section). Under the influence of radiant energy the vanes rotate with the shiny surfaces leading, this effect being due to residual gas in the bulb.*

explanation of the radiometer's action must take into account the residual gas in the bulb, because the device does not work if an extremely low pressure is maintained. It is necessary to suppose that the black surfaces reach a higher mean temperature than the shiny surfaces when light is incident, while the gas remains at a fairly constant temperature. Collisions of the gas molecules with the vanes are not instantaneous but allow the molecules to reach the local surface temperature. As a result, molecules leave the black surfaces with a higher mean velocity than those leaving the shiny surfaces; thus more backward impulse is given to the black surfaces and the vanes rotate with the shiny surfaces leading.

(c) Calculation of gas pressure

We see from the foregoing discussion of the radiometer that thermal equilibrium between the gas and the enclosure is essential before we can calculate the pressure exerted by molecular collisions. Provided that equilibrium exists, the mean kinetic energy of molecules leaving the walls is the same as that of molecules arriving and the net momentum transfer is the same for both classes of molecules if the directions of arrival and departure are randomly distributed. The impulse due to an arriving molecule depends on its velocity before collision, so a complete calculation must take into account both the speed and angular distributions of the molecules.

The exact distribution of molecular speeds does not finally affect the calculation of gas pressure, but we shall use a probability function $f(v)\,dv$ in defining the appropriate mean speeds. Since $f(v)\,dv$ represents the probability of a molecule having speed between v and $(v + dv)$ and the total integrated probability must be unity, we can "normalize" the function $f(v)$ by imposing the condition

$$\int_0^\infty f(v)\,dv = 1. \qquad [2.1.5]$$

The mean speed $\bar{v}$ is then defined by the expression

$$\bar{v} = \int_0^\infty v f(v)\,dv. \qquad [2.1.6]$$

The mean square speed is found similarly

$$\overline{v^2} = \int_0^\infty v^2 f(v)\, dv. \qquad [2.1.7]$$

In the Maxwellian distribution (Figure 2.5) the curve is not symmetrical about the peak which defines the most probable speed (v_0), so that the mean speed $\bar{v}$ is slightly higher than v_0 and the root-mean-square value is higher than both v_0 and $\bar{v}$.

We now consider the class of molecules arriving at a small area ΔA with velocity $\mathbf{v}$ at angle θ to the normal (Figure 2.3) and we shall assume that the molecules are point-masses so that no intermolecular collisions can occur. The number of collisions per second in this class is equal to the number of molecules in a prism of slant height v on base ΔA, that is,

$$nv \cos \theta\, \Delta A,$$

where n is the number of molecules per unit volume. The probability of molecules arriving at angles between θ and $(\theta + d\theta)$ is a function of θ since we have to take solid-angle effects into account. The effective solid angle ($d\Omega$) of collection between cones of semiangle θ and $(\theta + d\theta)$ is defined as the area cut off on a sphere centered at the common apex divided by the square of the sphere's radius. Referring to Figure 2.3, we see that the area cut off between the cones is

$$2\pi r \sin \theta\, r\, d\theta,$$

and we find

$$d\Omega = 2\pi \sin \theta\, d\theta \text{ steradians (sr).} \qquad [2.1.8]$$

The total solid angle surrounding any point is 4π sr so that the fraction represented by $d\Omega$ is

$$\frac{d\Omega}{4\pi} = \tfrac{1}{2} \sin \theta\, d\theta, \qquad [2.1.9]$$

and this is the probability that the molecular direction lies within the angular limits specified, provided that the motions are completely random.

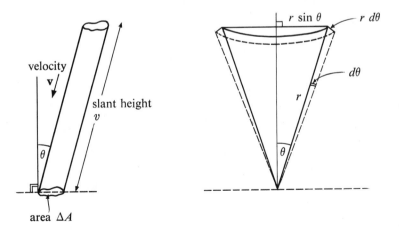

FIGURE 2.3 *Collisions of gas molecules with the wall of an enclosure; on the left the number of molecules with velocity* **v** *arriving at angle θ is estimated; on the right the effective solid angle between cones of semiangle θ and $(\theta + d\theta)$ is found.*

The expression obtained by combining all the foregoing expressions, that is,

$$nv \cos \theta \, \Delta A \, f(v) \, dv \, \tfrac{1}{2} \sin \theta \, d\theta, \qquad\qquad [2.1.10]$$

represents the number of molecules with speeds between v and $(v + dv)$ arriving at ΔA in one second, within the angular range θ to $(\theta + d\theta)$. To find the number of molecules striking ΔA per second we immediately integrate over all speeds and over the angular range from $\theta = 0$ to $\theta = \dfrac{\pi}{2}$ radians (rad),

$$\tfrac{1}{2} n \, \Delta A \int_0^\infty v f(v) \, dv \int_0^{\pi/2} \cos \theta \sin \theta \, d\theta = \tfrac{1}{4} n \bar{v} \, \Delta A. \qquad\qquad [2.1.11]$$

The momentum transferred to the wall by arriving molecules can be resolved into normal and tangential components and of these the tangential components cancel out when a large number of molecules is considered. The normal momentum transfer at a single collision is

$$mv \cos \theta,$$

so the total normal force (ΔF) on area ΔA becomes

$$\Delta F = \tfrac{1}{2} nm \, \Delta A \int_0^\infty v^2 f(v) \, dv \int_0^{\pi/2} \cos^2 \theta \sin \theta \, d\theta$$

$$= \frac{nm\overline{v^2} \, \Delta A}{6} \qquad\qquad [2.1.12]$$

and the pressure is

$$\frac{\Delta F}{\Delta A} = \frac{nm\overline{v^2}}{6}.$$

In accordance with our assumption of thermal equilibrium between the wall and the gas, we must add an equal force for the molecules leaving the wall. The total pressure is therefore

$$P = \frac{nm\overline{v^2}}{3} = \frac{\rho \overline{v^2}}{3}. \qquad\qquad [2.1.13]$$

The final result is the same as that obtained in the simple theory but we now have a more thorough analysis of molecular collisions with the walls of an enclosure. The theory is still idealized to the extent that no allowance has been made for intermolecular forces or the finite size of the molecules. It is well known that corrections can be applied to the ideal gas equation to account for deviations from ideal behavior, for example, in Van der Waals' equation. However, no completely satisfactory equation of state has been developed in closed form and modern investigations are based on an equation embodying infinite series,

$$PV = RT(1 + C_1 V^{-1} + C_2 V^{-2} + \cdots), \qquad\qquad [2.1.14]$$

where the "virial coefficients" C_1, C_2, and so forth are functions of T. The behavior of these coefficients depends on the details of interaction forces between pairs of molecules in the gas. In this connection, it should be mentioned that molecules can be treated simply as centers of force acting on each other, an idea which goes back to Michell and Boscovich in the eighteenth century. By suitable combination of a short-range attractive force and a stronger repulsion at very short distances, it is possible to account satisfactorily for the general behavior of virial coefficients, at least in the monatomic gases.*

* T. Kihara, Rev. Mod. Phys., **25**, 831 (1953).

2.2 The Classical Boltzmann Statistics

The theoretical expression $f(v)$ for the distribution of molecular speeds in a gas was first obtained by Maxwell and it can be derived in several ways. The most powerful method is that of statistical mechanics, in which we find the most probable energy distribution for a large number N of molecules in random motion. The motion is subject to two conservation conditions. The total internal energy E is supposed to be constant, so if we divide the molecules into a large number of energy groups, with N_1 molecules having energy ε_1, N_2 with energy $\varepsilon_2, \ldots, N_i$ with energy ε_i, we can write

$$\sum_i N_i \varepsilon_i = E.$$

Also the total number of molecules is constant

$$\sum_i N_i = N.$$

The classical expression for the most probable number of molecules with energy ε_i is then

$$\bar{N}_i \propto \exp\left(-\frac{\varepsilon_i}{kT}\right), \qquad [2.2.1]$$

where $k = $ Boltzmann's constant.

Thus the probability of a molecule having energy ε_i decreases exponentially with ε_i; but the relative probability of having a high energy increases as the temperature rises.

(a) *Derivation of Boltzmann's energy distribution*

A great deal of analysis is required before a satisfactory basis for the statistical theory can be recognized. The following outline may serve to illustrate the type of argument employed in deriving Boltzmann's relation. According to the second law of thermodynamics a system tends to reach a condition of maximum entropy and this condition represents the state of equilibrium. In statistical mechanics the entropy S is defined in terms of the number of *complexions* (C) of the assembly, where C is the total number of ways in which a given configuration can be set up. The fundamental relation between S and C is

$$S = k \ln C, \qquad [2.2.2]$$

where k is Boltzmann's constant and natural logarithms are employed throughout the analysis.

To find C we divide the N molecules into energy groups, although, strictly speaking, the energies vary continuously in classical physics and to that extent the treatment is more suitable for quantum systems which have well-defined energy states. If we assign equal statistical weights to all the groups, the number of ways of arranging the N molecules is

$$C = \frac{N!}{N_1! \, N_2! \ldots N_i! \ldots}. \qquad [2.2.3]$$

Hence,

$$S/k = \ln C = \ln N! - \sum_i \ln N_i!$$

The numbers N_i are supposed to be so large that to a sufficient degree of accuracy we can use Stirling's theorem in the approximate form

$$\ln N! = N \ln N - N$$

and find

$$S/k = N \ln N - N - \sum_i (N_i \ln N_i - N_i)$$

$$= N \ln N - \sum_i N_i \ln N_i. \qquad [2.2.4]$$

Thermal equilibrium is fixed by finding the state of maximum entropy consistent with the conditions of conservation. We employ the method of Lagrange and write a new function

$$S'/k = S/k - \alpha \sum_i N_i - \beta \sum_i N_i \varepsilon_i,$$

where α, β are undetermined factors.* If, now, we regard the N_i as continuous variables and impose the condition

$$\frac{\partial}{\partial N_i}\left(\frac{S'}{k}\right) = 0 \qquad \text{when} \quad N_i = \bar{N}_i, \qquad [2.2.5]$$

we shall be able to maximize the value of S while ensuring the constancy of N and E. The condition of thermal equilibrium then becomes

$$0 = \frac{\partial}{\partial N_i}\left[\sum_i N_i \ln \sum_i N_i - \sum_i N_i \ln N_i - \alpha \sum_i N_i - \beta \sum_i N_i \varepsilon_i\right] \qquad \text{when} \quad N_i = \bar{N}_i,$$

$$0 = \ln N + 1 - \ln \bar{N}_i - 1 - \alpha - \beta \varepsilon_i,$$

or

$$\bar{N}_i = N \exp\left(-\alpha - \beta \varepsilon_i\right). \qquad [2.2.6]$$

The parameters α and β perform different roles in the theory. Since we have

$$\sum_i \bar{N}_i = N,$$

$$\exp\left(-\alpha\right) \sum_i \exp\left(-\beta \varepsilon_i\right) = 1,$$

or

$$\exp\left(\alpha\right) = \sum_i \exp\left(-\beta \varepsilon_i\right).$$

This sum is called the *partition function* of the assembly and will be written $\sum$. If there are two or more gases mixed together, it is found that the α factors are different for the different components of the mixture but that the β factors are identical. It follows that β can perform the role of temperature, which is necessarily constant throughout a mixed assembly in thermal equilibrium. For each type of molecule in the mixture α is related to the Helmholtz free-energy function.

The relation between β and the temperature T defined in thermodynamics can be deduced as follows. The first law of thermodynamics may be written

$$dE = T\, dS - P\, dV.$$

In an assembly at constant volume the absolute temperature is therefore

$$T = \left(\frac{\partial E}{\partial S}\right)_V.$$

* See, for example, T. M. Apostol, *Calculus* (Blaisdell Publishing Co., New York, 1692) Vol. II, p. 206.

The total internal energy E can be expressed as the series

$$E = \sum_i \bar{N}_i \varepsilon_i$$

$$= N \exp(-\alpha) \sum_i \varepsilon_i \exp(-\beta \varepsilon_i), \qquad [2.2.7]$$

and the entropy divided by Boltzmann's constant is

$$S/k = N \ln N - \sum_i \bar{N}_i \ln \bar{N}_i$$

$$= N \ln N - N \exp(-\alpha) \sum_i \exp(-\beta \varepsilon_i)[\ln N - \alpha - \beta \varepsilon_i]$$

$$= N \ln N - N \ln N + N\alpha + \beta \sum_i \bar{N}_i \varepsilon_i$$

$$= N\alpha + E\beta. \qquad [2.2.8]$$

Hence

$$E = \frac{S}{k\beta} - \frac{N\alpha}{\beta}$$

and

$$T = \frac{\partial E}{\partial S} = \frac{1}{k\beta},$$

or

$$\beta = 1/kT. \qquad [2.2.9]$$

The Boltzmann energy distribution therefore becomes

$$\bar{N}_i = N \exp\left(-\alpha - \frac{\varepsilon_i}{kT}\right)$$

$$= \frac{N}{\Sigma} \exp\left(-\frac{\varepsilon_i}{kT}\right). \qquad [2.2.10]$$

(b) Applications of Boltzmann's result

A very simple example of the Boltzmann distribution is afforded by molecules in a gas at constant temperature in a uniform gravitational field, that is, the density distribution in an atmosphere when g and T are constant. The change in hydrostatic pressure due to a thin horizontal layer (dH) of gas with density ρ is

$$-dP = g\rho \, dH$$

(the minus sign being introduced to ensure that P decreases with increasing height H). The ideal gas relation for 1 kilomole gives

$$P = \frac{RT}{V} = \frac{RT\rho}{M},$$

where

$$M = N*m = \text{molecular weight in kg}$$

and

$$R = N*k = \text{the ideal gas constant.}$$

In terms of the density ρ the equation becomes

$$-d\rho = \frac{mg\rho\, dH}{kT}$$

with the solution

$$\rho = \rho_0 \exp\left(-\frac{mgH}{kT}\right), \qquad [2.2.11]$$

if ρ_0 is the density at the reference layer $H = 0$. Now mgH represents the potential energy of a molecule of mass m at height H above the reference layer, so we have obtained a Boltzmann type of distribution in which ε is identified as the potential energy per molecule.

A practical example of the use of Boltzmann's relation is the classic determination of k, and hence of N^*, by Perrin, who employed a suspension of colloidal particles in a liquid. These comparatively massive particles are kept in suspension by the Brownian motion and their distribution in height follows the exponential law of Equation (2.2.11), provided that they are of uniform mass. Gamboge particles of different sizes were sorted out by prolonged centrifuging to produce a group of fairly uniform mass (m). After settling in a liquid for some time to reach "sedimentation equilibrium" they were observed through a microscope. The numbers of particles counted in a layer of fixed thickness varied with height H in the expected manner and the constant factor (mg'/kT) was extracted (g' being the effective value of g when buoyancy of the liquid has been allowed for). Difficulties were encountered in estimating the mass m with sufficient accuracy, but after several years of work Perrin was able to publish a value for k in 1912. The corresponding N^* (6.8×10^{26}) differs by more than 10% from the accepted value, but Perrin's experiments provided an essential link between kinetic theory and other investigations in atomic physics.

2.3 The Maxwellian Distribution of Molecular Speeds

The mean square speed of molecules in a gas may be calculated directly from its pressure and density, with the aid of Equation (2.1.13). If, however, the mean speed ($\bar{v}$) or the most probable speed is required, it is necessary to know the exact form of the molecular speed distribution, first worked out by Maxwell. The Maxwellian distribution is useful as an introduction to the classical theorem of equipartition of energy, outlined in Section 2.4. It is also important in experiments on molecular beams, where a stream of molecules escapes from a hot oven into an evacuated space and the fraction of molecules in a given speed range must be known. Another application is to the evaporation of molecules from a liquid surface, and, by analogy, to the "evaporation" of nuclear particles from a highly excited nucleus.

In deriving the Maxwellian velocity distribution from the results of Boltzmann's statistical analysis, we are concerned chiefly with the kinetic energies of the gas molecules. Ignoring any other types of energy which the molecules may possess, we may write the energy of one molecule in the form

$$\varepsilon = \tfrac{1}{2}mv^2 = \tfrac{1}{2}m(v_x^2 + v_y^2 + v_z^2), \qquad [2.3.1]$$

where v_x, v_y, v_z are the components of the velocity $\mathbf{v}$ parallel to Cartesian axes Ox, Oy, Oz.

All the velocity variables in Equation (2.3.1) are essentially continuous, whereas our statistical analysis was based on discrete energy groupings denoted by $\varepsilon_1, \varepsilon_2, \ldots, \varepsilon_i$. We therefore have to find out how to apply the results of the simplified Boltzmann treatment to

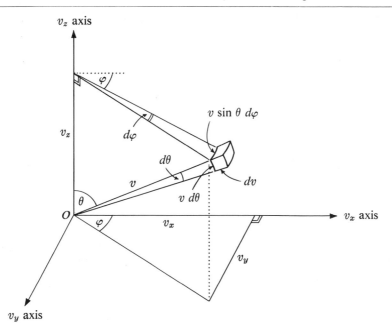

FIGURE 2.4   *Coordinates in "velocity space": the velocity of a particle can be represented by a point with Cartesian coordinates* (v_x, v_y, v_z). *In this space an element of "volume" can be denoted by* $v^2 \sin \theta \, dv \, d\theta \, d\varphi$ *in spherical polar coordinates* (v, θ, φ).

the problem of continuous variables in three dimensions (unlike the atmosphere problem, which was confined to one dimension). The question is whether we can assign equal statistical weights to any particular configuration of the velocity variables. It turns out that the Boltzmann results can be taken over directly into the velocity representation provided that we assign equal statistical weight to equal volumes of "velocity space." This "space" is obtained by representing the components (v_x, v_y, v_z) as variables on conventional Cartesian axes (Figure 2.4) so that v (the speed) is equivalent to the "distance" in velocity space from the origin O to the point (v_x, v_y, v_z) because

$$v^2 = v_x^2 + v_y^2 + v_z^2.$$

In this representation an element of "volume" is $dv_x \, dv_y \, dv_z$ in Cartesian terms and the Boltzmann relation leads directly to the triple velocity distribution

$$f(v_x, v_y, v_z) \, dv_x \, dv_y \, dv_z \propto \exp\left(-\frac{\varepsilon}{kT}\right) dv_x \, dv_y \, dv_z,$$

which is the product of three independent distributions

$$\exp\left(\frac{-mv_x^2}{2kT}\right) dv_x \exp\left(\frac{-mv_y^2}{2kT}\right) dv_y \exp\left(\frac{-mv_z^2}{2kT}\right) dv_z. \qquad [2.3.2]$$

The result implies that the most probable value of v_x or v_y or v_z taken independently is zero, but this happens because a molecule can have a high speed (v) with almost no velocity component parallel to, say, the direction Ox.

   In the derivation of the Maxwellian function $f(v) \, dv$ from the triple distribution $f(v_x, v_y, v_z)$ of Equation (2.3.2), the Cartesian coordinates (v_x, v_y, v_z) are transformed into spherical polar coordinates (v, θ, φ). The element of "volume" $(dv_x \, dv_y \, dv_z)$ becomes

$$v^2 \sin \theta \, dv \, d\theta \, d\varphi,$$

as may be seen from Figure 2.4. The exponential Boltzmann factor is expressed once again in terms of v and we have

$$f(v) \, dv \, d\theta \, d\varphi \propto \exp \left(\frac{-mv^2}{2kT} \right) v^2 \sin \theta \, dv \, d\theta \, d\varphi,$$

where the occurrence of the $\sin \theta$ term indicates a completely random distribution of direction, as in Equation (2.1.9). We can integrate over all angles and finally obtain the Maxwellian function

$$f(v) \, dv \propto v^2 \exp \left(\frac{-mv^2}{2kT} \right) dv. \qquad [2.3.3]$$

This function is plotted against v in Figure 2.5 for arbitrary values of the parameters; it is seen to rise from the origin sharply to a peak and then to fall almost equally sharply.

The theoretical result can be checked against the fundamental energy relations of kinetic theory by calculating the mean kinetic energy per molecule,

$$\tfrac{1}{2}m\overline{v^2} = \tfrac{1}{2}m \int_0^\infty v^2 f(v) \, dv.$$

So far we have not employed any constant in the speed distribution $f(v)$. If we introduce a constant C in Equation (2.3.3)

$$f(v) \, dv = Cv^2 \exp \left(-\frac{mv^2}{2kT} \right) dv,$$

we can evaluate C with the aid of the normalization condition [Equation (2.1.5)]

$$\int_0^\infty f(v) \, dv = C \int_0^\infty v^2 \exp \left(-\frac{mv^2}{2kT} \right) dv = 1.$$

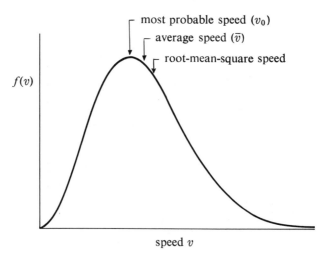

FIGURE 2.5   *The Maxwellian distribution of molecular speeds (v) in a gas at arbitrary temperature; for air at STP the most probable speed is about 400 m/sec.*

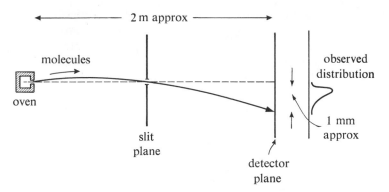

FIGURE 2.6   *The apparatus of Estermann and Stern for measuring molecular velocities by deflection in the Earth's gravity field; the molecules emerge from a hot oven in a vacuum system and form a beam defined by slits.*

The mean kinetic energy per molecule then becomes

$$\frac{\frac{1}{2}m \int_0^\infty v^2 v^2 \exp\left(-mv^2/2kT\right) dv}{\int_0^\infty v^2 \exp\left(-mv^2/2kT\right) dv}.$$

Integrals of this type can be determined from the standard definite integral

$$\int_0^\infty \exp\left(-\xi x^2\right) dx = \frac{1}{2}\sqrt{\frac{\pi}{\xi}}, \qquad [2.3.4]$$

where ξ is an arbitrary parameter.

By repeated differentiation with respect to ξ we can deduce the following results

$$-\frac{\partial}{\partial \xi} \int_0^\infty \exp\left(-\xi x^2\right) dx = \int_0^\infty x^2 \exp\left(-\xi x^2\right) dx = \frac{1}{4}\sqrt{\frac{\pi}{\xi^3}}, \qquad [2.3.5]$$

$$\frac{\partial^2}{\partial \xi^2} \int_0^\infty \exp\left(-\xi x^2\right) dx = \int_0^\infty x^4 \exp\left(-\xi x^2\right) dx = \frac{3}{8}\sqrt{\frac{\pi}{\xi^5}}. \qquad [2.3.6]$$

If we substitute v for x and $(m/2kT)$ for the parameter ξ we find

$$\frac{1}{2}m\overline{v^2} = \frac{1}{2}m\frac{3}{2\xi} = \frac{3kT}{2} \qquad [2.3.7]$$

as in the simple kinetic theory.

It is possible to test the Maxwellian formula experimentally by passing a beam of molecules through some kind of velocity selector. The beam is generated by a small furnace in a vacuum system and is defined by slits. In the experiments of Estermann, Simpson, and Stern* (Figure 2.6), the gravity field was used to sort out molecules of different speeds. The observed distribution of molecules arriving at a distant collector may be translated into a corresponding speed distribution. Agreement between experiment and theory is generally

* I. Estermann, O. C. Simpson, and O. Stern, Phys. Rev., **71**, 238 (1947).

good but discrepancies occur in the low-speed region, possibly because of nonequilibrium conditions in the beam extracted from the furnace.*

2.4   The Equipartition Theorem and Specific Heats

(a) Statement of the theorem

The classical statistics of Maxwell and Boltzmann not only gave a profound treatment of molecular motions in a gas but was capable of extension to other problems in heat. So far only the translational energy of molecules has been considered, but it is easy to imagine how certain types of molecule can have rotational and vibrational energy in addition. In the solid state, transport of the molecules or atoms is highly unlikely and rotation is inhibited, so vibrational energy is likely to be dominant. The question of dealing with these different types of motion resolves itself into the problem: how much energy, on the average, will these different forms take up in an assembly at equilibrium?

Suppose that we form the sum of the translational, rotational, and vibrational energies of a molecule and write

$$\varepsilon = \varepsilon_T + \varepsilon_R + \varepsilon_V,$$

where

$$\varepsilon_T = \tfrac{1}{2}mv^2 = \tfrac{1}{2}m(v_x^2 + v_y^2 + v_z^2) \qquad [2.4.1]$$

and

$$\varepsilon_R = \tfrac{1}{2}\mathscr{I}_1\omega_1^2 + \tfrac{1}{2}\mathscr{I}_2\omega_2^2 + \cdots, \qquad [2.4.2]$$

where $\mathscr{I}_1, \mathscr{I}_2, \ldots$ are the principal moments of inertia and $\omega_1, \omega_2, \ldots$ are the corresponding angular velocities. The vibrational term ε_V is the sum of separate terms, depending on the number of vibrational modes; each term is composed of two parts, the kinetic energy and the potential energy of oscillation. For pure harmonic vibrations we have

$$\varepsilon_V = \sum_i (p_i^2/2m_i + 2\pi^2 v_i^2 q_i^2), \qquad [2.4.3]$$

where $m_i, p_i, v_i,$ and q_i are, respectively, the mass involved, the linear momentum, the frequency, and the displacement in one particular mode of vibration.

It is evident that the expression for ε may contain many terms and that each term is quadratic in type (so long as the vibrations are harmonic). We have shown that the three terms in ε_T have total energy $3kT/2$ on the average [Equation (2.3.7)]. It is not difficult to prove from the basic distribution in $v_x, v_y,$ and v_z [Equation (2.3.2)] that each of the three terms has mean energy $\tfrac{1}{2}kT$. This result can be extended by applying the Boltzmann distribution to each of the possible quadratic terms in ε. The theorem of equipartition of energy, adumbrated by Clausius and stated clearly by Maxwell in 1860, predicts that each quadratic term will contribute, on the average, $\tfrac{1}{2}kT$ per particle to the total internal energy of the assembly. This important theorem is based firmly on classical mechanics and statistics and should have far-reaching consequences: therefore experimental tests of its predictions are particularly valuable in testing the whole basis of classical theory.

(b) Applications of the theorem

One straightforward application of the theorem is to mixtures of gases and to the Brownian motion of colloidal particles suspended in a gas. Since colloidal particles and the

* See R. C. Miller and P. Kusch, Phys. Rev., **99,** 1314 (1955).

gas molecules themselves must always have three translational terms in ε, the mean kinetic energy per particle or molecule should be $3kT/2$ and the equality of mean kinetic energies yields

$$\tfrac{1}{2}m\overline{v^2} = \tfrac{1}{2}M\overline{V^2}, \qquad [2.4.4]$$

where m, v refer to one group and M, V to the other.

The equipartition theorem finds important application in the theory of specific heats, since the specific heat at constant volume is simply the derivative of the internal energy with respect to temperature. Suppose that in some substance there are F quadratic terms in the expression for ε, including two terms for each mode of vibration, then the total internal energy of N^* molecules should be, on the average,

$$E = FN^*(\tfrac{1}{2}kT). \qquad [2.4.5]$$

F is often referred to as the effective number of *degrees of freedom* of the molecule and it clearly depends on the type of molecular structure. The specific heat (C_v) of one kilomole of the substance at constant volume can be derived as follows:

$$C_v = \frac{\partial E}{\partial T} = \tfrac{1}{2}FN^*k = \tfrac{1}{2}FR \ \text{J/}^\circ\text{K}. \qquad [2.4.6]$$

In the more familiar heat units, R is very nearly 2 kcal/$^\circ$K so that C_v should be approximately F kcal/$^\circ$K per kilomole.

Moreover, in an ideal gas the two principal specific heats (C_p at constant pressure, C_v at constant volume) are related by Mayer's equation

$$C_p - C_v = R \qquad \text{(in mechanical units)}$$

so that

$$C_p = R(\tfrac{1}{2}F + 1) \ \text{J/}^\circ\text{K} \qquad [2.4.7]$$

and the ratio of the two specific heats becomes

$$\gamma = C_p/C_v = \frac{F + 2}{F}. \qquad [2.4.8]$$

The classical theory therefore makes clear predictions concerning the specific heats of an ideal gas in terms of the parameter F.

The minimum value of F in a gas is 3, because the molecules always have translational energy, so the corresponding maximum value of γ is 5/3. Experiments on the inert gases helium, neon, argon, krypton, and xenon yield results for C_v and C_p agreeing very closely with the theory for $F = 3$. We regard the molecules of these gases as single atoms in motion, without any rotation or vibration; this is a fairly satisfactory model, although the atoms would have to be literally point-masses for rotation to be inconceivable.

In the diatomic gases, each molecule has three principal axes of rotation, two perpendicular and one parallel to the line joining the two atoms, also one mode of vibration along the interatomic line. If we ignore the possibility of vibration and forbid rotation about the line joining the atoms, we find that $F = 5$ and $\gamma = 7/5$. This actually seems to be the situation in gases like hydrogen, oxygen, and nitrogen at ordinary temperatures, but other diatomic gases possess γ values rather below 1.4, indicating that some vibration may occur. More complex molecules have a wide range of γ values and the classical theory gives no clear guidance as to which types of motion are to be admitted in each case.

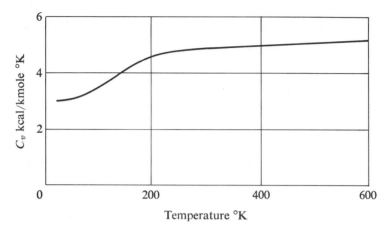

FIGURE 2.7   *The specific heat of hydrogen gas at constant volume plotted against the absolute temperature; at very low temperatures the value of C_v is close to that for a monatomic gas but it rises to a level indicative of rotational motions of the diatomic molecules at ordinary temperatures.*

The situation may be appreciated by considering the variation with temperature of the specific heat of a gas like hydrogen. Figure 2.7 shows that at very low temperatures C_v is close to 3 kcal/°K, the value for a monatomic gas. At higher temperatures C_v rises to about 5 kcal/°K, which is characteristic of a diatomic gas with two rotational degrees of freedom. The specific heat continues to rise slowly at very high temperatures, where presumably vibrational energy is present to a limited extent. The evidence shows clearly that

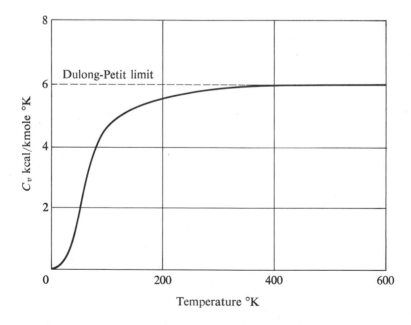

FIGURE 2.8   *The calculated specific heat at constant volume of a typical metal (derived from measurements of C_p for silver) plotted against the absolute temperature; at very low temperatures C_v approaches zero, but at ordinary temperatures it approximates to the Dulong-Petit value of 6 kcal/kmole °K.*

degrees of freedom are effective to different amounts at different temperatures, a phenomenon with no obvious explanation in the classical theory. This breakdown in the equipartition of energy in gases provided the first significant indication that the basic postulates of classical theory are inadequate where atomic systems are concerned.

Further evidence of the breakdown of equipartition is provided by the specific heats of metals and other solids. We suppose that a solid consists of molecules or single atoms or ions disposed in a rigid lattice; in simple metals the only motions allowed are vibrations of the atoms about their mean positions. Such vibrations can be resolved into three components parallel to the Ox, Oy, and Oz directions and each resolved vibration mode counts two terms in the enumeration of F, so ideally $F = 6$. Thus C_v should be nearly 6 kcal/°K for one kilomole. Values of C_p should be only slightly higher than this, because of the low expansion coefficients of solids, and it is C_p which is measured in the laboratory.

It is well known that the product of atomic weight and specific heat is close to 6 kcal/°K in many metals (the rule of Dulong and Petit), and this result agrees with the equipartition theory. However, the specific heats of solids vary appreciably with temperature and in general the classical value is reached only at high temperatures. Figure 2.8 shows the behavior of a typical metal (silver); the C_v curve (derived from experimental data for C_p) rises sharply from very low values near 0°K to near the theoretical 6 kcal/°K at ordinary temperatures. Certain solids (for example, carbon) have C_v values much lower than the Dulong-Petit limit even at elevated temperatures, but in general the behavior of simple solids is similar to that shown in Figure 2.8 with some differences in the temperature scale. Here again we have a serious breakdown in application of the classical equipartition theorem, although its predictions seem to be accurate when the temperature is high enough. One of the most important early achievements of the quantum theory was its accounting for the general behavior of specific heats at different temperatures (see Section 8.1).

2.5 Transport Phenomena in Gases

(a) Finite size of molecules

In the calculation of gas pressure according to kinetic theory it was assumed that the molecules are point-masses and that they collide only with the walls of the vessel. In fact there is considerable evidence that they have finite volume and collide frequently with each other. For example, it was estimated that the number of molecules hitting an area ΔA in one second is $\frac{1}{4}n\bar{v}\,\Delta A$ [Equation (2.1.11)]. If a hole of size ΔA is cut in the wall, the quoted expression should represent the number of molecules escaping per second, provided that they do not collide with each other. Simple estimates show that the formula gives rates of escape at least 100 times too great to fit the observations. The discrepancy may be explained by supposing that the molecules jostle each other in the mass motion of escape, which is thereby slowed down and resembles a diffusion process rather than direct escape.

It is found that the finite size of molecules has great influence on all transport phenomena such as diffusion and viscosity in gases. On the other hand, the theory of gas pressure (Section 2.1) is not materially affected, because of the random molecular motions in gases at rest, and the effects of intermolecular forces are important only at low temperatures. In the theory of virial coefficients [Equation (2.1.14)] no precise molecular diameter is introduced, but a repulsion of very short range is substituted. Nevertheless, the concept of a finite molecular diameter (d) is valuable in a first treatment of transport phenomena in gases.

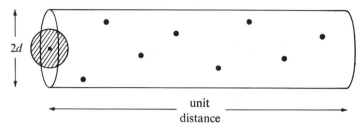

FIGURE 2.9   *Calculation of the mean free path of spherical gas molecules; a fixed diameter (d) is assumed and one molecule is supposed to sweep a path with double this diameter through a gas of point-molecules.*

A most useful parameter in the theory is the *mean free path* (L), defined as the average distance traveled by a molecule between collisions with other molecules. This quantity can be related to the molecular diameter by a conventional argument. In order to find the number of molecules struck by a given molecule in traveling unit distance, we imagine the one molecule to have double the normal diameter and to be sweeping through a gas of point-molecules (Figure 2.9). The number struck is equal to the number in a cylinder of *radius d* and of unit length. Thus

$$\text{Number of collisions} = n\pi d^2,$$

where n = number of molecules/unit volume.

The average distance between collisions is the reciprocal of this

$$L = \frac{1}{n\pi d^2}. \qquad\qquad [2.5.1]$$

The mean free path should therefore be independent of the molecular velocity and inversely proportional to the density (and therefore the pressure) of the gas. The simple treatment takes no account of the motion of the "target" molecules; more elaborate theories have been developed to allow for this motion and for the persistence, after collision, of velocity components parallel to the velocity before collision. According to Jeans,* the best value of L for use in the theory of viscosity is very close to the formula quoted, so Equation (2.5.1) will be employed in further developments.

Estimates of L are necessarily somewhat approximate, but if we assume that "air molecules" have an effective diameter of about 3 Ångstroms (Å) (1 Å = 10^{-10} m) we find that L is about 10^{-7} m in air at ordinary temperature and pressure. Thus the collisions between molecules are extremely frequent unless we reduce the pressure considerably. In many applications (for example, Knudsen's apparatus of Figure 2.1) it is essential to maintain pressures below 10^{-7} atm to ensure that the mean free path is longer than the longest dimension of the apparatus. Experimental methods have been developed for measuring L directly but, owing to technical difficulties, these are less satisfactory than indirect determinations based on the viscosity of the gas.

(b) The viscosity of a gas

The theoretical derivation of gaseous viscosity follows from the relations established in Section 2.1. The gas as a whole is supposed to have a drift velocity $\mathbf{u}$ in the x direction,

* J. H. Jeans, *Introduction to the Kinetic Theory of Gases* (Cambridge University Press, New York, 1959) p. 163.

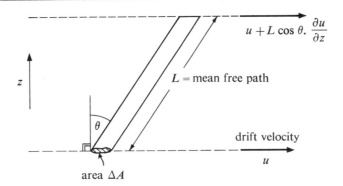

FIGURE 2.10 *The calculation of gaseous viscosity based on the transfer of momentum across planes perpendicular to the general drift velocity* **u.**

where the magnitude u is negligible compared with the molecular speeds. Near a boundary, u is reduced nearly to zero by viscous effects, and a transverse velocity gradient $\partial u/\partial z$ is set up. According to the definition of the viscosity coefficient η the laminar flow is maintained by a tangential stress equal to $\eta(\partial u/\partial z)$.

The stress across an area ΔA parallel to the x direction can be calculated from kinetic theory if it is assumed that at each collision a molecule adopts the local drift velocity. The area ΔA in a layer with drift velocity u receives molecules at an angle θ to the normal at the rate

$$\tfrac{1}{2}nvf(v)\, dv \cos \theta \sin \theta\, d\theta\, \Delta A \qquad \text{[from Equation (2.1.10)]}$$

for molecular speeds between v and $(v + dv)$.

On the average these molecules have traveled a distance L from their previous collisions, which were in a layer with a different drift velocity. Referring to Figure 2.10 we see that their previous drift velocity was of magnitude

$$u + L \cos \theta \frac{\partial u}{\partial z},$$

if we ignore higher derivatives of u with respect to z. In this class, therefore, an extra momentum $\left(mL \cos \theta\, \dfrac{\partial u}{\partial z}\right)$ per molecule is given up to the ΔA layer. The net transfer of momentum per second across the area ΔA is obtained by integrating the expression (2.1.10), multiplied by the momentum term, over the full angular range from $\theta = 0$ to $\theta = \pi$ rad, which allows for molecules arriving from layers above and below ΔA. The force across ΔA is then

$$\Delta F = \tfrac{1}{2}nmL \frac{\partial u}{\partial z} \Delta A \int_0^\infty vf(v)\, dv \int_0^\pi \cos^2 \theta \sin \theta\, d\theta.$$

The tangential stress becomes

$$\frac{\Delta F}{\Delta A} = \tfrac{1}{3}nmL\bar{v} \frac{\partial u}{\partial z}$$

so that the coefficient of viscosity is

$$\eta = \frac{nmL\bar{v}}{3} = \rho \frac{L\bar{v}}{3}. \qquad [2.5.2]$$

More refined calculations of this quantity have been made but the above result is sufficiently accurate to yield results of physical importance. We can substitute the value of (nL) from Equation (2.5.1) and obtain

$$\eta = \frac{m\bar{v}}{3\pi d^2}.$$ [2.5.3]

The viscosity should therefore be independent of the gas pressure, since $\bar{v}$ depends only on the absolute temperature for a given gas. This unexpected result was confirmed experimentally by Maxwell over a wide range of pressures. However, at very low pressures the mean free path becomes comparable with the dimensions of conventional apparatus so η can no longer be defined in terms of the simple theory. In this region the viscosity falls to values much lower than the theoretical results.

It also follows from Equation (2.5.3) that the viscosity should increase with increasing temperature, because of the velocity term, and this unexpected behavior is confirmed by experiment. However, Sutherland showed that η does not vary simply with $\bar{v}$ but has a complex behavior, due presumably to variations in the effective molecular diameter d. It appears that d varies with the violence of the collisions and this can be understood if we regard molecules as centers of force. If a short-range repulsion acts between pairs of molecules the effective molecular diameter must decrease with increasing molecular speed, a deduction in accord with the viscosity data.

(c) *Diffusion and thermal conductivity*

Calculations can also be carried out to find the diffusion coefficient (D) and thermal conductivity (K) of an ideal gas. The quantity D is defined as the ratio of molecular flux (the number of molecules crossing unit area per second) to the gradient of molecular density, $\partial n/\partial z$. The net flux of molecules across an area ΔA follows from Equation (2.1.10), with the molecular density (n) replaced by the appropriate density at the mean-free-path distance, namely $\left(n + L\cos\theta\,\dfrac{\partial n}{\partial z}\right)$. We obtain

$$\text{Flux} = \tfrac{1}{2}\Delta A \int_0^\infty vf(v)\,dv \int_0^\pi \left(n + L\cos\theta\,\frac{\partial n}{\partial z}\right)\cos\theta\sin\theta\,d\theta,$$

that is,

$$D\frac{\partial n}{\partial z}\Delta A = \tfrac{1}{3}L\bar{v}\frac{\partial n}{\partial z}\Delta A$$

or

$$D = \tfrac{1}{3}L\bar{v}.$$ [2.5.4]

The coefficient D may be used in problems involving random molecular motion in a gas (where mass motion is ignored), provided that the mean free path is considerably less than the dimensions of the apparatus concerned.

Entirely similar calculations lead to an expression for the thermal conductivity of an ideal gas

$$K = \tfrac{1}{3}nmL\bar{v}s_v,$$ [2.5.5]

where s_v is the specific heat per *kilogram* of the gas at constant volume, that is, $s_v = C_v/M$ (M = molecular weight). Over a wide range of pressures the conductivity is independent of the pressure, but it increases with rising temperature. At very low pressures the variation of thermal conductivity with pressure is of some practical importance because it is the basis of pressure gauges of the Pirani type.

In these applications of kinetic theory it has been assumed that the molecules attain local thermal equilibrium at each collision, and this is a pronounced weakness of the theory. A test of the results is provided by the ratio

$$\frac{K}{\eta s_v},$$

which should be exactly 1 if the simple treatment is correct. More elaborate calculations yield results as high as 2.5 for this ratio, and experimental data agree fairly well with the empirical relation

$$\frac{K}{\eta s_v} = \tfrac{1}{4}(9\gamma - 5).$$

These and other results serve to show that the simple kinetic theory of transport effects, based on a fixed molecular diameter, is a good qualitative guide to the behavior of gases but is far from precise quantitatively.

(d) Molecular diameters

In 1865 Loschmidt outlined a method whereby measurements of gaseous viscosity can be used to yield estimates of molecular diameter (d) and the number N^*. The viscosity involves the quantity m/d^2 [Equation (2.5.3)], and an independent figure for the quantity m/d^3 can be obtained from the density of the same substance in the condensed state, as follows. It is well known that at temperatures well below the critical point the density of a liquid does not change very much; in this region, therefore, the molecules must approach a close-packed configuration. To a sufficient degree of accuracy, we can imagine each molecule occupying a cubical space of size equal to the effective molecular diameter (d) and write

Liquid density: $\quad \rho_L = m/d^3$ approximately.

If this equation is combined with Equation (2.5.3), separate figures for m and d are obtainable.

If the molecular mass (m) is known, the number of molecules (N^*) in a kilomole is readily found. Loschmidt's method gives somewhat variable results, owing to the difficulty of defining molecular conditions in a liquid. However, the modern figure for N^* may be employed to find m for any gas, and the viscosity data then yield useful estimates of the molecular diameter (d) and the mean free path (L). In this way we find that the common gases, whether they are monatomic or diatomic in structure, have effective molecular diameters in the region of a few Ångstroms. It is clear, nevertheless, that the interaction between two molecules is a complex phenomenon, and refined methods are required to link molecular properties with the behavior of gases in bulk.

FOR FURTHER READING

Kinetic theory:

J. H. JEANS, *Introduction to the Kinetic Theory of Gases* (Cambridge University Press, New York, 1959).

E. H. KENNARD, *The Kinetic Theory of Gases* (McGraw-Hill Book Co., New York, 1938).

Thermodynamics:

E. SCHRÖDINGER, *Statistical Thermodynamics* (Cambridge University Press, New York, 1960).

M. BORN, *The Natural Philosophy of Cause and Chance* (Oxford University Press, New York, 1949).

Brownian motion:

J. PERRIN, *Atoms*, translator, D. L. Hammick (D. Van Nostrand Co., Princeton, 1916).

A. EINSTEIN, *Investigations on the Theory of the Brownian Movement*, translator, A. D. Cowper (Dover Publications, New York, 1956).

Molecular Beams:

K. F. SMITH, *Molecular Beams* (Methuen Monographs, J. Wiley & Sons, New York, 1955).

PROBLEMS FOR CHAPTER 2

DATA REQUIRED:

Number of molecules per kilomole: $N^* = 6.0 \times 10^{26}$
Number of molecules per m^3 in gas at STP (Standard Temperature and Pressure) = 2.7×10^{25}
Pressure of one standard atmosphere = 10^5 N/m² approximately
Boltzmann constant: $k = 1.4 \times 10^{-23}$ J/°K

2.1. If the last breath of Julius Caesar occupied about 350 cm³ at STP and all the molecules were evenly spread through the Earth's atmosphere, how many of Julius Caesar's molecules do the average person's lungs contain? Take the average lung capacity to be 3000 cm³, the Earth's radius as 6400 km, and the atmosphere to be a uniform layer 8 km deep.

2.2. Calculate the root-mean-square speed of oxygen molecules at a pressure of 1 atm when the density is 1.44 kg/m³. What is the relation between this result and the speed of sound in oxygen under the same conditions?

2.3. Show that the molecules leaving area A in Knudsen's apparatus (Figure 2.1) with the angular distribution given by Equation (2.1.10) are uniformly distributed over the inner surface of the spherical enclosure.

2.4. Suppose that the gas in a Crookes radiometer has a density 1.5×10^{-7} kg/m³ at a constant temperature of 300°K. If the opposite faces of a vane differ in temperature by 1°, estimate:

(a) the difference in root-mean-square molecular speeds of molecules leaving opposite sides of the vane,

(b) the net pressure acting on the vane in consequence.

2.5. Estimate the number of molecules per second striking 1 mm² of the wall of a large enclosure containing nitrogen (mol. wt. = 28) at STP. Assuming that the molecules are point-masses, calculate how long it would take for 1 g of the gas to escape through a 1 mm² hole into a perfect vacuum, the internal pressure being maintained constant at 1 atm.

2.6. In an experiment on colloidal particles of average mass 6×10^{-17} kg and average density 1.25 times that of water, the numbers of particles observed at different heights (H) in a water suspension at 300°K were as follows:

H (in 10^{-6} m)	0	15	25	50
Numbers	480	310	225	95

Plot a semilogarithmic graph and from the average slope calculate k and N^*. Assume $R = 8.3 \times 10^3$ J/°K.

2.7. Show that the Maxwellian speed distribution $f(v)\,dv$ may be converted into an energy distribution of the form

$$F(\varepsilon)\,d\varepsilon \propto \sqrt{\varepsilon}\, \exp\left(-\frac{\varepsilon}{kT}\right) d\varepsilon,$$

where ε is the kinetic energy per molecule. Use this expression to prove that the most probable value of ε is $\frac{1}{2}kT$ and the mean value is $3kT/2$.

2.8. With the aid of Maxwell's distribution of molecular speeds, show that the most probable speed (v_0) is related to the mean speed $(\bar{v})$ and the root-mean-square speed (v_{rms}) by the equation

$$v_0 = \frac{\bar{v}\sqrt{\pi}}{2} = \sqrt{\tfrac{2}{3}}\,v_{\mathrm{rms}}.$$

2.9. In an Estermann-Stern experiment a beam of caesium atoms (at. wt. = 133) emerges horizontally from an oven, which is effectively at 500°K, and travels a horizontal distance of 3 m before being detected. Find the root-mean-square speed of the caesium atoms and calculate the net vertical deflection for this speed.

2.10. It is observed that smoke particles suspended in a gas at 300°K possess a root-mean-square speed, due to Brownian motion, of about 5 cm/sec. Estimate the average mass of a smoke particle on the assumption that there is equipartition of kinetic energy between the particles and the molecules of the gas.

2.11. Outline the standard transport theory to arrive at the thermal conductivity of a gas in the form

$$K = \frac{nmL\bar{v}s_v}{3}.$$

Hence find the ratio of the thermal conductivities of helium (mol. wt. = 4, mol. diam = 2.4×10^{-10} m, $s_v = 3.1$ J/g°K) and nitrogen (mol. wt. = 28, $d = 3.7 \times 10^{-10}$ m, $s_v = 0.73$ J/g°K) at the same temperature and pressure. Suggest a method for the physical detection of small quantities of helium in a flow of air.

2.12. Calculate the mean free path for hydrogen molecules at STP, given that the effective molecular diameter is 2.7×10^{-10} m. Also find the mean molecular speed and the mean time between molecular collisions.

2.13. Calculate the diffusion coefficient D for carbon dioxide (mol. wt. 44) at STP, given that its effective molecular diameter is 4.6×10^{-10} m. Carbon dioxide under these conditions is kept in two large vessels, connected by a pipe of cross-sectional area 1 mm² and of length 0.1 m. The total pressure is 1 atm throughout but initially one vessel contains 0.8 atm of normal CO_2 and 0.2 atm of radioactive CO_2. What is the rate of flow of radioactive molecules from one vessel to the other, assuming that the diffusion coefficient is nearly the same for both kinds of molecules?

2.14. Given that the viscosity of argon gas (mol. wt. = 40) is 2.1×10^{-5} mks unit at 1 atm pressure and a gaseous density of 1.8 kg/m³, also that liquid argon has a density of about 1.4×10^3 kg/m³, estimate the effective diameter and mass of an argon molecule, and find a value for N^*.

2.15. Calculate the mean free path for oxygen molecules at STP if the effective molecular diameter is 3.5×10^{-10} m. Hence find the viscosity of the gas, assuming that the mean molecular speed is 420 m/sec.

2.16. Show that the entropy S and internal energy E of an assembly which possesses a partition function Σ based on discrete energy states can be determined from the relations

$$S = Nk \frac{\partial}{\partial T}(T \ln \Sigma),$$

$$E = NkT^2 \frac{\partial}{\partial T}(\ln \Sigma).$$

Hence find the relation between the Helmholtz free energy $(E - TS)$ and the parameter α of Equation (2.2.6).

2.17. Suppose that an assembly contains atoms which can exist in two possible states (of equal statistical weight) with energies 0 and ε. Find the partition function and show that the specific heat at constant volume has a maximum value and then varies approximately as T^{-2} when the temperature T reaches the region where $kT \gg \varepsilon$.

2.18. In a similar assembly to that of Problem 2.17, suppose that the atoms can exist in states of energy $0, \varepsilon, 2\varepsilon, \ldots, r\varepsilon, \ldots$, where r varies from zero to infinity. Find the partition function and show that the specific heat at constant volume rises to a steady value at high temperatures.

CHAPTER III

෯෯෯෯෯෯෯෯෯෯෯෯෯෯෯෯෯෯෯෯෯෯෯෯෯෯෯෯෯෯෯෯

CHARGED SUBATOMIC PARTICLES

During the early years of the nineteenth century several major discoveries were made concerning the properties of electric current. In 1800 Nicholson and Carlisle discovered the phenomenon of electrolysis, in which the chemical bonds of certain compounds (known as *electrolytes*) are broken by the passage of a current. The laws of electrolysis were stated by Faraday in 1832 and these could be explained most simply in terms of ionic migration. According to the ionic theory, an electrolyte consists of free positive and negative ions which move to opposite electrodes during electrolysis. This idea was applied successfully to many problems of physical chemistry by Arrhenius and others. As a result it appeared probable that in certain substances chemical combination depends on the electrostatic attraction between opposite charges attached to different atoms or parts of the molecules.

Some of the most important physical advances of the late nineteenth century came from the study of electrical conduction in gases. After 1855 improved vacuum techniques enabled Plücker, Hittorf, and Crookes to investigate the properties of cathode rays. In 1897, J. J. Thomson produced strong evidence in favor of the theory that cathode rays are beams of subatomic particles, now called electrons. The electron theory was rapidly applied in many fields and Millikan's experiments (from 1911 onward) made it clear that the electronic charge is a fundamental unit of electricity.

J. J. Thomson went on to analyze the positive rays occurring in discharge tubes and by 1912 he had evolved a technique for separating ions of different atomic mass and charge. In isolating two stable isotopes of neon he provided the explanation of fractional atomic weights in chemistry. By this time both the massive positive ions and much lighter electrons had been identified and, although the details of atomic structure remained obscure, it was evident that the stability of atoms depends on electrostatic forces.

The many important applications of charged-particle beams (especially those of electrons) could not have been realized without the development of high-vacuum techniques. The control of such beams is usually effected by the use of electric and magnetic fields, which are capable of precise definition in a vacuum. On the other hand, the motions of charged particles in matter are often complex because of interactions with atomic fields. Particular interest attaches to the conditions inside metallic solids (which are supposed to contain free electrons in large numbers) and in ionized gases. Since the days of Thomson and Rutherford, basic research on ionization has often been prosecuted by nuclear physicists engaged in developing efficient detectors of charged particles. More recently, interest has been directed to the highly ionized *plasma* state of matter: investigations in plasma physics are largely devoted to the complex interactions between plasma and electromagnetic fields, which may be used to control the behavior of plasma at high temperatures.

3.1 Ions and Ionic Solids

(a) *The ionic theory*

When an electric current is passed through an electrolyte, such as the solution of an inorganic salt in water, different chemical products appear at the two electrodes. Here we have the first clear indication that positive and negative charges may be attached to different parts of a molecule. Further evidence can be obtained from Faraday's laws of electrolysis, which may be combined in the statement that one-gram equivalent of any substance requires a fixed amount of charge [close to 96,500 coulombs (C)] for release in electrolysis. This unit of charge is called "the Faraday" and its existence suggests that there is some more fundamental unit operative in atomic structures.

According to the ionic theory, an electrolyte is dissociated into ions which carry positive and negative charges and which therefore turn up at different electrodes during electrolysis. For example, sodium chloride does not exist as a molecule NaCl but only as positive sodium ions (Na^+) and negative chlorine ions (Cl^-), which become mobile when the solid is melted or dissolved in water. In the solid state the substance is held together by electrostatic forces and it requires a highly "polar" liquid like water (which has a very high dielectric constant) to weaken the forces of cohesion sufficiently and cause solution.

The ionic theory met great opposition because it ran counter to the well-established chemical concept of a molecule. Nevertheless, it was successful in explaining many properties of inorganic substances and in predicting the electrical behavior of solutions containing "weak" electrolytes (Ostwald's dilution law). The theory was less successful in dealing with "strong" electrolytes like sodium chloride, which are completely ionized, but Debye and Hückel showed that the difficulties are caused by the ions' tendency to attract each other, even when in solution.

If we adopt the hypothesis that a monovalent ion (for example Na^+ or H^+ or Cl^-) carries a fundamental unit of charge (denoted by $\pm\, e$), we must interpret the Faraday as the total charge on one-gram equivalent of these ions. The total charge on 1000 g of ions, that is, a kilomole (consisting of N^* monovalent ions), is therefore

$$N^*e = 9.65 \times 10^7 \text{ C}, \qquad\qquad [3.1.1]$$

and, substituting $N^* = 6 \times 10^{26}$ approximately, we obtain

$$e = 1.6 \times 10^{-19} \text{ C}.$$

Moreover, the Faraday yields an estimate of the specific charge (the ratio of charge to mass) of the H^+ ion, if we assume that the atomic weight of hydrogen (1.008 in terms of the standard C^{12} unit) is very nearly the same as the mass (in kg) of 1 kmole of hydrogen ions. Thus for the lightest positive ions we get

$$\text{Specific charge} = \frac{N^*e}{M} = \frac{9.65 \times 10^7 \text{ C}}{1.008 \text{ kg}}$$

$$= 9.57 \times 10^7 \text{ C/kg}. \qquad\qquad [3.1.2]$$

The fundamental charge unit defined by Equation (3.1.1) was called "the electron" by Stoney in 1874, but later the name was transferred to the negatively charged subatomic particles discovered in cathode rays. It is noteworthy that direct measurements of the electron's charge (for example by Millikan's oil-drop method) agree closely with the value estimated above for monovalent ions. This result suggests that ions are formed by the transfer of one or more electrons between atoms or groups of atoms when chemical combination takes place. The theory of electrovalence applies chiefly to the elements on the left of the periodic table (Appendix II), to the transition metals and to certain halogens which readily form ions. Other types of valence are dominant in compounds containing those elements in the middle columns of the table which do not readily form ions.

(b) Ionic crystals

The ionic theory also leads to consideration of the types of solid structure which may be formed of positive and negative ions held together by electrostatic attraction. In Figure 3.1 we picture a particularly simple lattice, that of solid sodium chloride, in which Na^+ and Cl^- ions are disposed in a cubic array. Each sodium atom is surrounded by six chlorine atoms as nearest neighbors and each chlorine atom by six sodium atoms. Thus each type of ion forms a *face-centered cubic* lattice and this structure is consonant with the well-known cubic symmetry of sodium chloride crystals. A perfect lattice of this type corresponds to a single "supermolecule," $(NaCl)_n$, where n is a large number.

Many properties of ionic solids can be interpreted in terms of lattice structures similar to the structure of sodium chloride. For example, in the solid anhydrous state such crystals

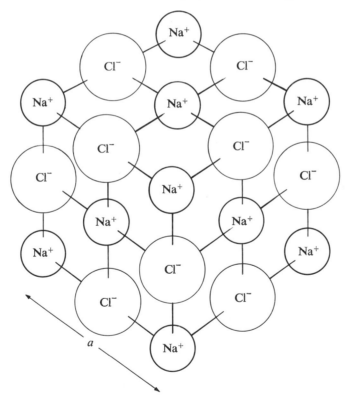

FIGURE 3.1 *The lattice structure of solid sodium chloride which forms cubic crystals of high stability; each sodium ion is surrounded by six chlorine ions and each chlorine ion by six sodium ions. The lattice constant a is the side of the cubic unit cell.*

should be poor conductors of electricity. Measurements show that, at temperatures well below the melting point, electrical conduction depends chiefly on the presence of impurities, but near the melting point a certain amount of ionic migration does take place. In the liquid state, conduction takes place with difficulty owing to the low mobility of ions which are so closely aggregated with ions of the opposite sign. It is interesting to note that when "molecular" beams of sodium chloride are formed in a vacuum by the usual techniques, the "molecules" often consist of aggregates of Na^+ and Cl^- ions, but very rarely of $NaCl$ itself.

An important parameter in the study of crystal lattices is the size of the *unit cell*, which is the smallest unit repeated exactly throughout the lattice. In a cubic structure the lattice constant is the side of the unit cube (denoted by a in Figure 3.1). This parameter may be calculated from the density of the solid if the type of lattice is known. For example, in sodium chloride each unit cell contains eight subcells of side $\frac{1}{2}a$ and each subcell is of such a size that it can be arranged to surround one ion (of either type) in an infinite lattice. In a very large lattice, say a cube of side 1 m, the number of subcells is found to be

$$\left(\frac{2}{a}\right)^3 \quad \text{if } a \text{ is expressed in meters.}$$

This is the number of ions in the cube, but the number of $NaCl$ "molecules" is one-half of this, so, if M is the molecular weight, the mass of the meter cube (that is, the density) is

$$\rho = \tfrac{1}{2}m\left(\frac{2}{a}\right)^3 \quad \text{in} \quad kg/m^3,$$

where m is the mass per molecule and $N^*m = M$.

The lattice constant a can then be calculated from the equation

$$\rho = \frac{4M}{N^*a^3}, \qquad\qquad [3.1.3]$$

which is equivalent to the assumption that each unit cell contains four "molecules."

The results of x-ray analysis confirm the simple picture of conditions in an ionic solid. Indeed, x-ray measurements of lattice constants are so accurate that the method described for finding a is now reversed and provides the most reliable way of determining N^*. The x-ray wavelengths are found by experiments with gratings and are then used to fix the lattice constants of a high-quality crystal of known structure and density. In this way N^* is found to be

$$6.023 \times 10^{26} \text{ molecules/kilomole,}$$

and division of the Faraday by N^* gives the fundamental ionic charge

$$e = 1.6021 \times 10^{-19} \text{ C.}$$

3.2 The Discovery of the Electron

We have seen that the conduction of electric current through electrolytes can be described by precise laws and is supposed to be due to the presence of ions with fixed charges. Normally gases are excellent insulators but they can be rendered conducting by several methods involving ionization of the molecules, for example, by irradiation with x rays, ultraviolet radiation, or alpha particles. It is to be emphasized that this ionization process is irregular, because many different kinds of ions may be formed in the same gas. For example, a gas like oxygen may contain molecular ions (O_2^+ or O_2^-) or atomic ions, which are liable to recombine with each other to form neutral molecules. For this reason, early studies of electrical discharges in gases did not immediately yield fundamental results. At fairly low pressures (around 10^{-4} atm) a column of glowing gas fills most of the discharge tube and this column emits characteristic spectral lines of the elements present. The column is highly ionized and the properties of the plasma can be studied with the aid of probe techniques introduced by Langmuir.

As improved techniques for the attainment of high vacua became available, it was found possible to extend the observations into a low-pressure region where the gas no longer glows, although an appreciable current is still passing. Here the walls of the glass tubes were seen to fluoresce strongly under the influence of rays which seemed to come from the cathode of the discharge tube. These "cathode rays" were investigated by Hittorf, Crookes, Perrin, and others. The following properties were established:

(i) the rays travel in straight lines except in the presence of electric or magnetic fields (no gravitational effects are detectable);

(ii) their deflections in electromagnetic fields indicate that the rays are negatively charged, and this was checked by direct collection on an insulated plate;

(iii) when the rays are stopped by matter, heat is produced;

(iv) the rays are capable of penetrating thin metal foils which are opaque to light;

(v) the rays carry momentum, for example, they can cause a light paddle-wheel to rotate.

The last property was taken to show that the rays consist of material particles, although the existence of a pressure due to pure radiation could not be ruled out. The penetrating property was seen as a serious objection to the particle theory because at that time the atoms in a solid were visualized as forming an impenetrable barrier of matter. However, estimates of the velocity of cathode rays by Wiechert and others were somewhat lower than the velocity of light *in vacuo*; these results, combined with the negative-charge indications, cast doubt on the theory that the rays consist of electromagnetic radiations of some type.

In 1897, J. J. Thomson produced decisive evidence concerning the velocity and specific charge of the cathode rays. He succeeded in obtaining consistent deflections of the rays by electrostatic fields and he compared the results with deflections produced by magnetic fields. Assuming that the rays were negatively charged particles, he showed that their velocities agreed with previous estimates and were consistent with the accelerating voltage applied to the discharge tube. The specific charge (e/m) of the particles was measured repeatedly with different gases in the tube and all gave the same value (within the limits of experimental error). Thomson found, as an average value

$$\frac{e}{m} = 1.3 \times 10^{11} \text{ C/kg,}$$

a result over 1000 times the figure for hydrogen ions [Equation (3.1.2)].

Assuming that there is some relation between the specific charges of cathode rays and hydrogen ions, we may consider two extreme cases. On the one hand, the cathode-ray particles could be as massive as hydrogen atoms with a very much higher charge than the hydrogen ion; or, on the other hand, they might carry the same charge and be much less massive than the hydrogen atom. Since the other evidence suggested that the cathode rays are the same for all elements, Thomson concluded that the particles are subatomic, with

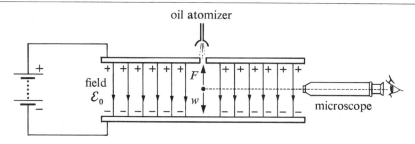

FIGURE 3.2 *Millikan's method of measuring the electronic charge. The motion of single oil-droplets introduced into the space between two parallel plates is influenced by the weight (w) and the force (F) due to the uniform electrostatic field $\mathscr{E}_0$ acting, in this case, on the net negative charge carried by the droplet.*

masses less than 10^{-3} of that of the hydrogen atom. He went on to find e/m values for the negatively charged particles emitted from metals by the thermionic and photoelectric effects and showed that they agreed with the cathode-ray results.

Although satisfactory evidence about the specific charge of the "electrons" was now available, it remained to find the magnitude of the charge (e) so that the mass (m) of a single particle might be calculated. Experiments by Townsend, Thomson, and H. A. Wilson succeeded in giving estimates of e with the right order of magnitude, but the best early results were those of Millikan, who used oil droplets moving in a uniform vertical electric field. A pair of horizontal parallel plates connected to a battery provided a uniform field region (Figure 3.2), where the force exerted on a charged droplet could be found by studying its motion through the air. If, for example, the effective weight (w) of a droplet carrying n electronic charges is exactly canceled by electrostatic force due to a field of magnitude $\mathscr{E}_0$, we obtain the equilibrium condition

$$w = ne\,\mathscr{E}_0. \qquad [3.2.1]$$

In practice, the oil droplets were allowed to drift slowly either upwards or downwards, according to whether the field was slightly greater or less than the value $\mathscr{E}_0$. The resistance to motion of a sphere through a viscous fluid is given by Stokes' law, which may be written

$$\text{Resistance} = 6\pi\eta r v_d, \qquad [3.2.2]$$

where η is the viscosity of air,
   r is the radius of the sphere,
   v_d is the drift speed.

Thus in a field of strength ($\mathscr{E}_0 \pm \delta\mathscr{E}$), the drift speed is determined by an equation of the form

$$w \pm 6\pi\eta r v_d = ne(\mathscr{E}_0 \pm \delta\mathscr{E}).$$

If the field is switched off, the terminal speed (v_f) of the droplet in free fall is given by

$$w = 6\pi\eta r v_f,$$

where

$$w = \frac{4\pi}{3}\,\rho r^3 g$$

and ρ stands for the difference in density between the oil and air. Thus the radius r can be found from the free-fall speed v_f and can then be substituted in the equation

$$6\pi\eta r(v_f \pm v_d) = ne(\mathscr{E}_0 \pm \delta\mathscr{E}) \qquad [3.2.3]$$

in order to find the net charge (ne).

Millikan carried out many measurements of the quantity (*ne*) and derived a value for *e* which was, in fact, about 1 % too low, owing to errors in the viscosity coefficient as applied to very small droplets.

Despite this systematic error Millikan obtained clear evidence that the total charge (*ne*) is an integral multiple of some basic unit, which is identified as the charge on one electron. The most important feature of the oil-drop type of experiment is its clear demonstration that electric charge is *quantized*, that is, it appears only in multiples of some basic unit. Recent research has led to the discovery of many new kinds of particles; it remains a remarkable fact that all subatomic charged particles, whether stable or unstable, possess the same charge ($\pm e$) to a high order of accuracy.

Accurate measurements of the specific charge of electrons enable us to fix the electronic mass (*m*) as
$$m = 9.1091 \times 10^{-31} \text{ kg},$$

or 1/1837 of the mass of a neutral hydrogen atom. Apart from the neutrino, which is believed to have zero rest mass, the electron is the lightest entity conventionally regarded as a "particle" and it is by far the most important item in theoretical chemistry as well as atomic physics.

3.3   The Motion of Charged Particles in Electric and Magnetic Fields

Many of the applications of charged-particle beams depend on their characteristic properties of deflection in electric and magnetic fields. These properties are used in various ways and combinations in the design of mass spectrographs (Section 3.4), particle accelerators (Section 9.1), cathode-ray tubes, and electron microscopes. Here we survey the basic principles involved in applications where the Newtonian laws of mechanics are obeyed, that is, where the particle velocities are small compared with the velocity of light. Throughout this section each particle will be assigned charge $+e$ and mass *m*.

(a) Uniform electrostatic field (Figure 3.3)

If a charged particle of speed v_0 enters an electric field, of intensity $\mathscr{E}$, at right angles to the lines of force, it will be deflected transversely. The transverse acceleration (*a*) is given by

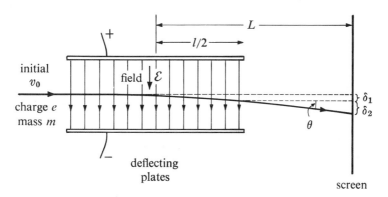

FIGURE 3.3   *Deflection of positively charged particles entering a uniform electrostatic field at right angles to the lines of force. δ_1 is the deflection in the field region, δ_2 is the deflection in the space between the plates and the screen.*

the relation

$$a = \frac{e\mathscr{E}}{m} = \frac{eV}{md} \qquad\qquad [3.3.1]$$

if the field is maintained by a potential difference V between parallel plates, distance d apart. If the horizontal distance traveled in the field is l, the time spent is $t = l/v_0$. From this we calculate the transverse deflection in the field

$$\delta_1 = \tfrac{1}{2}at^2 = \frac{e\mathscr{E}l^2}{2mv_0^2} . \qquad\qquad [3.3.2]$$

If the particle now enters a field-free region and finally strikes a screen at a distance L from the center of the parallel plates, there is an extra transverse deflection away from the center line, given by

$$\delta_2 = (L - \tfrac{1}{2}l)\tan\theta = (L - \tfrac{1}{2}l)\frac{e\mathscr{E}l}{mv_0^2},$$

where θ is the deflection angle at which the particle leaves the field. The total transverse deflection is therefore

$$\delta = \delta_1 + \delta_2 = \frac{e\mathscr{E}lL}{mv_0^2} . \qquad\qquad [3.3.3]$$

In practice corrections have to be applied for the effects of the fringing field where the beam enters and leaves the parallel-plate system. A straightforward extension of the theory enables us to calculate the trajectory of particles entering the field at any angle.

(b) Nonuniform electrostatic fields

In the first case considered, the charged particles were injected perpendicular to the uniform electrostatic field, that is, parallel to the equipotential surfaces within the field. In general, positively charged particles tend to follow lines of force and therefore to cross equipotential surfaces at right angles. This property can be used to focus particle beams to some extent if the field is designed to have equipotential surfaces with lens-shaped configurations.

In the simplest case of a series of equipotential planes parallel to each other (although not necessarily equidistant), particle trajectories are refracted according to a precise law. Suppose that a particle is incident at one plane with velocity $\mathbf{v}_0$ at angle θ_0 relative to the normal and leaves the set of planes with velocity $\mathbf{v}$ at angle θ (Figure 3.4). Then if $-\Delta V$ is the potential difference between first and last planes, the final kinetic energy is

$$\tfrac{1}{2}mv^2 = \tfrac{1}{2}mv_0^2 + e\Delta V.$$

However, the increase in velocity is due entirely to changes in the normal component of the velocity, that is, the tangential component remains constant, or

$$v\sin\theta = v_0\sin\theta_0,$$

whence

$$\frac{\sin\theta_0}{\sin\theta} = \sqrt{1 + \frac{2e\Delta V}{mv_0^2}} . \qquad\qquad [3.3.4]$$

If ΔV is positive, positive particles are "refracted" toward the normal by an amount depending on the original angle and on the ratio of $e\Delta V$ to the original kinetic energy.

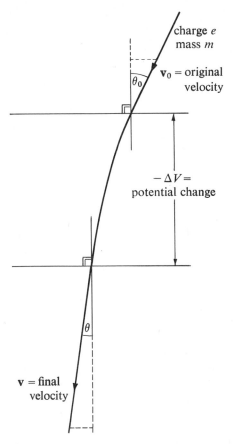

FIGURE 3.4 *"Refraction" of positively charged particles passing through a region where the equipotential surfaces are parallel and in which the net change in electrical potential is* $-\Delta V$.

In practice the paths of particles in complex fields have to be found by ray-tracing methods, but the principles may be illustrated by reference to an important feature of many accelerators (Figure 3.5). A beam is being accelerated across the gap between two coaxial tubes or similar electrodes, where the equipotential surfaces form a lens-shaped system in the

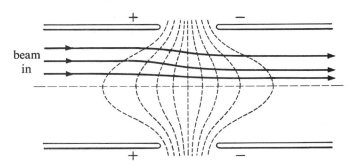

FIGURE 3.5 *Passage of a beam of positively charged particles through the gap between two coaxial "drift tubes" where the equipotential surfaces act like a lens in focusing the beam towards the central axis.*

central region. The early converging effect is stronger than the later divergence because of the particles' increase in speed. The net result is that particles off the axis are deflected inward and the beam is focused to some extent. Equation (3.3.4) shows that the focusing effect decreases as the energy of the beam increases and it is negligible in the high-energy region of an accelerator.

(c) *Uniform magnetic field perpendicular to the beam*

The deflection of a beam of charged particles in a magnetic field is entirely equivalent to the effect of the field on a wire carrying electric current. The basic definition of electrodynamics leads to the Lorentz formula for the force exerted by field **B** on a particle with velocity $\mathbf{v_0}$

$$\mathbf{F} = e[\mathbf{v_0} \times \mathbf{B}].$$

Since the force **F** is always perpendicular to the velocity no work is done on the particle, which is therefore deflected into a circular path of constant speed v_0 and radius r.

The radius of the particle's orbit (Figure 3.6) is found by equating $|\mathbf{F}|$ with the mass multiplied by the centripetal acceleration

$$F = ev_0B = \frac{mv_0^2}{r},$$

whence

$$Ber = mv_0, \qquad\qquad [3.3.5]$$

that is, the radius of curvature is proportional to the momentum of the particle. The period

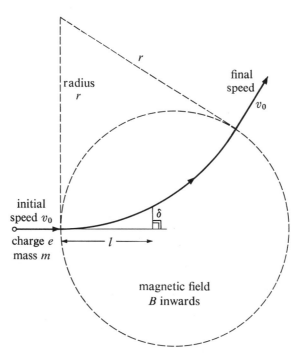

FIGURE 3.6   *Deflection of positively charged particles in a uniform magnetic field at right angles to the original velocity v_0. δ is the deflection after a distance l in the field parallel to v_0.*

of revolution (T) in a complete orbit is given by

$$T = \frac{2\pi r}{v_0} = \frac{2\pi m}{Be} \qquad [3.3.6]$$

and the frequency of revolution (often called the *cyclotron frequency*) is

$$\nu = \frac{Be}{2\pi m}, \qquad [3.3.7]$$

which is independent of the speed and radius of the orbit.

The transverse deflection of a particle in the field can be found with the aid of Figure 3.6, where the arc of its circular path is intercepted at a distance l, measured parallel to the original direction of motion. From the geometry of the circle, we obtain the relation

$$\delta(2r - \delta) = l^2.$$

This quadratic equation may be solved to find δ, provided that l is less than r. For small deflections we may ignore the δ^2 term and approximate the path to a parabola, obtaining

$$\delta = \frac{l^2}{2r} = \frac{Bel^2}{2mv_0}. \qquad [3.3.8]$$

This approximate expression shows that the deflection is proportional to the specific charge and the field B.

(d) Uniform magnetic field at any angle

If a particle enters a field with velocity $\mathbf{v}_0$ at angle θ to the lines of force, the velocity components are $v_0 \cos \theta$ parallel to the field and $v_0 \sin \theta$ perpendicular to it. The first component remains unchanged, while the second gives rise to a circular motion with radius

$$r = \frac{mv_0 \sin \theta}{Be}.$$

The resultant path is a spiral with the particle returning periodically to touch a line through its starting point parallel to the field; the axis of the spiral is along a line of force.

The period of revolution in the spiral depends, as before, only on the field B and the specific charge

$$T = \frac{2\pi r}{v_0 \sin \theta} = \frac{2\pi m}{Be}.$$

If, now, we have a slightly divergent beam of particles emerging from a hole with the average direction parallel to the uniform field $\mathbf{B}$, the beam will be repeatedly focused on to the axis as a result of the spiral motion. The component of the velocity along the axis is $v_0 \cos \theta$ and after n periods of the spiral the distance traveled parallel to the axis is

$$d_n = v_0 \cos \theta \, nT.$$

If the angle θ is small, $\cos \theta$ is very nearly 1 so the focal distances are given by the expression

$$d_n = n \frac{2\pi m v_0}{Be}, \qquad [3.3.9]$$

that is, they are equally spaced along the axis (Figure 3.7).

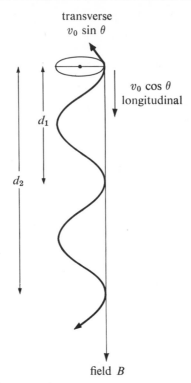

transverse
$v_0 \sin \theta$

$v_0 \cos \theta$
longitudinal

d_1

d_2

field B

FIGURE 3.7 *Spiral path of a charged particle entering a uniform magnetic field B at angle θ to the lines of force. The velocity component parallel to field remains constant while the transverse component describes a circular orbit which brings the particle back to the original line of force at distances $d_1, d_2, \ldots, d_n$.*

(e) Crossed electrostatic and magnetic fields

We have seen that a uniform electrostatic field deflects a beam of charged particles in the plane containing the beam and the lines of force. If a magnetic field is applied, also transverse to the beam but perpendicular to the electrostatic field, the extra deflection is in the same plane as the electrostatic deflection, so that the total deflection in a distance l parallel to the original direction becomes

$$\delta = \delta_E \pm \delta_M = \frac{e\mathscr{E} l^2}{2mv_0^2} \pm \frac{eBl^2}{2mv_0},$$

provided that the magnetic field B is weak.

J. J. Thomson succeeded in measuring e/m for cathode rays by a method in which the deflection produced by an electrostatic field was exactly canceled by that due to a co-extensive magnetic field. The net force on the particles was zero at all points, giving the condition

$$ev_0 B = e\mathscr{E}$$

or

$$v_0 = \frac{\mathscr{E}}{B}. \qquad [3.3.10]$$

Thomson's estimates of the velocity agreed with independent measurements made by Wiechert (at similar accelerating voltages) and they could be substituted in the appropriate deflection formula [Equation (3.3.3) or (3.3.8)] to find the specific charge e/m. The system of crossed electrostatic and magnetic fields is often used as a *velocity-selector*, the operation of which is independent of the charge and mass of the particles injected.

(f) The plane magnetron

This method for measuring the specific charge of particles was used by J. J. Thomson to investigate the electrons emitted from metals by thermionic and photoelectric action. It employs simultaneous acceleration and deflection of the low-speed electrons ejected from the metal surface. Suppose particles of charge $+e$ are emitted from a surface or filament in the plane $x = 0$ (Figure 3.8) and are accelerated by a uniform electrostatic field $\mathscr{E}$ toward a collector plate in the plane $x = l$. A uniform magnetic field B is applied parallel to the Oz direction with the result that the particles are deflected to the left, in the Oy direction. Under suitable conditions the beam is diverted away from the collector and no current flows between the plates. The "cutoff" condition may be found from the equations of motion in the x and y directions. Parallel to Ox we have the relation

$$m\frac{d^2x}{dt^2} = e\mathscr{E} - Be\frac{dy}{dt},$$

and parallel to Oy

$$m\frac{d^2y}{dt^2} = Be\frac{dx}{dt}.$$

The latter equation is integrated, and, assuming that the particles started off with zero velocity at $x = 0$, we find

$$\frac{dy}{dt} = \frac{Be}{m}x,$$

which is substituted in the first equation to give

$$\frac{d^2x}{dt^2} + \frac{B^2e^2}{m^2}x = \frac{e\mathscr{E}}{m}.$$

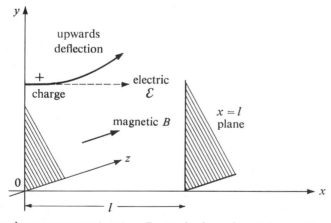

FIGURE 3.8 *The plane-magnetron situation. Positively charged particles start from the plane $x = 0$ and are accelerated by a uniform electrostatic field $\mathscr{E}$ toward the plane $x = l$, but are deflected by a uniform magnetic field B perpendicular to the plane xy. If B is strong enough, the current between $x = 0$ and $x = l$ is cut off.*

The equation may be solved by the substitution

$$x = \frac{m\mathscr{E}}{B^2 e}\left(1 - \cos\frac{Bet}{m}\right),$$ [3.3.11]

which satisfies the boundary conditions at $x = 0$. To find the cutoff condition we find the maximum value of x and put it equal to l; this maximum occurs at $(Bet/m) = \pi$ rad, so

$$l = \frac{2m\mathscr{E}}{B_c^2 e}\qquad (B_c = \text{cutoff field}).$$

Or, if V is the potential difference applied between the plates,

$$\mathscr{E} = \frac{V}{l}$$

and

$$\frac{e}{m} = \frac{2V}{B_c^2 l^2}.$$ [3.3.12]

In practice the field B is increased until the current between the plates disappears and e/m is calculated from the cutoff field B_c. At higher fields the particles describe cycloidal paths and return to the plane $x = 0$. A similar procedure may be followed with a cylindrical magnetron tube, in which particles are accelerated from a central filament toward a coaxial collector and are deflected by a magnetic field parallel to the cylindrical axis. The equations of motion are more complicated in this case but the cutoff field may be found from the simple relation

$$\frac{e}{m} = \frac{8V}{B_c^2 r^2}\qquad (r = \text{radius of the cylinder}).$$

3.4   Positive Rays and Isotopes

(a) Positive rays

The presence of positive rays traveling from the anode toward the cathode in a gas-discharge tube was detected by Goldstein in 1886, and these rays were investigated by Wien and others. It was shown that they are more easily deflected by fields than the cathode rays and that they can be detected with photographic plates, but accurate experiments were hindered by two factors which did not affect the work on cathode rays:

(i) the positive rays include ions of several kinds with different masses and charges;

(ii) their speeds are extremely variable because of frequent collisions with molecules of the residual gas in the discharge tube.

These difficulties were finally overcome when J. J. Thomson succeeded in measuring the specific charge of certain rays by the "parabola" method. The ions passed through a fine hole in the cathode of a discharge tube (Figure 3.9) into an evacuated space where they were influenced by *parallel* electrostatic and magnetic fields. This arrangement causes deflections both in the x and y directions as viewed on the detecting photographic plate, but ions of the same specific charge (q/M) are found to lie on a single parabolic trace. This result is derived from the deflection equations (3.3.3) and (3.3.8), as follows.

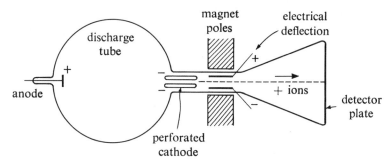

FIGURE 3.9   *J. J. Thomson's apparatus for analyzing the positive rays from a gas discharge; these pass through a hole in the cathode and are deflected by parallel electrostatic and magnetic fields.*

If the electrostatic field $\mathscr{E}$ is parallel to the y axis, the deflection in distance L (from the center of the deflecting plates) is

$$y = \frac{q\mathscr{E}lL}{Mv_0^2}.$$

A magnetic field B along the y axis produces a deflection parallel to the x axis given approximately by

$$x = \frac{qBlL}{Mv_0} \qquad \text{(for small } B\text{)}.$$

Elimination of the original speed v_0 then yields the relation

$$y = \frac{M\mathscr{E}}{qB^2Ll} x^2 \qquad\qquad [3.4.1]$$

so that the equation represents a parabola. In practice only a part of the full curve was recorded because the ions have a maximum velocity, which corresponds to a certain minimum deflection. The origin of the curve was located, however, by taking a second exposure with the electric or the magnetic field reversed; in this way, unambiguous results were obtained for the specific charge (q/M) for the first time.

(b) Isotopes

In Thomson's experiments several parabolic traces were always recorded and the number of these depended on the gas in the tube and the conditions of operation. Thus if a compound like methane (CH_4) was used, there would be traces due to $CH_4(+)$, $CH_3(+)$, also doubly charged ions and ions from traces of air and other impurities. For this reason, identification of the ion beams was extremely difficult. Eventually, however, it became clear that the monatomic gas neon consistently gave two parabolic traces corresponding to the same charge. The atomic masses were estimated at 20 and 22 for the two types of ion, whereas the accepted atomic weight of neon was 20.2. This evidence, combined with contemporary evidence from the natural radioactive series (see Section 6.1), showed that fractional atomic weights assigned to chemical elements are due to mixtures of *isotopes*, with identical chemical properties but different atomic masses. As is now well known, all elements have isotopes, either stable or unstable according to their nuclear properties, and isotopic masses are nearly, though not quite, integral multiples of the mass of the hydrogen atom.

Although the discovery of isotopes cleared up one of the major problems in chemistry, there remained considerable interest in the small discrepancies between the isotopic masses

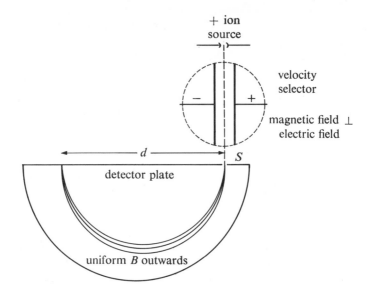

FIGURE 3.10   *The Bainbridge type of mass spectrograph in which positive ions pass through a velocity selector before entering a large vacuum chamber, where they are deflected by a uniform magnetic field B. The 180° deflection results in a focusing action as shown.*

and the nearest whole numbers. For a given isotope or *nuclide*,* the atomic mass number (*A*) is integral and is sometimes referred to as the *baryon number*. The precise atomic mass is expressed in carbon units (u), based on the definition that the neutral atomic mass for the isotope $_6C^{12}$ is exactly 12u. For example, the mass of the "ordinary" hydrogen atom, $_1H^1$, is 1.0078252u, where $1u = 1.6604 \times 10^{-27}$ kg.

The development of nuclear physics has made precise measurements of isotopic mass extremely important. The first accurate "mass spectrograph" was built by Aston in 1919 and it employed double focusing of the positive rays to produce sharp lines on a photographic detector. A simpler type of instrument, due to Dempster and Bainbridge (Figure 3.10), employs a large magnet to bend the positive-ion beam through an angle of 180°, thus sorting out ions of the same specific charge. The ions first pass through a velocity-selector of the crossed-field variety (Section 3.3.e), then emerge from a slit *S* into a large vacuum chamber where the uniform magnetic field bends their paths into semicircles. It may be seen that small errors in direction as the ions emerge from *S* are largely canceled by the focusing action of the field. The ions are finally recorded on a photographic plate or they may be allowed to pass through a second slit into a current detector.

In instruments designed for accurate mass measurements the most important factor is the resolving power for separating masses which are close together. In the 180° magnetic-field type the ion path has a radius of curvature

$$r = \frac{Mv}{Bq},$$

and the distance from the slit *S* to the final focus on the photographic plate is the diameter $d = 2r$. For two groups of ions with the same charge and a small difference in mass (ΔM),

* The word *nuclide* is given to a nuclear species identified by its charge number (*Z*) and mass number (*A*).

the corresponding difference in orbit diameter is

$$\Delta d = \frac{2v}{Bq}\Delta M,$$

so that

$$\frac{\Delta d}{d} = \frac{\Delta M}{M}, \qquad\qquad [3.4.2]$$

provided that the initial speed v is constant. To achieve high resolution, therefore, large magnets must be used.

In later types of mass spectrograph, high resolution is attained by repeated focusing of the ion beam. The aim of an experiment is not to find masses directly but to measure the ionic mass, and hence the isotopic mass, in terms of the carbon standard $_6C^{12} = 12u$. The most precise method for building up a table of accurate masses consists in matching ionic "doublets," that is, pairs of positive ions with very nearly the same specific charge. For example, the mass of a singly charged hydrogen molecule, $H_2(+)$, may be compared with that of a singly charged atom of the "heavy hydrogen" isotope, $D(+)$, usually called deuterium. The very small difference between doublet lines can be measured accurately and the method yields much greater precision than a direct comparison of masses. The singly

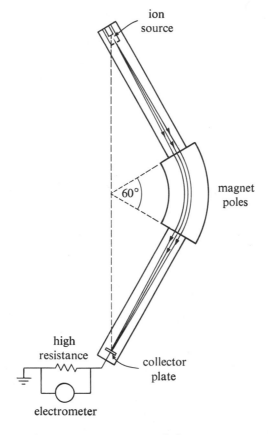

FIGURE 3.11 *Nier type of mass spectrometer used for measurements of isotopic abundance. The positive ions are magnetically deflected through 60° before being collected on an insulated plate and the ion current is measured with an electrometer.*

charged deuterium molecule, $D_2(+)$, with a mass of approximately 4 units (u) has very nearly the same specific charge as a triply charged carbon atom, $_6C^{12}(+++)$, which has a mass of 12u *less* three electrons. Repeated doublet comparisons lead to the establishment of standard masses for hydrogen and deuterium, in terms of the carbon unit. It is then convenient to use various hydrocarbons in finding the masses of other elements. For example, the methane molecule (CH_4) has a mass close to the mass of the oxygen isotope $_8O^{16}$, which may be standardized in terms of carbon and hydrogen. It should be noted that all mass data refer to the *neutral atoms*, each with a full complement of electrons, and suitable corrections must be made to find the masses of ions or bare nuclei.

A different type of instrument, called the mass spectrometer, is employed for measuring the abundance of isotopes in a mixture. In the Nier mass spectrometer (Figure 3.11) ion beams are focused by means of a magnet giving 60° deflection, with the source, detector, and the center of the magnet arcs all lined up. The beam falls on an insulated plate connected to the grid of an electrometer tube, which amplifies the signal sufficiently for recording via a dc amplifier. Different beams may be detected on different collectors simultaneously or they may be recorded successively by varying the magnetic field. This technique is of the highest importance in geophysics for measuring lead-isotope ratios and in physical chemistry and biology for the estimation of "tracers" consisting of stable isotopes. Such tracer isotopes can be injected into a complex molecular situation and their routes through various reactions are followed with the aid of the mass spectrometer.

3.5 The Electron Theory of Metals

(a) *The classical theory*

According to the results of J. J. Thomson's experiments, all atoms contain negatively charged electrons of small mass and high mobility, and this suggests a possible explanation of the high electrical conductivity of metallic solids. In 1900 Drude and Thomson independently proposed a theory, later developed by Lorentz, according to which a metal contains considerable numbers of free electrons traveling through a lattice of relatively immobile positive ions. The idea was confirmed experimentally in 1916 by Tolman and Stewart, who found that sudden stoppage of a rapidly-rotating coil of wire caused a pulse of current due to the persisting momentum of the free electrons. The classical electron theory attempted to explain the properties of metals in terms of kinetic concepts, including the ideas employed in Section 2.5.

In the metallic state, the atoms are supposed to lose their valence electrons (usually 1 or 2 per atom) to the "gas" of free electrons, so that the atoms are left positively charged. The positive ions are disposed in some form of crystal lattice, which is held together by the interactions of the ions with the electron gas. If there is equipartition of energy between the electrons and the lattice, which is at temperature T, we may write the kinetic energy of the electrons as

$$\tfrac{1}{2}m\overline{v^2} = \frac{3kT}{2} \quad \text{[from Equation (2.3.7)]}.$$

Also, if the electrons possess a Maxwellian velocity distribution, the square of the mean speed is

$$\bar{v}^2 = \frac{8kT}{\pi m} \quad \text{(Problem 2.8)}.$$

We now have to consider the effects of applying a uniform electrostatic field $\mathcal{E}$ to the assembly of electrons which are in random motion. It is clear that there will be a general drift antiparallel to the field direction (since the electrons carry negative charge) super-imposed on the random motion. Provided that this drift is much slower than the mean electron speed $\bar{v}$ it is possible to calculate the mean drift speed $\bar{u}$ in terms of a mean free path (L), defined for collisions of the electrons with ions of the lattice. Neglecting the drift speed u compared with v, we estimate the mean free time between collisions (τ) to be

$$\tau = \frac{L}{\bar{v}}. \qquad [3.5.1]$$

The field $\mathcal{E}$ exerts a force on each electron causing acceleration

$$\mathbf{a} = \frac{(-e)\mathcal{E}}{m}$$

and in time τ the gain in velocity antiparallel to $\mathcal{E}$ is

$$\mathbf{a}\tau = \frac{(-e)\mathcal{E}L}{m\bar{v}}.$$

Assuming that the electron is effectively stopped at each collision terminating a mean free path L, the mean drift velocity is

$$\bar{\mathbf{u}} = \tfrac{1}{2}\mathbf{a}\tau = \frac{(-e)\mathcal{E}L}{2m\bar{v}}. \qquad [3.5.2]$$

In a conductor of cross-sectional area A, containing n atoms per unit volume, each atom contributing z electrons to the electron gas, we can calculate the electron current $\mathbf{I}$ from the expression

$$\mathbf{I} = nz(-e)\bar{\mathbf{u}}A$$
$$= \frac{nze^2LA\mathcal{E}}{2m\bar{v}}. \qquad [3.5.3]$$

Assuming that each electron experiences a field of magnitude $\mathcal{E}$ due to an electrical potential difference (V) applied to the conductor of length l, we find

$$\mathcal{E} = V/l$$

and

$$I = \frac{nze^2LA}{2m\bar{v}l}V.$$

If the electrical conductivity of the material is σ,

$$I = \frac{\sigma A}{l}V,$$

so that theoretically

$$\sigma = \frac{nze^2L}{2m\bar{v}}. \qquad [3.5.4]$$

This simple version of the Drude-Lorentz theory serves to demonstrate certain important features of the classical treatment:

(i) by introducing a mean free path L, the drift speed is made proportional to the field, and it follows that Ohm's law should be obeyed;

(ii) the sign of the electrical "carriers" is immaterial since I is proportional to e^2;

(iii) the calculated conductivity should decrease with increasing temperature according to the variation of the term $\bar{v}$ in the denominator, that is, we should find $\sigma \propto T^{-\frac{1}{2}}$.

In fact, the electrical conductivity of most pure metals approximates to a T^{-1} variation, indicating that the simple theory is inadequate. More refined versions of the classical theory result in different numerical factors in the expression (3.5.4) but the essential features remain unchanged. It would appear that the artificial introduction of the mean free path L is an unsatisfactory device in dealing with the motion of electrons in a lattice.

(b) The law of Wiedemann and Franz

It is possible to devise a numerical test of the theory by comparing the electrical conductivity with the thermal conductivity of the same metal, on the assumption that the high thermal conductivities observed in metals are due to electron motions and are not properties of the lattice. This method has the effect of eliminating the factor L, because in the kinetic theory we found the thermal conductivity to be

$$K = \frac{nzm\bar{v}Ls_v}{3} \qquad \text{[from Equation (2.5.5)]}$$

for (nz) particles per unit volume, with effective specific heat s_v per unit mass. According to Equation (2.3.7) the specific heat for particles in translational motion is

$$s_v = \frac{3k}{2m}.$$

We therefore obtain

$$\frac{K}{\sigma} = \frac{2m^2\bar{v}^2 s_v}{3e^2} = \frac{m\bar{v}^2 k}{e^2}$$

or, with the substitution, $\bar{v}^2 = \frac{8kT}{\pi m}$, the ratio becomes

$$\frac{K}{\sigma} = \frac{8k^2T}{\pi e^2}. \qquad [3.5.5]$$

This equation expresses the law of Wiedemann and Franz, which is obeyed approximately by most metals. Not only do we find the correct type of variation with temperature, but we can also test the numerical value of the ratio $K/\sigma T$. According to the simple theory above we should find

$$\frac{K}{\sigma T} = \frac{8k^2}{\pi e^2} = 1.89 \times 10^{-8} \text{ mks units.}$$

For copper, we have the following data:

$T^\circ K$	K W/m$^\circ$K	σ mho/m	Ratio: $K/\sigma T$
273	3.85×10^2	6.40×10^7	2.2×10^{-8}
573	3.76	2.78	2.4
973	3.50	1.52	2.4.

Other metals give rather similar values of the quantity $K/\sigma T$ and, to this extent, the classical theory agrees with observation. At the same time, we have adduced no real evidence for the basic assumptions of the theory, concerning the electron carriers and the existence of an effective mean free path L. The expression (3.5.4) for the electrical conductivity contains the product (zL) and we have as yet no independent evidence about either factor (z or L).

(c) *The Hall effect*

Valuable information concerning the carriers of electric current is obtained from an effect discovered by Hall in 1879. When an electric current is passed through a thin metal strip which is placed perpendicular to a powerful magnetic field, an electromotive force is set up in the metal, perpendicular both to the field and the current. The effect may be understood by reference to Figure 3.8, in which an electric field $\mathscr{E}$ accelerates positive charges in the x direction, while a magnetic field $\mathbf{B}$ is applied across the current in the direction of the z axis. The charges are deflected in the y direction, producing a transverse current equivalent to that set up by an electric field in the y direction.

The Hall coefficient R_H for a material may be defined in terms of the transverse current density $\mathbf{j}_t$ (the current per unit area transverse to the main current) or the transverse electric field $\mathscr{E}_t$. Assuming that these are related by the same electrical conductivity σ as the longitudinal current and field, we can write

$$\mathbf{j}_t = \sigma \mathscr{E}_t.$$

The coefficient R_H is conventionally defined by the relation

$$\mathscr{E}_t = R_H[\mathbf{j} \times \mathbf{B}], \qquad [3.5.6]$$

where $\mathbf{j}$ is the longitudinal current density (along Ox in Figure 3.8). Hence, by substituting $\mathbf{j} = \sigma \mathscr{E}$, we find

$$\mathbf{j}_t = R_H \sigma^2[\mathscr{E} \times \mathbf{B}]. \qquad [3.5.7]$$

We see that, for positive charges, the coefficient R_H, as defined by Equation (3.5.6), is positive. If we dealt with negative charges instead, their motion would be to the left in Figure 3.8, but the magnetic field would deflect them in the same direction as the positive charges are deflected. The net result, for negative charges, must be an effective transverse electromotive force in the negative y direction, therefore a *negative* sign for R_H. It follows that a determination of the sign of R_H establishes the sign of electric charges carrying current.

The magnitude of the Hall coefficient can be estimated from the classical theory with the aid of relations established in Section 3.3f. The equations of motion for positive charges starting from the plane $x = 0$ with zero velocity yielded the solution for displacement parallel to the applied field

$$x = \frac{m\mathscr{E}}{B^2 e}\left(1 - \cos\frac{Bet}{m}\right), \qquad \text{[from Equation (3.3.11)]}$$

which leads to the velocity component in the x direction

$$\frac{dx}{dt} = \frac{\mathscr{E}}{B}\sin\frac{Bet}{m}.$$

If we assume that the time between collisions (τ) is so short that the quantity Bet/m is always small, we find the approximate velocity $u_x = \dfrac{e\mathscr{E}t}{m}$. If this expression is averaged over the time interval from $t = 0$ to $t = \tau$, the result is identical with the mean drift velocity $\bar{u}$ of Equation (3.5.2).

The transverse velocity component of the positive charges is

$$\frac{dy}{dt} = \frac{Be}{m}x = \frac{\mathscr{E}}{B}\left(1 - \cos\frac{Bet}{m}\right),$$

and for small time intervals we can replace the cosine term by the first two terms of the cosine expansion, obtaining

$$u_y = \frac{e^2 B \mathscr{E} t^2}{2m^2} \text{ , approximately.}$$

The mean drift velocity in the y direction is found by averaging the u_y expression over the time interval τ

$$\bar{u}_y = \frac{1}{\tau} \int_0^\tau u_y \, dt = \frac{e^2 B \mathscr{E} \tau^2}{6m^2} . \qquad [3.5.8]$$

The transverse current density j_t can be calculated

$$j_t = nze\bar{u}_y = \frac{nze^3 B \mathscr{E} \tau^2}{6m^2}$$

or, in terms of the conductivity $\left(\sigma = \dfrac{nze^2 \tau}{2m} \right)$,

$$j_t = \frac{2\sigma^2}{3nze} B \mathscr{E}. \qquad [3.5.9]$$

Comparison of this expression with Equation (3.5.7) shows that the Hall coefficient R_H is related to the carrier charge density in the material by the equation

$$R_H = \frac{2}{3nze} . \qquad [3.5.10]$$

Thus measurements of R_H should yield estimates of the product (nze) for metals, and the derived values of nze can be used to find the mean free time τ or the mean free path L. Moreover, the number of atoms per unit volume (n) is readily calculated from the atomic weight (M) and the density (ρ) with the equation

$$n = \frac{N^* \rho}{M} , \qquad [3.5.11]$$

which is related to Equation (3.1.3). Hence the number of electrons contributed per atom (z) may be calculated.

Experimental data for copper at 273°K are as follows:

Hall coefficient: $R_H = -7.2 \times 10^{-11}$ mks

Mass density: $\rho = 8.9 \times 10^3$ kg/m³

Atomic weight: $M = 63.5$

Calculated atomic density, from Equation (3.5.11),

$$n = \frac{6.0 \times 8.9 \times 10^{29}}{63.5}$$

$$= 8.4 \times 10^{28} \text{ atoms/m}^3$$

Number of free electrons per atom, from Equation (3.5.10),

$$z = \frac{0.67 \times 10^2}{8.4 \times 1.6 \times 7.2} = 0.7 \text{ approximately}$$

Moreover, we can use the conductivity equation (3.5.4), together with the observed Hall coefficient of copper, to find the mean free path and mean free time: the results are

$$L = 8.1 \times 10^{-9} \, \text{m}; \quad \tau = 7.8 \times 10^{-14} \, \text{sec.}$$

These results are eminently reasonable, but difficulties of interpretation arise when other metals are considered. Zinc, which is next to copper in the first transition series, has a *positive* Hall coefficient ($R_H = +10^{-10}$ mks approximately). Nor is this a rare phenomenon. The magnitudes of observed Hall coefficients are consistent with values of z close to 1, but it is clear that the simple electron theory cannot attach meaning to Hall coefficients of the wrong sign.

(d) Difficulties of the theory

Further difficulties are encountered when the specific heats of metals are studied. It has been shown in Section 2.4 that metals like copper possess the classical atomic heat (nearly 6 kcal/kmole °K), except at low temperatures, and that this result is entirely due to lattice vibrations. If, now, we adopt the basic postulate of the electron theory of metals, the z free electrons per atom must contribute considerably to the specific heat. The equipartition relation of Equation (2.3.7) indicates that the total internal energy of 1 kmole of the metal should be

$$E = 3RT + z \frac{3RT}{2}$$

and the specific heat of 1 kmole at constant volume becomes

$$C_v = 3R + \frac{3Rz}{2}. \tag{3.5.12}$$

This expression suggests that the atomic heat of a typical metal should be about 8 to 9 kcal/kmole °K, significantly higher than the experimental results.

The various difficulties arising in the electron theory of metals admitted of no easy solution and many aspects of quantum theory had to be developed before the picture cleared. The failure of classical theory in the realm of specific heats was no new thing, but could perhaps be explained as due to the breakdown of equipartition in the mixed assembly of massive ions and mobile electrons. The theory's partial success with the Wiedemann-Franz ratio indicated that electron mobility probably accounts for the high thermal conductivities of metals, but against this was the baffling positive Hall coefficient in certain metals. Fortunately the essential correctness of the electron theory was demonstrated by two effects in which electrons are emitted from metal surfaces, by the action of heat and of light.

3.6 The Thermionic and Photoelectric Effects

Both the thermionic effect, discovered by Edison in 1883, and the photoelectric effect in metals, detected first by H. Hertz in 1887, depend on the emission of electrons from a metal, or from a conducting solid such as graphite. Reliable experimental data are obtained only if the solid surfaces are clean and emission takes place into an evacuated space, where the electrons may be detected by the current drawn to a positively charged plate. Under normal conditions, only electrons are emitted and the identity of the particles was established by

J. J. Thomson's experiments to measure their specific charge (Section 3.3.f). These results provided support for the idea that electrons exist in metals in a highly mobile state.

(a) Diode characteristics

The most significant features of thermionic emission may be studied with a simple diode tube, in which the electron current flows through the space between an incandescent filament and an anode sealed into the bulb. Experiments lead to the following conclusions:

(i) the current depends on the anode potential in a complex manner (Figure 3.12); when the applied potential difference is low, the current rises fairly slowly from zero, but at high potentials it flattens off to a saturation value;

(ii) the saturation current (I_0) depends very sensitively on the nature of the filament and its temperature, the current rising with increasing temperature much more rapidly than the usual power-law relations.

The first observation may be explained on the assumption that the current is restricted at low field intensities by the presence of electrons outside the filament, which constitute a "space-charge" barrier to electrons escaping from the filament. At high anode potentials the space charge disappears and the saturation current is limited only by the intrinsic emission of the filament, which depends chiefly on the material and its temperature.

In the space-charge-limited region, a characteristic current-voltage relation was established by Child and Langmuir. We may derive this relation by considering electron flow in one direction only, for example between plane-parallel electrodes (Figure 3.13). Suppose that at any plane between the cathode ($x = 0$) and the anode ($x = l$), the potential is V, the field intensity $\mathscr{E}$, and the local electron density is n electrons/m³. The space-charge density is then

$$-ne \text{ C/m}^3$$

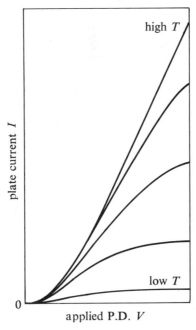

FIGURE 3.12 *Current-voltage curves obtained with a parallel-plate diode at different filament temperatures. At low voltages the current is limited by space charge but rapidly reaches a saturation value if the temperature is low.*

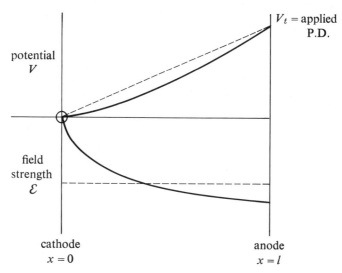

potential
V

V_t = applied
P.D.

field
strength
$\mathscr{E}$

cathode
$x = 0$

anode
$x = l$

FIGURE 3.13   *Variation of electric field strength ($\mathscr{E}$) and potential (V) in the region between parallel plates when space-charge effects are dominant. The dotted lines show the field and potential when no space charge is present.*

and Poisson's equation in one dimension takes the form

$$\frac{d^2V}{dx^2} = \frac{ne}{\varepsilon_0},$$ [3.6.1]

where ε_0 is the permittivity of free space.

The current density per unit area of cross section perpendicular to the field is constant for all x and its *magnitude* is given by the relation [from Equation (3.5.3)]

$$j = \frac{I}{A} = neu,$$

where u is the mean speed of the electrons.

The electrons are supposed to be accelerated from the cathode at potential $V = 0$ to the anode at $V = V_t$. If we assume that they were emitted with negligible speed, we can find the mean speed at any point with potential V from the energy equation

$$\tfrac{1}{2}mu^2 = eV,$$ [3.6.2]

so that

$$ne = \frac{I}{A}\sqrt{\frac{m}{2eV}}$$

$$= \varepsilon_0 \frac{d^2V}{dx^2} \qquad \text{by Poisson's equation.}$$

Solution of this differential equation is achieved by substituting for the potential gradient as follows:

$$\mathscr{E} = -\frac{dV}{dx},$$

$$\frac{d^2V}{dx^2} = \frac{dV}{dx}\frac{d}{dV}\left(\frac{dV}{dx}\right) = \mathscr{E}\frac{d\mathscr{E}}{dV},$$

so that

$$\mathscr{E} \, d\mathscr{E} = \frac{I}{\varepsilon_0 A} \sqrt{\frac{m}{2e}} \, V^{-\frac{1}{2}} \, dV.$$

The space charge is supposed to be effective in reducing the field to zero near the cathode, so we integrate the equation with the boundary condition $\mathscr{E} = 0$ when $V = 0$ and obtain

$$\tfrac{1}{2}\mathscr{E}^2 = \frac{I}{\varepsilon_0 A} \sqrt{\frac{m}{2e}} \, 2V^{\frac{1}{2}} .$$

The field intensity is therefore related to the potential V by the equation

$$\mathscr{E} = -\frac{dV}{dx} = \left(\frac{4I}{\varepsilon_0 A} \sqrt{\frac{m}{2e}} \right)^{\frac{1}{2}} V^{\frac{1}{4}}.$$

Integration with the boundary condition $V = 0$ at $x = 0$ yields

$$4V^{\frac{3}{4}} = 3 \left(\frac{4I}{\varepsilon_0 A} \sqrt{\frac{m}{2e}} \right)^{\frac{1}{2}} x.$$

Finally, substitution of the anode condition

$$V = V_t \qquad \text{at} \qquad x = l$$

gives the current-voltage relation

$$I = \frac{4\varepsilon_0 A}{9l^2} \sqrt{\frac{2e}{m}} \, V_t^{\frac{3}{2}}, \qquad\qquad\qquad [3.6.3]$$

which is the Child-Langmuir result for a plane-parallel diode.

The power-law relation

$$I \propto V_t^{\frac{3}{2}}$$

is typical of conditions where space-charge effects are dominant. It should be noted, however, that at very small potential differences the relation may not be obeyed because of small "contact-potential" differences between cathode and anode. At high voltages, also, the space charge is effectively removed and the current is limited by the intrinsic emission from the cathode.

(b) The work function φ

The variation of the saturation current with temperature was first explained by Richardson in terms of the electron theory of metals. Despite the difficulties of the early theory, it provides a useful picture of the energy relations of electrons inside and outside a solid surface. The positive lattice ions must attract the electrons to some extent, so the electrons inside the metal have negative potential energy relative to their potential energy outside. This difference in potential energy constitutes a "potential barrier" which tends to prevent the free electrons from escaping. In Figure 3.14 we plot the potential energy per electron as a function of distance along a line passing through a few lattice points near the edge of the metal. At each lattice point the potential energy becomes very large in the negative sense, although the electrons presumably do not fall into low-energy states because of the bound electrons remaining on each atom of the metal. In between the atoms the potential energy is supposed to be smoothed out to an average value for electrons in the "valence" or conduction levels. Taking the average energy outside the metal to be zero, we denote the

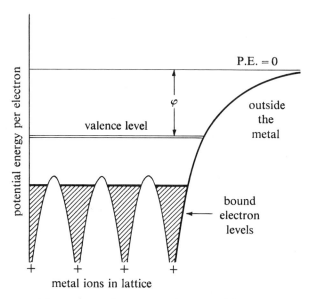

FIGURE 3.14 *The potential energy per electron as a function of distance near the surface of a metal. The "free" electron level (the valence level) is at energy* $-\varphi$ *relative to the space outside the metal, so each electron must surmount a barrier* φ *in order to leave the metal surface.*

average valence-electron energy inside the metal as $-\varphi$, where φ is defined as the energy required to extract an electron from the valence level and release it with zero kinetic energy outside the metal surface.

In practice the *work function* of the metal surface (φ) is often expressed in electron volts, because in many experimental arrangements the kinetic energies of electrons are estimated by measuring the retarding potential difference (in volts) which is required to stop the electron flow. In the case of an electron beam accelerated from rest by an applied potential difference (V_a) we have, from Equation (3.6.2),

$$\tfrac{1}{2}mv^2 = eV_a$$

so the kinetic energy acquired by one electron in passing through a potential difference of 1 V is 1.6×10^{-19} J. This is a convenient unit in many branches of atomic physics and it is frequently abbreviated as eV.

In Richardson's theory of the thermionic effect, the electrons in the valence band of the metal are all supposed to have potential energy $-\varphi$ per electron, but some electrons may have sufficient kinetic energy to surmount the potential barrier. By applying the Boltzmann statistics to the electron assembly, we can estimate the probability of an electron escaping.* The number of electrons with kinetic energy ε is given by the classical expression

$$N(\varepsilon) \propto \exp\left(-\frac{\varepsilon}{kT}\right),$$

where the exponential term will clearly dominate the behavior of $N(\varepsilon)$ as a function of temperature T. An electron can escape at the surface only if ε exceeds the barrier height φ.

* It should be recognized that electrons in a metal actually obey the statistics of Fermi and Dirac (see Section 7.15); however, the present treatment is sufficiently accurate for the purpose of discussion.

Concentrating on the dominant exponential term, we can find the total probability of escape by integrating over all values of ε exceeding φ

$$P(> \varphi) \propto \int_{\varphi}^{\infty} \exp\left(-\frac{\varepsilon}{kT}\right) d\varepsilon = kT \exp\left(-\frac{\varphi}{kT}\right). \qquad [3.6.4]$$

This classical result shows clearly why the saturation current in a diode varies extremely rapidly with the filament temperature T. Different theories give different powers of T in front of the exponential term, but the latter is so powerful that in practice satisfactory straight lines are obtained by plotting $\ln I_0$ against T^{-1}. The slope of such a graph leads directly to a determination of the work function φ. It is found that φ depends on the state and cleanliness of the metal surface, but consistent experimental results are obtainable with metals like tungsten; φ values for metals vary in the region between 2 and 5 eV.

(c) The photoelectric effect

The photoelectric effect in metals consists in the ejection of electrons from the surface by the action of light, notably by ultraviolet radiation. The phenomenon was investigated in 1902 by Lenard, who showed that the number of electrons emitted per second is proportional to the intensity of the incident light. The maximum energy of the electrons, however, does *not* depend on the intensity, as would be expected on the basis of the wave theory of light; the energy is related only to the frequency of the incident light and the metal used. No photoelectric emission occurs at all below a certain threshold frequency, whatever the intensity of the light. This is undoubtedly paradoxical from the wave point of view—apparently "waves" of infinitesimal amplitude are capable of ejecting electrons with energies as great as those ejected by large-amplitude waves. Moreover, it was found later that, even with weak sources of light, the electrons are emitted almost instantaneously when the light is turned on; there is no "induction period" which would enable energy to be built up before being concentrated on one electron.

The intense difficulties of interpretation raised by the photoelectric effect were partially removed by Einstein in 1905. He boldly adopted Planck's hypothesis of 1900 that radiant energy does not occur in continuously divisible amounts but is quantized in discrete units depending on the frequency (v) of the light. The Planck energy quantum is

$$\varepsilon = hv, \qquad [3.6.5]$$

where h is Planck's constant, the "quantum of action" with the numerical value 6.6×10^{-34} J sec. An alternative way of expressing the quantum relation is in terms of the angular frequency (ω), when we write

$$\varepsilon = \hbar\omega, \qquad [3.6.6]$$

where $\hbar$ (the "Dirac h") is Planck's constant divided by 2π.

Einstein supposed that in the photoelectric effect each ejected electron received its energy from one quantum of the incident light. Allowing for the work done in extracting the electron from the metal, that is, the work function φ, he produced a simple equation for the maximum kinetic energy of emission

$$\tfrac{1}{2}mv^2 = hv - \varphi. \qquad [3.6.7]$$

This gives a linear relation between the electron energy ($\tfrac{1}{2}mv^2$) and the frequency v; the occurrence of a threshold for emission is seen if we write $\varphi = hv_0$, when the equation becomes

$$\tfrac{1}{2}mv^2 = h(v - v_0). \qquad [3.6.8]$$

No emission can occur until the frequency exceeds the value ν_0, which is directly proportional to the work function of the metal.

Einstein's photoelectric equation was tested experimentally by Hughes and by Millikan, who established its accuracy over a wide range of frequencies and measured the value of h, which agreed with independent measurements. Determinations of the work function φ have also been made for several metals, and the results for tungsten agree satisfactorily with data obtained from the thermionic effect.* It is clear that the quantum theory of radiation gives a correct account of the photoelectric effect in metals; the remaining difficulties lie in reconciling the new ideas with older views concerning the nature of light. A great body of experimental evidence exists in support of the wave theory, but this theory seems inadequate to deal with interactions between atoms and radiation, a subject explored in the next chapter.

3.7 Ionization in Gases

(a) Ion-chamber characteristics

The study of electrical discharges in gases at low pressure led to the discovery of cathode rays and the identification of the electron (Section 3.2), also to the analysis of positive rays (Section 3.4). Other investigations were carried out, by J. J. Thomson and Rutherford among others, into the conductivity of gases at normal and high pressures. In order to obtain steady currents in an ionization chamber at ordinary pressure, it is necessary to provide a constant external source of ionization, such as an x-ray tube operated nearby or a radioactive deposit inside the chamber. The currents produced are extremely small but may be measured by means of a high resistance in series with the chamber (Figure 3.15), with an electrometer to record the potential drop across the resistance.

When the ionization current is plotted against the potential difference applied across the chamber, it is found that Ohm's law is not obeyed (Figure 3.16). The current rises from zero toward a saturation value (I_0) which depends only on the amount of ionization supplied by the x rays or radioactive material. In the saturation region, therefore, nearly all the ions created must be collected by the electrodes. At lower voltages some phenomenon obviously causes loss of ions, while at high voltages excess current can be obtained as a result of ion-multiplication processes.

The behavior of ions in a gas subjected to an electric field is extremely complex, but a discussion of the data is possible if we introduce the following concepts:

(i) the ionic mobility (μ_+ for positive ions, μ_- for negative ions) is defined as the ratio of the mean drift speed (u_+ or u_-) to the electric field intensity ($\mathscr{E}$);

(ii) a recombination coefficient (α) may be defined for simple binary processes in which positive and negative ions recombine to form neutral molecules;

(iii) the diffusion coefficient (D_i) for ions is defined in a way similar to that for molecules (Section 2.5c);

(iv) in strong fields ion multiplication is important and the *first Townsend coefficient* (ζ) is introduced to account for electron-induced "avalanche" processes.

A complete analysis is not easily presented, but the main features of the curve in Figure 3.15 deserve consideration. In the first place, suppose that an arbitrary lifetime (τ) is

* C. Herring and M. H. Nichols, Rev. Mod. Phys., **21**, 185 (1949).

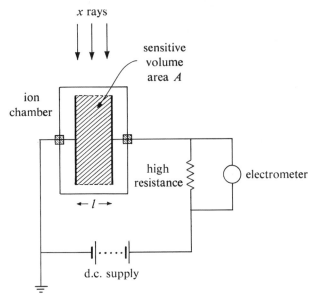

FIGURE 3.15 *Circuit for measuring the ionization current in a gas subjected to the action of x rays. The parallel-plate chamber has an effective volume of (lA) if the plates are close together.*

assigned to each ion and that a constant mobility (μ) obtains, so that we can write

$$u = \mu\mathscr{E} \quad \text{[by analogy with Equation (3.5.2) in the theory of metals].} \quad [3.7.1]$$

Then one electrode can collect ions which are within a distance ($u\tau$) and if ($u\tau$) is less than the interelectrode separation (l), the current is proportional to ($u\tau$) and therefore to $\mathscr{E}$. On the other hand, if ($u\tau$) is considerably greater than the distance l, all ions are collected and the saturation current is recorded.

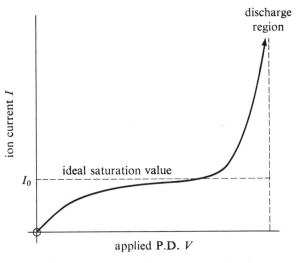

FIGURE 3.16 *The variation of ionization current (for a constant ionizing source) with the applied voltage in a gas at normal pressure. Ion losses prevent saturation at low voltages and ion multiplication leads to discharge at high voltages.*

The product $(u\tau)$ therefore provides a simple criterion for judging the approach of I to its saturation value, which can be worked out as follows. In a parallel-plate chamber of electrode area A, let

$$I_0 = \text{saturation current}$$

and

$$Q = \text{number of ion pairs created per unit volume per second.}$$

If all the ions are singly charged (with charge e), the saturation current collected at either electrode is

$$I_0 = QAle \qquad [3.7.2]$$

so that the quantity Q is readily estimated from experimental data.

At small voltages we can find the *I-V* relation in terms of the ion mobilities. The current is the sum of the positive and negative charges flowing through the gas per second; across any plane parallel to the electrodes the current (of singly charged ions) is

$$I = A(n_+ eu_+ + n_- eu_-)$$
$$= eA(n_+ \mu_+ + n_- \mu_-)\mathscr{E}', \qquad [3.7.3]$$

where n_+, n_- are the numbers of ions per unit volume,
$\quad \mathscr{E}'$ is the local field strength (which may be modified by the presence of space charge).

Under ideal conditions, the situation is simplified by the equality of the positive and negative ion concentrations (although this cannot obtain near the electrodes). If we assume that

$$n_+ = n_- = n_0$$

and that $\mathscr{E}' = V/l$, the current is

$$I = n_0 eA(\mu_+ + \mu_-)\frac{V}{l}.$$

Also, the steady-state ion concentration n_0 is related to the ion-creation rate Q and the effective ion lifetime

$$n_0 = Q\tau,$$

so that the current-voltage relation should be linear

$$I = QeA\tau(\mu_+ + \mu_-)\frac{V}{l}. \qquad [3.7.4]$$

The rate of recombination of the positive and negative ions is important in determining the lifetimes of the ions. In simple binary collisions, the recombination rate per unit volume of gas is proportional to the product of the local ion concentrations

$$\frac{-dn_+}{dt} = \frac{-dn_-}{dt} = \alpha n_+ n_-.$$

In fact this equation also is highly idealized because many different recombination processes are important in actual gases. Adopting the equation in the case where Q ion pairs are created per unit volume per second and the ion concentrations are equal everywhere $(n_+ = n_- = n)$, we find

$$\frac{dn}{dt} = Q - \alpha n^2. \qquad [3.7.5]$$

In the steady state, $\dfrac{dn}{dt} = 0$ and we have $n_0 = \sqrt{\dfrac{Q}{\alpha}}$. The effective lifetime is

$$\tau = \frac{n_0}{Q} = \frac{1}{\sqrt{Q\alpha}} \, .$$

The exact meaning of the quantity τ is found by solving Equation (3.7.5) in the case when the source of ions is switched off at $t = 0$. We have

$$\frac{dn}{dt} = -\alpha n^2 \qquad \text{for} \quad t > 0$$

with the solution

$$\alpha t = \frac{1}{n} - \frac{1}{n_0}$$

or

$$n = \frac{n_0}{1 + t/\tau} \, . \tag{3.7.6}$$

This relation shows that the ion concentration falls to half its value in time τ and that the rate of decrease is very slow. Indeed the mean lifetime is strictly infinite and the use of τ is therefore somewhat unsatisfactory. Nevertheless the relation between n and t is supported by experimental evidence and various measurements of the recombination coefficient α have been made; with I, Q, and τ determined under suitable conditions, Equation (3.7.4) yields an estimate for the sum of the ion mobilities. This result may be compared with independent data concerning the individual mobilities.

(b) Diffusion and mobility

A process which introduces complications into the theory for the weak-field situation is that of diffusion, which has been ignored so far. We define the coefficient D_i for some type of ion by the same relation as that used in kinetic theory

$$\frac{dn}{dt} = A D_i \frac{dn}{dx} , \tag{3.7.7}$$

where only motions in the x direction are considered. If the mean drift speed is u, we may write

$$nuA = A D_i \frac{dn}{dx} ,$$

so that

$$u = \frac{D_i}{n} \frac{dn}{dx} \, .$$

The ions are supposed to be of the same character as the gas molecules exerting pressure on a surface, so that we can relate the concentration gradient dn/dx to an equivalent pressure gradient dP/dx through the kinetic equation

$$P = \frac{nm\overline{v^2}}{3} ,$$

whence

$$dP = \frac{m\overline{v^2}}{3} \, dn$$

and

$$\frac{dP}{P} = \frac{dn}{n} \, .$$

The drift speed is therefore expressible in terms of dP/dx

$$u = \frac{D_i}{P} \frac{dP}{dx}.$$

Now the pressure difference (dP) multiplied by the area A is the force (dF) acting on the ions in a volume of dimensions A by dx, containing ($nA\,dx$) ions. The force per ion is therefore

$$\frac{dF}{nA\,dx} = \frac{A\,dP}{nA\,dx} = \frac{uP}{nD_i}.$$

This effective force due to diffusion is compared with the electrostatic force due to the field $\mathscr{E}$ in order to find a relation between the diffusion coefficient D_i and the ion mobility. Using Equation (3.7.1), we write down the force per ion

$$e\mathscr{E} = \frac{eu}{\mu}$$

and, if this expression is identified with $\dfrac{uP}{nD_i}$, we find

$$\frac{\mu}{D_i} = \frac{ne}{P}. \qquad [3.7.8]$$

For singly charged ions, therefore, there is a constant ratio between μ and D_i. Its numerical value can be found by substituting $P = 10^5$ N/m², $n = 2.7 \times 10^{25}$ m^{-3} at STP, and $e = 1.6 \times 10^{-19}$ C into Equation (3.7.8), when we obtain

$$\frac{\mu}{D_i} = 43 \text{ V}^{-1}. \qquad [3.7.9]$$

In 1900 Townsend used independent measurements of D_i and μ to obtain a value for e, but this result was necessarily approximate. The relation (3.7.9) is often employed to find D_i from the measured mobility of an ion. It is interesting to note that values of D_i are much less than the diffusion coefficients for neutral molecules derived either from Equation (2.5.4) or by experiment. This surprising effect is attributed to clustering of neutral molecules around an ion, which causes its mobility to be much less than that of a neutral molecule by itself.

Even more pronounced deviations from the estimates of kinetic theory are observed for negative ions in certain gases such as pure argon or nitrogen. In these cases it is clear that the negative carriers are electrons, with high effective mobility. Since electrons lose very little energy when they collide elastically with massive molecules, in an electric field they may gain energy greatly exceeding the equipartition energy. Such an effect might indeed be present in electron motions within a metal also, but there the massive lattice ions are much closer together than the molecules in a gas.

In practice the electron drift speeds are expressed graphically as functions of the parameter ($\mathscr{E}/P$) and the curves obtained are usually complex. Where an electron mobility (μ_e) can be usefully defined, the electron diffusion coefficient (D_e) is calculated from the relation

$$\frac{\mu_e}{D_e} = \frac{ne}{\eta P}.$$

In this equation the quantity η is the ratio of the mean electron energy to the mean energy of a molecule and it may reach large values (several hundreds) in some cases.

(c) Ion multiplication

Electron speeds are particularly important in the region where ion multiplication first occurs (Figure 3.16), because at moderate voltages only electrons are likely to have energy sufficient to ionize the molecules of a gas. Townsend carried out measurements of the ion current in a chamber where the mean field $\mathscr{E}$ was kept constant at a high value while the electrode separation (l) was increased steadily. In the ion-multiplication region he found that the current increased exponentially with l according to the relation

$$I = I_0 \exp{(\zeta l)}. \qquad [3.7.10]$$

If it is assumed that an electron creates, on the average, ζ ion pairs for each unit length traveled in the gas, the equation of ion growth is

$$dn = \zeta n \, dl$$

with the solution

$$n = n_0 \exp{(\zeta l)}. \qquad [3.7.11]$$

Here n is the electron density and ζ is supposed to be constant if $\mathscr{E}$ is constant. Under these conditions, the electrons lose considerable energy at each ionizing collision and their average energy does not increase, despite the high field. With electrons maintaining a constant mean speed, the current relation (3.7.10) follows directly from the ion-density equation (3.7.11).

With the introduction of the first Townsend coefficient ζ it is possible to treat the problems of ion multiplication produced by electrons in gases at normal pressures. Over a limited region of applied fields $\mathscr{E}$ the total ion current collected remains proportional to the saturation current (I_0) and therefore to the ion-creation rate Q. This region is employed in the operation of "proportional counters," which are cylindrical ionization chambers designed to record the passage of ionizing particles through the gas. In the ion-multiplication region of Figure 3.16, the electrical signal given by the counter is considerably larger than the signal obtained in the saturation region. For this reason the proportional counter is often used to detect low-energy particles, although there are also advantages in using a counter in the saturation region if the particles spend sufficient energy in the gas (see Section 9.2).

The cylindrical ion counter can be rendered extremely sensitive by raising the applied voltage until the gas is able to go into overall discharge whenever an ion appears; this is the principle of the "Geiger-Müller" counter, which produces an avalanche effect every time an ionizing particle passes through it. Thus the signal is independent of the original number of ions produced by the particle. This feature is a great advantage in recording weakly ionizing particles, but the Geiger counter's lack of discrimination is often a drawback in practice and proportional counters are therefore preferred in many experimental situations.

FOR FURTHER READING

Conduction in gases:

J. J. THOMSON and G. P. THOMSON, *The Conduction of Electricity through Gases*, (Cambridge University Press, New York, 1928) Vol. I, 3rd ed.

L. B. LOEB, *Fundamental Processes of Electrical Discharges in Gases* (J. Wiley & Sons, New York, 1939).

Electron optics:

J. R. PIERCE, *The Theory and Design of Electron Beams* (D. Van Nostrand Co., Princeton, 1949).

Mass spectrometers:

K. T. BAINBRIDGE, article in *Experimental Nuclear Physics*, ed., E. Segré, (J. Wiley & Sons, New York, 1953) Vol. I.

PROBLEMS FOR CHAPTER 3

DATA REQUIRED:

Specific charge of the electron: 1.76×10^{11} C/kg
Specific charge of the H^+ ion: 9.6×10^7 C/kg
Electronic charge: $e = 1.6 \times 10^{-19}$ C
Boltzmann's constant: $k = 1.4 \times 10^{-23}$ J/°K
Planck's constant: $h = 6.6 \times 10^{-34}$ J sec
Velocity of light *in vacuo*: $c = 3.0 \times 10^8$ m/sec
Number of molecules per kilomole: $N^* = 6.0 \times 10^{26}$

3.1. A solution of sodium chloride (mol.wt. 58.5) is electrolyzed and it is found that a current of 1 A liberates 1.3×10^{-3} kg of chlorine (at.wt. 35.5) in one hour. Sodium chloride crystals of density 2.17×10^3 kg/m³ are analyzed by x rays and the unit cell parameter (*a* in Figure 3.1) is found to be 5.6×10^{-10} m. From these data calculate the charge on a monovalent ion.

3.2. The salts potassium fluoride (KF, mol.wt. 58.1) and potassium chloride (KCl, mol.wt. 74.6) both possess the cubic crystalline structure of sodium chloride (Figure 3.1). The density of KF is 2.48×10^3 kg/m³ and that of KCl is 1.98×10^3 kg/m³: show that these figures are consistent with the idea that the effective size of ions in one column of the periodic table increases with increasing atomic weight.

3.3. In a Millikan oil-drop experiment, a certain droplet was found to fall freely in air at a steady rate of 1.15×10^{-4} m/sec, between horizontal plates 3 mm apart. When an electrical potential difference of 400 V was applied between the plates, the droplet rose steadily at 1.2×10^{-5} m/sec; while at 300 V, the droplet fell steadily at 1.8×10^{-5} m/sec. Find the magnitude of the charge on the drop, given that the viscosity of air is 1.8×10^{-5} mks units, and the density of the oil used was 900 kg/m³.

3.4. In a cathode-ray tube electrons are accelerated from rest through a potential difference V_a before passing between deflecting plates maintained at constant potential difference V. Show that the deflection of the beam depends only on V, V_a, and the dimensions of the tube and plates. Calculate the deflection produced on a screen 30 cm away from deflecting plates 2 cm long and 0.7 cm apart when $V = 20$ V and $V_a = 1000$ V.

3.5. Show that the expression (3.3.4) for the "refraction" of particles at a set of equipotential surfaces gives the correct result for the deflection of particles entering a uniform field parallel to the equipotential surfaces (Figure 3.3).

3.6. In an experiment to determine e/m for electrons by J. J. Thomson's method, the particles were deflected by a uniform electrostatic field of 5×10^4 V/m applied between plates 0.05 m long. The deflection produced on a screen placed 0.3 m away from the center of the plates was 0.05 m. This deflection was exactly canceled by applying a magnetic field of strength 10^{-3} weber/m² coextensive with the electric field. Find the speed of the electrons, their specific charge, and the accelerating voltage.

3.7. In a cathode-ray tube electrons are accelerated through a potential difference of 600 V before entering a magnetic field at right angles to their initial velocity and of strength 8×10^{-4} weber/m². Calculate the radius of curvature of the electron paths in the field; also the deflection of the electrons measured transverse to their original direction after they have traveled 0.05 m in the field (measured parallel to their original direction). Compare the result of using the quasi-parabolic approximation with the exact result.

3.8. In an experiment to measure e/m for electrons, the particles are accelerated from rest through a potential difference V_a and then pass through a small hole. An axial magnetic field of strength 10^{-3} weber/m² focuses an electronic image of the hole on to a screen 0.5 m from the hole. If this is the first focus, find V_a, also the value of V_a which would give a second-order focus at the same distance.

3.9. In a plane-magnetron type of experiment (Figure 3.8) electrons are emitted from the surface $x = 0$ with initial velocity v_0 (parallel to the x direction). Show from energy considerations or otherwise that the cutoff magnetic field B_c is related to the distance l and voltage V by

$$B_c = \frac{1}{l}\sqrt{\frac{2m}{-e}} \left\{ V + \frac{mv_0^2}{(-2e)} \right\}^{1/2}.$$

Hence devise an experimental method for testing Einstein's photoelectric equation (3.6.7).

3.10. A beam of H⁺ ions passes for 0.1 m through a region which is subject to a uniform electrostatic field of 10^5 V/m and a magnetic field of 10^{-1} weber/m² acting in parallel, both perpendicular to the ion beam. What is the pattern traced by the ions on a screen placed at the end of this region?

3.11. In a Bainbridge type of mass spectrograph (Figure 3.10) carbon ions are accelerated and those of speed 10^5 m/sec are filtered so as to pass into a uniform magnetic field of strength 5×10^{-2} weber/m². They are bent through a total angle of 180° before they strike a detector plate. Calculate the diameter of the trajectory of singly-charged C^{12} ions, also the separation of C^{12} and C^{13} ions on the plate.

3.12. Prove analytically that the separation (Δd) of ions, of the same charge but differing by ΔM in mass, on the plate of a 180° mass spectrograph is given by

$$\frac{\Delta d}{d} = \frac{\Delta M}{2M},$$

if the ions are accelerated through a fixed potential difference before they enter the magnetic field.

3.13. In a high-resolution mass spectrograph, the difference in specific charge (q/M) between $C^{12}(+ + +)$ ions and $D_2(+)$ ions is measured as 0.705%, the deuterium ions having the lower specific charge. Under similar conditions, the difference in specific charge between $H_2(+)$ ions and $D(+)$ ions is found to be 0.0775%, the hydrogen molecules being the more massive. Given that one electron has a mass of 0.000549u, find the neutral atomic masses of D and H in carbon-12 units (u).

3.14. Proton (H⁺ ions) are accelerated in a cyclotron by a radio-frequency field which is in resonance with the frequency of revolution of the protons in a uniform magnetic field B. If $B = 0.8$ weber/m², calculate the correct frequency for resonance.

3.15. Assuming that the classical electron theory of metallic conduction applies to carbon (at.wt. 12), which has a conductivity of 2×10^4 mho/m at 300°K and density 2.3×10^3 kg/m³, show that the number of free electrons per atom (z) is much less than 1 if the mean free path is supposed to exceed the (graphite) lattice spacing of 6.7×10^{-10} m.

3.16. If each atom in metallic gold (at.wt. 197, density 19.3×10^3 kg/m³) contributes one electron to the "electron gas," what is the Hall coefficient R_H for this metal? In practice R_H may be measured by finding the angular shift of equipotential lines in a long, thin specimen of the metal when the transverse magnetic field is switched on. Suppose that a thin gold strip carries a current density of 10^7 A/m² in a transverse field $B = 1.0$ weber/m²: what is the angular displacement of equipotential lines if the conductivity of gold is 5×10^7 mho/m?

3.17. An experiment on the saturation current obtained from a tungsten filament at different temperatures yielded

Temp. °K	1900	2000	2200	2300	2500
I_0 (μA)	0.7	1.6	21	65	480

Plot a graph to test Richardson's relation [Equation (3.6.4)] (retaining only the exponential term) and hence find the work function for tungsten approximately.

3.18. Show that the energy of a light quantum (V in eV) is related to the corresponding wavelength (λ in m) by
$$\lambda V = 1.24 \times 10^{-6} \text{ V m.}$$

Hence find the wavelength (*in vacuo*) corresponding to the photoelectric threshold for sodium metal, if the work function is 2.46 eV.

3.19. Measurements of the ionic diffusion coefficient and mobility for negative oxygen ions gave (at $P = 10^5$ N/m²)
$$D_i = 4 \times 10^{-6} \text{ m}^2/\text{sec:} \quad \mu = 1.8 \times 10^{-4} \text{ m}^2/\text{V sec.}$$

Calculate an approximate value for the charge per ion.

3.20. If the ion concentration (n) and the electric-field intensity ($\mathscr{E}$) are nearly uniform in a parallel-plate chamber, show that Equations (3.7.2) and (3.7.3) lead to a current-voltage relation of the type
$$V^2 = \frac{I^2 \alpha l^3}{eA(I_0 - I)(\mu_+ + \mu_-)^2}$$
if diffusion effects are negligible.

3.21. In a cylindrical magnetron, electrons are emitted with negligible velocity from a fine axial filament and travel toward the cylindrical anode, of radius r, maintained at potential V relative to the filament ($V = 0$). An axial magnetic field is applied and this supplies a deflecting torque acting on the electrons. Use the energy and angular-momentum relations to show that the cutoff field (B_c) is given by $B_c^2 r^2 = \dfrac{8mV}{(-e)}$.

3.22(a) Set up Poisson's equation in cylindrical coordinates for the special case where the potential V is a function only of the radius (r).

(b) Apply the equation to the problem of space charge in a cylindrical diode with anode radius b and an axial filament of negligible radius. Assume that V can vary with r only according to a simple power law, and use the constancy of the total current (I) to derive the relation
$$I/l = \frac{8\pi\varepsilon_0}{9b} \sqrt{\frac{2e}{m}} V_t^{3/2},$$
where I/l is the current per unit length of the diode (assumed to be very long).

❖❖❖❖❖❖❖❖❖❖❖❖❖❖❖❖❖❖❖❖❖❖❖❖❖❖❖❖❖❖❖❖❖❖

CHAPTER IV

ATOMIC INTERACTIONS
WITH RADIATION

One of the greatest achievements of nineteenth-century physics was the electromagnetic theory of radiation, formulated by Maxwell in the early 1860's. Not only did this theory put physical optics on an entirely new basis, but it suggested a means by which radiation can act upon atoms, namely, through the interactions of electric and magnetic fields with charged particles forming part of the atomic structure. The growing body of evidence concerning the existence of such particles led in due course to the classical electron theory of Lorentz, in which the interactions of electrons with the electromagnetic field were fully developed. This theory was able to account for many observed phenomena like dispersion, scattering, and the "normal" Zeeman effect.

However, a detailed theory of atomic interactions must aim to explain the vast amount of spectroscopic data concerning spectral lines emitted by the atoms of different elements. The work of Balmer, Rydberg, and others showed that hydrogen and the alkali metals emit lines which form distinct series, but all attempts to account for these series by classical methods failed. It became clear that light possesses certain properties which are not embodied in the electromagnetic theory, despite the successes of that theory in the realms of radio propagation and physical optics.

These new properties of radiation were discovered by Planck in 1900. His studies of the continuous "blackbody" radiation convinced him that the equipartition theorem cannot apply to an assembly of electromagnetic waves in an enclosure, and he boldly introduced the quantum hypothesis, according to which radiant energy is available only in discrete amounts. The quantum theory accounted for the blackbody energy distribution and was successfully applied by Einstein to the photoelectric effect in metals and the specific heats of solids. Not only did the new theory explain phenomena in which equipartition breaks down but it also provided the essential clue toward solving the problems of interaction between atoms and radiation.

The discovery of x rays by Röntgen in 1895 stimulated research in many fields but the electromagnetic character of the rays was not established for several years. Indeed the development of quantum theory raised profound questions concerning the nature of radiation in general. As early as 1910 W. H. Bragg pointed out that x rays probably partake of the nature of both electromagnetic waves and corpuscles possessing definite energy and momentum. On the one hand, experiments on polarization and diffraction phenomena demonstrated the wavelike behavior of x rays; on the other hand, studies of the photoelectric and Compton effects revealed properties similar to those of particles. The introduction of quantum theory therefore means that simple models cannot be retained in the realm of optics—a fully developed theory must include within its formalism both the wave and corpuscle aspects of radiation.

4.1 The Dispersion and Scattering of Light

(a) Electromagnetic interactions with matter

The theory of electromagnetic radiation cannot be presented briefly but some of its results are very important in the treatment of atomic interactions. The bulk properties of a material are described in terms of the refractive index, the electrical permittivity, and the magnetic permeability. Of these the permittivity (ε) is necessarily related to the electric *polarization*, which is supposed to depend on induced or permanent electric dipoles in the constituent molecules. If we can determine the average dipole moment per molecule (**p**), the total polarization (**P**) of an assembly containing N molecules per unit volume is

$$\mathbf{P} = N\mathbf{p}. \qquad [4.1.1]$$

The electric displacement (**D**) in the specimen is related to the displacement with the specimen removed (**D**$_0$) according to the equation

$$\mathbf{D} = \mathbf{D}_0 + \mathbf{P}. \qquad [4.1.2]$$

If the material is isotropic and fields in only one direction are considered, we may simplify the treatment, dividing the equation throughout by the electric field intensity $\mathscr{E}$ to find

$$\varepsilon = \varepsilon_0 + \frac{Np}{\mathscr{E}}, \qquad [4.1.3]$$

where ε = permittivity of the material,
$\quad\ \varepsilon_0$ = permittivity of free space.
$\mathscr{E}$ is assumed to be the field acting on each atom, which is very nearly the same as the external field, provided that polarization effects are comparatively slight inside the material.

The electromagnetic theory leads to a general expression for the wave velocity in a material

$$c_m = \frac{1}{\sqrt{\varepsilon\mu}}, \qquad [4.1.4]$$

where μ is the magnetic permeability of the material. Similarly, the velocity in a vacuum is

$$c = \frac{1}{\sqrt{\varepsilon_0\mu_0}}.$$

The refractive index (n), relative to a vacuum, for any material is therefore

$$n = \frac{c}{c_m} = \sqrt{\frac{\varepsilon\mu}{\varepsilon_0\mu_0}}. \qquad [4.1.5]$$

In materials with very slight magnetic interactions, $\mu = \mu_0$ very nearly, so we may write

$$n^2 = \frac{\varepsilon}{\varepsilon_0} = 1 + \frac{Np}{\varepsilon_0\mathscr{E}}. \qquad [4.1.6]$$

(*b*) *Theory of dispersion*

Now let us suppose that an atomic electron is executing simple harmonic motion of angular frequency ω_0 in the absence of any incident electromagnetic field. The frequency ω_0 is related to some characteristic frequency of the atom and may be identified with that of a spectral line, although the classical theory has no basis for calculating ω_0 directly. Indeed, according to classical theory one would expect to observe harmonics of angular frequencies $2\omega_0, 3\omega_0, \ldots$ in the atomic spectrum, but these are not found. The electromagnetic treatment is therefore phenomenological rather than fundamental.

The equation of motion of the electron is written

$$\frac{d^2x}{dt^2} + \omega_0^2 x = 0$$

on the assumption that damping effects (due, for example, to losses of energy by radiation) are negligible. The rest of the atom or molecule is supposed to be so massive that its motion is slight and the effective dipole moment is found from the electron displacement only. Since the electron is charged (charge $-e$), an incident electromagnetic wave exerts a force on it due to the electric field vector $\mathscr{E}$, which varies harmonically at some arbitrary angular frequency ω. The interaction is similar to that producing forced vibrations of a mechanical system, and, for an electric field parallel to the x direction, the equation of motion becomes

$$\frac{d^2x}{dt^2} + \omega_0^2 x = \frac{-e\mathscr{E}}{m},$$

where m is the electronic mass. The field $\mathscr{E}$ varies with time t according to the function

$$\mathscr{E} = \mathscr{E}_0 \exp(i\omega t),$$

where we have employed the complex exponential form $\exp(i\omega t)$ to represent a sinusoidal variation. The exponential function can be expressed as the sum of real and pure imaginary terms with the aid of de Moivre's theorem

$$\exp(i\omega t) = \cos \omega t + i \sin \omega t.$$

Thus, if we chose to introduce a cosine function initially, we could follow through the analysis with the complex exponential and take the real part of the final solution. Alternatively, we could choose a sine function initially and take the imaginary part of the final solution. In many applications, the complex exponential function can be employed throughout, and it is particularly useful in describing the polarization properties of radiation (see Section 4.2).

A particular integral of the equation of motion, representing forced vibrations of the electron, is

$$x = \frac{-e\mathscr{E}_0 \exp(i\omega t)}{m(\omega_0^2 - \omega^2)}. \qquad [4.1.7]$$

The corresponding dipole moment per electron is

$$p = -ex = \frac{e^2\mathscr{E}_0 \exp(i\omega t)}{m(\omega_0^2 - \omega^2)}.$$

Thus if z is the number of electrons per atom involved in the oscillation of angular frequency ω_0 and all these electrons act independently, the effective refractive index, calculated from Equation (4.1.6), is given by the equation

$$n^2 = 1 + \frac{Nze^2}{m(\omega_0^2 - \omega^2)\varepsilon_0}. \qquad [4.1.8]$$

The most striking feature of this result is the resonant behavior induced when the incident angular frequency ω approaches the value ω_0. Theoretically the amplitude of electron vibrations (and the refractive index) would be infinite at $\omega = \omega_0$, but this difficulty can be avoided by the introduction of a small damping term in the equation of motion. Ignoring this necessity, we can list the main physical consequences of Equation (4.1.8) as follows:

(i) the refractive index goes through a violent change at frequencies close to a "natural" frequency of the atoms: this phenomenon involves the effect known as *anomalous dispersion* and can be observed in the vicinity of strong absorption lines, for example those of sodium vapor in the visible region;

(ii) near the resonance frequency, strong scattering effects occur because of reradiation of energy by the vibrating electrons;

(iii) at very high frequencies, where ω is much greater than any resonance frequency ω_0, the refractive index n is close to unity, but is always slightly less than this limiting value: the *phase* velocity of the wave therefore becomes greater than c (although the *group* velocity must be less than c in all cases);

(iv) a plasma, that is, an assembly of ions and free electrons (in which $\omega_0 = 0$ effectively), always has a refractive index less than 1: this accounts for the reflection of radio waves by ionized layers in the high atmosphere, to an extent determined by the electron density (N per unit volume).

In the extreme case of a plasma of high density, it is possible for the permittivity to vanish, which has the result of allowing high-frequency "plasma oscillations" to develop. The *plasma frequency* ω_p is found from the condition

$$\frac{\varepsilon}{\varepsilon_0} = 1 - \frac{Ne^2}{m\omega_p^2\varepsilon_0} = 0$$

yielding

$$\omega_p = \sqrt{\frac{Ne^2}{m\varepsilon_0}}. \qquad [4.1.9]$$

(c) Theory of scattering

The classical theory may be developed further by regarding each oscillating electron as an effective electric dipole which is capable of radiating electromagnetic waves. Analysis of the dipole field in the "wave zone" (far away from the source) shows that the electric field vector $\mathscr{E}'$ and the magnetic field vector $\mathscr{H}'$ are perpendicular both to each other and to the radius vector **r** drawn from the source. Moreover, the magnitude of each field vector is proportional to the sine of the angle θ between the dipole moment **p** and radius **r**. Hence the polar diagram for the field magnitude is a circle tangential to the dipole in any plane containing the dipole vector **p** (Figure 4.1); also there is no emission along the dipole line.

These results can be used in a treatment of the scattering of light by atomic electrons. Suppose that a beam of light, plane polarized so that the electric vector $\mathscr{E}$ is parallel to Ox, is incident in the y direction upon an atom at O containing an electron (Figure 4.2). The intensity of the incident beam, that is, the flux of energy per second across unit area, is

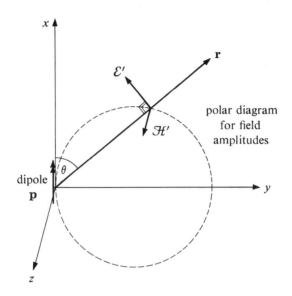

FIGURE 4.1 *Electromagnetic radiation from an oscillating electric dipole in the "wave zone." The vectors $\mathcal{E}'$, $\mathcal{H}'$, and* **r** *are perpendicular to each other; the magnitude of each field vector is proportional to* $\sin \theta$, *hence the circular polar diagram.*

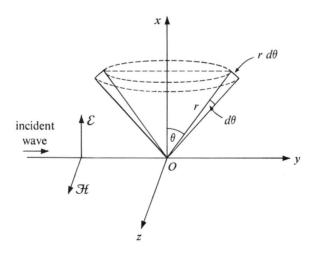

FIGURE 4.2 *Calculation of the scattering of an incident electromagnetic wave by an electron at 0. The scattered amplitude is uniform over a ring-shaped surface between cones of semiangle θ and $(\theta + d\theta)$ and the intensity is integrated over all angles between $\theta = 0$ and $\theta = \pi$ radians.*

given by the magnitude of the Poynting vector

$$\mathbf{I} = [\mathscr{E} \times \mathscr{H}], \tag{4.1.10}$$

where we can write $\mathscr{E} = \mathscr{E}_0 \cos \omega t$, also $\mathscr{H} = \mathscr{H}_0 \cos \omega t$.
The mean intensity, averaged over several oscillations, becomes, in terms of the *amplitudes* $\mathscr{E}_0$ and $\mathscr{H}_0$,

$$I_0 = \tfrac{1}{2}\mathscr{E}_0\mathscr{H}_0$$

$$= \frac{1}{2}\sqrt{\frac{\varepsilon_0}{\mu_0}} \, \mathscr{E}_0^2 \qquad \text{in free space.}$$

Since the incident wave is polarized parallel to Ox the electron's forced vibrations will cause reradiation of energy chiefly in the yz plane. At a point some distance from O with polar coordinates (r, θ) the amplitude of the radiated field is

$$\mathscr{E}_0' = \frac{-e \sin \theta}{4\pi\varepsilon_0 c^2 r} \left\langle \frac{d^2x}{dt^2} \right\rangle, \tag{4.1.11}$$

where $\left\langle \dfrac{d^2x}{dt^2} \right\rangle$ represents the acceleration amplitude at the time when the wave left the point O. From the expression in Equation (4.1.7) we find that the acceleration is

$$\left\langle \frac{d^2x}{dt^2} \right\rangle = \frac{e\omega^2\mathscr{E}_0}{m(\omega_0^2 - \omega^2)}$$

so that the amplitude of the scattered wave at (r, θ) becomes

$$\mathscr{E}_0' = \frac{-e^2\omega^2\mathscr{E}_0 \sin \theta}{4\pi\varepsilon_0 c^2 rm(\omega_0^2 - \omega^2)}. \tag{4.1.12}$$

By analogy with Equation (4.1.10) we find the mean scattered intensity in the direction represented by angle θ as

$$I' = \frac{1}{2}\sqrt{\frac{\varepsilon_0}{\mu_0}} \, \mathscr{E}_0'^2$$

$$= \frac{1}{2}\sqrt{\frac{\varepsilon_0}{\mu_0}} \frac{e^4\omega^4\mathscr{E}_0^2 \sin^2 \theta}{(4\pi\varepsilon_0)^2 c^4 r^2 m^2(\omega_0^2 - \omega^2)^2}. \tag{4.1.13}$$

This scattered intensity is the flux of energy per second across a unit area and may be denoted by dE/dA, where E is the radiated *power*. The element of area dA may be extended to cover the surface area between cones of semiangle θ and $(\theta + \theta)$ with slant height r (Figure 4.2), since the intensity I' is constant over this surface. From Equation (2.1.8), derived from Figure 2.3, we know that

$$dA = 2\pi \sin \theta \, d\theta \, r^2.$$

After a little rearrangement the expression for the element of power radiated becomes

$$dE = \frac{2\pi I_0 e^4\omega^4}{(4\pi\varepsilon_0)^2 c^4 m^2(\omega_0^2 - \omega^2)^2} \sin^3 \theta \, d\theta.$$

The total scattered power is obtained by integration over the entire angular range between $\theta = 0$ and $\theta = \pi$ rad

$$E = \frac{2\pi I_0 e^4 \omega^4}{(4\pi\varepsilon_0)^2 c^4 m^2 (\omega_0^2 - \omega^2)^2} \int_0^\pi \sin^3 \theta \, d\theta$$

$$= \frac{8\pi}{3} \left(\frac{e^2}{4\pi\varepsilon_0 mc^2} \right)^2 \frac{\omega^4}{(\omega_0^2 - \omega^2)^2} I_0. \qquad [4.1.14]$$

The scattering is naturally proportional to the incident intensity I_0, which is the power per unit *area* in the arriving wave front. In order to express the magnitude of the scattering conveniently, we introduce the concept of the *scattering cross section* (σ_{sc}), which is defined here by the equation

$$E = I_0 \sigma_{sc} \qquad [4.1.15]$$

and indicates the effective area of the atom for scattering. This concept of a "cross section" is very widespread, especially in nuclear physics, but should not be taken literally. A given atom or nucleus has many different "cross sections" for different processes, the data being used to express the probabilities of the various processes occurring.

The classical scattering cross section per electron for electromagnetic radiation is written

$$\sigma_{sc} = \frac{8\pi}{3} \left(\frac{e^2}{4\pi\varepsilon_0 mc^2} \right)^2 \frac{\omega^4}{(\omega_0^2 - \omega^2)^2} . \qquad [4.1.16]$$

Two important results emerge from this formula:

(i) at low frequencies, where $\omega_0 \gg \omega$, the cross section is proportional to ω^4 or to λ^{-4}: we then have *Rayleigh scattering*, as exemplified by scattering of light in the atmosphere, where short wavelengths are scattered much more than longer wavelengths;

(ii) at very high frequencies, where $\omega \gg \omega_0$, the cross section approaches a constant value, known as the *Thomson scattering cross section*

$$\sigma_{sc}^T = \frac{8\pi}{3} \left(\frac{e^2}{4\pi\varepsilon_0 mc^2} \right)^2 . \qquad [4.1.17]$$

The latter result, due to J. J. Thomson, applies chiefly to the scattering of x rays by atoms containing a small number of electrons each. The electrons are supposed to remain bound in the atom and the scattered radiation is coherent with the incident beam. Other types of scattering and absorption of radiant energy by atoms occur in the x-ray region, but these have to be treated by quantum methods, since the wave theory is no longer applicable at very high frequencies.

The expression enclosed in parentheses in Equation (4.1.17) has the numerical value

$$\frac{e^2}{4\pi\varepsilon_0 mc^2} = 2.8 \times 10^{-15} \text{ m} \qquad [4.1.18]$$

for electrons and is often referred to as the *classical electron radius* (r_0). Lorentz attempted to formulate a complete scheme of electrodynamics in which electrons of finite size might be incorporated, but he encountered great difficulties due to the intense interactions at very short distances. In such a context r_0 is the distance within which the electromagnetic field properties are strongly modified by the electron's own interactions. In modern theories an electron is regarded as a point-particle and it is necessary to subtract certain infinite terms in the total energy expression so that a finite total interaction can be handled. This unsatisfactory procedure indicates that we need new methods of dealing with phenomena which involve distances of the order of r_0.

4.2   The Zeeman and Faraday Effects

(a) *The "normal" Zeeman effect*

A remarkable phenomenon concerning the interaction of radiating atoms with a uniform magnetic field was discovered by Zeeman in 1896 and was interpreted by Lorentz in terms of the classical theory of electrons. Briefly, the light emitted by a gas-filled discharge tube, which is placed between the poles of a powerful magnet, is found to have its spectral lines split into several components. In several elements there are two components when the tube is viewed along the magnetic field direction and three when viewed perpendicular to the field. This "normal" Zeeman effect may be understood if we consider electrons revolving in circular orbits of angular frequency ω_0 within the atom, where ω_0 represents the natural angular frequency of the spectral line examined.

The circular orbit hypothesis is not inconsistent with the harmonic-oscillator model used previously in the theory of dispersion, since a uniform circular motion can be decomposed into two simple harmonic vibrations along perpendicular diameters of the orbit. The phase relations of two perpendicular harmonic vibrations are of some importance in the theory of optical polarization. If, for instance, we write the x and y displacements as functions of time t according to the equations

$$x = A \cos \omega t; \qquad y = A \sin \omega t;$$

the two oscillations are of the same angular frequency (ω) but are $\pi/2$ radians out of phase. Combination of x^2 and y^2 results in the circular orbit

$$x^2 + y^2 = A^2.$$

Alternatively, we may write (with $i = \sqrt{-1}$)

$$x + iy = A(\cos \omega t + i \sin \omega t)$$

$$= A \exp(i\omega t).$$

In the complex plane, this expression represents a circular motion at radius A in the direction of ωt increasing, that is, *counterclockwise* in the usual convention. Likewise

$$x - iy = A \exp(-i\omega t)$$

represents a *clockwise* motion in the xy complex plane.

A classic experiment by Fresnel showed that plane-polarized light can be split into two beams circularly polarized in opposite directions. This decomposition is equivalent to the algebraic relation

$$x = A \cos \omega t = \tfrac{1}{2}A[\exp(i\omega t) + \exp(-i\omega t)]$$

for light polarized in the x direction. Fresnel's explanation of the optical activity exhibited by certain crystals and solutions was based on the supposition that in these materials the two circularly polarized beams travel at different speeds. When the light emerges from the material the two components have different phase relations from their condition at entry and they recombine to form plane-polarized light with the plane of polarization rotated to some extent about the beam direction. Suppose, for example, that a beam initially polarized in the x direction emerges with its two components differing in phase by angle δ and represented conveniently by

$$\tfrac{1}{2}A \exp{(i\omega t)}; \qquad \tfrac{1}{2}A \exp{(-i\omega t + \delta)}.$$

The algebraic sum of these expressions may be written

$$\tfrac{1}{2}A \exp\left(i\frac{\delta}{2}\right)\left[\exp\left(i\omega t - i\frac{\delta}{2}\right) + \exp\left(-i\omega t + i\frac{\delta}{2}\right)\right] = A \exp\left(i\frac{\delta}{2}\right)\cos\left(\omega t - \frac{\delta}{2}\right)$$

$$[4.2.1]$$

so the amplitude is still A but the plane of polarization has been rotated through an angle of $\dfrac{\delta}{2}$. Thus if we can estimate the phase difference δ the angle of rotation follows.

Returning to the circular electron orbits, we consider first an undisturbed orbit in the xy plane and equate the centripetal force to some expression $f(r)$ which is a function of radius r only

$$m\omega_0^2 r = f(r).$$

If a uniform magnetic field **B** is now applied along the z axis this field will exert a force (**F**) on each electron according to the Lorentz expression

$$\mathbf{F} = -e[\mathbf{v} \times \mathbf{B}].$$

The vector product indicates that if the electron revolves counterclockwise in the xy plane and the field **B** is directed into the plane (Figure 4.3) the extra force **F** is directed radially outwards, whereas if the field **B** is reversed the force acts radially inwards. We can therefore write the total force on each electron as

$$f(r) \pm evB,$$

where $v = \omega r$ (the orbital speed of the electron).

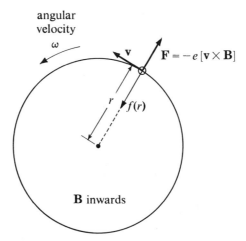

FIGURE 4.3 *The effect of an applied magnetic field **B** on an electron revolving counterclockwise in an orbit of radius r. The force **F** acts outwards, reducing the net centripetal force so that the angular velocity ω is less than the undisturbed value ω_0.*

The effect of the extra magnetic force was studied by Larmor, who showed that the radius of the orbit would remain constant for moderate fields B but that the electron speed must be increased or decreased. This follows from Faraday's law of electromagnetic induction, since a sudden increase of the field B sets up an electromotive force which must accelerate or decelerate the electron in its orbit. We can calculate the change in angular frequency $\Delta\omega$, which is assumed to be small, by writing the new angular frequency

$$\omega = \omega_0 + \Delta\omega$$

and the centripetal-force equation becomes

$$m\omega^2 r = f(r) \pm e\omega rB.$$

Elimination of the unknown $f(r)$ yields

$$mr(\omega^2 - \omega_0^2) = \pm e\omega rB,$$

that is,

$$m\,\Delta\omega(\omega + \omega_0) = \pm e\omega B.$$

The sum $(\omega + \omega_0)$ may be replaced by 2ω to a sufficient degree of accuracy, so the change in angular frequency is

$$\Delta\omega = \pm(eB/2m), \text{ approximately independent of } \omega_0. \qquad [4.2.2]$$

According to the *Larmor precession theorem*, the angular-momentum vector assigned to any electron orbit precesses about the lines of force of an applied magnetic field and the angular velocity of precession ($\Delta\omega$) is given by the above expression.

In a gas-filled discharge tube, the atoms are oriented in all possible directions relative to the magnetic field, but the foregoing results are readily applied. Any orbital motion can be resolved into harmonic vibrations parallel to the x, y, and z directions, with the same frequency but different amplitudes. If we view the gas *along* the magnetic field in the z direction, we see no light from the z components of vibration because of the electric-dipole property (Figure 4.1). The x and y components can be resolved into two circularly polarized motions in opposite directions and one of these has its frequency increased, the other decreased, by the field. From this aspect, therefore, the spectral line corresponding to ω_0 is split into two lines with opposite circular polarizations. These predictions may be verified by experiment, which also shows that:

(i) the charges responsible for radiation are *negative*;

(ii) the *specific charge e/m*, calculated from $\Delta\omega$, agrees closely with that of electrons produced in a cathode-ray tube.

If the gas is viewed from a direction *perpendicular* to the magnetic field, the z vibrations contribute radiation at the unchanged angular frequency ω_0 and this radiation is plane polarized with its electric vector parallel to the magnetic field lines. Either the x or the y components, or both, give spectral lines of changed frequency $\omega_0 \pm \Delta\omega$ and these are polarized with electric vectors perpendicular to the magnetic field.

The classical theory of the Zeeman effect was successful when applied to certain spectral lines of elements like neon and mercury. In 1897, however, Preston found "anomalous" Zeeman effects in the spectral lines of cadmium and it soon became clear that the excited atoms of many elements emit complex patterns of spectral lines when placed in a magnetic field. For example, the two D lines of sodium split into a total of 10 Zeeman lines instead of the six expected in the "normal" Zeeman effect. Despite this setback, the discovery of the Zeeman effect was of great importance in the development of atomic theory because it was nearly contemporaneous with the discovery of the electron. Moreover, Fitzgerald and others were able to link the Zeeman effect with another magneto-optical effect, discovered by Faraday in 1845.

(b) The Faraday effect

If plane-polarized light is passed through a dense isotropic medium (such as glass) which is subjected to an intense magnetic field parallel to the light path, the plane of polarization is rotated as though the medium were optically active. The angle of rotation α depends on the field B and the distance l traveled in the material according to the equation

$$\alpha = V_i Bl, \tag{4.2.3}$$

where V_i is Verdet's constant (for an isotropic material).

According to the classical theory of the Zeeman effect, the atoms of the material in field B should emit circularly polarized waves of slightly different frequency, which, in a dispersive medium, travel at slightly different speeds. Conversely, the material should transmit waves circularly polarized in opposite directions at different speeds, so that a phase difference is introduced and the plane of polarization is rotated, according to Equation (4.2.1). In principle the rotation can be calculated classically but in the solid and liquid states complex interactions cause deviations from the simple theory. In a gas or plasma the situation is simplified by the fact that, on the average, the electrons are very nearly half in the left-hand and half in the right-hand precession states. Under these conditions the refractive indices (n_1 and n_2) for two angular frequencies (ω_1 and ω_2) are given by Equation (4.1.8)

$$n_1^2 - 1 = (n_1 - 1)(n_1 + 1) = \frac{\frac{1}{2}Nze^2}{m\varepsilon_0(\omega_1^2 - \omega^2)}$$

and

$$n_2^2 - 1 = (n_2 - 1)(n_2 + 1) = \frac{\frac{1}{2}Nze^2}{m\varepsilon_0(\omega_2^2 - \omega^2)}.$$

If n_1 and n_2 are both close to unity, we may replace $(n_1 + 1)$ and $(n_2 + 1)$ each by 2 and find the difference in refractive indices

$$n_1 - n_2 = \frac{\frac{1}{2}Nze^2}{2m\varepsilon_0}\left[\frac{1}{\omega_1^2 - \omega^2} - \frac{1}{\omega_2^2 - \omega^2}\right].$$

Substitution of $\omega_1 = \omega_0 - \Delta\omega$, $\omega_2 = \omega_0 + \Delta\omega$, and $\Delta\omega = \dfrac{eB}{2m}$ gives

$$n_1 - n_2 = \frac{Nze^2}{4m\varepsilon_0}\frac{4\omega_0\Delta\omega}{(\omega_0^2 - \omega^2)^2} \quad \text{approximately}$$

$$= \frac{Nze^3B\omega_0}{2m^2\varepsilon_0(\omega_0^2 - \omega^2)^2}. \tag{4.2.4}$$

The phase difference (δ) introduced by passage through a distance l depends on the difference in refractive indices

$$\delta = (n_1 - n_2)\frac{\omega l}{c}$$

and the angle of rotation becomes

$$\alpha = \tfrac{1}{2}\delta = \frac{Nze^3B\omega\omega_0 l}{4m^2c\varepsilon_0(\omega_0^2 - \omega^2)^2}. \tag{4.2.5}$$

We see from this result that Verdet's constant depends on angular frequency in a complex manner, being very large near a resonance frequency ω_0, as is observed experimentally. Under normal conditions the Faraday rotation is very slight in gases but it has been detected in radio waves traversing the ionosphere, and in laboratory-produced plasma, where measurements of α may lead to estimation of the electron density N.

4.3 Blackbody Radiation

(a) The laws of Stefan and Wien

Although the classical theory of radiation did not provide any solution to the problem of interpreting atomic line spectra, it was fully expected that continuous or *thermal* radiation would prove susceptible to theoretical treatment. If an enclosure is maintained at a high uniform temperature the radiant energy within it reaches an equilibrium distribution depending on the temperature. This radiation may be studied by letting a little of it escape from a small hole in the wall; such radiation is called "blackbody" radiation, because from the external point of view the cavity is almost a perfect absorber of any radiation which enters the hole.

The properties of blackbody radiation were studied theoretically by treating the contents of the enclosure as a thermodynamic fluid exerting pressure ("radiation pressure") on the walls. In this way Boltzmann established the important result, first derived by Stefan from experimental data, that the energy density of the radiation (E/V) is proportional to the fourth power of the absolute temperature

$$\frac{E}{V} = sT^4, \qquad \text{where } s \text{ is constant.} \qquad [4.3.1]$$

Wien extended this type of theory to find the distribution of energy among the various frequencies present in the radiation. In terms of the angular frequency ω, Wien's result is

$$f(\omega) \, d\omega \propto \omega^3 g(\omega/T) \, d\omega, \qquad [4.3.2]$$

where $g(\omega/T)$ is an undetermined function of ω/T.

Experimental data concerning the function $f(\omega)$ were obtained, notably by Lummer and Pringsheim, and these data indicated that at a given temperature there is always an angular frequency (ω_m) where the energy density is a maximum. In Figure 4.4 the energy density per unit frequency is plotted against angular frequency, with the visible light region marked. At low temperatures there is very little emission except in the infrared (low-frequency) region, as one would expect. As the temperature rises, the energy increases at all frequencies in such a way that the area under the curve, representing the total energy density, varies as the fourth power of T. At the same time the peak in the curve moves to higher frequencies so that at very high temperatures ω_m lies in the visible region.

The behavior of the curves of Figure 4.4 is entirely in agreement with Wien's theory because we can use Equation (4.3.2) to derive a relation between the peak position (ω_m) and the temperature T. Writing the ratio $\omega/T = \xi$, $f(\omega)$ becomes

$$f(\omega) \propto \omega^3 g(\xi).$$

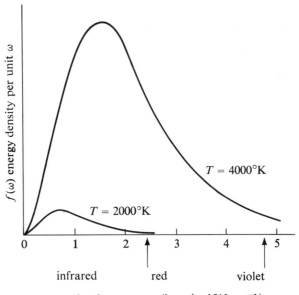

FIGURE 4.4 *Distribution of energy density per unit frequency range in blackbody radiation. The peak moves to high frequencies as the temperature rises.*

Differentiating with respect to ω and putting the derivative equal to zero at the peak $\omega = \omega_m$, we find that

$$3\omega_m^2 g(\xi) = -\frac{\omega_m^3}{T}\frac{\partial g}{\partial \xi}$$

or

$$3g(\xi) = -\xi\frac{\partial g}{\partial \xi}.$$

This equation in ξ is supposed to have some numerical solution $\xi = \alpha$ so that we obtain the result:

$$\frac{\omega_m}{T} = \alpha$$

(or in Wien's form, $\lambda_m T = $ constant).

This relation is well established both theoretically and experimentally but the exact form of the function $g(\xi)$ is not obtainable from the general thermodynamic treatment.

(b) Classical theory of blackbody radiation

The classical theory can be adapted in two ways to provide a derivation of the distribution function $f(\omega)$:

(i) in accordance with the theory of dispersion, we may consider a set of harmonic oscillators in the walls of the enclosure, absorbing and emitting radiation in such a way that equilibrium is maintained;

(ii) the electromagnetic waves can be studied in the cavity and suitable boundary conditions imposed to find the possible modes of vibration, each of which is equivalent to a classical harmonic oscillator.

The latter method will be outlined here because of its affinity with the methods of wave mechanics, but it should be emphasized that both methods give the same answer.

The wave method is based on the general wave equation for light of speed c in a vacuum

$$\frac{\partial^2 \Psi}{\partial x^2} + \frac{\partial^2 \Psi}{\partial y^2} + \frac{\partial^2 \Psi}{\partial z^2} = \frac{1}{c^2} \frac{\partial^2 \Psi}{\partial t^2}, \qquad [4.3.3]$$

where Ψ is an electromagnetic field variable which is a function of x, y, z, and t. For sinusoidal waves of angular frequency ω, we substitute

$$\Psi = \psi(x, y, z) \exp(i\omega t)$$

and obtain the space-dependent equation in Lapiacian form

$$\nabla^2 \psi + \frac{\omega^2}{c^2} \psi = 0. \qquad [4.3.4]$$

In a cubical cavity of side a we can impose boundary conditions which make the waves periodic in the distance a. A possible solution which is periodic separately in x, y, and z is

$$\psi = \psi_0 \sin\left(\frac{l\pi x}{a}\right) \sin\left(\frac{m\pi y}{a}\right) \sin\left(\frac{n\pi z}{a}\right),$$

where ψ_0 is the amplitude; l, m, and n are integers.

This particular solution has the property that $\psi = 0$ at the boundaries x, y, $z = 0$ or a. Substitution of the above function in the wave equation yields the condition

$$\frac{l^2\pi^2 + m^2\pi^2 + n^2\pi^2}{a^2} = \frac{\omega^2}{c^2}$$

or

$$l^2 + m^2 + n^2 = \frac{\omega^2 a^2}{\pi^2 c^2}. \qquad [4.3.5]$$

Any group of numbers (l, m, n) denotes a particular mode of vibration of the waves in the cavity and, at a given angular frequency, the above equation is the only limitation on the possible numbers. We may depict the l, m, n values as points on a cubic lattice with the l values plotted in units along the x axis, the m values along the y axis and the n values along the z axis. At very large values of l, m, n we may regard the distribution as almost continuous and Equation (4.3.5) represents the sphere of radius $\frac{\omega a}{\pi c}$ in (l, m, n) coordinates. In particular, all the points belonging to angular frequencies *less* than a certain value ω lie inside the positive octant of the sphere (Figure 4.5). If we now construct two octants of radius $\frac{\omega a}{\pi c}$ and $\frac{(\omega + d\omega)a}{\pi c}$, respectively, the volume enclosed between the spherical shells is equal to the *number* of modes of vibration between angular frequencies ω and $(\omega + d\omega)$. Thus the number distribution is

$$N(\omega)\, d\omega = \frac{4\pi r^2\, dr}{8}$$

$$= \frac{\omega^2 a^3\, d\omega}{2c^3\pi^2}, \qquad \text{if} \quad r = \frac{\omega a}{\pi c}.$$

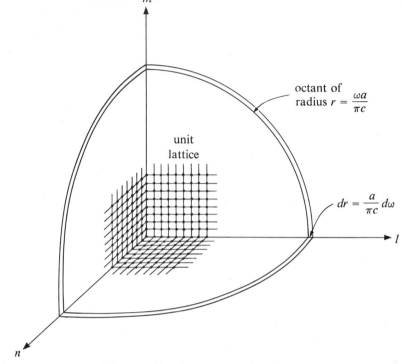

FIGURE 4.5 *Enumeration of the possible vibrational modes for waves in a cubical cavity. Each "lattice" point (l, m, n) represents one mode and the points within a positive octant of radius $r = \dfrac{\omega a}{\pi c}$ correspond to frequencies less than ω.*

This method for enumerating the possible modes of vibration in a closed system may be generalized to deal with volumes of any shape and waves of different types. It is found that the number of modes per unit volume is independent of the shape of the enclosure. The full theory of electromagnetic waves shows that the number of modes must be doubled to allow for the transverse polarizations, which effectively *double* the degrees of freedom. The number of waves *per unit volume* with angular frequencies between ω and $(\omega + d\omega)$ is

$$n(\omega)\, d\omega = \frac{\omega^2}{\pi^2 c^3}\, d\omega. \qquad [4.3.6]$$

Finally, in order to derive the *energy* density distribution $f(\omega)$, we must multiply the number of modes by the energy per mode at equilibrium. In the classical theory the natural assumption to make is that the equipartition theorem holds, in which case the mean energy per mode of vibration is

$$\bar{\varepsilon} = kT \qquad \text{(from Section 2.4).}$$

We then find the *Rayleigh-Jeans expression* for the energy distribution in classical theory

$$f(\omega)\, d\omega = \frac{\omega^2 kT}{\pi^2 c^3}\, d\omega. \qquad [4.3.7]$$

It is plain that this expression is incapable of giving anything like the curves of Figure 4.4 or Wien's law, because there is no maximum in the function $f(\omega)$. Indeed, the theory predicts that there should be an infinite amount of energy in the high-frequency regions of the spectrum, the so-called "ultraviolet catastrophe." Analysis of the problem leads to the conclusion that we have here another case of the breakdown of equipartition, somewhat similar to the failure of classical theory to explain the specific heats of gases and solids at low temperatures (Section 2.4). The analogy suggests that there may be some connection between the failure of classical expressions at high frequencies and low temperatures, that is, in the region where the parameter $\xi = \omega/T$ is large.

(c) Planck's hypothesis

The solution to this problem was given in 1900 by Planck, who tried the effect of assuming that not all frequencies partake equally of the energy because of an insufficiency in available energy at high frequencies. This assumption was embodied in the *quantum hypothesis* previously stated in Section 3.6c

$$\varepsilon = h\nu = \hbar\omega.$$

If the waves have their energy quantized, the atoms in the walls of the enclosure can emit or absorb energy only in amounts $\hbar\omega$, so each mode of vibration possesses energies equal to integral multiples of $\hbar\omega$, that is,

$$\varepsilon_n = n\hbar\omega, \qquad \text{where } n = 0, 1, 2, \ldots, \text{ and so forth.}$$

Planck calculated the mean energy per mode on the assumption that the probability depends on the Boltzmann expression

$$P(\varepsilon_n) \propto \exp\left(\frac{-\varepsilon_n}{kT}\right).$$

The partition function Σ is then, from Equation (2.2.10),

$$\Sigma = \sum_{n=0}^{\infty} \exp\left(\frac{-n\hbar\omega}{kT}\right)$$

and, writing the quantity $\dfrac{\hbar\omega}{kT} = \zeta$, we find

$$\Sigma = [1 - \exp(-\zeta)]^{-1}. \qquad [4.3.8]$$

From Problem 2.16, the mean energy per mode is calculated as

$$\bar{\varepsilon} = \frac{\bar{E}}{N} = kT^2 \frac{\partial}{\partial T}(\ln \Sigma)$$

$$= \frac{kT^2\,\hbar\omega}{kT^2} \frac{\exp(-\zeta)}{1 - \exp(-\zeta)}$$

$$= \frac{\hbar\omega}{\exp\left(\dfrac{\hbar\omega}{kT}\right) - 1}. \qquad [4.3.9]$$

The full Planck expression for the energy distribution is obtained by multiplying the distribution in number of modes $n(\omega)$ by the mean energy per mode, that is, we obtain

$$f(\omega)\,d\omega = \frac{\hbar\omega^3\,d\omega}{\pi^2 c^3\left[\exp\left(\dfrac{\hbar\omega}{kT}\right) - 1\right]}. \qquad [4.3.10]$$

This result is entirely consistent with Wien's formula of Equation (4.3.2) and there is always a peak in the function because at high frequencies $f(\omega)$ decreases exponentially with increasing frequency. This feature ensures that the total energy represented by the area under the curve is always finite. The Planck theory is not free from objection, because it combines the classical statistics with the quantum hypothesis in an arbitrary way, but it was significant historically in providing the first example of a theory which accounted for a breakdown in equipartition of energy. It pointed the way to successful treatments of the specific heats of solids and gases (see Problem 2.18).

(d) The Stefan and Wien constants

The Planck energy distribution [Equation (4.3.10)] agrees very closely with the experimental data of Figure 4.4 and also determines the numerical values of the Stefan-Boltzmann constant [s in Equation (4.3.1)] and the Wien constant ($\lambda_m T$). Values of $\hbar$ found from these quantities agree with each other and with photoelectric determinations (Section 3.6c).

The total energy density in the enclosure is found by direct integration of the expression $f(\omega)\, d\omega$ over all frequencies

$$\frac{E}{V} = \int_0^\infty f(\omega)\, d\omega$$

$$= \frac{(kT)^4}{\pi^2 c^3 \hbar^3} \int_0^\infty \frac{\zeta^3\, d\zeta}{(\exp \zeta - 1)}.$$

The integral is evaluated by series and we find

$$\frac{E}{V} = sT^4$$

with

$$s = \frac{\pi^2 k^4}{15 c^3 \hbar^3}.$$

[4.3.11]

In order to find Wien's constant we first express the energy distribution as a function of wavelength by the substitution of

$$\lambda = \frac{2\pi c}{\omega} \quad \text{and} \quad -d\lambda = \frac{2\pi c}{\omega^2}\, d\omega$$

into

$$f(\omega)\, d\omega = -F(\lambda)\, d\lambda.$$

We obtain

$$F(\lambda)\, d\lambda = \frac{-\hbar \omega^3}{\pi^2 c^3 (\exp \zeta - 1)} \frac{d\omega}{d\lambda}\, d\lambda$$

$$= \frac{\hbar \omega^5\, d\lambda}{2\pi^3 c^4 (\exp \zeta - 1)}$$

or

$$F(\lambda)\, d\lambda = \frac{\text{constant } d\lambda}{\lambda^5 \left[\exp \left(\dfrac{2\pi c \hbar}{kT\lambda} \right) - 1 \right]}.$$

[4.3.12]

The position of the peak in $F(\lambda)$ is found by setting the derivative of F equal to zero

$$\frac{\partial F}{\partial \lambda} = 0 \quad \text{at} \quad \lambda = \lambda_m,$$

whence

$$5\left[\exp\left(\frac{2\pi c\hbar}{kT\lambda_m}\right) - 1\right] = \frac{2\pi c\hbar}{kT\lambda_m}\exp\left(\frac{2\pi c\hbar}{kT\lambda_m}\right).$$

We therefore require the root of the transcendental equation

$$5\exp(y) - 5 = y\exp(y), \quad\text{where}\quad y = \frac{2\pi c\hbar}{kT\lambda_m}.$$

The root is found by numerical methods to be $y = 4.965$, and Wien's constant becomes

$$\lambda_m T = \frac{2\pi c\hbar}{4.965k} = 2.9 \times 10^{-3}\,\text{m}^\circ\text{K}. \tag{4.3.13}$$

It should be noted that the peak in the wavelength distribution $F(\lambda)$ does *not* occur in the same place as the peak found by maximizing the function $f(\omega)$, owing to the introduction of the $\frac{d\omega}{d\lambda}$ factor in the derivation of Equation (4.3.12).

4.4 Atomic Energy States

(a) Ionization potentials

The classical theory of radiation was capable of explaining various optical properties of matter in bulk, such as dispersion and scattering, but failed to deal with atomic interactions in detail. Several lines of evidence were developed to show that the quantum theory is essential for the understanding of characteristic line spectra and the various energy states of an atom.

It is well known that the characteristic spectrum of an element is usually emitted when the element is present in a gas discharge (Section 3.2) and we have seen that under such conditions the atoms are ionized. In Section 3.7 ionization in gases was treated in a general way without reference to the details of physical processes involved. A simple method for investigating the ionization of different elements consists in bombarding the gas or vapor with electrons of known energy to detect the onset of ion multiplication and spectrum emission. For example, we may use a diode tube, containing a little of the element under investigation, in the circuit of Figure 4.6. If the current through the tube is plotted against

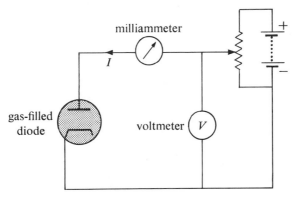

FIGURE 4.6   *Simple circuit for measuring the first ionization potential (W_0) for an element in the form of a gas or vapor. The current-voltage curve shows a steep rise when the applied voltage exceeds W_0.*

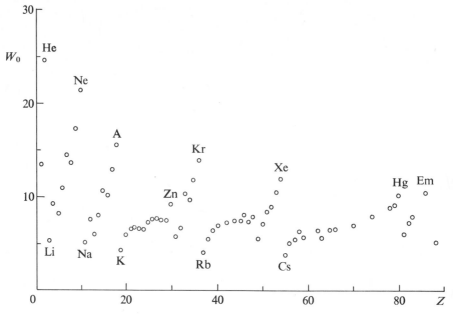

FIGURE 4.7 *Plot of the first ionization potential (W_0) against atomic number (Z) for the elements.*

the applied potential difference, the graph looks very much like the curve for a vacuum diode (Figure 3.12) at low voltages. This similarity indicates that the electrons from the cathode are reaching the anode with very nearly the full kinetic energy, that is, any collisions with the gas atoms are elastic. At higher voltages the behavior may be complex, but usually the current rises steadily until it reaches a well-marked ionization region. Here there is a sudden steep increase in current due to ion multiplication in the gas. Simultaneously, the gas emits *all* its characteristic spectral lines, although certain lines are emitted at lower voltages. From the graph it is possible to estimate the *first ionization potential* of the element

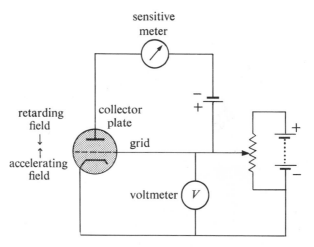

FIGURE 4.8 *Circuit for measuring the excitation potential of a gas or vapor (the Franck-Hertz experiment). Electrons accelerated to and through the grid meet a retarding field, with the result that the collector current is sensitive to small losses of energy by the electrons to the atoms of the gas.*

(W_0), which is the least amount of energy required to extract one electron from the atom and is usually expressed in electron volts.

This and other methods may be used to find ionization potentials and the results are of considerable interest when W_0 is plotted against the atomic number (Z) of the element, as shown in Figure 4.7. Comparison of the plot with the periodic table (Appendix II) reveals that the sharp maxima always occur at the inert gases (helium through emanation) and pronounced minima at the alkali metals (lithium through caesium). We also see that the transition metals and the rare earths have very uniform values of W_0, in accord with their close chemical similarities within the groups. Finally there are certain suggestions of structure between the main peaks, for example, the subsidiary peaks at elements like zinc and mercury. These features must be taken into account when the details of atomic structure are worked out.

Figure 4.7 shows that the energy required to ionize an atom depends on its place in the periodic table, W_0 being large for the inert gases and small for the alkalis. We know that the alkalis readily form positive ions by the loss of one electron per atom to some other atom or acceptor, such as a halogen atom. After the neutral atom has been ionized (by the supply of energy W_0) the atom emits spectral lines which are characteristic of the neutral atom, *not* of the ion. This phenomenon can be understood if we suppose that the ion captures a free electron, emitting radiation while the electron is being bound into the atom. The process does not occur in electrovalent solids (such as sodium chloride, Figure 3.1) because no free electrons are available.

(b) Excitation potentials

The process by which atoms absorb and emit radiation may be studied further by measurements of the *excitation potentials*, which are the energies at which individual spectral lines can be emitted. A classic experiment was performed in 1914 by J. Franck and G. Hertz,* who accelerated electrons through a known potential difference (V) applied between the grid and cathode of a tube containing mercury vapor (Figure 4.8). Many of the electrons passed through the grid toward a collector plate which was maintained at a small negative potential relative to the grid. Despite the retarding field between the grid and collector, a current was recorded in the collector circuit when the accelerating voltage V became appreciable. With this arrangement Franck and Hertz were able to investigate the conditions under which *inelastic* collisions of electrons with the mercury atoms are important, since such collisions rob the electrons of energy and prevent them from reaching the collector plate.

Figure 4.9 shows a typical set of results from the Franck-Hertz experiment performed with mercury vapor. The plot of the collector current (I) against the accelerating voltage (V) shows a remarkable series of maxima and minima due to the inelastic collisions. It is found that below about 6 V the current rises steadily, but there is then a sharp drop due to the onset of inelastic behavior and subsequent minima occur at intervals of very nearly 4.9 V on the potential scale. These minima are accounted for by supposing that electrons of 4.9 eV kinetic energy have just sufficient energy to excite a mercury atom at one collision, those of 9.8 eV to cause excitation twice (in different mercury atoms), and so on. The first minimum is actually higher than 4.9 eV because of contact-potential effects, but these effects may be eliminated in finding the excitation potential by calculating the mean spacing of the higher minima.

* This experimental work followed the theoretical exposition of the energy-state concept by N. Bohr (see Section 6.4).

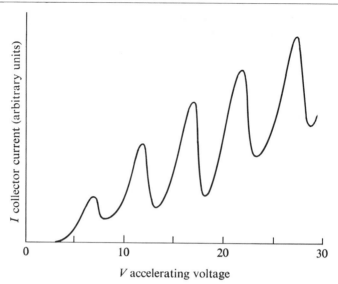

FIGURE 4.9   *Typical plot of collector current against accelerating voltage V for the Franck-Hertz experiment in mercury vapor. The peaks are spaced at about 4.9 volts apart.*

The immediate result of the Franck-Hertz experiment is to show that electrons of 4.9 eV energy are capable of losing considerable energy to the mercury atoms. The ionization potential of mercury is 10.4 eV, so no ionization can occur, but 4.9 eV is enough to excite the atoms into a state whence they can lose energy again by emitting radiation. In fact Franck and Hertz were able to show that a strong ultraviolet line is detected as soon as the accelerating voltage reaches the first minimum and that no other lines are found until higher voltages are employed. The ultraviolet line has a wavelength of 2537 Å and from Equation (3.6.5) (or Problem 3.18) we find that the corresponding quantum energy is just 4.9 eV. Therefore the energy lost to the atoms by the electrons reappears as one quantum per atom and we have located one excited state of the mercury atom at 4.9 eV above its ground state. A second excitation potential at 6.7 eV in mercury has been detected and this corresponds to a strong ultraviolet line at 1849 Å.

In this way we can get direct experimental evidence about atomic excited states which lie between the ground state and the energy at which ionization occurs. Atomic energy states are usually so complicated that only a few of the details can be worked out by these methods, but the principles for interpreting spectra are clear. Each state has a certain excitation potential (V_m) which measures its energy separation from the ground state. We can also assign an *effective* ionization potential W_m to each state, although only the ionization potential of the ground state (W_0) is normally measurable. By conservation of energy, we have

$$W_0 = W_m + V_m \qquad \text{for any state,}$$

if all quantities are taken as positive. The angular frequency (ω_{mn}) of a spectral line emitted or absorbed when the atom makes a transition from one state (m) to another (n) is given by the quantum relation

$$\hbar\omega_{mn} = W_m - W_n. \qquad [4.4.1]$$

In energy-level diagrams it is conventional to register all W values as negative, because the potential energy of an electron in an atom is negative, and the zero of energy represents

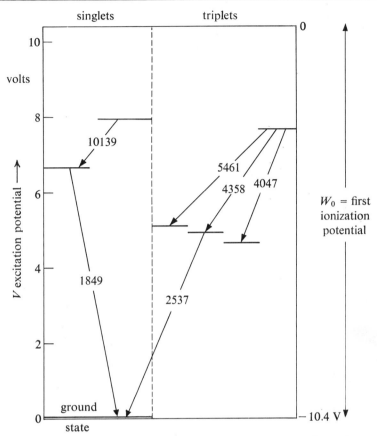

FIGURE 4.10 *Energy-level diagram for the mercury atom, showing the relation between excitation potentials and the ionization potential (W_0). The two main "resonance" lines connect excited states with the ground state. Wavelengths of several optical transitions are shown in Ångstroms.*

the separation of an electron from the atom, that is, single ionization. Figure 4.10 shows some of the energy-level structure of the mercury atom and a few of the characteristic lines produced by transitions between the different states. In this particular atom the states are divided into *singlet* and *triplet* types, which do not readily combine with each other.

(c) Spectroscopic series

The science of spectroscopy became highly developed during the latter years of the nineteenth century and out of the wealth of data certain empirical rules began to emerge. In 1885 Balmer showed that the visible spectrum of atomic hydrogen contained lines which were derivable from a formula

$$\lambda = \lambda_0 \frac{m^2}{m^2 - 4} \quad \text{with } m = 3, 4, \ldots, \text{ and so forth.}$$

This expression can be rearranged in terms of angular frequencies

$$\omega = \omega_0 \left(\frac{1}{2^2} - \frac{1}{m^2} \right), \qquad [4.4.2]$$

where ω_0 is a constant for the Balmer lines.

Rydberg was able to show that many atoms analogous to hydrogen, for example the alkali metals, possessed lines agreeing with the general formula

$$\frac{1}{\lambda} = R\left[\frac{1}{a^2} - \frac{1}{(m + b)^2}\right],$$ [4.4.3]

where R is known as Rydberg's constant, a is close to an integer, m takes integral values, and b is a small correction (constant in any series).

Despite these clarifications, no theoretical explanation was forthcoming at the time, although it is now evident that Equations (4.4.2) and (4.4.3) are similar in form to the quantum equation (4.4.1).

A great advance was recorded by the Ritz combination principle of 1908, according to which the spectral frequencies of one element can often be represented as sums or differences of other spectral frequencies. This observation may be understood in the light of quantum theory (see Figure 4.10) since, if the atom can pass from one state to another in several different ways, the net energy change is constant and therefore the sum of frequencies emitted depends only on the initial and final states. The quantum interpretation therefore directed attention away from the spectral lines themselves and toward the problem of locating energy levels and explaining them theoretically.

Although the quantum condition (4.4.1) is most often applied to optical frequencies, it is important also in the radio-frequency region, where characteristic lines of atoms and molecules occur. These lines represent minute changes in energy due to transitions between levels lying very close together. For example, the ground state of the hydrogen atom is known to be split very slightly, because a strong radio-frequency absorption is observed at a wavelength of 21 cm. The corresponding energy difference is found to be

$$\hbar\omega = \frac{hc}{\lambda} = 6 \times 10^{-6}\ \text{eV},$$

a *hyperfine* splitting due, in this case, to a small magnetic interaction between the electron and the hydrogen nucleus. This spectral line is of extreme importance in radio astronomy because interstellar hydrogen emits a detectable amount of the 21 cm radiation and as a result the general distribution of hydrogen in a galaxy can be determined. Experiments have been undertaken to measure the Zeeman splitting of this line and hence to find the magnitude of magnetic fields in interstellar regions.

4.5   The Statistics of Energy Levels

(a) Einstein's treatment of blackbody radiation

Atomic energy levels are important not only in the detailed theory of atoms but also in their statistical aspect. In 1916 Einstein published a derivation of the Planck distribution function in which new theoretical concepts were introduced. This derivation is based on the idea that atoms in excited states can contribute energy to the blackbody radiation in two ways—both *spontaneous* and *stimulated* emission being possible. For simplicity we shall deal with atoms possessing two states only, the ground state and an excited state, the energy separation being $\varepsilon = \hbar\omega$.

Suppose that at thermal equilibrium the number of atoms in the ground state is N_1 and the number in the excited state N_2, so that, according to Boltzmann's statistics, we should have

$$N_2 = N_1 \exp\left(\frac{-\varepsilon}{kT}\right).$$

Let the number of quanta available in the radiation with the correct angular frequency ω be represented by $f(\omega)$ and denote the probability of absorption per atom per quantum by B_{12}, so that the average number of absorptions per unit time by the ground-state atoms is

$$B_{12}N_1 f(\omega).$$

Also suppose that the probability of emission per unit time for each atom in the excited state is A; then the number of spontaneous emissions per unit time is

$$AN_2.$$

Here we must introduce a fundamental idea of quantum mechanics, namely, the principle that anything which stimulates a transition in one direction may equally well stimulate the reverse transition. In particular, the radiation density $f(\omega)$ which governs the probability of absorption by atoms in the ground state can also cause *stimulated emission* from the excited state. Formally, the probability of stimulated emission is written B_{21} so that the number of such transitions per unit time is

$$B_{21}N_2 f(\omega).$$

According to quantum mechanics, however, $B_{12} = B_{21} = B$, so that we can write the condition of dynamic equilibrium

$$BN_1 f(\omega) = AN_2 + BN_2 f(\omega)$$

or

$$f(\omega) = \frac{AN_2}{B(N_1 - N_2)}.$$

Using the Boltzmann relation to find the ratio N_2/N_1 we obtain

$$f(\omega) = \frac{A/B}{\exp\left(\dfrac{\hbar\omega}{kT}\right) - 1}. \qquad [4.5.1]$$

The theory is incomplete because the ratio A/B cannot be derived without a detailed treatment of the emission and absorption processes, as given by quantum mechanics. However, we may use the *Correspondence principle* of Niels Bohr to convert Equation (4.5.1) into the Planck relation. According to Bohr any quantum expression must reduce to the corresponding classical expression in the limit when $\hbar \to 0$. In the denominator of Equation (4.5.1) we have

$$\left[\exp\left(\frac{\hbar\omega}{kT}\right) - 1\right] \to \frac{\hbar\omega}{kT} \qquad \text{as } \hbar \to 0,$$

so that

$$f(\omega) \to \frac{kTA}{\hbar\omega B}.$$

If we identify this expression with the Rayleigh-Jeans formula [Equation (4.3.7)], we find

$$A/B = \frac{\hbar\omega^3}{\pi^2 c^3}$$

and the full expression for the energy distribution becomes

$$f(\omega) = \frac{\hbar\omega^3}{\pi^2 c^3 \left[\exp\left(\dfrac{\hbar\omega}{kT}\right) - 1 \right]},$$

which is Planck's result [Equation (4.3.10)]. Here $f(\omega)$ has been derived on the basis of classical statistics and the Correspondence principle. In fact a thorough application of quantum statistics is necessary for a satisfactory treatment of the blackbody problem.

(b) The maser principle

The process of stimulated emission has acquired great theoretical and practical significance in recent years. In the practical field it makes possible the design of various *maser* devices, the name being an abbreviation of "microwave amplification by stimulated emission of radiation."* These devices were developed to produce a radio-frequency amplifier which is almost free from the noise affecting conventional amplifiers. Under suitable conditions the stimulated emission from excited atoms or molecules may be much stronger than the reverse absorption process, with the result that a weak input signal of the correct frequency can stimulate a larger output. In the original ammonia maser a beam of ammonia molecules, which normally consists of two groups in slightly different energy states, is sent through an electrostatic field which separates the groups into two beams. The slightly excited molecules enter a cavity resonator, where a weak input signal at the resonant frequency of 24,000 Mc/sec is amplified as a result of the energy supplied by the ammonia molecules through stimulated emission. This type of maser can be used to make highly stable oscillations at the resonant frequency.

The three-level maser is of wider application because it can be run continuously without any beam-separation device; some types can be used at different frequencies through the use of materials in which the separation of levels depends on an applied magnetic field. Suppose that we have a system in which absorption of radiation (ω_2) leads rapidly to the second excited state S_2 (Figure 4.11). It may happen that many of the excited atoms do not immediately revert to the ground state but go into the first excited state S_1, which is *metastable*, that is, it has a comparatively long mean lifetime. The Einstein theory shows that the ratio A/B is lower for S_1 than for S_2, so it is possible for the first excited state S_1 to have A very low (for spontaneous emission) and yet to possess an appreciable value of B (the stimulated emission factor). This situation allows the first excited state to be populated by a large number of atoms when radiant energy at angular frequency ω_2 is supplied in large quantities, since these atoms can pass to S_1 indirectly via S_2. In this way the ratio N_2/N_1 is artificially made greater than 1, which is impossible under normal conditions of thermal equilibrium. If, now, a weak signal of frequency ω_1 is applied (in addition to the exciting radiation of frequency ω_2), this signal is strongly amplified by stimulated emission from the large number of atoms in the first excited state S_1.

Masers were originally developed to work in the microwave region, where low-noise amplification is particularly valuable, but more recently *optical masers* or "lasers" have

* J. P. Gordon, "The Maser," Scientific American, **199**, No. 6, 42 (1958).

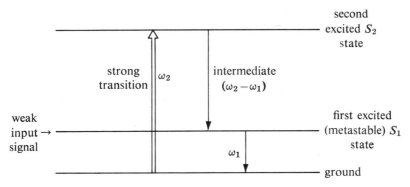

FIGURE 4.11 *Action of a 3-level maser. A supply of energy at the "pumping" frequency ω_2 causes strong transitions to the second excited state and, indirectly, population of the first excited state which is normally slow to emit radiation of frequency ω_1. Incoming radiation of this frequency stimulates emission from the first excited state and an amplified output signal is obtained.*

been produced.* In the ruby laser, for example, chromium atoms in a ruby crystal are excited by high-intensity light and deexcitation occurs in an avalanche of stimulated-emission processes because the emitted light is repeatedly reflected within the crystal. The light emitted by such a device has the property of being highly *coherent* since the atoms radiate in phase with each other. The effective bandwidth is thereby greatly reduced and the light waves become as precisely defined as radio waves. It is possible, for example, to produce very narrow and very intense beams of light by this method and numerous applications of the optical maser are expected.

4.6 The Nature of X Rays

(a) Properties of x rays

X rays were discovered in 1895 by Röntgen, who observed fluorescence in a material placed near a cathode-ray tube and found that photographic plates became fogged in the same vicinity, even when the plates were wrapped in black paper. The penetrating radiation was shown to have the following properties:

(i) it is not deflected by electrostatic or magnetic fields, nor does it exhibit appreciable reflection, refraction, or diffraction effects;

(ii) it penetrates matter to an extent which depends on the atomic weights of the elements involved, for example lead absorbs x rays much more strongly than aluminum;

(iii) it causes ionization in gases, ejects photoelectrons from metals, and affects photographic plates.

It will be seen that these properties do not fit in with conventional ideas about either waves or corpuscles, although many physicists supposed that the x rays must consist of streams of neutral particles. In the context of classical physics, the problem of identification resolves itself into the question whether the rays travel at the same speed as light in a vacuum and exhibit characteristic wave properties such as polarization, diffraction, and interference. The theory of electromagnetic waves (Section 4.1) already predicted that, at very short wavelengths, refraction effects must be slight and high penetrating

* A. L. Schawlow, "Optical Masers," Scientific American, **204**, No. 6, 52 (1961).

power would also be consistent with classical ideas. For this reason the particle theory was opposed by physicists who considered that x rays must be electromagnetic radiation of very short wavelength.

The first "wavelike" property demonstrated with x rays was that of polarization, detected by Barkla in 1904. Following the classical treatment of Section 4.1, it may be argued that scattered x rays should be polarized with their electric-field vector perpendicular to the plane containing the incident and scattered radiation (the yz plane of Figure 4.2). Barkla's experimental arrangement (Figure 4.12) allowed the unpolarized beam of x rays from the target of a cathode-ray tube to fall upon a carbon scatterer at O. The rays scattered in the z direction were intercepted by a second carbon scatterer placed close to the first but outside the limits of the primary beam. A detector moving in a plane parallel to the xy plane was able to record the effects of x rays scattered twice, through 90° each time. The results showed that a maximum intensity of doubly scattered x rays was recorded when they emerged from the second scatterer parallel to the y direction. Very little double scattering occurred in the x direction. This observation is in accord with classical theory because the rays scattered from O along Oz should be polarized in the x direction and the forced electron oscillations in the second scatterer cannot radiate in the direction of oscillation.

Later Barkla extended the measurements to find the scattering cross section of carbon for x rays. He found that, if Thomson's formula [Equation (4.1.17)] is correct for carbon, there must be in each carbon atom about 6 electrons effective in scattering. This result agrees somewhat fortuitously with the atomic number (Z) of the element, if this number is defined as the ordinal when all the elements are arranged in sequence of atomic weights. Historically, Barkla's result was important in showing that in light elements the number of electrons per atom is approximately half of the atomic weight.

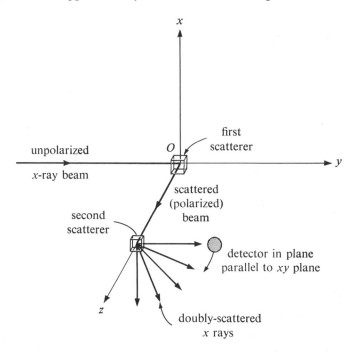

FIGURE 4.12   *Barkla's experiment on the polarization of x rays by scattering. Rays scattered twice show maximum intensity in a direction parallel to the original (unpolarized) beam.*

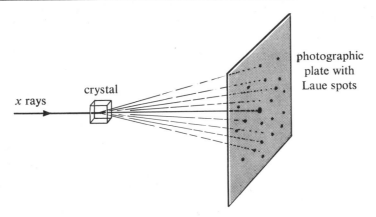

FIGURE 4.13 *Arrangement for detecting Laue diffraction of x rays by a crystal, which acts like a three-dimensional grating and produces diffraction spots on a photographic plate.*

The scattering process is also of interest in establishing that the effective scattering power of an atom or ion for x rays depends on the number of electrons present. This result is important in the electrovalent type of solid lattice (Figure 3.1), which consists of ions only. For example, in potassium chloride the ions K^+ and Cl^- happen to possess 18 electrons each, although the neutral atoms contain 19 and 17, respectively. From the x-ray point of view, therefore, all the lattice points are identically occupied and the structure is equivalent to a *simple cubic* lattice with its lattice constant one-half of the correct size.

In 1911 Laue suggested that x rays should be appreciably diffracted by a regular crystal since the layers of atoms in the crystal lattice might act as a three-dimensional grating of suitable dimensions. The experiment was first carried out in 1912 by Friedrich and Knipping, who passed a beam of x rays through a zinc sulfide crystal with a photographic plate placed on the other side (Figure 4.13). Most of the x rays went through the crystal to form a central spot on the plate but, after long exposure, the plate recorded additional spots in a regular pattern and these agreed with the diffraction theory. Later technical developments made x-ray analysis into the most powerful method for investigating the structure of matter in the solid state.

Early attempts to measure the wavelengths of x rays with ruled gratings failed because of the large disparity between the grating spacing (several thousand Ångstroms) and the wavelengths (a few Ångstroms). Finally, however, Compton was successful in obtaining diffraction patterns when x rays fell on ruled gratings at grazing incidence. The theory of Section 4.1 shows that at very high frequencies the refractive index of a material is slightly less than 1, so by passing the radiation in a fine beam very close to the surface of the grating it is possible to obtain total reflection of the beam. In addition to the reflected rays, diffracted beams of different orders are found and these beams are used to standardize the x-ray wavelength in terms of metric units. In this way lattice constants can be measured very accurately from x-ray crystal diffraction patterns and the method leads to a determination of the constant N^* and the electronic charge e (Section 3.1).

(b) Waves and quanta

The identification of x rays as electromagnetic radiations of short wavelength was contemporaneous with the discovery that they exhibit pronounced quantum effects. As early as 1896, J. J. Thomson investigated the ionization of gases by x rays. In 1910 W. H.

Bragg pointed out that this is an indirect process in which the x rays eject photoelectrons from the atoms and the electrons cause the ionization. The photoelectric effect in gases obeys the same rules as the photoelectric effect in metals, with the important difference that the work function is characteristic of the individual atoms and not of the atoms interacting strongly together, as in a metal. Bragg showed that the maximum energy of a photoelectron is very nearly equal to the energy of electrons striking the target in the x-ray tube. Such an effect is inexplicable in terms of waves, which dissipate their energy as they spread out from a source and can hardly concentrate all their energy on one particle.

In the quantum theory, however, the whole of a quantum can be given to one electron in the photoelectric effect. Each x-ray quantum originated in the slowing down or stoppage of an electron in the target of the x-ray tube. Although this process gives rise to quanta of different energies, it is clear that the maximum quantum energy must be equal to the kinetic energy per electron in the beam. The quantum theory therefore gives a straightforward account of the energy relations observed by Bragg. At the same time, the wave model provides a picture of the decreasing yield of photoelectrons as the distance from the target increases. As the x rays get further from the tube, the *probability* of ejecting a photoelectron becomes smaller and smaller, but this does not rule out the production of individual photoelectrons of high energy.

It is evident, therefore, that radiation behaves like both waves and corpuscles in different types of experiment. In order to reconcile the two pictures, it is necessary to emphasize once more the *statistical* nature of our knowledge about atomic processes—in fact we do not directly observe a quantum influencing one atom or an electron scattering electromagnetic waves. Our experimental data usually refer to large assemblies of atoms and quanta; hence it is possible to regard the diffraction pattern produced on a screen by x rays or visible light as the sum of contributions by many quanta. In the modern view the pattern represents a probability function for quanta to reach the screen at various places and this function is determined by the wave aspects of radiation. The pattern is only seen when quanta accumulate in sufficient numbers to even out the inevitable statistical fluctuations. For example, in 1909 Taylor[*] carried out an experiment on the interference pattern produced by a light source so feeble that no more than one quantum could traverse the apparatus at any time. Nevertheless the pattern built up slowly on a photographic plate was exactly the same as the pattern produced by a strong light source. If Taylor's experiment is repeated with a bank of photoelectric cells, each cell records only occasional counts due to individual quanta and statistical data have to be accumulated before wave behavior can be detected. It is therefore necessary to retain the wave formulation when the behavior of many quanta is to be predicted, but atomic interactions occur through individual quanta.

4.7 The Analysis of Crystal Structure[†]

(a) The Bragg method

The Laue method for analyzing crystal structures with x rays involves the diffraction of waves by a three-dimensional lattice, each atom of which acts as a scatterer of the incident x rays. The analysis can be simplified greatly by a method developed by W. H. Bragg and

[*] G. I. Taylor, Proc. Cambridge Phil. Soc., **15**, 114 (1909).
[†] This section may be read in conjunction with the treatment of solids in Chapter 8; it is included here for the convenience of placing together all the sections on x rays.

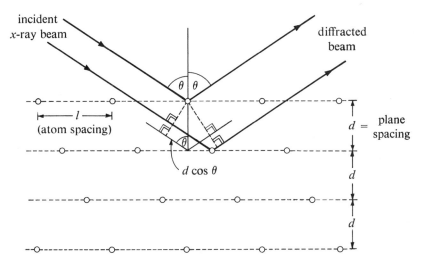

FIGURE 4.14 *The condition for strong (Bragg) reflection from a set of crystal planes at distance d apart is that the path difference between successive scattered waves is a whole number of wavelengths; by construction it is shown that the path difference is 2d cos θ for any atomic pattern.*

W. L. Bragg in 1913. Suppose that x rays of wavelength λ are incident at angle θ on a crystal face, in a plane containing a row of surface atoms spaced at intervals l (Figure 4.14). The surface atoms scatter the x rays coherently, to a degree given approximately by the Thomson formula [Equation (4.1.17)] for each electron in the atom. It follows from Huyghens' principle that the scattered waves reinforce each other in the direction making angle θ with the normal, that is, the "diffracted" beam obeys the law of reflection. Other diffracted beams would be observable if a single surface layer was present but in practice the other layers of atoms in the crystal contribute appreciably and have the effect of restricting the scattered beam to that angle where the reflection law is obeyed.

The reflection condition is necessary but not sufficient to give a strong diffraction maximum; we must now consider the effects of the different layers of atoms in the crystal, spaced at intervals d (measured perpendicular to the surface). If the atoms lie directly beneath each other, the path difference between waves scattered by one atom and its neighbor at angle θ to the normal, is simply

$$2d \cos \theta.*$$

The same path difference is obtained if the atoms do not lie beneath each other, as may be seen from Figure 4.14. If, now, this path difference is an integral multiple of the wavelength, strong *Bragg reflection* will occur from this crystal face, provided that

$$2d \cos \theta = N\lambda, \qquad \text{where } N = 1, 2, 3, \ldots . \qquad [4.7.1]$$

The same result can be obtained by treating the Laue spots (Figure 4.13) as due to reflections from planes suitably oriented in the crystal.

In practice, the direction of incident x rays is defined by slits and the crystal is placed on a rotating table (Figure 4.15). A suitable detector, for example, an ion chamber or a Geiger counter, is placed so that it records x rays "reflected" from the surface at the correct angle θ,

* In x-ray work it is conventional to use, instead of the angle θ, the angle between the incident beam and the crystal *face*; however, this practice causes some confusion and has been avoided here.

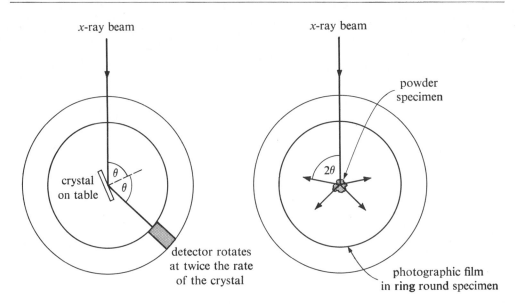

FIGURE 4.15   *Two experimental methods for Bragg analysis of crystal structure. On the left, a crystal face is rotated relative ot the incident x-ray beam so that the detector, rotating at twice the rate, picks out the Bragg reflections. On the right, a polycrystalline specimen is placed in the path of the beam and the Bragg reflections produce lines on the surrounding photographic film.*

equal to the angle of incidence. The Bragg angles for strong reflection are located by rotating the crystal slowly and the detector at *twice* the rate, so that the condition of reflection is maintained. This method was employed by the Braggs both in examining x-ray spectra and in analyzing crystals.

If we wish to use the Bragg method for crystal analysis, it is desirable that x rays of a single wavelength fall on the crystal; the existence of sharp characteristic x-ray lines emitted by metal targets renders this plan feasible. If necessary, thin metal filters can be introduced to isolate a particular line of suitable wavelength. When a single crystal is studied in all possible orientations, several values of the parameter d are found. The same happens when a powder or a polycrystalline specimen is investigated; here the specimen need not be rotated, since small crystals of many orientations occur in it, and the Bragg lines are conveniently recorded on a photographic film surrounding the specimen (Figure 4.15). The question now arises: what is the relation between any particular d value and the lattice constants of the crystal? The answer to this question involves the specification of particular planes by means of the *Miller indices*, which we shall illustrate by reference to cubic lattices.

(b) *Plane spacings in a cubic lattice*

The reason for the existence of different d values may be seen directly by consideration of a cubic lattice such as that of Figure 3.1, where the unit cell contains atoms in several layers. Not only do layers occur with the spacing $d = a$ but there are parallel layers with $d = \frac{1}{2}a$, inclined layers with $d = \frac{a}{\sqrt{2}}$, and so on. A convenient way of enumerating the different planes is to use the Miller indices (h, k, l) which are proportional to the *reciprocals* of the intercepts of a particular plane on the Cartesian axes (Figure 4.16). In these coordinates the equation of the plane is

$$hx + ky + lz = a \qquad [4.7.2]$$

with intercepts

$$x = \frac{a}{h}, \qquad y = \frac{a}{k}, \qquad z = \frac{a}{l}.$$

For example, the (110) plane is at 45° to the x and y axes and parallel to the z axis, while the (111) plane is a diagonal across the corner of the unit cell near the origin. In a cubic lattice the three axes are interchangeable so (110) and (101) or (011) are not distinguished. It is conventional to write the indices (h, k, l) with $h \geqslant k \geqslant l$.

If we multiply the Miller indices (h, k, l) of a plane by any whole number we necessarily obtain a parallel plane closer to the origin, for example, the (222) plane is half-way between (111) and the origin. In Bragg reflection from the lattice, a first-order line corresponding to (222) spacing is the same as a second-order ($N = 2$) line from the (111) planes. For this reason the number N is usually omitted from Equation (4.7.1) and the full sequence of Miller indices is employed.

The spacing (d) between parallel planes denoted by a particular set of indices (h, k, l) is found by calculating the length of a perpendicular from the origin on to the nearest plane of the set. Standard geometrical techniques lead to the general result for cubic lattices

$$d = \frac{a}{\sqrt{h^2 + k^2 + l^2}}, \qquad [4.7.3]$$

which may be checked by considering special cases. If, then, experimental data yield several values of d for a crystal we need to know the (h, k, l) values at each reflection to be sure of a. The situation is complicated by the fact that not all (h, k, l) values are represented in the sequence of reflections, which depends on the symmetry properties of the unit cell. For

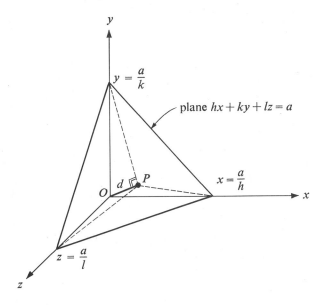

FIGURE 4.16 *Identification of any plane in a cubic lattice by means of the Miller indices (h, k, l). The effective plane spacing d is found by dropping a perpendicular from the origin 0 on to the plane $hx + ky + lz = a$, where a is the lattice constant.*

these reasons there is no general method for determining lattice structures and a certain amount of trial and error may be necessary before a consistent solution is reached.

(c) The structure of metals

One very important group of solids requiring analysis consists of the pure metals, in which, as we have seen, positively charged ions form a lattice which is held together by the "gas" of free electrons. Here the problem of x-ray analysis is simplified by the identity of all the scattering centers, and possible structures may be investigated by packing together a large number of identical spheres in a limited volume. It is clear that we obtain the closest packing in one plane by forming the triangular array shown in Figure 4.17, where each sphere touches six neighbors. The next layer on top of this will have its spheres centered in alternate spaces left between the spheres of the lower layer. Each sphere in the lower layer now touches three spheres in the upper layer and in a complete three-dimensional structure there must be an extra three below the first layer, making a total of 12 nearest neighbors for any atom in a close-packed lattice of identical atoms.

Examination of Figure 4.17 shows that two different kinds of close-packed structures exist, according to the way in which successive layers of atoms are stacked up. If the third layer of atoms is placed so that each atom is diametrically over an atom in the first layer, we have a simple alternation of the pattern in a direction perpendicular to the plane of the first layer. Thus the structure is columnar or prismatic and it obviously has hexagonal symmetry. *Hexagonal close packing* is exemplified by several metals, including magnesium.

The second way in which close packing can be attained is by stacking a third layer of atoms so that each is centered in a space which is not occupied by atoms in the first or second layers. Fourth and fifth layers then repeat the sequence of the first and second layers and the net result is an isotropic structure in which no particular axis is preferred. Examination of the position of any one atom relative to its lower neighbors (Figure 4.18) shows that the lattice is in fact cubic, the threefold symmetry corresponding to the symmetry of a cube viewed from one corner, that is, in a direction perpendicular to the (111) plane. This structure is often termed *face-centered cubic* because the unit cell has atoms at all eight corners and at the centers of all six faces (Figure 4.18). It is the same structure as that of *either* the

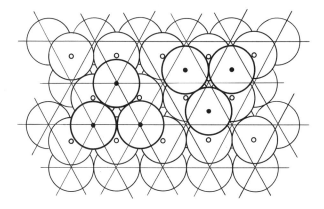

FIGURE 4.17 *Two ways in which identical spheres may be built up into a close-packed structure. The first layer has its spheres centered at the triangular lattice points, the second layer has centers marked* ○, *and the third layer may be centered either above the first layer (hexagonal close-packing, left) or in the unoccupied gaps (cubic close-packing, right).*

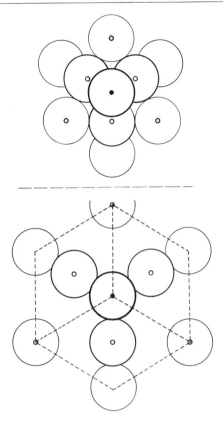

FIGURE 4.18   *Above: view of a typical atom in the cubic close-packed structure and its relations to neighboring atoms. Below: the same structure expanded to show its identity with the face-centered cubic lattice, viewed perpendicular to the (111) plane.*

positive ions *or* the negative ions in the sodium chloride lattice (Figure 3.1) and so an infinite metallic lattice of this type must contain four atoms per unit cell. Among metals, face-centered cubic structure is exhibited by copper, nickel, and lead.

Another form of cubic structure is obtained when each unit cell contains one central atom in addition to eight corner atoms, that is, it is *body-centered*. In such a system each atom is surrounded by eight nearest neighbors and the lattice is less densely populated than a close-packed lattice. Such a structure is exemplified by tungsten and iron (the "α-modification" at ordinary temperatures).

Most metals belong to one or other of the crystal types described and analysis by the Bragg method enables the structure to be identified, the procedure being particularly simple for cubic lattices. It is found that face-centered cubic crystals give strong reflections only from those planes in which h, k, and l are all even or all odd, that is, all the Miller indices have the same *parity*. Numbering these planes in turn, we find the sequence

$$111, 200, 220, 222, 311, 331, 333, 400, \ldots.$$

The values of d found from the observed angles of reflection are therefore inspected to see if they fit in with the above sequence. Once the correct structure has been identified, it is possible to determine the lattice constant (a) with considerable precision in terms of the x-ray wavelength used. Equation (3.1.3) can then be used to check the consistency of the result.

Body-centered cubic lattices give strong reflections only from those planes in which the *sum* $(h + k + l)$ is even, that is, in this case we have the sequence

$$110, 200, 211, 220, 222, 310, 321, \ldots$$

which is recognisably different from the face-centered reflection sequence. Again, the constant a can be found once the sequence of d values has been identified.

4.8   X-Ray Spectra

(a) Continuous and line spectra

The x rays emitted from the target of a cathode-ray tube may be analyzed conveniently with the aid of a Bragg spectrometer in which a single crystal plane is used as reflector, that is, in Equation (4.7.1) only one value of d is considered. The results of a typical experiment are shown in Figure 4.19, where the increasing angle θ corresponds to decreasing wavelength. Certain features are immediately relevant to the study of x-ray spectra:

(i) there is a continuous background of radiation extending up to a definite cutoff, corresponding to a certain minimum wavelength;

(ii) superimposed on the continuous spectrum are sharp lines which are found to be characteristic of the element used as the cathode-ray target.

The continuous background of "white x rays" is interpreted in terms of the *bremsstrahlung**

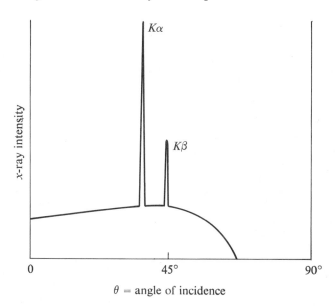

FIGURE 4.19   *Investigation of x-ray spectra by the Bragg method. A continuous background of "bremsstrahlung" extends up to a maximum angle corresponding to a definite minimum wavelength. Superimposed on the background there may be sharp lines which are characteristic of the target in the x-ray tube, for example, the Kα and Kβ lines shown.*

* This means "radiation from slowing-down processes."

mechanism, by which electrons impinging on the target suffer repeated small losses of energy by distant interactions with the atoms. At each small impact the loss of energy is radiated as a quantum and, since all values of the energy loss can occur up to a maximum imposed by the original kinetic energy of the electrons, the spectrum is necessarily continuous. Moreover, the maximum angular frequency (ω_{max}) of the x rays must be given by the *Duane-Hunt law*

$$\hbar\omega_{max} = \text{Electron } KE \doteq e\text{V}, \qquad [4.8.1]$$

where V is the accelerating voltage applied to the electrons. This relation has been verified in detail and it provides an accurate way of finding Planck's constant when the electronic charge is known.

In 1906 Barkla found that when x rays strike a scatterer "secondary x rays" are emitted in addition to the scattered x rays coherent with the incident beam. The secondary rays are always of longer wavelength than the incident rays and are due to the ionization of atoms in the scatterer. Following ionization, each atom captures an electron and the reorganization of inner electrons is supposed to involve the emission of high-energy quanta. The secondary rays are identical in wavelength with the characteristic x-ray lines produced by electron bombardment of a target made of the same element, so we deduce that emission of the characteristic lines follows ionization of atoms by the incident electrons. The characteristic lines occur in definite groups, corresponding to Barkla's $K, L, M, \ldots$ series. For example, the K series always consists of a strong "$K\alpha$" line (resolved into two close lines in heavy elements) and a weaker "$K\beta$" line at a slightly shorter wavelength (as in Figure 4.19), while the L, M series are more complicated. X-ray spectra differ from the lines in the optical region in that they have the same general character for all medium and heavy elements, whereas optical spectra change markedly from one element to the next. This fact and the high-energy changes involved in x-ray emission indicate that we are dealing with the inner structure of the atoms.

(b) Moseley's law

The study of K lines emitted by different elements led to a remarkable discovery by Moseley in 1913. The frequency of a particular type of line, say the $K\alpha$ line, varies smoothly from one element to the next in the periodic table and is proportional to the square of the atomic number (Z). If we use the atomic weight instead, the relation is much less satisfactory, so Moseley's work was the first to establish the atomic number as characteristic of the chemical nature of an element. His experiments on the $K\alpha$ and $K\beta$ lines emitted by a series of metals between calcium and zinc showed quite clearly the existence of a gap between calcium and titanium, as maintained by Mendeleev (Figure 1.1). Moseley's results also established the correct order of cobalt and nickel, which have very similar atomic weights.

More detailed investigations show that the angular frequency of $K\alpha$ lines obeys a relation of the type

$$\omega \propto (Z - a)^2, \qquad [4.8.1]$$

where a is a constant of the order of one unit. This result applies only to the K series at low Z values, but within limits the relation is highly accurate, as may be seen in Figure 4.20, where the square root of the angular frequency is plotted against the atomic number for both $K\alpha$ and $L\alpha$ lines. Further observations show that the higher series must involve the outer structure of the atom, since the quantum energies are low and the sequences of lines approach the complexity of optical spectra.

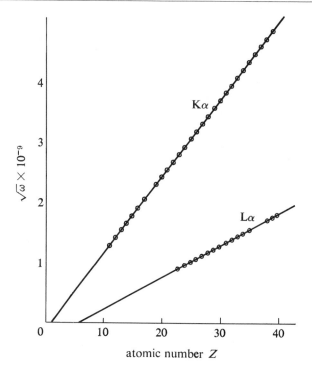

FIGURE 4.20   *The Moseley diagram. The square root of the angular frequency plotted against atomic number Z for the Kα and Lα lines of light elements.*

4.9   The Absorption of X Rays

(a) Absorption coefficients and cross sections

Several effects contribute to the scattering and absorption of x rays and the different processes are often difficult to disentangle. If we concentrate on pure absorption processes, we can define the rate of absorption in terms of an *absorption cross section*, analogous to the scattering cross section of Equation (4.1.15). Suppose that a homogeneous beam of x rays, of intensity I_0, is incident upon a material of thickness x which reduces the intensity to I. In the material let there be n atoms per unit volume, related to the mass density ρ (for an element) by the equation

$$n = \frac{N^*\rho}{M},$$
[4.9.1]

where M stands for the atomic weight.

In a thin layer, of thickness dx, placed at right angles to the beam, the number of atoms per unit *area* is $n\,dx$. Each of these atoms presents an effective area for absorption of σ_{ab}, hence the probability of absorption in this layer is $n\sigma_{ab}\,dx$. The loss of intensity $(-dI)$ is proportional to the actual intensity (I) and, introducing the probability expression, we find

$$-dI = n\sigma_{ab}I\,dx,$$

an equation with the solution

$$I = I_0 \exp{(-n\sigma_{ab}x)}.$$
[4.9.2]

An alternative way of writing this expression is

$$I = I_0 \exp(-\mu x). \qquad [4.9.3]$$

where μ is the *absorption coefficient*

$$\mu = n\sigma_{ab}. \qquad [4.9.4]$$

(b) Photoelectric absorption

It has already been mentioned that x rays are capable of ejecting photoelectrons from metals and from gases; indeed this process occurs with all forms of matter and it is very similar to the photoelectric effect in metals (Section 3.6). The most important new feature revealed by experiments with x rays is the necessity of introducing several different work functions (W_k, W_l, and so forth) in Einstein's quantum equation

$$KE \text{ of electron} = \hbar\omega - W. \qquad [4.9.5]$$

The situation may best be appreciated by study of the absorption coefficient μ as a function of the incident x-ray frequency ω (Figure 4.21). Although the general trend of the curve is downwards as the angular frequency increases, there are pronounced maxima associated with sharp absorption "edges." Thus, whenever the frequency reaches some critical value, for example, ω_k or ω_l in the diagram, the absorption rises suddenly, indicating the onset of some process which was not present at lower frequencies. The interpretation in terms of work

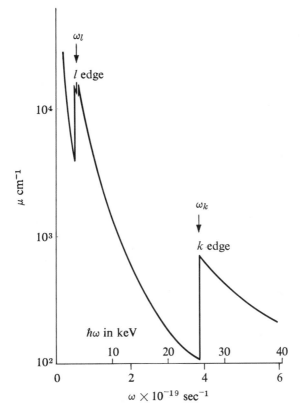

FIGURE 4.21 *The absorption coefficient for silver (on a logarithmic scale) plotted against the angular frequency and quantum energy in the x-ray region. The l and k absorption edges are prominent (the l edge consists of three discontinuities close together).*

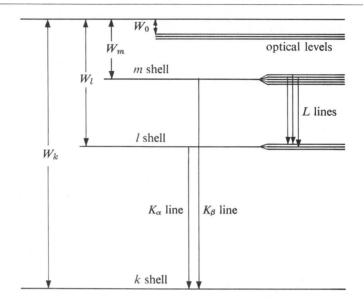

FIGURE 4.22 *General scheme of atomic energy levels operative in x-ray spectra (not to scale).*
Under high resolution all the lines appear complex because of the splitting of the main energy levels.
Here W_0 represents the "first ionization potential" of Section 4.4 and is in fact
much smaller than any of the other W values.

functions (W) is that at each absorption edge the energy becomes sufficient to ionize a
certain level in the atom; so if we write

$$W_k = \hbar\omega_k, \qquad W_l = \hbar\omega_l, \qquad \text{and so forth,}$$

the W values in eV represent ionization potentials for *inner* levels of the atom.

The photoelectric effect therefore consists of x-ray absorption, with ejection of an
electron from one of the inner parts of the atom; this process does not immediately terminate, because there is now a gap in the level which was ionized. We suppose that an
electron will now fall from a higher level into the ionized level and emit radiation, which
appears as a secondary x ray. In this way a cascade of x rays can be emitted until eventually
a stray electron is captured by the atom into one of its outermost layers, where optical
transitions occur. Following the quantum rule [Equation (4.4.1)] the frequencies of all the
secondary x rays can be calculated once the W values are known. The $K\alpha$ lines, for instance,
are due to transition from the "l" electron shell to the lowest "k" shell, so we write

($K\alpha$): $$\hbar\omega = W_k - W_l,$$ [4.9.6]

where the W values are regarded as positive.

The $K\beta$ lines are due to transitions from the "m" to the "k" shell, so are of slightly higher
frequency

($K\beta$): $$\hbar\omega = W_k - W_m.$$

Here we have denoted x-ray lines by capitals, K, L, and so forth and the levels by small
letters k, l, and so forth, in an attempt to avoid the confusion between shells and lines
which often arises in x-ray work. Figure 4.22 shows some of the relations between the
various characteristic lines and energy levels of a heavy atom, the diagram being drawn in the

convention of Figure 4.10 with the *W* values *negative* to indicate the work done in extracting an electron from the various levels. Except in the "*k*" and "*l*" shells considerable subdivision occurs among the various levels and the line patterns become correspondingly complex.

(c) The Compton effect

At frequencies higher than the "*k*" absorption edge an element displays very little photoelectric absorption but a new type of scattering becomes important. This is a type of "inelastic" scattering in which the x rays lose energy, so the process is akin to absorption in the energy sense. By the quantum rule the scattered x rays must have lower frequency and hence longer wavelength than the incident beam. The effect was detected by Compton, who analyzed the radiation scattered from carbon with a Bragg spectrometer. He obtained patterns like those in Figure 4.23, where at each angle of scattering there is a component at the same wavelength as the original plus a second component of much longer wavelength. The change in wavelength ($\Delta\lambda$) between the first and second components is given as a function of the angle of scattering (θ) by the simple relation

$$\Delta\lambda = 2.4 \times 10^{-12} (1 - \cos\theta) \text{ m.} \qquad [4.9.7]$$

Compton not only demonstrated the accuracy of this formula but also provided a simple interpretation which had revolutionary effects on scientific thinking about the quantum theory. So far we have considered the quantum as a discrete amount of energy in the radiation field and we have seen that the statistical distribution of such quanta over a

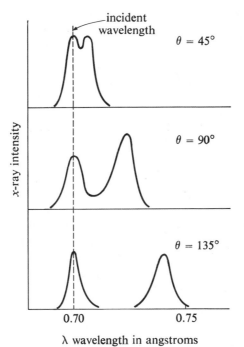

FIGURE 4.23 *Analysis of the x rays scattered by carbon at various angles θ to show the Compton effect. In addition to a group of the same wavelength as the incident beam there is a component of longer wavelength attributed to "inelastic" scattering of the x rays by electrons.*

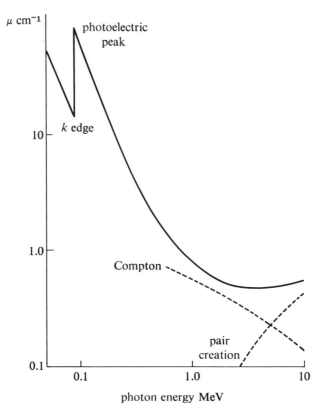

FIGURE 4.24   *The total attenuation coefficient (μ) for lead in the high-energy x-ray region, plotted against the photon energy (on a log-log scale). The Compton and pair-creation contributions are represented approximately by the dotted lines.*

surface is given by the classical wave theory. Compton showed that the quantum must be endowed with linear momentum, some of which can be imparted to a single electron in a collision process, when the recoiling electron takes up the energy which is lost by the quantum. The quantum therefore takes on many of the properties of a classical particle and the word *photon* is often used to denote the "particle" of an electromagnetic radiation field, as distinct from the word *quantum* which is more general and usually refers to energy. The way in which the Compton cross section varies with photon energy is shown in Figure 4.24*; like the photoelectric effect, the process becomes less probable as the energy increases.

(d) Pair creation

For many years it was believed that all forms of electromagnetic interaction decrease in probability in the high-energy region. However, in 1932 the positive electron or *positron* was discovered by Anderson in cosmic rays and investigation proved that positive and negative electrons are produced simultaneously in pairs when high-energy photons encounter matter. This *pair-creation* process has a threshold (for electrons) at a photon energy of 1.02 MeV. At higher energies the sum of the electrons' kinetic energies is very nearly

* The coefficient shown by the dotted line is the sum of the Compton scattering and energy-absorption contributions.

equal to the difference between the photon energy and the threshold energy

$$K(e^+) + K(e^-) = \hbar\omega - 1.02 \text{ MeV.} \qquad [4.9.8]$$

It therefore appears that the threshold energy was spent in "creating" the two charged particles; we have clear evidence here about the interrelation of matter and energy.

The pair-creation process cannot take place in free space* but usually occurs in the field of an atomic nucleus, which recoils with the excess momentum imparted by the photon; there is a certain loss of kinetic energy to the nucleus, but this is very small in practice because of its large mass compared with the mass of an electron. The cross section for pair creation increases with increasing photon energy and also increases with the atomic number (Z) of the element concerned. In the case of lead, the photon absorption is appreciable above 5 MeV and it provides the greater part of the total attenuation cross section above this energy (see Figure 4.24). The *total* cross section therefore falls to a broad minimum in the 5-MeV region and then rises once more.

The positron was the first particle to be discovered with "antiparticle" properties, that is, it is similar to its opposite number, the negative electron or *negatron*, in all properties except its opposite charge. The positron is entirely stable *in vacuo* but, when it meets a negative electron, the two particles may annihilate each other, in this way reversing the pair-creation process. Slow positrons usually annihilate with slow electrons to emit two photons per pair of disappearing electrons; since each type of electron contributes 0.51 MeV energy, the balance equation reads

$$e^+ + e^- \rightarrow 2\hbar\omega = 1.02 \text{ MeV.} \qquad [4.9.9]$$

Annihilation radiation, consisting of 0.51 MeV photons, is often detected when positrons encounter matter, which slows down the positrons and provides the negative electrons for annihilation. The pair-creation and pair-annihilation processes serve to emphasize the new relations between matter and radiation which emerge in the high-energy region.

FOR FURTHER READING

Electrical theory:
W. H. PANOFSKY and M. PHILLIPS, *Classical Electricity and Magnetism* (Addison-Wesley Publishing Co., Cambridge, Mass, 1955).

Classical electron theory:
H. A. LORENTZ, *The Theory of Electrons* (Dover Publications, New York, 1952).

X rays:
A. H. COMPTON and S. K. ALLISON, *X rays, in Theory and Experiment* (D. Van Nostrand Co., Princeton, N.J. 1935) 2nd ed.

Simple crystal structures:
A. HOLDEN and P. SINGER, *Crystals and Crystal-growing* (Science Study Series, Doubleday & Co., New York, 1960).

X rays and matter:
K. H. SPRING, *Photons and Electrons* (Methuen Monographs, J. Wiley and Sons, New York, 1960) 2nd ed.

---

* This is a consequence of the conditions of conservation of energy and momentum as applied to this process. See Problem 5.16.

PROBLEMS FOR CHAPTER 4

DATA REQUIRED

Number of molecules per kmole: $N^* = 6.0 \times 10^{26}$
Electronic charge: $e = 1.60 \times 10^{-19}$ C
Specific charge: $e/m = 1.76 \times 10^{11}$ C/kg
Velocity of light in vacuum: $c = 3.0 \times 10^8$ m/sec
Permittivity: $\varepsilon_0 = \dfrac{1}{36\pi \times 10^9}$ mks approximately
Planck's constant: $h = 6.6 \times 10^{-34}$ J sec
Boltzmann's constant: $k = 1.38 \times 10^{-23}$ J/°K

4.1. (a) Show that the dispersion formula [Equation (4.1.8)] may be put in the form:
$n^2 = A + \dfrac{B}{\lambda^2}$ (A, B, constants) if the wavelength λ is considerably greater than the resonance wavelength λ_0.

(b) Experiments yield the following data concerning the refractive index of water (mol.wt. = 18) at different wavelengths:

$\lambda = 4047$	4861	5893	6708 Å
$n = 1.3428$	1.3371	1.3330	1.3308

Use these data to test the foregoing relation and calculate the effective resonance wavelength (λ_0), also the number of electrons per molecule (z) active in dispersion.

4.2. In a highly ionized region the refractive index is given by the relation

$$n^2 = 1 - K\lambda^2 \qquad (K \text{ is constant}).$$

Prove that the group velocity of electromagnetic waves $\left(u_G = \dfrac{\partial v}{\partial(1/\lambda)}\right)$ is always less than the velocity in vacuum (c) although the phase velocity (c/n) exceeds c.

4.3. Find a general relation for total reflection of radio waves of angular frequency ω by an ionosphere layer of electron density N per m³ when the waves arrive at an angle of incidence θ (measured in vacuum). If radio waves of angular frequency $\omega = 5 \times 10^7$ sec⁻¹ are incident normally upon a certain layer and are just totally reflected, what is the value of N for this layer?

4.4. Calculate the number of atoms per cubic meter in graphite (at.wt. = 12, density = 2.3×10^3 kg/m³), also the Thomson scattering cross section per atom if $Z = 6$. Hence find the fraction of the intensity of an x-ray beam which is scattered by a block of graphite 2 cm thick, assuming that no other interactions occur.

4.5. Calculate the percentage Zeeman splitting (in terms of frequency) of the 21 cm hydrogen line by an interstellar magnetic field of strength $B = 10^{-8}$ weber/m².

4.6. Show that (i) in the normal Zeeman effect the lower frequency component of the doublet seen along the magnetic field direction is circularly polarized in the same sense as the electron flow in coils producing the magnetic field; (ii) in the normal Faraday effect with plane-polarized light traveling along magnetic lines of force, the rotation is clockwise as viewed from the source of the light.

4.7. Estimate the Faraday rotation in degrees per centimeter for radio waves of wavelength 4 cm passing through an ionized gas containing 4×10^{17} electrons/m³ subject to a magnetic field of 10^{-2} weber/m² in the direction of travel. (Substitute $\omega_0 =$ the plasma frequency ω_p for the gas.)

4.8. With the aid of Planck's distribution function [Equation (4.3.10)] find the angular frequency (ω_m) at which the energy per unit frequency range is a maximum for blackbody radiation at temperature $T = 6000°K$. Compare the wavelength corresponding to this frequency with the wavelength given by the Wien relation [Equation (4.3.13)].

4.9. The value of Stefan's blackbody constant σ is usually quoted as the energy radiated per second from unit area at absolute temperature $T = 1°K$. Show that this constant σ is related to the energy-density constant s of Equation (4.3.11) by the equation

$$\sigma = \tfrac{1}{4}cs \quad (c = \text{velocity of light}).$$

Hence calculate the value of σ absolutely.

4.10. The principal excitation potential in atomic hydrogen is 10.2 eV and the first ionization potential (W_0) is 13.6 eV. Show that Balmer's formula [Equation (4.4.2)] can be accounted for if we assume that hydrogen possesses a series of levels with effective ionization potentials given by the formula

$$W_m = \frac{13.6}{m^2}\,\text{eV} \quad (m = 1, 2, 3, 4, \text{ and so forth}).$$

Draw an energy-level diagram for the hydrogen atom and locate lines which should be found in the ultraviolet region.

4.11. Suppose that we could construct a three-level maser based on the "normal" Zeeman splitting of a simple energy level, what magnetic field would be needed to operate a radio-frequency amplifier in the millimeter-wavelength region? (Assume $\omega = 10^{12} \text{ sec}^{-1}$)

4.12. In a Taylor experiment on the "interference of photons," light of wavelength 6000 Å travels from a source to a screen 1 m away and forms an interference pattern. What is the maximum wattage of the source if there must be, on the average, no more than one photon in the apparatus at any time?

4.13. In an experiment to analyze the crystal structure of metallic copper (at.wt. = 63.5, density 8.9×10^3 kg/m³) x rays of wavelength 1.54 Å were incident on a copper foil and strong Bragg reflections were found at the following angles of incidence

$$\theta = 68°8' \quad 64°33' \quad 52°38' \quad 44°53'.$$

Show that the data are consistent with a face-centered cubic lattice and calculate the lattice constant (a) both from the density and the x-ray data.

4.14. Prove that in an infinite body-centered cubic lattice there are two atoms per unit cell if all atoms are identical. Calculate the lattice constant for tungsten (at.wt. = 184, density 19.3×10^3 kg/m³) and find the angles θ at which strong Bragg reflections occur for a wavelength of 2.5 Å.

4.15. Use the data of Problem 3.2 to find the Bragg angles for x rays of wavelength 4.0 Å incident upon a crystal of potassium chloride. (A "simple cubic" structure reflects from all possible planes.)

4.16. In an experiment to test Moseley's law electrons of maximum energy 20 keV strike metallic targets made of aluminum $(Z = 13)$, copper $(Z = 29)$, and tungsten $(Z = 74)$. In the first two cases $K\alpha$ lines are observed and these x rays make strong Bragg reflections (in first order, $N = 1$) from a certain crystal at angles of incidence

$$\theta = 30° \text{ for Al}; \qquad \theta = 80° \text{ for Cu}.$$

Compare the ratio of the wavelengths of the lines with the prediction of Moseley's law. No K lines from tungsten are found; why?

4.17. Experiments show that the ionization potential of the "k" shell for different elements is as follows:

$$W_k = 1.56 \qquad 3.6 \qquad 7.1 \qquad 9.65 \qquad \text{keV}$$
$$Z = 13 \qquad 19 \qquad 26 \qquad 30.$$

Derive a relation between W_k and Z, and use this relation together with Moseley's law to draw general conclusions about the behavior of W_l at different values of Z.

4.18. Calculate the least voltage required across an x ray tube to produce x rays:

 (i) of the "Compton" wavelength 0.024 Å;

 (ii) capable of ionizing the "k" shell of copper ($Z = 29$);

(iii) giving first-order reflection at $\theta = 45°$ from a crystal of plane spacing $d = 3.0$ Å.

4.19. Secondary x rays of the K series from copper are passed through aluminum foils, each of thickness 4×10^{-5} m. The counting rate of a Geiger tube (after correction for background) varied with the number of absorbers as follows:

Number of foils: 0   1   2   3   4
Counts/min   8000 4700 2800 1650 970

Calculate the mean absorption coefficient of aluminum (at.wt. = 27, density 2.7×10^3 kg/m³) for the copper K lines and hence the absorption cross section per atom.

4.20. Show that if very high-energy x rays are incident on matter the back-scattered Compton radiation is of nearly constant wavelength. Would it be possible to find a "k" absorption edge at this wavelength (among existing chemical elements)?

4.21. An *electron-pair spectrometer* measures the energy of x rays by detecting electron-positron coincidences in the apparatus shown in Figure 4.25. The magnetic field bends the particles in opposite directions so that they are recorded in detectors. If each detector is placed 5 cm from the source of pairs and coincidences are found at a magnetic field

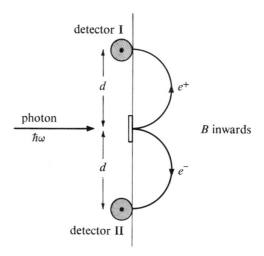

FIGURE 4.25 *Electron-pair spectrometer.*

$B = 2 \times 10^{-2}$ weber/m², what is the energy of the incident photons? (A nonrelativistic calculation is sufficiently accurate here.)

4.22. Show that the total energy radiated per second from an oscillating electrical dipole of angular frequency ω, length l, and current amplitude i_0, is

$$E = \frac{(\omega i_0 l)^2}{3c^3(4\pi\varepsilon_0)}.$$

Hence calculate the "radiation resistance" in ohms for an isolated quarter-wave antenna.

✿✿✿✿✿✿✿✿✿✿✿✿✿✿✿✿✿✿✿✿✿✿✿✿✿✿✿✿✿✿✿✿✿✿

CHAPTER V

PHOTON MECHANICS
AND RELATIVITY

Studies of the interactions of radiation with matter revealed that radiant energy exists in quanta and that the photons of the radiation field possess well-defined momentum as well as energy. The Compton effect is readily explained by supposing that photons collide with individual electrons and lose energy in the process; while the phenomenon of pair creation shows that radiant energy can be converted into rest-mass of the created particles. It appears from these properties of the photon that classical mechanics does not account satisfactorily for the behavior of bodies moving at very high speed and some new form of mechanics is needed to deal with the mass-energy relations discovered. A suitable scheme of mechanics is provided by the *special* theory of relativity, formulated by Einstein in 1905.

The theory of relativity originated in the difficulties which are encountered in the electromagnetic theory of light whenever we consider the medium which is assumed to convey the electromagnetic waves (the "aether"). Repeated efforts to detect motion of the Earth relative to the aether failed; the alternative proposition that the Earth drags the aether with it is also inconsistent with experimental results. During the years 1899 to 1904 Poincaré re-examined the classical principle of relativity and proposed to remove the aether difficulty by representing the speed of light *in vacuo* (*c*) as a fixed maximum speed. Meanwhile Lorentz showed that classical transformations from one *inertial frame* of reference to another are inconsistent with Maxwell's electromagnetic theory. The transformation required to preserve the invariance of Maxwell's equations and to keep the value of *c* constant was derived by Lorentz in 1903; this transformation is the basis of Einstein's theory.

The special theory of relativity is restricted to inertial frames of reference and further work was needed to extend the relativistic scheme to accelerated frames. This extension was brilliantly provided in 1915 by Einstein's *general* theory which incorporates an entirely new approach to the problem of gravitation. In the realm of atomic physics the general theory has been much less important than the special theory, probably because its results deviate very little in practice from the results either of the special theory or Newton's inverse-square law of gravitation. Later developments in atomic and nuclear physics depended heavily on the understanding of mass-energy relations as expounded in the special theory and on the condition of Lorentz invariance, which is required of any system of equations describing the behavior of high-speed particles. For example, quantum mechanics was originally developed in nonrelativistic forms but a relativistic equation of motion for the electron was required before phenomena such as the Compton effect and pair creation could be dealt with in detail.

5.1 Radiation Pressure and Photon Momentum

(a) Radiation pressure

It is clear from a study of the Compton effect (Section 4.9) that photons carry linear momentum, some of which may be imparted to electrons by a collision mechanism. The idea that radiation has momentum associated with it is by no means new, since Maxwell found this to be a necessary consequence of the electromagnetic theory. However, Compton's analysis suggested that there is a one-to-one relation between the scattered photon and the recoiling electron; this deduction was supported by the experiments of Bothe and Geiger, who found that the scattering is effectively simultaneous with the recoil process. In order to treat the Compton effect in detail we need to know the linear momentum of a single photon.

One important phenomenon ascribed to the momentum of radiation is the pressure it exerts on any absorbing or reflecting surface. In the classical theory the pressure is related to the total energy density of the incident radiation. For example, if a beam of light is represented instantaneously by electromagnetic vectors $\mathscr{E}$ and $\mathscr{H}$, and the beam is incident normally upon a perfect absorber, the power absorbed per unit area is the magnitude of the Poynting vector [Equation (4.1.10)], that is,

$$I = |\mathscr{E}|\,|\mathscr{H}|.$$

The energy delivered to the absorber appears as work done in the recoil process, if the absorber is free to move. The force exerted on unit area, that is, the radiation pressure P, multiplied by the speed (c) of the radiation, is therefore equal to the power absorbed (I)

$$Pc = I. \qquad [5.1.1]$$

Thus the pressure P is the ratio of the energy absorbed per unit area per second to the speed of radiation. It follows that I/c represents the energy present per unit volume (E/V) in the radiation field outside the absorber, so that

$$P = E/V \text{ for normal incidence.} \qquad [5.1.2]$$

If the irradiated surface is a very good conductor of electricity, and therefore wholly reflecting, the treatment is modified because the reflected wave cancels out the incident electric vector at the surface. The magnetic vector, however, is doubled and the interaction between this field and electric currents induced in the surface layers results again in a normal force. The pressure is again equal to the total energy density of the radiation, which is, in this case, *twice* the amount due to the incident wave by itself.

Radiation pressure is believed to be of great importance inside the stars, which are presumably prevented from gravitational collapse by the intense flow of energy outwards from their interiors. In the laboratory, measurements of P are rendered difficult by the well-known radiometer effect discovered by Crookes (Section 2.1). However, if the gas pressure in a bulb is reduced to a very low value it is possible to make a delicately suspended metal foil move under the influence of an intense beam of light. Experiments by Lebedev (1900) and Nichols and Hull[*] (1903) showed that the radiation pressure can be measured with some accuracy. Nichols and Hull employed two silvered glass vanes suspended by a torsion fiber

---

[*] E. F. Nichols and G. F. Hull, Phys. Rev., **17**, 27 (1903).

in a bulb. Allowing for the effects of gas molecules in the bulb, they found that the beam of light from an arc lamp exerted a force of 1.05×10^{-9} N on one vane. The incident energy flux was estimated by matching its heating effect on a blackened disk with heat supplied electrically to a similar disk, both disks being equal in area to the glass vanes. The energy incident per second on the disk was found to be 0.165 J, so that the calculated force due to pressure P on an absorber of this area (A) becomes

$$F = AP = AI/c = \frac{0.165}{3 \times 10^8} = 0.55 \times 10^{-9} \text{ N}.$$

Assuming that the disk was a perfect absorber and that the silvered vanes were perfect reflectors, we should expect the measured force to be exactly twice the above figure; the results yield a discrepancy of about 5 % between the observed and calculated pressure. In general the theory was tested to an accuracy of about 6 %.

Further experiments by Poynting and Barlow* in 1909 showed that reflecting surfaces do in fact experience about twice the pressure found for absorbing surfaces when the same beam of light is incident. This result is readily explained in terms of a corpuscular or photon theory of radiation, since the reflection of a photon at full velocity from a surface imparts twice as much impulse to the surface as the impulse due to an absorption process.

(b) *Photon momentum*

We may use the expression for radiation pressure [Equation (5.1.2)] to derive the momentum of a photon in free space. If N photons, each of momentum p and energy $\hbar\omega$, strike unit area of an absorbing surface at normal incidence every second, the force exerted is

$$P = Np.$$

The energy density of incident radiation is equal to the total photon energy ($N\hbar\omega$) divided by the volume of a cylindrical element on unit area as base with height equal to the photon speed (c). According to Equation (5.1.2) therefore

$$P = E/V = \frac{N\hbar\omega}{c} ,$$

whence

$$p = \frac{\hbar\omega}{c} \qquad\qquad [5.1.3]$$

or in terms of Planck's constant h and the wavelength λ

$$p = h/\lambda. \qquad\qquad [5.1.4]$$

This fundamental relation has been tested in several ways and it is the basis of Compton's treatment of x-ray scattering by free electrons. In 1933 Frisch performed an experiment which showed that atoms emitting light of energy E in a certain direction experience recoil of total momentum E/c, in agreement with the above equations. A further consequence of the momentum-wavelength relation is that light changes its momentum when it enters a dense medium, which causes a change in wavelength. This effect has been investigated by R. V. Jones and his collaborators,† with the result that the theoretical predictions have been verified within experimental errors of the order of 1 to 2 %.

---

* J. H. Poynting and G. Barlow, Proc. Roy. Soc. London, **A83**, 534 (1910).
† R. V. Jones, Nature, **171**, 1089 (1953).

If we visualize a process whereby certain atoms emit and others absorb radiation, it is clear that linear momentum cannot be conserved at every stage in the process unless the radiation field carries momentum in definite amounts. The experimental evidence agrees with the electromagnetic theory in assigning momentum proportional to the energy of the field (for a fixed speed c). In terms of photons, or any corpuscular type of radiation, this relation represents a considerable breakaway from classical mechanics, in which the momentum of a particle is proportional to the square root of the kinetic energy (for a fixed mass). Indeed Planck showed that the usual kinetic energy expression ($\frac{1}{2} mv^2$) cannot apply to quanta because it yields incorrect results for the pressure of radiation. If, therefore, we require a system of mechanics which accounts for the properties of photons as well as classical particles, a radical revision of the fundamental principles is indicated. Historically the new mechanics arose out of difficulties encountered in optics, but the inadequacy of classical mechanics in dealing with high-speed particles became evident during the years following the introduction of relativity theory.

Several properties of a mechanical nature (for example, energy and linear momentum) have already been ascribed to photons and these properties are demonstrated when interactions of matter with radiation occur. We should also take into account the *vector* character of the electromagnetic field, which suggests that photons possess angular momentum, represented by a vector directed along the axis of propagation, when they belong to a circularly polarized beam of light. This problem has been explored theoretically by Heitler and experimentally by Beth,* who, in 1936, showed that circularly polarized light does exert a torque on half-wave plates of quartz which change the state of polarization. The results agree with the supposition that the quantized unit of angular momentum associated with a photon has magnitude $\hbar$ or $h/2\pi$. We see, therefore, that Planck's constant is related to a basic unit of angular momentum and this role of h is equally important with its original definition as the ratio of energy to frequency for a quantum.

5.2 Inertial and Gravitational Effects of Photons

(a) Effective mass of a photon

Several arguments may be advanced to support the idea that a photon has effective mass or inertia, which depends on its energy, being much greater for the high-frequency radiations (for example, x rays) than for low frequencies. A simple treatment due to Einstein suffices to establish the required result. Consider a rigid enclosure of total mass M isolated from the rest of the universe (Figure 5.1) and let a photon of energy $\hbar\omega$ be emitted from one end then absorbed at the other end. At emission the whole enclosure must recoil because of the photon momentum and the recoil speed is v, where

$$Mv = \frac{\hbar\omega}{c}.$$

If the photon is absorbed after traveling a distance L between the ends, the recoil action is stopped but the enclosure as a whole will have moved a distance s given by the equation

$$s = \frac{vL}{c} = \frac{\hbar\omega L}{Mc^2}.$$

* R. A. Beth, Phys. Rev., **50**, 115 (1936).

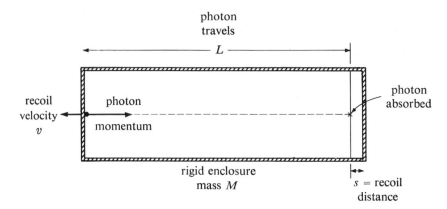

FIGURE 5.1 *Einstein's argument concerning the effective mass m* of a photon. A rigid isolated enclosure of mass M is moved slightly by the momentum of a photon traveling internally from one end to the other, but the center of mass is supposed to stay in the same place.*

Now it is a principle of mechanics that no system can move its center of mass by purely internal rearrangements so we can assume that the center of mass has stayed in the same place throughout and that an effective mass m^* has been transferred with the photon. The magnitude of m^* can be determined by the principle of moments; on the assumption that m^* is much less than the mass M, we have directly

$$m^*L = Ms,$$

whence

$$m^*c^2 = \hbar\omega. \qquad [5.2.1]$$

Although this argument applies only to photons and requires complete isolation of the system (that is, no aether of any kind is introduced), the result has very wide applications in that it expresses the general equivalence of mass with energy. For example, it gives the correct threshold energy for the phenomenon of electron pair creation (Section 4.9); if the combined rest mass of the two particles is substituted for m^* in the foregoing expression, we find the photon energy at threshold to be

$$\hbar\omega = 2m_ec^2, \qquad [5.2.2]$$

where m_e = mass of each electron.
In the usual mks units $m_ec^2 = 8.2 \times 10^{-14}$ J = 0.51 MeV so the threshold is 1.02 MeV, in agreement with experiment.

(b) Gravitational effects

The effective mass m^* is readily calculated for a photon of known energy but the question arises: does a photon respond to a gravitational field in the way expected for a mass m^*? Light certainly appears to travel in straight lines in the Earth's field but it may be surmised that a very intense gravitational field, such as the field of the Sun at its surface, has appreciable effects. The theoretical arguments hinge on the *Principle of Equivalence*, according to which all entities endowed with inertia must respond to a given gravitational field in such a way that the ratio of gravitational force to mass is constant. This principle may be tested by comparing inertia determinations, made, for example, with a ballistic balance, with weight determinations, based on a spring balance, for a whole series of objects. More accurately, Newton showed that simple pendulums of the same length have the same period whatever mass or material is used; this result would follow from the principle. The most accurate tests reported in detail are those of Eötvös (1922) who showed that all forms of matter which are easily available obey the equivalence principle to an accuracy of about 1 part in 10^8. More recently Dicke has substantiated Eötvös' results and the link between gravitation and inertia may be taken as established, at least for matter under the usual laboratory conditions. However, this does not mean that photons necessarily obey the principle of equivalence, since we have already found that their momentum-energy relation differs from that of a classical particle.

One test of the gravitational interaction of photons, proposed by Einstein, consists of measuring a small shift in frequency when radiation passes between two points differing in gravitational potential. For example, suppose that a photon travels from an intense gravitational field to a weaker one; by the principle of conservation of energy, the change in potential energy per photon should cause a shift toward the red end of the visible spectrum, $\Delta\omega$, such that, if $\Delta\Phi$ is the change in gravitational potential, we have

$$\hbar\,\Delta\omega = m^*\,\Delta\Phi.$$

Since

$$\hbar\omega = m^*c^2,$$

we obtain

$$\frac{\Delta\omega}{\omega} = \frac{\Delta\Phi}{c^2}.$$

[5.2.3]

In the Earth's field the change in gravitational potential due to a change ΔH in vertical height is

$$\Delta\Phi = g\Delta H,$$

provided that ΔH is so small that g is effectively constant. Thus with ΔH of the order 20 m and g about 10 m/sec^2

$$\frac{\Delta\omega}{\omega} \approx 2 \times 10^{-15}.$$

This is an extremely small frequency shift but it has been detected in laboratory experiments by Pound and Rebka,* who worked with the very narrow gamma-ray line emitted by the iron isotope Fe^{57}. The results of the experiments agreed with theoretical predictions within a possible systematic error of 10%.

An alternative test of the gravitational frequency shift is provided by light which leaves the surface of a star (where the gravitational field is intense) and arrives at the Earth's surface (where the field is comparatively small). Under such conditions the change in potential, for a star of mass M and radius R, is

$$\Delta\Phi = \frac{GM}{R},$$

where G is the gravitational constant of Newton. The "red shift" becomes

$$\frac{\Delta\omega}{\omega} = \frac{GM}{Rc^2}.$$

[5.2.4]

For the Sun, with $M = 2 \times 10^{30}$ kg and $R = 7 \times 10^8$ m, this fractional shift amounts to about 2×10^{-6}, corresponding to about 10^{-2} Å change in visible wavelengths. In practice the effect is difficult to disentangle from Doppler shifts due to relative motion of the source and observer. Finlay-Freundlich analyzed the data available in 1954 and concluded that they do not agree very well with the theory. However, there are other stars which exhibit a

* R. V. Pound and G. A. Rebka, *Phys. Rev. Letters*, **4**, 337 (1960).

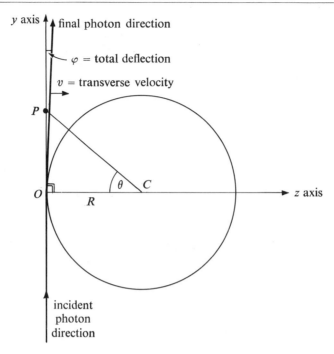

FIGURE 5.2   *A photon of effective mass m* passes a sphere of mass M, radius R, at grazing incidence. The deflection is supposed to be so small that a point P on the y axis (the original photon direction) is close to the actual photon path and the photon speed is c throughout.*

much larger red shift of spectral lines than the Sun. The white-dwarf companion of Sirius appears to have $\dfrac{\Delta\omega}{\omega} \approx 7 \times 10^{-6}$. If the theory is correct, such stars must have an extraordinarily high mean density and it is believed that normal atomic structure breaks down under special conditions obtaining in the stellar interior.

The most direct test of the gravitational interaction of photons consists of the observation of lateral displacements when light passes very close to the Sun. Measurements have been carried out when the Sun was totally eclipsed by the Moon, because of the intense glare at other times, and enough observations have been made to show that the positions of stars seen close to the Sun's limb are apparently displaced in directions consistent with gravitational deflection of the photons. The magnitude of the effect can be estimated by a classical calculation in which the photon is supposed to have gravitational mass equal to its effective mass m^*.

Let a photon travel at grazing incidence to a sphere of mass M and radius R, as in Figure 5.2, where the coordinate axes are Oz along the radius at the point of contact O and Oy perpendicular to Oz. Since the deflection is supposed to be very slight, any point P on the axis Oy lies close to the actual photon trajectory. If we count time $t = 0$ at the instant of contact and the photon speed is c, we may write

$$OP = y = ct = R \tan \theta,$$

where θ is the angle OCP at the center C of the sphere.

It follows that
$$dy = c\, dt = R \sec^2 \theta \, d\theta.$$

At P the gravitational force (F) on the photon is taken to be

$$F = \frac{GMm^*}{R^2 \sec^2 \theta} = m^*a,$$

so that the acceleration resolved perpendicular to OP is

$$a_z = \frac{dv}{dt} = \frac{GM}{R^2 \sec^2 \theta} \cos \theta,$$

where v represents the *transverse* velocity component, perpendicular to OP. Transforming the variable from t to θ, we obtain

$$\frac{dv}{d\theta} = \frac{dv}{dt}\frac{dt}{d\theta} = \frac{GM}{cR} \cos \theta.$$

This equation may be integrated directly and imposition of the boundary condition $v = 0$ when $\theta = -\pi/2$ rad leads to

$$v = \frac{GM}{cR} (1 + \sin \theta).$$

When the photon has finally passed the Sun we can find the final transverse velocity by substituting $\theta = +\pi/2$, that is,

$$\text{Final } v = \frac{2GM}{cR}.$$

The total angular deflection of the photon is obtained by taking the ratio of the final transverse velocity to the tangential velocity, which is always close to c. We find

$$\text{Deflection: } \varphi = \frac{2GM}{c^2R} \text{ rad.} \qquad [5.2.5]$$

This result is twice the fractional gravitational frequency shift for the same sphere, that is, for the Sun the angle is 4×10^{-6} radian, or 0.88 sec of arc. The effect is so small that the exact magnitude is still subject to considerable experimental errors. The best results show that at grazing incidence the deflection is close to 2.0 sec, at least twice the classical result. Einstein's general theory of relativity predicts a deflection twice the value obtained above and so is in much better agreement with observation than Newton's theory. At the same time more accurate measurements are required for a precise test of possible theories.

5.3 Newton's Laws of Motion

In the foregoing sections we have described some of the properties of the photon, which clearly does not behave like a classical particle. In order to obtain a more complete description of the mechanics of fast particles we need the theories of relativity which are specially associated with the name of Einstein. However, it may be advisable first to explore the basis of classical mechanics, as expressed in Newton's laws of motion. These laws provided the foundation of all physical theory until the beginning of the twentieth century and they must obviously be at least a good approximation to the correct relations. On the other hand, all the implications of these basic laws were never fully worked out, as was emphasized by

Mach from 1872 onward. For example, there is no immediate explanation for the principle of equivalence, which links inertia with the gravitational interactions of a body. Since the time of Mach several physicists have sought a more profound interpretation of mechanical laws and the search continues.

Newton's first law, which expresses the principle of inertia expounded by Galileo, states that a body acted upon by no forces (or by forces which cancel out) must stay at rest or move with constant velocity. These two conditions are therefore equivalent in dynamics and all the laws of mechanics must be the same in a system moving uniformly as they are in the system at rest. It follows from this principle that no observer can detect his own uniform motion in a straight line, except by reference to some other object, and all measurements of velocity are purely relative. For example, the Earth is traveling at great speed in its orbit round the Sun but terrestrial observers detect this motion only by reference to objects outside the solar system, since the centripetal acceleration happens to be too small to measure. Likewise we suppose that the whole solar system is traveling at high speed relative to the constellation Hercules, the spectral lines of which show significant Doppler shifts, but these measurements do not convey any information about motion of an absolute nature. Newton realized that only relative velocity measurements are made in practice but he tried to introduce the concept of "absolute space" for reasons connected with the second law of motion.

The second law of Newton states that a force acting on a body produces a change in momentum such that, if the mass remains constant, the body accelerates at a rate proportional to the applied force. This is in fact true only if the observations are carried out in an *inertial frame* of reference, that is, one which is moving uniformly and is not affected by external fields. In a noninertial frame, for example one which is accelerating or rotating about some axis, forces arise which are not related to measurements in the frame itself. Thus on the Earth's surface we can detect rotation about the polar axis by means of Foucault's pendulum, which maintains a direction fixed relative to the distant stars but changes its orientation in the local reference frame. It is possible to introduce "fictitious" forces, for example centrifugal and Coriolis forces, to account for phenomena observed in noninertial frames of reference.

Newton analyzed the problem of acceleration by the aid of a simple experiment with a rotating bucket of water. At first the bucket was set spinning by means of a twisted rope suspension while the water remained stationary and level. Later the water took on part of the spinning motion and adopted a paraboloidal surface as the result of "centrifugal" effects; to be more explicit, its inertia made it try to maintain motion in a straight line toward the outside of the bucket. Newton then stopped the bucket but the water continued to revolve with a paraboloidal surface. He interpreted this observation by supposing that the shape of the water surface is determined by its rotation relative to "absolute space," not by its relation to the bucket or to the laboratory. In other words, Newton found it necessary to postulate the existence of absolute acceleration although all experience indicates that velocity measurements are strictly relative.

A possible solution to the acceleration problem was mentioned by Berkeley and later developed in detail by Mach. If we imagine that matter in the universe as a whole, and particularly the sphere occupied by the most distant detectable masses, provides a reference frame which is significant in our laboratory experiments, we can measure accelerations relative to this frame. Then the surface of the water in the bucket depends on its motion relative to the universe. The difference between this approach and that of Newton is that here we ascribe inertial effects to some form of interaction between the object under investigation and actual masses in the universe, whereas Newton used "empty space" as a reference frame. Mach argued that if the distant masses interact with an object in such a way that, when it is accelerated relative to the masses, it is acted upon by a retarding force proportional to the acceleration, the origin of inertia can be understood. Moreover, if the interaction responsible for inertia is of a gravitational type (though not the static interaction of Newton's theory) it follows that inertia and gravitational mass are intimately connected, as required by the principle of equivalence.

Mach's principle of inertia has not been generally accepted, perhaps because it relies on weak nonstatic gravitational effects which are not directly detectable by present apparatus. On the other hand, it does provide a program for investigating gravitational effects and relating these to astronomical observations. A possible test of Mach's idea consists of detecting a slight anisotropy in a body's inertia due to interaction of the body with our local galaxy of stars, which form the Milky Way. The solar system is situated far from the center of the galaxy and it might be expected that the inertia differs by as much as one part in 10^7 when measured in a direction toward the galactic center and then perpendicular to this direction. Experiments have been carried out to test the *scalar* character of inertia and some evidence is available to rule out any anisotropy as great as one part in 10^7. This conclusion does not demolish Mach's principle but it does suggest that some overriding condition ensures the spherical symmetry of distant interactions. One might strengthen the principle of equivalence with the postulate that gravitational mass, regarded as the source of a field, is strictly scalar and isotropic, which would require inertia to have the same properties.

The third law of Newton is important chiefly in emphasizing the symmetry of all two-body interactions, so that gravitational force, for example, must be proportional to the product of the masses interacting. In other words the "active" mass, the source of the field, is identical with the "passive" mass on which the field acts. This principle is an essential part of Mach's argument about the principle of equivalence. With the aid of the third law, in the form of the principle of momentum conservation, we can set up a scale of inertial mass without reference to gravitation and this scale is important in the special theory of relativity (which excludes gravitational fields).

The arguments of this section may be summarized as follows:

(i) inertial frames of reference exist* and in these frames Newton's laws are a good approximation for bodies moving at low speed;

(ii) Newton's laws by themselves are consistent with the idea that all velocity measurements are purely relative;

(iii) if we adopt Mach's principle, we can explain the principle of equivalence and at the same time regard all measurements of acceleration as relative to the distant masses in the universe;

(iv) Mach's principle might lead to a slight anisotropy in the inertia of bodies in the solar system, but all the present evidence indicates that inertia is scalar.

5.4 The Special and General Theories of Relativity

Consideration of the classical laws of mechanics serves to emphasize the significance of inertial frames of reference for any successful theory. Any new scheme of mechanics must also allow for the equivalence of mass and energy, since it is found that the interrelation

* See L. I. Schiff, Rev. Mod. Phys., **36,** 510 (1964).

of these two concepts is of wider application than our original derivation from the properties of photons. Although no entirely satisfactory scheme has yet been developed, Einstein made two great contributions to the subject in the *special* and *general* theories of relativity and of these the special theory brings together many phenomena in the realm of high-energy physics.

The special theory is based on the principle that all inertial frames are equivalent so far as the laws of physics are concerned. It follows that there is no preferred frame of reference and all velocity measurements are relative, as required by the classical principle of relativity. However, Einstein extended the classical principle by postulating that the speed of light *in vacuo* (c) is the same for all observers in inertial frames and this statement represents the real departure from classical mechanics. The reason for including this postulate is bound up with difficulties inherent in the simple wave theory of light.

(a) Difficulties of the aether theory

During the nineteenth century the wave theory was generally regarded as secure except for difficulties concerned with the "aether" or medium in which the waves were supposed to travel. The aether apparently had incredible mechanical properties. For example, it should be rigid, to allow the transmission of transverse waves without appreciable attenuation, but it must also let planets and stars move through it at high speeds. Moreover, if motion of the Earth or some piece of apparatus relative to a fixed aether could be detected, the aether would act as a preferred frame of reference and the principle of relativity would be violated.

Experiments of many kinds have been carried out to detect motion of the Earth relative to the hypothetical aether. Since the Earth's speed (v) relative to the Sun is about 10^{-4} times that of light (c), one might devise a "first-order" experiment in which effects proportional to the ratio $v/c \approx 10^{-4}$ are measured. Modern techniques are beginning to realize these possibilities. For example, Townes and his collaborators[*] have employed two ammonia masers (see Section 4.5) in which the beams of ammonia molecules traveled in opposite directions; when the emitted signals were mixed suitably, a beat frequency was detected, owing to the Doppler shift caused by relative motion of the molecules. When the whole apparatus was rotated in various directions to change its orientation with respect to presumed "aether drifts," no systematic change in the beat frequency could be detected. The limits of experimental error corresponded to aether-drift velocities of the order of 10^{-3} times the Earth's speed (v) relative to the Sun, so this first-order experiment by itself appears to rule out any detectable motion of the Earth relative to the aether.

However, it may be that more subtle effects of aether drift are present and a "second-order" experiment, depending on terms of the type v^2/c^2, may yield significant results. In 1887 Michelson and Morley performed a famous experiment designed to detect aether-drift effects by means of a sensitive optical interferometer. In this instrument (Figure 5.3) two beams of light pass to and fro over paths fixed at right angles to each other before being recombined to produce interference fringes visible at the eyepiece. When light traverses a total distance $2L$ *in vacuo*, the time taken should be $t_0 = 2L/c$ in the absence of aether-drift effects. If, however, there is a velocity **v** of the apparatus relative to the aether and this is parallel to one light path (the "parallel arm"), the total time elapsed should differ from t_0 if the classical laws of velocity addition are obeyed. On this assumption the time should be

$$t_2 = \frac{L}{c+v} + \frac{L}{c-v} = \frac{2Lc}{(c^2 - v^2)} = \frac{t_0}{(1 - v^2/c^2)}$$

[*] J. P. Cedarholm, G. F. Bland, B. L. Havens, and C. H. Townes, *Phys. Rev. Letters*, **1**, 342 (1958).

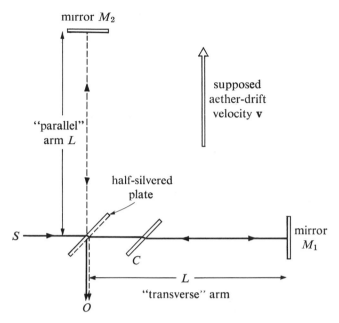

FIGURE 5.3 *The principle of the Michelson-Morley apparatus. Light from the source S is split into two beams traveling over perpendicular paths (the "parallel" and "transverse" arms, each of length L) to mirrors M_1 and M_2 which reflect the light back and the beams recombine to form interference fringes seen at O. The compensating plate C corrects for the extra thickness of glass traversed by the beam reflected at M_2.*

which differs from t_0 by a second-order factor. With the same assumption, the time taken for light to travel a distance $2L$ perpendicular to the velocity **v** (the "transverse arm") should be

$$t_2 = \frac{2L}{(c^2 - v^2)^{1/2}} = \frac{t_0}{(1 - v^2/c^2)^{1/2}},$$

since the speed of travel across a stream of speed v is $(c^2 - v^2)^{1/2}$, by Pythagoras' theorem.

The difference between t_1 and t_2 is extremely small, of the order of 3×10^{-16} sec when $v/c = 10^{-4}$ and the arms are 10 m long. Nevertheless the interference technique is so sensitive that this difference corresponds to an appreciable fraction of a wavelength of light, hence a detectable shift in the interference pattern. Michelson and Morley mounted the apparatus on a raft floating in mercury and the raft was rotated steadily about a vertical axis so that the parallel and transverse arms were interchanged repeatedly. No systematic shifts in the interference pattern were detected during long periods of observation. Later the experiment was repeated by Miller,* who claimed to have found a small systematic aether drift, but Joos performed a similar experiment with elaborate precautions and obtained no shifts within experimental errors equivalent to an aether drift (v) less than $10^{-5}c$. This limit has been reduced still further in experiments using optical masers.†

It is worthy of mention that in 1925 Michelson and Gale carried out an interferometer experiment in which the Earth's *rotational* motion was instrumental in causing a shift in the

---

* For a review of Miller's work, see R. S. Shankland, S. W. McCuskey, F. C. Leone, and G. Kuerti, Rev. Mod. Phys., **27**, 167 (1955).
† See A. L. Schawlow, "Advances in Optical Masers," Scientific American, **209**, No. 1, 34 (1963).

observed fringe pattern. This experiment gave results consistent with the classical fixed-aether theory, although that theory cannot be reconciled, in its simple form, with the null result of the Michelson–Morley experiment. From the point of view of mechanics, the positive Michelson–Gale result serves to emphasize the difference between inertial frames, which are entirely equivalent, and noninertial frames, in which apparently "absolute" effects are detectable, by optical or mechanical means.

(b) Possible explanations

The null results of the various aether-drift experiments stimulated a great deal of enquiry and several possible explanations were put forward. Among these suggestions were the following:

(i) the aether might be carried along with the Earth—this would explain the failure to detect relative motion, but it is inconsistent with observed stellar aberration and with the Michelson–Gale results;

(ii) the "emission" theory of Ritz suggested that the speed of light may be affected by motion of the source—this is conceivable in terms of a corpuscular theory of light, but is inconsistent with observations of double stars and with experimental results obtained by Majorana and by Michelson with moving mirrors*;

(iii) Fitzgerald and Lorentz pointed out that the parallel arm of a Michelson interferometer might be contracted by the aether motion while the transverse arm remained unaffected—such a contraction would normally be unobservable because any measuring instruments must be affected in the same way as the apparatus and so the hypothesis cannot be tested unless some other physical changes occur at the same time.

The contraction hypothesis, put forward by Fitzgerald and independently by Lorentz, was the first indication that distance measurements may depend on relative motion between the observer and the measured object. In order to account for the null result of Michelson and Morley's experiment, the changed length of the parallel arm of the apparatus would have to be

$$L' = L(1 - v^2/c^2)^{\frac{1}{2}}. \qquad [5.4.1]$$

Lorentz derived the same result from the condition that Maxwell's electromagnetic equations should remain invariant under transformations from one inertial frame to another. The Lorentz scheme involves changes in time coordinates under the same transformation and is best developed by Einstein's method. Here we should emphasize that no physical effects of any supposed contraction were detected in experiments carried out to find, for example, stresses set up in various materials by the aether drift. Moreover, Kennedy and Thorndike performed a Michelson–Morley type of experiment in which the two arms were of somewhat different length. Interference fringes were obtained and these did not shift when the apparatus was rotated, showing that no simple contraction hypothesis is tenable.

The difficulties encountered by the aether theory became apparently insuperable and during the years 1900 to 1905 both Poincaré and Lorentz maintained that a fundamental revision of ideas about space and time measurements and about relative velocity was overdue. Einstein obviated a great deal of argument by basing his special theory on the invariance of the speed of light *in vacuo* (c) for all inertial coordinate systems. This principle automatically accounts for the null results of first-order and second-order experiments on "aether drift." He went on to derive the Lorentz transformation and showed that all

---

* A recent examination of the question is by J. G. Fox, Am. J. Phys., **33**, 1 (1965).

existing experimental data were consistent with the theory. Moreover, he was able to incorporate mass-energy equivalence into the theory and to lay the foundations for many future developments in atomic physics.

(c) The general theory of Einstein

Nevertheless the special theory was severely restricted by the exclusion of noninertial frames and of fields which can cause acceleration of bodies. In 1915 Einstein published his general theory, in which gravitational fields are incorporated by a new principle of geometry. Instead of using conventional Euclidean coordinates for space-time, Einstein adopted a Riemannian geometry in which the metric is "curved," to an extent which depends on the local gravitational field. The presence of matter is supposed to distort the properties of space-time in such a way that a test body describes a unique path (the *geodesic*) which is defined geometrically, not by dynamic factors. Despite this revolutionary approach to mechanics, it is possible to devise a theory in which Newton's law of gravitation appears as the first approximation to a more general law. In practice the general theory agrees with Newton's law to a high degree of accuracy and it incorporates the results of the special theory.

Experimental tests of the general theory are not easily devised or carried out, and there is a great need for more accurate tests to decide between possible theories. The only considerable discrepancy between the predictions of Newton's and Einstein's theories concerning the solar system is in the precession of the perihelion of Mercury's orbit about the Sun. Newton's theory allows a precession of 531 seconds of arc per century, after calculation of all known effects, whereas the observed precession amounts to 574 sec of arc. The difference of 43 sec is given almost exactly by the general theory of relativity, as due to small deviations from the inverse-square law of gravitation.

The general theory also predicts a deflection of light by the Sun amounting to 1.76 sec at grazing incidence.* We have seen in Section 5.2 that this prediction agrees fairly well with observations. The theory gives the same result as the simple treatment of Section 5.2 for the gravitational frequency shift, which is now well established by the experiments of Pound and Rebka. Apart from these subtle effects, the theory finds its widest application in the field of cosmology, since it provides a fundamental approach to the problems of matter and gravitation as existing over large intervals of space and time. Again, modern techniques are reaching the stage where some experimental tests of rival theories may be feasible.†

5.5 The Lorentz Transformation

(a) The Galilean scheme

In classical mechanics the transformation from one inertial frame (0) to another (0′) which moves at uniform velocity v relative to 0 is accomplished by means of the *Galilean* equations (for motion in one dimension)

$$x' = x - vt \quad \text{and} \quad t' = t, \qquad [5.5.1]$$

where (x, t) are the space and time coordinates of an event in the system 0, and
(x', t') are the corresponding coordinates in frame 0′.

---

* This result can also be derived with the special theory: see L. I. Schiff, Am. J. Phys., **28**, 340 (1960).
† See M. G. Adam, Proc. Roy. Soc. (London), **A270**, 297 (1962).

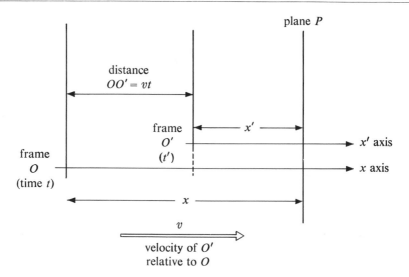

FIGURE 5.4 *The "Galilean" transformation from one inertial frame 0 to another, 0', moving at relative velocity v. If the times t = t' = 0 when the frames coincide, the distance 00' is vt at any subsequent time t. An event in plane P can be recorded as (x, t) or (x', t').*

The space transformation may be appreciated by reference to Figure 5.4, in which the frames 0 and 0' are supposed to coincide at time $t = t' = 0$ and the difference in x co-ordinates is increasing steadily with time because of the relative velocity v, that is,

$$x' - x = vt.$$

The classical transformation is consistent with Newton's laws of motion and the principle of relativity, since if a body of fixed mass m is accelerated by force F in frame 0, we have

$$F = m \frac{d^2x}{dt^2}.$$

From Equation (5.5.1) the velocity recorded in frame 0' is

$$\frac{dx'}{dt'} = \frac{dx}{dt} - v \quad (\text{since } t = t')$$

hence

$$\frac{d^2x'}{dt^2} = \frac{d^2x}{dt^2} \quad \text{since } v \text{ is constant.}$$

Thus for a constant mass

$$F' = m \frac{d^2x'}{dt^2} = m \frac{d^2x}{dt^2} \quad \text{in frame 0'}$$

and the second law of Newton is valid in both frames, that is, $F = F'$, as shown by experiment. Moreover, if we write the velocity of a particle, as measured in frame 0, as $u = \frac{dx}{dt}$ and, as measured in 0', as $u' = \frac{dx'}{dt}$, the classical transformation yields the relation

$$u' = u - v. \qquad\qquad [5.5.2]$$

This velocity relation is traditional in mechanics and was employed in considering the time intervals (t_1 and t_2) required by light beams to traverse the arms of the Michelson–Morley apparatus (Section 5.4).

(b) *The problem of simultaneity*

Einstein's emphasis on the invariance of the speed of light *in vacuo* necessarily led to a revision of the velocity transformation [Equation (5.5.2)], and a change in the basic distance and time relations [Equation (5.5.1)]. Einstein pointed out that, since light travels at the highest speed yet measured and this speed is presumed to be the maximum attainable for transmission of signals, it is not possible for observers in different inertial frames to use the same time scale. It is allowed that two observers can synchronize clocks at the same place and time (so that $t = t' = 0$, as before) but there is no guarantee that the clocks will continue at the same rate when the observers move apart, because the finite maximum speed of signals prevents direct synchronization of clocks in different places.

Suppose, for example, that a long railroad train is traveling at uniform velocity relative to the ground, and that two lightning flashes strike the two ends of the train (Figure 5.5). A passenger at the center of the train might see the flashes simultaneously, in which case he would argue, quite correctly, that the flashes were simultaneous in the train's frame of reference, because he is equidistant from the two ends. Of course, the light signals took a certain time to reach the passenger and during this time the train moved forward relative to the ground. An observer on the track who was exactly opposite the passenger when the latter saw the flashes could not record the flashes as simultaneous because, in the Earth's reference frame, he is closer to the front lightning strike than the rear one. It follows that two observers in uniform relative motion cannot judge distant events as simultaneous even when the observers are instantaneously at the same place. Similar arguments may be adduced to show that clocks in different reference frames do not work at the same rate.

In order to avoid serious errors of principle, therefore, we must base our relativistic transformation scheme on the soundest possible evidence. We take the invariance of the

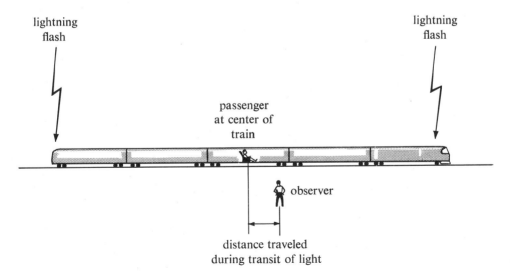

FIGURE 5.5 *Einstein's argument concerning simultaneity. The passenger at the center of the train decides that two lightning flashes are simultaneous, but the observer on the track, who is opposite the passenger when he receives the light signals, cannot judge the flashes to be simultaneous.*

speed of light *in vacuo* as being established by the optical experiments and we assume the Galilean equations [Equation (5.5.1)] to be correct at low relative velocities. The Lorentz transformation is then set up and it remains to be seen if the relativistic mechanics leads to new conclusions which are in agreement with experimental results.

(c) The Lorentz scheme

In deriving the Lorentz equations, we first assume that the transformation is linear in space and time coordinates, so that one event in frame 0 corresponds to one and only one event in frame 0'. We modify the classical equation for the $x \leftrightarrow x'$ transformation by introducing a constant γ, with the condition that $\gamma \to 1$ as $v \to 0$, that is,

$$x' = \gamma(x - vt), \qquad [5.5.3]$$

which goes over into Equation (5.5.1) at low relative velocities. There is a similar reverse transformation from frame 0' to 0 which is symmetrical with respect to Equation (5.5.3) except for the sign of v, which is reversed (as may be seen from Figure 5.4), that is,

$$x = \gamma(x' + vt'). \qquad [5.5.4]$$

We then find, by substitution, that the time transformation is

$$t' = \gamma\left[t + \frac{x(1 - \gamma^2)}{\gamma^2 v}\right]. \qquad [5.5.5]$$

This expression shows that t' is not equal to t unless $\gamma = 1$, which we rule out as giving the classical equations once more.

Now suppose that a beam of light travels a distance x *in vacuo* in time t, measured in frame 0, so that

$$x = ct.$$

The same distance in frame 0' is measured as

$$x' = \gamma(ct - vt)$$

and the time elapsed, from Equation (5.5.5), is

$$t' = \gamma\left[t + \frac{ct(1 - \gamma^2)}{\gamma^2 v}\right].$$

Imposing the condition that all observers in inertial frames find the same speed of light (c), we obtain

$$c = \frac{x'}{t'} = \frac{(c - v)}{1 + \dfrac{c(1 - \gamma^2)}{\gamma^2 v}}$$

which reduces to

$$\gamma^2(1 - v^2/c^2) = 1.$$

The positive root is chosen for γ and the Lorentz transformation equations from frame 0 to 0' become

$$x' = \frac{x - vt}{(1 - v^2/c^2)^{\frac{1}{2}}} \qquad \text{and} \qquad t' = \frac{t - vx/c^2}{(1 - v^2/c^2)^{\frac{1}{2}}} \qquad [5.5.6]$$

with the reverse transformations

$$x = \frac{x' + vt'}{(1 - v^2/c^2)^{\frac{1}{2}}} \qquad \text{and} \qquad t = \frac{t' + vx'/c^2}{(1 - v^2/c^2)^{\frac{1}{2}}}. \qquad [5.5.7]$$

The consequences of these equations are far-reaching, but certain results are derived immediately.

(d) Length contraction

Suppose that in frame 0 we find the length L of a body, at rest in that frame, by measuring two coordinates x_1 and x_2 (at any time we like) and writing

$$L = x_2 - x_1.$$

In the frame 0′ the same length must be measured by taking coordinates x_1' and x_2' at the *same* time t'; otherwise the relative motion will render the measurements meaningless. With this condition we can write

$$L' = x_2' - x_1'.$$

Using the reverse transformation [Equation (5.5.7)], we find

$$L = \frac{L'}{(1 - v^2/c^2)^{1/2}}$$

or

$$L' = L(1 - v^2/c^2)^{1/2}. \qquad [5.5.8]$$

It follows that measurements of length carried out in this way in a system which is moving relative to the frame where the measured object is at rest always give results which are *less* than the "true" length L.* This is the meaning of the supposed Fitzgerald contraction effect, which should be regarded not as a physical distortion but as a consequence of the method of measurement in a universe where the principle of relativity is obeyed.

(e) Time dilation

Suppose that an observer in frame 0 records an interval T between two events t_1 and t_2 which occur at the *same* coordinate x in his system, so that he may write

$$T = t_2 - t_1.$$

In another frame 0′ an observer would record the same events as t_1' and t_2' and his measurements would in fact give different x' coordinates because of the relative motion, but this is irrelevant to the problem of time relations. The interval T' recorded in 0′ is

$$T' = t_2' - t_1'$$

and the transformation equations (5.5.6) yield

$$T' = \frac{T}{(1 - v^2/c^2)^{1/2}}. \qquad [5.5.9]$$

We see in this case that the interval recorded in 0′ is *greater* than the interval recorded by a clock which is stationary relative to the place where the events occurred. This "dilation" of time is independent of the velocity direction, since only v^2 appears in the expression. Thus if some process of frequency $\nu = 1/T$ is going on in a body traveling at speed v relative to an observer the frequency recorded by the observer is

$$\nu' = 1/T' = \nu(1 - v^2/c^2)^{1/2}. \qquad [5.5.10]$$

The frequency is always reduced, whichever way the body moves; thus in optical spectra there is a shift toward the red end of the visible region, quite apart from the usual Doppler

---

* Note, however, that the *appearance* of a fast object does not correspond to a simple contraction: see V. F. Weisskopf, Phys. Today, **13**, No. 9, 24 (1960).

shifts. This effect is sometimes called the "transverse" Doppler effect because it is still present when emitters move across the line of sight (when there is no Doppler shift proper). Experiments by Ives and Stilwell* on the spectral lines emitted by atoms moving at high speed have shown that this very slight frequency shift exists and is consistent with the above relation.

(f) Cosmic-ray muons

An illustration of the combined effects of length contraction and time dilation is supplied by the high-speed particles known as *muons* which are present in cosmic rays. These particles have a mean lifetime at rest of about 2×10^{-6} sec and they are produced high in the Earth's atmosphere by the action of incident rays. This raises an interesting paradox, because the lifetime is apparently much too short to allow the muons to reach sea level. Even if they travel at the speed of light the distance covered in 2 μsec is only 600 m. However, we should remember that the lifetime was measured with muons at rest in the laboratory frame and that v/c is quite appreciable for cosmic-ray muons on their way through the atmosphere. The effective lifetime (in the Earth's frame of reference) should therefore be much longer than 2 μsec, in fact about 15 times as long. Thus the muons can travel several kilometers through the atmosphere and therefore have a good chance of reaching sea level.

It is instructive to consider the same problem in the muon's coordinate system. Here the lifetime is always 2×10^{-6} sec but the atmosphere is moving past at high speed. Owing to the Lorentz contraction effect, the thickness of the atmosphere is reduced by a factor of about 15 and again the probability of the muon reaching sea level is greatly enhanced. The two descriptions are therefore entirely equivalent. Experiments on muons have demonstrated the validity of Equation (5.5.9) for these particles.†

(g) Laboratory-produced mesons

The relation between measured time intervals in different frames can be tested experimentally in high-energy laboratories where various kinds of *mesons* are produced artificially. For example, charged π *mesons* are known to decay, on the average, within a period of about 5×10^{-8} sec. It is found that measurements of the mean lifetime of π mesons in flight give different results at different speeds. Either we have to suppose that π mesons made in different laboratories with different speeds have different lifetimes (although all other properties are the same) or we can relate all measurements to the frame in which the meson is at rest. If the Lorentz time-dilation equation (5.5.9) is employed to find the "true" mean lifetime, all the results agree with a single value of 2.5×10^{-8} sec.

(h) The transformation of velocities (in one dimension)

If we measure the velocity u_x of a certain body moving parallel to the x axis in frame 0 and intend to calculate the velocity u'_x in frame 0', we proceed as follows.
In frame 0' we have

$$u'_x = \frac{dx'}{dt'}$$

and from the Lorentz equations (5.5.6) we find

$$dx' = \frac{dx - v\,dt}{(1 - v^2/c^2)^{1/2}} \quad \text{and} \quad dt' = \frac{dt - \dfrac{v\,dx}{c^2}}{(1 - v^2/c^2)^{1/2}},$$

* H. E. Ives and G. R. Stilwell, J. Opt. Soc. Am., **28**, 215 (1938), and H. E. Ives, J. Opt. Soc. Am., **37**, 810 (1947). See also: C. W. Sherwin, Phys. Rev., **120**, 17 (1960).
† B. Rossi and D. B. Hall, Phys. Rev., **59**, 223 (1941); also D. H. Frisch and J. H. Smith, Am. J. Phys., **31**, 342 (1963).

so that

$$u'_x = \frac{u_x - v}{\left(1 - \dfrac{u_x v}{c^2}\right)}.$$ [5.5.11]

This relativistic expression replaces the classical equation (5.5.2). It has the effect that, no matter how many velocities add up by transformations from one frame to another, the final result is always less than c, unless the original velocity happened to be c, in which case the transformed velocities are always c. For, if we substitute $u_x = c$ in the above equation, we find

$$u'_x = \frac{c - v}{1 - v/c} = c.$$

An experimental test of the velocity formula (5.5.11) may be obtained by the use of light signals which travel in a dense medium at a speed somewhat less than c, namely c/n, where n is the refractive index of the medium. In 1851 Fizeau performed an experiment in which two beams of light were passed through water before being combined to produce interference fringes. When the water was moved at high speed (v) relative to the laboratory, in such a way that one light beam traveled parallel and the other antiparallel to the direction of water flow, the interference fringes were displaced. The displacement corresponded to a change in the velocity of light in the water relative to the laboratory, but was only about one-half of the effect predicted on the basis of the classical equation (5.5.2). The Lorentz scheme predicts that the velocity should be

$$u' = \frac{u \pm v}{1 \pm \dfrac{\bar{u}v}{c^2}} \qquad \text{with} \qquad u = c/n,$$

the $+$ or $-$ sign depending on which light beam is considered. Binomial expansion of the denominator then yields the approximate result

$$u' = c/n \pm v \mp v/n^2$$
$$= c/n \pm v(1 - 1/n^2).$$ [5.5.12]

The correction factor $(1 - 1/n^2)$ was first given by Fresnel in his theory of "partial aether drag" and it accounts for a wide range of experimental results, including those of Fizeau, which were substantiated later by Michelson and Morley and by Zeeman.

(i) Three-dimensional transformations

The postulates of the special theory require that relative motion of two inertial frames in one direction, say the x direction, does not affect space measurements in perpendicular directions. In three dimensions, therefore, we add to Equation (5.5.6) the equations

$$y' = y \qquad \text{and} \qquad z' = z.$$

It should be noted, however, that velocity components measured in the y and z directions do not remain unchanged by the relative velocity (v), because of the alteration in time scale. If

$$u_y = \frac{dy}{dt} \qquad \text{and} \qquad u'_y = \frac{dy'}{dt'},$$

then from Equation (5.5.6),

$$dt' = \frac{dt - \dfrac{v\,dx}{c^2}}{(1 - v^2/c^2)^{1/2}},$$

so that

$$u'_y = \frac{u_y(1 - v^2/c^2)^{1/2}}{\left(1 - \dfrac{vu_x}{c^2}\right)} \qquad [5.5.13]$$

and likewise for the transformation of u_z.

5.6   Momentum, Mass, and Energy in the Special Theory

(a) Elastic collision of identical masses

If we define the inertial mass m of a body by the condition that linear momentum, the product of mass and velocity, is conserved in a collision (Newton's second and third laws), we find that the mass as measured by an observer varies with the relative velocity between the observer and the body. This result is a direct consequence of the Lorentz transformation and it may be illustrated by the following simple example, due to Lewis and Tolman.

Let two observers 0 and 0' move toward each other with relative velocity v so that their antiparallel paths define the x, x' direction and are separated laterally by a distance $y = 2Y$. Let each throw a smooth ball of rest mass m_0 in such a way that the balls make a perfectly elastic collision with each other and each ball returns to each observer with the same speed as the speed with which it was projected. Viewed from frame 0 the process is somewhat as shown in Figure 5.6 (upper part). The ball A is thrown by 0 at speed u in the y direction, perpendicular to the direction of relative motion. At some point given by $y = Y$, the ball A encounters ball B, which was launched by 0' at point B_1 and after the collision will return to 0' at point B_2. The situation is perfectly symmetrical between observers 0 and 0', because the balls are defined to be identical in the same frame, so 0' will see ball B travel out to Y and back over the same path, the speed being u both ways.

If, now, we require the components of the velocity of A in frame 0', we must use the Lorentz velocity transformations (5.5.11) and (5.5.13)

$$u'_x = \frac{u_x - v}{1 - \dfrac{u_x v}{c^2}} \qquad \text{and} \qquad u'_y = \frac{u_y(1 - v^2/c^2)^{1/2}}{1 - \dfrac{u_x v}{c^2}}.$$

In frame 0 we had $u_x = 0$ and $u_y = u$ (before collision) so that the same components, as measured in 0', are

$$u'_x = -v \qquad \text{and} \qquad u'_y = u(1 - v^2/c^2)^{1/2}.$$

Applying the principle of conservation of momentum in the frame 0', we postulate that the total change in momentum of B is the same as the total change in the y component of A's momentum and find

$$2m_A u'_y = 2m_B u,$$

whence

$$m_A = \frac{m_B}{(1 - v^2/c^2)^{1/2}} = \frac{m_0}{(1 - v^2/c^2)^{1/2}}. \qquad [5.6.1]$$

Now we can make u as small as we like compared with v, so that, with the paths closer and closer together, we approximate to a grazing collision in which only the relative velocity v

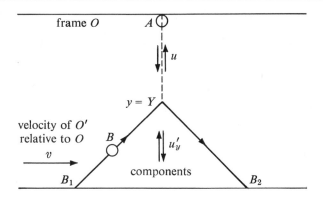

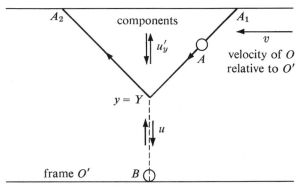

FIGURE 5.6 *Above: in O's frame of reference the ball A travels out to Y, rebounds from ball B, which is projected by O' at B_1, and returns to O while B carries on to B_2; the y components of velocity are $\pm u$ for A and $\pm u'_y$ for B. Below: the same events as seen from frame O', in which B travels out to Y and back while A travels from A_1 to Y and thence to A_2.*

is involved. On the assumption that the same mass ratio obtains in the limiting case where no collision occurs, we can say that the mass of A as measured by 0' must remain greater than the rest mass m_0 under all conditions when the relative velocity v exists. It is noteworthy that the mass remains a scalar because the variation with speed depends on v^2 and is independent of direction.

(b) Inelastic collisions

In the foregoing example, the kinetic energy of the bodies (however defined in terms of mass and velocity) remained constant because the collision was assumed to be perfectly elastic. It is instructive to consider an inelastic collision between two masses which are equal in the same frame. Suppose two particles of rest mass m_0 approach each other with opposite velocities (each of magnitude u) in frame 0, as in Figure 5.7, then coalesce. The conservation of momentum requires that the combined mass remains stationary in this frame (the center-of-momentum frame) and in this frame the mass of each (before collision) is given by Equation (5.6.1) as

$$m = \frac{m_0}{(1 - u^2/c^2)^{1/2}}.$$

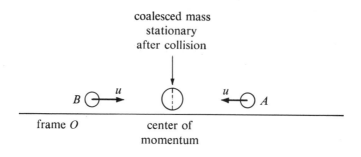

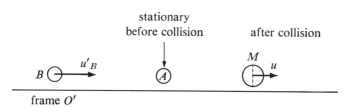

FIGURE 5.7 *An inelastic collision between two identical bodies A and B. Above: in the center-of-momentum frame O each mass m has speed u before collision and the coalesced mass is stationary afterwards. Below: in the frame O′ in which A was originally stationary, B has mass m'_B and speed u'_B before collision and the combined mass M has speed u after the collision.*

Now transform the same problem into a frame moving at velocity u relative to the center-of-momentum frame. In this new frame 0′ one mass (A) is stationary (and has rest mass m_0) before collision. The other mass (B) has net velocity given by Equation (5.5.11) as

$$u'_B = \frac{u + u}{1 + u^2/c^2}.$$

The mass m'_B of B in the frame 0′ should be, from Equation (5.6.1),

$$m'_B = \frac{m_0}{(1 - u'^2_B/c^2)^{1/2}} = \frac{m_0(1 + u^2/c^2)}{(1 - u^2/c^2)}.$$

In 0′ both masses travel at speed u after collision (since they were stationary in frame 0) and they may be supposed to have a combined mass M which can be found by applying the condition of momentum conservation in frame 0′. We have

$$m'_B u'_B + 0 = Mu,$$

whence

$$M = \frac{2m_0}{(1 - u^2/c^2)}.$$

On the other hand, if M were the mass of two separate bodies, each of rest mass m_0, moving at speed u, we should get a different result, namely,

$$M' = \frac{2m_0}{(1 - u^2/c^2)^{1/2}}.$$

It is clear that M is greater than M' and the difference must be due to the fact that the bodies coalesced at collision. Before the collision the bodies had kinetic energy in frame 0 but in this frame all the kinetic energy disappeared on collision, and was translated into some form of internal energy, for example, heat or excitation energy. The possession of this extra energy results in the inertia M (in frame $0'$) being greater than the total inertia of two separate bodies, showing that mass-energy equivalence is a necessary consequence of the Lorentz scheme.

Although kinetic energy is not conserved in the inelastic collision considered, we can establish a conservation equation involving mass as defined by Equation (5.6.1). If, in frame $0'$, we add the *relativistic masses* before collision, we find

$$m_A' + m_B' = m_0 + \frac{m_0(1 + u^2/c^2)}{(1 - u^2/c^2)}$$

$$= \frac{2m_0}{(1 - u^2/c^2)} = M.$$

Even in the inelastic collision, therefore, the total relativistic mass is constant and we deduce that this quantity combines the classical concepts of mass and energy in an invariant which is characteristic of relativity theory.

(c) Experimental tests

Experimental confirmation of the variation of mass with velocity has been obtained in experiments in which the specific charge (e/m) of electrons is measured. Between 1900 and 1910 Kaufmann and Bucherer independently determined the specific charge for beta rays (electrons) of velocities up to $0.7c$ and showed that the results varied very closely as $(1 - v^2/c^2)^{1/2}$. If it is assumed that the elementary electric charge is constant, the results are consistent with the relativistic mass variation. Later experiments have demonstrated the accuracy of Equation (5.6.1) over a wider range of speeds. But the most impressive evidence for the correctness of the theory is the successful design and operation of high-energy accelerators such as proton synchrotrons, which take in low-speed particles and guide them accurately through an "acceleration cycle" which ends in the region $v/c \approx 0.99$.

The operation of electron synchrotrons is also of great interest because at energies above a few MeV the electrons travel around in circular orbits with effectively constant speed. This is a direct consequence of Equation (5.5.11), which shows that repeated additions of speed to a "relativistic" particle bring its speed fractionally closer to c, which remains unreachable as the upper limit to particle speeds. Energy is supplied to the beam in ever-increasing amounts, and, in a sense, this is devoted to increasing the mass per particle; but strictly we should regard the entire process as one which increases the mass from the rest value m_0 to higher and higher values as the speed approaches c.

(d) Mass, energy, and momentum

The exact relation between energy supplied and the increase in mass can be obtained by setting up a scheme of relativistic dynamics and deducing the kinetic energy from the work done in accelerating the body. Newton's second law of motion is retained in the form

$$\text{Force: } F = \frac{d}{dt}(mv) = \frac{d}{dt}\left[\frac{m_0 v}{(1 - v^2/c^2)^{1/2}}\right]. \qquad [5.6.2]$$

The work done (dK) by such a force in time dt may be found as

$$dK = F\,dx = Fv\,dt, \quad \text{(in one dimension)}.$$

The work done over a period in which the speed increases from zero to a final value V is given by the integral

$$K = \int_{v=0}^{V} dK = m_0 \int_0^V v \, d\left[\frac{v}{(1 - v^2/c^2)^{1/2}}\right]$$

or

$$K = m_0 \left.\frac{v^2}{(1 - v^2/c^2)^{1/2}}\right|_0^V - m_0 \int_0^V \frac{v \, dv}{(1 - v^2/c^2)^{1/2}}$$

$$= \frac{m_0 V^2}{(1 - V^2/c^2)^{1/2}} + m_0 c^2 (1 - V^2/c^2)^{1/2} - m_0 c^2,$$

whence

$$K = mc^2 - m_0 c^2. \qquad [5.6.3]$$

Here the mass m is the relativistic mass given by Equation (5.6.1), and K stands for the kinetic energy. The result links up directly with the photon relation [Equation (5.2.1)] in showing that the conversion from mass to energy is effected by multiplication of the mass by c^2. Moreover it is clear that the relativistic mass is equivalent to a *total energy content* (rest-mass energy plus kinetic energy)

$$E = mc^2 = \frac{m_0 c^2}{(1 - v^2/c^2)^{1/2}}. \qquad [5.6.4]$$

Expanding this expression by the binomial theorem, we find

$$E = m_0 c^2 + \tfrac{1}{2} mv^2 + \ldots, \qquad \text{at low speeds.}$$

The relativistic equation connecting total energy E and linear momentum p (in one dimension) is found from the expressions

$$E^2 = \frac{m_0^2 c^4}{1 - v^2/c^2} \qquad \text{and} \qquad p^2 = \frac{m_0^2 v^2}{1 - v^2/c^2}.$$

Multiplying the latter equation by c^2 and subtracting from the former equation, we find

$$E^2 - p^2 c^2 = m_0^2 c^4. \qquad [5.6.5]$$

This general relation is particularly significant when applied to a particle of zero rest mass, for example a photon or neutrino, because it yields

$$E^2 = p^2 c^2 \qquad \text{or} \qquad p = E/c,$$

as required by the theory of photons (Section 5.1). Such particles always travel at speed c, whatever their energy, and the momentum varies directly as the energy.

In several applications involving charged particles, the particle momentum is determined from the curvature of the particle's orbit in a magnetic field. Equation (3.3.5) may be taken over into relativistic mechanics with the substitution of the relativistic mass for the factor m, so that the relation becomes

$$Ber = mv = \frac{m_0 v}{(1 - v^2/c^2)^{1/2}}, \qquad [5.6.6]$$

where r is the radius of an orbit for a particle of speed v in field B.

(e) The Compton effect

Finally, we can apply the relativistic scheme of mechanics to the problem of a photon colliding with an electron, the process which is supposed to give rise to the Compton effect

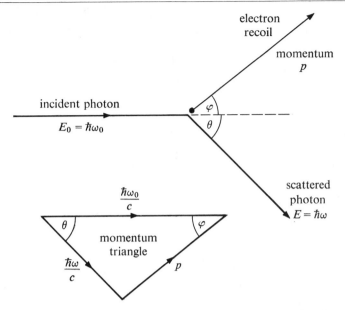

FIGURE 5.8   *The Compton effect interpreted as being due to the collision of a photon, incident with energy $E_0 = \hbar\omega_0$, and an electron, which is initially stationary. The electron recoils with appreciable energy and the scattered photon retains energy $E = \hbar\omega$, which varies with the angle θ.*

(Section 4.9). Consider an incident photon, of energy $E_0 = \hbar\omega_0$, in collision with an electron of rest mass m_0, which is initially stationary in the laboratory frame and recoils after collision with momentum p in a direction at angle φ to the direction of the incident photon (see Figure 5.8). The photon is supposed to be scattered with energy $E = \hbar\omega$ at an angle θ relative to its original direction. Then the momentum triangle of Figure 5.8 leads directly to the relation

$$c^2 p^2 = E_0^2 + E^2 - 2E_0 E \cos\theta.$$

The relativistic mass of the electron after collision (m) and its total energy (mc^2) are related to the momentum p by Equation (5.6.5)

$$m^2 c^4 = c^2 p^2 + m_0^2 c^4.$$

Also, by the principle of conservation of total energy

$$E_0 + m_0 c^2 = E + mc^2,$$

that is,

$$m^2 c^4 = (E_0 - E + m_0 c^2)^2.$$

If this expression is equated to the expression found from the momentum relation, the following identity is obtained

$$2E_0 E(1 - \cos\theta) = 2m_0 c^2 (E_0 - E). \qquad [5.6.7]$$

The relation between E and E_0 is most simply expressed in terms of the wavelengths, which are introduced by the equations

$$E = \hbar\omega_0 = \frac{hc}{\lambda_0} \qquad \text{and} \qquad E = \hbar\omega = \frac{hc}{\lambda}.$$

The equation then reduces immediately to

$$\Delta\lambda = \lambda - \lambda_0 = \frac{h}{m_0 c}(1 - \cos\theta), \qquad [5.6.8]$$

that is, the change in wavelength depends only on the angle θ, and the characteristic wavelength shift is found as

$$\frac{h}{m_0 c} = 2.4 \times 10^{-12}\text{m} = 0.024 \text{ Å},$$

which is known as the *Compton wavelength* for electrons. The theory therefore yields precisely the same result as Compton's experiments (Section 4.9). The agreement indicates that both the interpretation of the phenomenon and the energy-momentum relations used in the theory are essentially correct. The Compton effect has also been detected with protons as the scattering particles. In this process the shift in wavelength is necessarily very small because of the high value of the rest mass m_0, so photons of high energy (about 100 MeV per photon) have to be employed. The probability of Compton processes occurring must be calculated with the aid of quantum mechanics, which was developed in the years immediately after Compton's discovery.

FOR FURTHER READING

Mach's Principle:
   D. W. SCIAMA, *The Unity of the Universe*, Anchor Books (Doubleday and Co., New York, 1961).
The aether theory:
   E. T. WHITTAKER, *History of the Theories of Aether and Electricity*, 2 vols. (Harper Torchbooks, Harper & Row, New York, 1960).
Michelson's experiments:
   A. A. MICHELSON, *Studies in Optics* (University of Chicago Press, Chicago, 1927).
Relativity theory:
   A. EINSTEIN, *Relativity*, translator, R. W. Lawson (Crown Publishers, New York, 1961).
   H. A. LORENTZ, A. EINSTEIN, H. MINKOWSKI, and H. WEYL, *The Principle of Relativity*, translators, W. Perrett and G. B. Jeffery (Dover Publications, New York).
   R. B. LINDSAY and H. MARGENAU, *Foundations of Physics* (Dover Publications, New York, 1957).
   W. PAULI, *Theory of Relativity* (Pergamon Press, New York, 1958).

PROBLEMS FOR CHAPTER 5

DATA REQUIRED:

Velocity of light *in vacuo*: $c = 3.0 \times 10^8$ m/sec
Gravitational constant: $G = 6.6 \times 10^{-11}$ mks
Boltzmann's constant: $k = 1.4 \times 10^{-23}$ J/°K
Planck's constant: $\hbar = 1.05 \times 10^{-34}$ J sec
Electron volt: 1 eV $= 1.6 \times 10^{-19}$ J

5.1.(a) Prove, by the methods of Section 2.1, that in a perfectly reflecting enclosure the mean radiation pressure on each wall due to photons moving at random is

$$P = \frac{E}{3V}, \qquad \text{where } \frac{E}{V} \text{ is the energy density.}$$

(b) Regarding the assembly of photons as a system obeying the first law of thermo-dynamics, prove that the energy density (and hence the radiation pressure) is proportional to the fourth power of the absolute temperature (the Stefan–Boltzmann law).

(c) With the aid of the Stefan constant s of Equation (4.3.11) estimate the temperature at which the radiation pressure in the enclosure is 1 atm (10^5 N/m²).

5.2. Estimate the annual loss of mass by the Sun, given that the *solar constant* (the maxi-mum energy received from the Sun by unit area of the Earth's surface) is about 8 J per minute per square cm. The distance from the Earth to the Sun is 1.5×10^8 km.

5.3.(a) Calculate the classical angle of deflection per meter of path for a photon moving perpendicular to the Earth's gravitational field ($g = 10$ m/sec²).

(b) Show that the total deflection for a photon passing the Earth at grazing incidence (and undergoing no atmospheric refraction) is the result of (a) multiplied by the Earth's diameter.

5.4. Calculate the gravitational frequency shift ($\Delta\omega/\omega$) of photons traveling from an Earth satellite, which is in a circular orbit of radius 9000 km, to the Earth's surface (of radius 7000 km). Assume $g = 10$ m/sec² at the Earth's surface.

5.5. Assume that the observed red shift of spectral lines emitted by Sirius B, namely, $\Delta\omega/\omega = 7 \times 10^{-6}$, is due solely to the gravitational field at the surface of the star, find the mean density of the star, given that its mass is about 1.7×10^{30} kg.

5.6. In Michelson and Morley's experiment to detect "aether drift" (Figure 5.3) the paral-lel and transverse arms were each about 10 m long. Show that the expected difference in time caused by the Earth's orbital speed ($v \approx 10^{-4}c$) corresponded to a shift of $1/6$ of a wave-length for visible light ($\lambda = 6 \times 10^{-7}$m).

5.7. With the aid of the three-dimensional transformation scheme provided by Equation (5.5.6) and Section 5.5.f, prove that the equation for a spherical light wave spreading out from a point *in vacuo* is invariant under the Lorentz transformation. Show that the velocity component transformations of Equations (5.5.11) and (5.5.13) lead to the same result, if we put

$$u^2 = u_x^2 + u_y^2 + u_z^2 = c^2.$$

5.8. Calculate the fractional frequency shift ($\Delta\nu/\nu$) caused by time dilation in a beam of atoms moving at a speed of 10^3 m/sec across the line of sight, as in the experiment of Ives and Stilwell. What would be the corresponding change in wavelength for a spectral line of wavelength 6000 Å?

5.9. Consider an Earth satellite revolving in a circular orbit of radius R. Compare the gravitational frequency shift of signals sent from the satellite to a point directly "below" it on the Earth's surface (radius R_0) with the red shift caused by the time-dilation effect, neglecting the speed of the Earth's surface compared with the orbital speed of the satellite. Hence show that, in this approximation, there is zero total frequency shift when $R = 1.5R_0$.

5.10.(a) Two identical bodies approach each other head-on, each with speed $0.9c$ in the center-of-momentum frame; what is the speed of either one, as measured in the frame of reference of the other body?

(b) Expressing a high speed (u) as ($c - v$), where v/c is small, show that the addition of u to u results in a total speed equal to c *less* terms of order v^2/c^2.

5.11. In Fizeau's experiment, light beams passed in opposite directions through water, of refractive index $\frac{4}{3}$, flowing at approximately 7 m/sec parallel to the light paths. If the total path length of each beam in water was 6 m calculate the shift in the number of wavelengths ($\lambda = 6 \times 10^{-7}$ m) caused by the water flow.

5.12. Planck argued that the *flux* of energy (defined as the total energy density multiplied by the speed of transmission) should be, in general, equal to the momentum density multiplied by c^2; show that this principle, established for electromagnetic waves in Section 5.1, applies to a beam of relativistic particles.

5.13. In classical physics the "mass" of a body is often taken to be the ratio of force applied to the acceleration produced. Show that the relativistic Equation (5.6.2) leads to different values for this ratio when the acceleration is imposed (i) parallel and (ii) perpendicular to the velocity **v** (which is the relative velocity of the body and observer).

5.14.(a) Calculate the rest-mass energy of a proton (of mass 1.67×10^{-27} kg) in MeV.

(b) What is the value of v/c for a proton with kinetic energy (K) equal to its rest-mass energy?

5.15. A π meson of rest mass 273 times that of the electron (which is equivalent to 0.51 MeV) has a kinetic energy of 70 MeV as measured in the laboratory. Calculate:

(i) its speed relative to the laboratory;

(ii) its effective mass compared with that of an electron at rest;

(iii) its expected lifetime, if the mean lifetime of π mesons at rest is 2.5×10^{-8} sec.

5.16. Use the relativistic expressions for energy and momentum of a particle to show that a photon cannot produce an electron pair (electron plus positron) in free space, if the laws of conservation of energy and momentum are to be obeyed.

5.17. A beam of photons, each of energy 17 MeV, falls on a metal foil and electron pairs are ejected from the far side. If a magnetic field is applied (as in Figure 4.25) so that positive and negative particles of equal energy are detected simultaneously, find the field required to produce maximum counting rate in detectors placed 0.5 m apart.

5.18.(a) Show that, in high-energy accelerators of the synchrotron type, the magnetic field (B) needed to confine particles of kinetic energy K and rest-mass energy E_0 in orbits of radius r is given by the relation

$$B^2 e^2 r^2 c^2 = K(K + 2E_0), \qquad \text{where } e \text{ is the charge.}$$

(b) Hence find the field strength at the end of the acceleration cycle in an electron synchrotron of maximum beam energy 70 MeV and orbit radius 0.5 m (here $E_0 = 0.51$ MeV).

❧❧❧❧❧❧❧❧❧❧❧❧❧❧❧❧❧❧❧❧❧❧❧❧❧❧❧❧❧❧❧❧❧❧❧

CHAPTER VI

THE NUCLEAR ATOM

It may be said that the study of nuclear physics commenced in 1896 with the discovery of Becquerel that salts of uranium emit rays which penetrate matter to some extent and affect photographic plates. The study of *radioactivity* was pursued energetically by Pierre and Marie Curie, who isolated the new radioactive elements polonium and radium, and by Rutherford, who with various collaborators investigated radioactive series and the properties of alpha rays. Remarkable features of the new phenomenon were the apparently spontaneous release of considerable amounts of energy and the completely random sequence exhibited by individual radioactive decay processes. It was found that the activity displayed by a given quantity of a radioactive element is quite unaffected by chemical combination and by normal changes in physical conditions. Moreover, radioactive characteristics differ markedly from one isotope to another of the same element; it follows that radioactivity is a property of the massive positive part of an atom.

Although immense progress was made between 1900 and 1910 in the quantum theory of radiation, no successful model of atomic structure was evolved, possibly because too much importance was attached to the old concept of the atom as an impenetrable entity. The essential new idea was provided in 1911 by Rutherford, who analyzed the results of alpha-particle scattering experiments and showed that the positive charge in an atom is concentrated in a very small *nucleus* at the center. It then became possible to regard the electrons as loosely bound planetary particles, organized into shells by virtue of their orbital motion. In 1913 Niels Bohr succeeded in giving a prescription for electron orbits in terms of quantized angular momentum and he went on to explain the spectrum of atomic hydrogen. Despite the patent inconsistencies of the semiclassical Bohr theory, it remains a major landmark in scientific thought and it is still valuable as a model for calculating the orders of magnitude of classically conceived quantities, such as electron speeds and orbital radii in simple atoms.

6.1 Radioactive Series

(a) Alpha, beta, and gamma rays

Early experiments on radioactivity were carried out with the aid of photographic plates to detect the emitted rays or with charged electroscopes which are sensitive to the ionization produced by the passage of the rays through air. At least two kinds of rays were distinguished by Rutherford, who found that uranium preparations emit strongly ionizing *alpha rays*, with a short range in matter, and weakly ionizing *beta rays* with a much longer range.

143

Later these rays were separated in magnetic fields and the deflections showed that the alpha rays carry positive charge and the beta rays negative charge. In addition, Villard discovered the highly penetrating *gamma rays*, which are unaffected by magnetic and electric fields.

The nature of the alpha, beta, and gamma rays was elucidated by numerous experiments of the type used in studying cathode rays (Sections 3.2 and 3.3) and positive rays (Section 3.4). Beta rays are readily deflected by magnetic fields and electrostatic deflection is also achieved without difficulty; the results show that the specific charge is similar to that of electrons. More detailed experiments by Kaufmann and Bucherer showed, indeed, that the more energetic beta rays have specific charge varying with velocity and this result is in accord with the relativistic mass variation expressed in Equation (5.6.1). At this stage it became clear that beta rays consist of fast electrons. They are moderately penetrating in matter but possess no well-defined range, partly because there is a continuous "spectrum" of energies at emission, even from a single radioactive isotope.

The alpha rays emitted by uranium, radium, and other elements were found to travel in almost straight lines through matter. W. H. Bragg showed that a given element produces alpha rays with a characteristic range in air, corresponding to a definite initial energy, and this property may be used in identifying the emitter. Deflection of the rays by electric and magnetic fields was achieved only with great difficulty, but in 1906 Rutherford found that their specific charge is about half the specific charge of a hydrogen ion [Equation (3.1.2)]. In 1908 Rutherford and Geiger developed an electrical counter capable of recording the passage of a single particle. With its aid they determined the total number of alpha particles emitted in one second by a gram of pure radium. This unit of radioactivity, called the *curie*, was found to be approximately 3.4×10^{10} particles per second.* The positive charge carried by a known number of particles was then measured and the charge per particle came out to be 3.2×10^{-19} C, or twice the elementary charge.

These measurements indicate that an alpha particle is four times as massive as a hydrogen ion and should therefore be the positive part of a helium atom. This deduction was verified by Rutherford and Royds, who enclosed a small quantity of radon (a radioactive gas) in a thin-walled glass tube sealed into the side of a discharge tube. The alpha particles from radon were able to penetrate the thin wall into the discharge tube, where they spent most of their energy and eventually became neutral helium atoms. This supposition was proved by the appearance, after a few days, of the characteristic line spectrum of helium, in a tube which was originally free from the element.

The nature of the gamma rays was established by experiments on crystal diffraction, which showed that they are x rays of short wavelength and that they exhibit a *line spectrum* characteristic of the emitter. Later discoveries established the fact that a nucleus emits a gamma ray only after a radioactive transformation from some parent nucleus. The transformation may leave the residual body in an excited state and the emission of a gamma ray removes the excess energy without changing the nuclidic identity. The spectrum of gamma rays therefore yields information about the energy levels of the residual nuclide.

(b) The existence of series

The fact that the radioactive heavy elements form well-defined *series*, that is, chains in which successive radioactive transformations occur, was established only after prolonged experiments involving physical and chemical separations of the different elements. For example, in 1900 Owens and Rutherford observed that the activity of thorium preparations was varying in a baffling way and they traced this effect to the influence of air currents on the samples. It appeared that there is a gaseous *emanation*, called thoron, among the decay

---

* A more accurate figure for the curie is 3.7×10^{10} disintegrations/sec.

products of thorium. This gas is itself radioactive and its decay products can be collected on a negatively charged needle placed in the gas. In this way the members of the thorium series below thoron may be separated from those above thoron. Later work showed that thoron does not come directly from thorium but from an intermediate body called thorium X. This discovery first indicated the existence of radioactive chains.

In 1900 Dorn discovered a gaseous emanation from radium and this became known as radon. Like thoron, it is inert chemically but its chief radioactive characteristic, a mean lifetime of a few days, is entirely different from that of thoron, which is about a minute. Nevertheless Rutherford and Soddy showed that the two kinds of emanation have very similar freezing points. Eventually it was realized that the different emanations are isotopes of the same element, now called emanation (Em). This element fits into the periodic table (Appendix II) as an inert gas below xenon. Its emission from radium is explained if we write a balanced equation to represent the alpha decay of radium

$$_{88}Ra^{226} \rightarrow {}_{86}Em^{222} + {}_2He^4. \qquad [6.1.1]$$

Here the upper figures are the mass numbers of the isotopes concerned and the lower figures are the atomic charge numbers (Z), which determine the positions of the elements in the periodic table.

An early example of chemical separation of short-lived isotopes was Crookes' discovery that a substance (Uranium X) extracted from uranium carries all the beta activity of the original sample. Soddy then showed that pure uranium exhibits only alpha activity but the beta activity of Uranium X grows again in uranium which has been purified. Later experiments established the occurrence of two beta-active bodies, now called UX_1 and UX_2, in the UX fraction; moreover, these give rise to a new isotope of uranium, U^{234}. It had long been known that radium must be a descendant of uranium, but Soddy showed that there must be an intermediate body between the two elements. After several years of work Boltwood identified this intermediate nuclide as an active element which he called ionium and which is chemically identical with thorium. In this way the beginning of the uranium–radium series was worked out and the sequence of transformations takes a form shown in Figure 6.1, where each emitter is specified by its unique combination of atomic mass number (A) and atomic charge number (Z).

The existence of radioactive series was deduced as early as 1902 by Rutherford and Soddy, but the full details of three naturally occurring sequences were not worked out for many years. (See Appendix III). In 1912 Fajans and Soddy independently defined the nature of isotopes and their work received support from the contemporary discoveries of J. J. Thomson concerning the isotopes of neon (Section 3.4). In the natural radioactive series each member decays either by alpha or beta emission, except for a few cases in which the probabilities for the two processes to occur are comparable and the chain "branches" into two sequences. The emission of an alpha particle causes the A number to decrease by four and the Z number to decrease by 2, as shown in Equation (6.1.1). Beta emission causes no appreciable change in mass but raises the charge number by 1, since the loss of a single negative charge is equivalent to the gain of a positive charge.

Since the mass numbers change by zero or 4 only, there are, in theory, four possible radioactive series among heavy elements, namely, those whose mass numbers are represented by

$4n$ the thorium series commencing with Th^{232},

$4n + 1$ not found naturally on Earth,

$4n + 2$ the uranium–radium series commencing with U^{238} (Figure 6.1),

$4n + 3$ the actinium series commencing with U^{235},

where n is an integer in all cases.

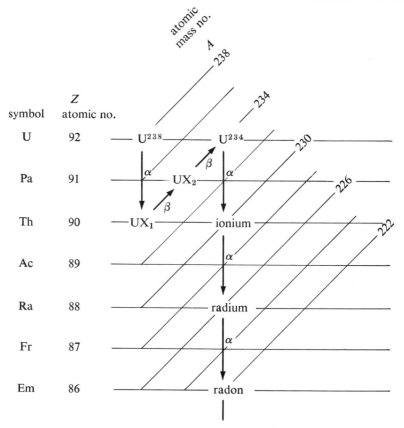

FIGURE 6.1 *The beginning of the natural uranium-radium radioactive series, represented on a diagram in which lines of equal atomic number (Z) are horizontal and lines of equal atomic mass number (A) are at 45° to the horizontal. (See also Appendix III.)*

The end product of the three natural series is in each case an isotope of lead, indicating that this element exhibits higher nuclear stability than the elements above it.

The rules observed by processes of alpha and beta emission are clearly consistent with the principle of conservation of electric charge; moreover, the conservation of mass number (A) indicates that, although small mass changes occur as a result of electron emission and energy changes, the nucleus maintains a constant number of massive units, now called *baryons*, throughout radioactive processes. In the modern view, the protons and neutrons forming a nucleus add up to make a total baryon number equal to A and this number is invariant during all nuclear processes.

6.2   The Statistics of Radioactive Decay

The statistical aspects of radioactive decay merit attention because of their significance in both practical and theoretical fields. Practically, the statistical fluctuations in measurements of radioactivity place limitations on the accuracy of experimental determinations.

Theoretically, the fact that basic changes in nuclear structure occur apparently at random, although governed by general probability factors, is an essential guide in the development of quantum mechanics. The statistical interpretation of atomic processes, which is necessary in the study of radioactivity, has been extended to cover the entire field of atomic theory.

(a) Counting fluctuations

If a Geiger counter is used to record individual events caused by radioactive decay, the events appear to form a random sequence and statistical analysis may be employed to demonstrate this. For example, experiments can be carried out to find the distribution in numbers (N) of particles emitted in a fixed time (t) by a sample of constant mean activity. If we assume that in each unit time there is a constant probability (λ) for a particle to be emitted and recorded by the counter, we can calculate the distribution in numbers N as follows.

Let $P(N, t)$ be the probability of N events being recorded in time t. Then if we extend the time from t to $(t + dt)$, the probability of having $(N + 1)$ events is the sum of two probabilities:

(i) of having N events in time t and one event in the extra time dt, that is, the product $P(N, t) \cdot \lambda \, dt$,

(ii) of having $(N + 1)$ events in time t and none in the extra time. We can therefore write an equation

$$P(N + 1, t + dt) = P(N, t)\lambda \, dt + P(N + 1, t)[1 - \lambda \, dt]$$

or

$$P(N + 1, t + dt) - P(N + 1, t) = \lambda \, dt[P(N, t) - P(N + 1, t)].$$

Since $P(N + 1, t)$ is supposed to be a continuous function of time, although it is necessarily discontinuous in N, the derivative $\dfrac{dP(N + 1, t)}{dt}$ presumably exists and is given by the above equation as

$$\frac{dP(N + 1)}{dt} = \lambda[P(N) - P(N + 1)],$$

where the time symbols have been dropped for convenience.

This type of equation may be written for any integral $N \geqslant 0$. The special case, $N + 1 = 0$, yields the equation

$$\frac{dP(0)}{dt} + \lambda P(0) = 0$$

with the solution

$$P(0) = C \exp(-\lambda t).$$

Since, when $t = 0$, the probability of no events is 1, we find that the integration constant (C) is 1.

Proceeding from this solution to the equation for $N = 0$, we obtain

$$\frac{dP(1)}{dt} + \lambda P(1) = \lambda \exp(-\lambda t)$$

with the solution

$$P(1) = C' \exp(-\lambda t) + (\lambda t) \exp(-\lambda t),$$

where C' is an integration constant and the second term is the particular integral. Imposing the boundary condition $P(1) = 0$ when $t = 0$, we find that $C' = 0$. Repeated substitutions of this type lead to the solution for any N

$$P(N) = \frac{(\lambda t)^N}{N!} \exp(-\lambda t), \qquad [6.2.1]$$

which is a Poisson distribution in N, satisfying the necessary condition

$$\sum_{N=0}^{\infty} P(N) = 1.$$

The validity of this result was tested experimentally by Rutherford and Geiger in 1910 and at moderate counting rates it is well established. Very high counting rates may introduce discrepancies because of the finite "dead time" of the counter or similar effects in other types of detector.

Two parameters are particularly important in the statistics of counting, namely, the mean counting rate ($\bar{N}$) and the *variance* (σ^2) or mean square deviation from the mean value. In the counting interval t these quantities may be defined as

$$\bar{N} = \sum_{N=0}^{\infty} NP(N)$$

and

$$\sigma^2 = \sum_{N=0}^{\infty} (N - \bar{N})^2 P(N)$$

$$= \sum_{N=0}^{\infty} (N^2 - 2N\bar{N} + \bar{N}^2) P(N).$$

Taking the terms separately in the latter expression, the first is the mean square value of N, written

$$\overline{N^2} = \sum_{N=0}^{\infty} N^2 P(N),$$

so that the expression for the variance becomes

$$\sigma^2 = \overline{N^2} - 2(\bar{N})^2 + (\bar{N})^2 \quad \left(\text{since } \sum_{N=0}^{\infty} P(N) = 1 \right),$$

that is,

$$\sigma^2 = \overline{N^2} - (\bar{N})^2.$$

These quantities may be derived directly or from a *moment-generating function* $G(x)$, which is defined by the series

$$G(x) = \sum_{N=0}^{\infty} P(N) x^N, \qquad [6.2.2]$$

where x is an arbitrary parameter.

Differentiation of the generating function yields

$$\frac{dG}{dx} = \sum_{N=0}^{\infty} NP(N) x^{N-1}$$

and this function is written $G'(x)$ for convenience. The mean value of N is found by putting $x = 1$, that is,

$$G'(1) = \sum_{N=0}^{\infty} NP(N) = \bar{N}. \qquad [6.2.3]$$

A second differentiation of $G(x)$ leads to the relation

$$G''(x) = \frac{d^2G}{dx^2} = \sum_{N=0}^{\infty} N(N-1) P(N) x^{N-2}$$

from which we find

$$G''(1) = \overline{N^2} - \bar{N}$$

and the variance is

$$\sigma^2 = G''(1) + G'(1) - [G'(1)]^2. \qquad [6.2.4]$$

In the special case of the Poisson distribution given by Equation (6.2.1), the generating function is explicitly

$$G(x) = \sum_{N=0}^{\infty} \frac{(\lambda t x)^N}{N!} \exp(-\lambda t)$$

$$= \exp[\lambda t(x - 1)],$$

from which we find the mean

$$\bar{N} = G'(1) = \lambda t \qquad \text{(as expected from the definition of } \lambda)$$

and the variance

$$\sigma^2 = (\lambda t)^2 + \lambda t - (\lambda t)^2$$

$$= \lambda t = \bar{N}.$$

Thus in the Poisson distribution the root-mean-square deviation (σ) from the mean value is simply the square root of the mean value ($\bar{N}$). In counting experiments it is usual to express the possible error in any particular measurement by taking the square root of the total counts recorded, that is, the data are put in the form

$$N \pm \sqrt{N}.$$

(b) Radioactive decay

The random nature of radioactive decay events is also displayed by the manner in which the mean activity of a pure sample varies with time, although in many cases the change is so slow that the mean activity is effectively constant. It is found that all radioactive emitters obey an exponential law of decay, so that the mean activity of polonium, for example, always decreases to one-half in 140 days, whatever the original activity may have been (Figure 6.2). The same law applies to the number of radioactive atoms present, since this number determines the activity of the sample.

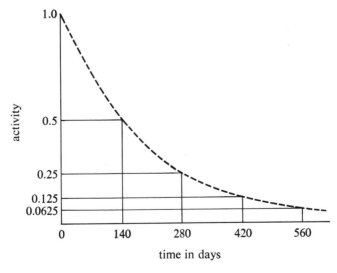

FIGURE 6.2　*The decay curve for the alpha activity of polonium, which has a half-life of 140 days.*

The law of decay may be understood in terms of the *decay constant* λ already introduced. If statistical fluctuations about the mean values are ignored, we may suppose that the number of atoms changed in unit time $(-dn)$ is proportional to the decay constant and to the number of atoms present (n). We write

$$-dn = \lambda n \, dt,$$

whence

$$n = n_0 \exp(-\lambda t), \qquad [6.2.5]$$

where n_0 is the number of atoms present at time $t = 0$.

The activity (a) of a sample is defined as the number of atoms decaying per unit time, so this quantity is

$$a = -\frac{dn}{dt} = \lambda n_0 \exp(-\lambda t). \qquad [6.2.6]$$

The *mean lifetime* (τ) is obtained by direct analysis of the exponential function and we find

$$\tau = 1/\lambda. \qquad [6.2.7]$$

In many applications, the *half-life* ($t_{1/2}$) is used and this quantity is related to the mean lifetime by the equation

$$t_{1/2} = \tau \ln 2 = 0.693\tau. \qquad [6.2.8]$$

It is possible to measure the mean lifetime or half-life of an emitter by plotting the logarithm of the activity against time, a straight line of slope $(-\lambda)$ being obtained. This method is feasible only if the lifetime is less than a century or so. Longer lifetimes are found by direct measurement of the decay constant λ; the activity (λn_0) is measured for a sample of known mass and composition, containing a calculable number of atoms (n_0). In this way the half-lives of the long-lived elements at the beginning of the natural radioactive series have been found; for Th^{232} the value is 1.4×10^{10} years, for U^{238} it is 4.5×10^9 years, and for U^{235} it is 7.1×10^8 years. Members of the missing "$4n + 1$" series have been produced artificially in nuclear reactors and it appears that they do not possess any half-lives longer than 1.6×10^5 years, the value for U^{233}. This evidence suggests that the history of the Earth's crust stretches over many million years, during which time all the "$4n + 1$" isotopes which might have existed must have changed into stable isotopes. Radioactive methods have now been developed into a powerful tool for determining geological age and several lines of evidence indicate that the effective age of the Earth is about 4.5×10^9 years. This period is comparable with the half-lives of both Th^{232} and U^{238}, the longest-lived members of the two most abundant radioactive series. The full details of the three natural series are shown in Appendix III, where it may be seen, for example, that the half-lives of alpha emitters range all the way from 1.4×10^{10} years (for Th^{232}) down to 3.0×10^{-7} sec (for ThC'). This fact alone suggests that the phenomenon of alpha-particle emission, though random in character, is governed by powerful restrictions which enable the probability of emission to vary enormously from one nuclide to another.

6.3   The Scattering of Alpha Particles by Nuclei

(a) Single and multiple scattering

Some of the most significant experiments on the subject of radioactivity were done with alpha rays, which have well-defined energies at emission and travel almost undeviated through matter. Crookes found that alpha particles striking a screen of zinc sulfide produce scintillations of light, which enabled early workers in this field to carry out counting experiments by visual examination of such screens. The culmination of several years' work came when the laws of scattering for alpha particles in metal foils were discovered.

It was known that even the thinnest gold foil contains many atoms per unit area, but alpha particles appear to pass through such foils with little deviation. Thus a great deal of the total cross-sectional area per atom offers very little resistance to the passage of positive particles which are massive compared with electrons, though much lighter than the gold atoms themselves. This fact alone suggests that the massive positive part of an atom occupies only a small fraction of the total cross-sectional area.

Careful experiments by Geiger showed that there is a detectable amount of small-angle scattering when the alpha particles penetrate gold foils and that the effect might be explained as the result of repeated small-angle scatterings by individual atoms. Geiger found that the most probable angle of scattering (θ_0) varied from about 1° to a few degrees, depending on the thickness of the foil used. Statistical analysis of the multiple scattering process indicates that at larger angles the probability of scattering should fall off very rapidly, according to the Gaussian distribution law

$$P(>\theta) \approx \exp{(-\theta^2/\theta_0^2)},$$

where $P(>\theta)$ represents the probability of scattering through an angle *greater* than θ. On this basis one can predict that any scattering through a large angle of the order of 90° is well-nigh impossible, the probability being much smaller than any measurable effect.

Contrary to this prediction, it was found by Geiger and Marsden that alpha particles are occasionally scattered through angles larger than 90°. Moreover, the numbers of these particles are proportional to the thickness of gold foil used, indicating that individual gold atoms are responsible for the large-angle deviations. In 1911 Rutherford* showed that these results can be explained only on the assumption that the alpha particles occasionally enter a strong field within the atom. This field was ascribed to the Coulomb repulsion between the positive alpha particle and the positive nucleus, and Rutherford found that the Coulomb law of force is obeyed to very small distances, of the order of 10^{-3} of the atomic radius. In this way he was able to establish the existence of a small positive nucleus at the center of each atom and to picture the atomic structure as a miniature solar system, with the extra-nuclear electrons in planetary orbits. Rutherford's theory of scattering was tested in a series of detailed experiments carried out by Geiger and Marsden, who reported their final results in 1913.†

(b) The Rutherford single-scattering formula

The theoretical problem of finding the path of a charged particle in a Coulomb field is very similar to the Kepler problem in the classical theory of gravitation, with the single difference that repulsion between the particle and the nucleus causes the particle orbit to be hyperbolic instead of elliptical. We shall assume that the alpha particle is much less massive than the "target" nucleus scattering the alpha particle, so that we can refer the geometrical situation to a fixed point (O in Figure 6.3) representing the target. A particle traveling from a great distance toward O is supposed to follow initially a path with *impact parameter* h_0, this parameter being the perpendicular distance between O and the projected path, that is, between the line Ox and the original velocity vector $\mathbf{v}_0$ in Figure 6.3. Since the target nucleus is fixed and the collision is elastic, the final kinetic energy of the particle is equal to its

* E. Rutherford, Phil. Mag., **21**, 669 (1911).
† H. A. Geiger and E. Marsden, Phil. Mag., **25**, 604 (1913).

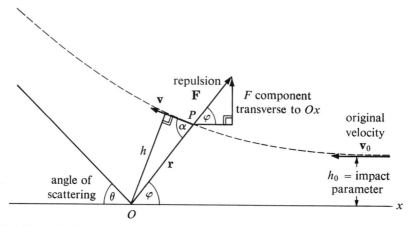

FIGURE 6.3   *The path of a positively charged particle near a massive nucleus placed at 0. The original direction represented by the velocity vector* $\mathbf{v}_0$ *is at a perpendicular distance* h_0 *(the "impact parameter") from the line 0x. At some time the particle is at P, with velocity* $\mathbf{v}$, *and* $\mathbf{r}$ *is the radius vector from 0, also h is the length of the perpendicular drawn from 0 to the tangent at P.*

original kinetic energy, but the final direction is at some angle θ to Ox, where θ is the angle measured in the scattering experiments.

At any point P on the particle's path, close to O, we can draw a radius vector $\mathbf{r}$ from O, making angle φ with the line Ox. At P the particle velocity is $\mathbf{v}$, directed along the tangent, and this vector can be resolved into two components

$$v_x \text{ (parallel to } Ox\text{)} \quad \text{and} \quad v_y \text{ (transverse to } Ox\text{)}.$$

The Coulomb force, directed along the radius $\mathbf{r}$, is of magnitude

$$F = \frac{Z_1 Z_2 e^2}{[4\pi\varepsilon_0]r^2},$$

where $Z_1 e$ and $Z_2 e$ are the charges on the alpha particle and the target nucleus, respectively, and ε_0 is the permittivity of the vacuum.*

The component of $\mathbf{F}$ transverse to Ox, that is, the force deflecting the particle from its original direction, is $F \sin \varphi$, and by Newton's second law of motion (for nonrelativistic particles) this force is equal to mass multiplied by transverse acceleration

$$m \frac{dv_y}{dt} = \frac{Z_1 Z_2 e^2}{[4\pi\varepsilon_0]r^2} \sin \varphi. \qquad [6.3.1]$$

This equation can be put into integrable form by use of the law of equal areas (Kepler's second law of planetary motion). Since the Coulomb force is central toward O, the angular momentum of the particle about O is constant and the radius vector sweeps out equal areas in equal times. In other words, if h is the length of the perpendicular from O to the tangent at P, the product (vh) is constant, or

$$v_0 h_0 = vh.$$

Now if α is the angle between the vectors $\mathbf{r}$ and $\mathbf{v}$ at P

$$h = r \sin \alpha$$

* The term $[4\pi\varepsilon_0]$ will be maintained in brackets throughout this chapter; if this term is omitted, calculations can be carried out conveniently in cgs units.

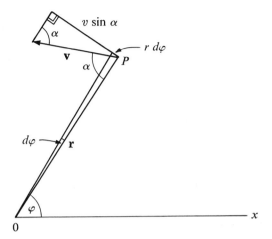

FIGURE 6.4 *The component of the velocity* **v** *transverse to the radius vector* **r** *can be expressed in two ways: either in terms of v and the angle* α, *or as* $r \dfrac{d\varphi}{dt}$, *where r dφ is the transverse arc covered in time dt.*

and the component of velocity transverse to **r** can be written in two ways, as shown in Figure 6.4,

$$v \sin \alpha = r \frac{d\varphi}{dt}.$$

It follows that the product (vh) is expressed in terms of r and φ by the equation

$$v_0 h_0 = vh = r^2 \frac{d\varphi}{dt}$$

and Equation (6.3.1) becomes

$$m \frac{dv_y}{dt} = \frac{Z_1 Z_2 e^2}{[4\pi\varepsilon_0] v_0 h_0} \sin \varphi \frac{d\varphi}{dt}. \qquad [6.3.2]$$

Thus the transverse velocity component (v_y) can be found in terms of φ by direct integration

$$v_y = \frac{Z_1 Z_2 e^2}{[4\pi\varepsilon_0] m v_0 h_0} \int_0^\varphi \sin \varphi \, d\varphi.$$

We find the final angle of deflection (θ) in the same way as the photon-deflection angle in Section 5.2, by calculating the final transverse velocity component ($v_y^{\max}$), as follows:

$$v_y^{\max} = \frac{Z_1 Z_2 e^2}{[4\pi\varepsilon_0] m v_0 h_0} \int_0^{\pi-\theta} \sin \varphi \, d\varphi$$

$$= \frac{Z_1 Z_2 e^2}{[4\pi\varepsilon_0] m v_0 h_0} (1 + \cos \theta).$$

Also, since the final alpha-particle speed is v_0 and its direction is at angle θ to the axis Ox, we have the equality

$$v_y^{\max} = v_0 \sin \theta$$

so that

$$2v_0 \sin \tfrac{1}{2}\theta \cos \tfrac{1}{2}\theta = \frac{Z_1 Z_2 e^2}{[4\pi\varepsilon_0]mv_0 h_0} 2 \cos^2 \tfrac{1}{2}\theta,$$

whence

$$h_0 = \frac{Z_1 Z_2 e^2}{[4\pi\varepsilon_0]mv_0^2} \cot \tfrac{1}{2}\theta. \qquad [6.3.3]$$

This is Rutherford's relation between the impact parameter (h_0) and the scattering angle (θ) for a charged particle scattered in a fixed Coulomb field. The same result is obtained by analyzing the path of the particle, which is a hyperbola with the target nucleus in one focus. In order to express the probability of scattering at various angles, we employ the concept of cross section, introduced in Section 4.1. All particles with impact parameter *less* than a certain value h_0 are scattered through angles *greater* than the corresponding θ given by Equation (6.3.3). Hence the area of a circle of radius h_0 is equal to the integrated cross section for scattering through all angles greater than θ, as may be seen from Figure 6.5. Writing the elementary cross section for scattering between angles θ and $(\theta + d\theta)$ as $d\sigma(\theta)$, we have the relation

$$\int_\theta^\pi d\sigma(\theta) = \pi h_0^2$$

and, by differentiation with respect to θ,

$$d\sigma(\theta) = -2\pi h_0 \, dh_0$$

$$= \pi \left\{ \frac{Z_1 Z_2 e^2}{[4\pi\varepsilon_0]mv_0^2} \right\}^2 \cot \tfrac{1}{2}\theta \operatorname{cosec}^2 \tfrac{1}{2}\theta \, d\theta. \qquad [6.3.4]$$

In the experiments of Geiger and Marsden, a thin metal foil was irradiated with alpha-particles emitted by a strong radon source and the scattered particles were detected by means of a small scintillation screen, which was examined through a microscope (Figure 6.6). The screen could be moved through a wide range of angles θ about the foil and the numbers of scattered particles were recorded. However, the results cannot be expressed directly in terms of the formula of Equation (6.3.4), because the solid angle of collection ($\Delta\Omega$) was constant in the experimental arrangement, whereas the formula gives the cross section for scattering into the entire solid angle between angles θ and $(\theta + d\theta)$. We may calculate the differential cross section for scattering per unit solid angle with the aid of Equation (2.1.8), which expresses the effective solid angle between cones of semiangle θ and $(\theta + d\theta)$ as

$$d\Omega(\theta) = 2\pi \sin \theta \, d\theta \text{ sr.}$$

Dividing this into Equation (6.3.4), we find the differential scattering cross section per unit solid angle

$$\frac{d\sigma}{d\Omega} = \left\{ \frac{Z_1 Z_2 e^2}{[4\pi\varepsilon_0]2mv_0^2} \right\}^2 \operatorname{cosec}^4 \tfrac{1}{2}\theta. \qquad [6.3.5]$$

With a scintillation screen placed perpendicular to the scattered beam at distance R from the foil, the solid angle of collection is

$$\Delta\Omega = \frac{\Delta A}{R^2} \text{ sr,}$$

where ΔA is the screen area, which is assumed to be small.

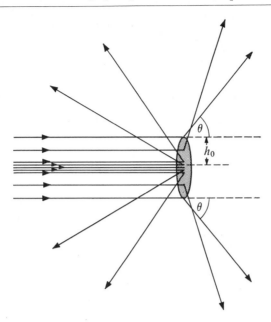

FIGURE 6.5 *The total cross section for Rutherford scattering through angles greater than a certain value θ is the area of a circle with radius equal to the impact parameter h_0 corresponding to that angle.*

The effective scattering cross section for detection on the screen is therefore

$$\Delta\sigma = \frac{\Delta A}{R^2}\left\{\frac{Z_1 Z_2 e^2}{[4\pi\varepsilon_0]2mv_0^2}\right\}^2 \operatorname{cosec}^4 \tfrac{1}{2}\theta. \qquad [6.3.6]$$

Finally, if Q is the total number of particles falling on a thin foil, of thickness t, containing n atoms per unit volume, the number of scattered particles recorded on the screen should be

$$\Delta Q = Qnt\,\Delta\sigma, \qquad [6.3.7]$$

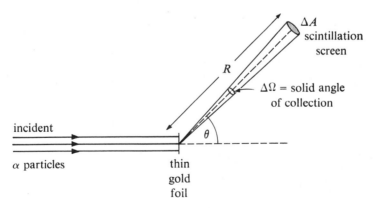

FIGURE 6.6 *Outline of the Geiger-Marsden apparatus for investigation of the scattering of alpha particles at various angles θ by a thin gold foil. The scintillation screen, of area ΔA, was moved to different angles but the solid angle of collection ΔΩ, remained constant and equal to $\dfrac{\Delta A}{R^2}$ steradians.*

as may be seen from Equations (4.9.3) and (4.9.4). The above equations express Rutherford's final result, which is to be tested against the experimental data.

(c) Experimental results

Geiger and Marsden carried out many observations with both gold and silver foils, recording the numbers of alpha particles scattered per minute at different angles. Owing to the radioactive decay of the radon source employed, all data had to be corrected so that they related to the initial activity; however, this feature was also useful because the comparatively rare large-angle scattering could be investigated while the source was still strong and the small-angle scattering at a later date, with the same geometrical arrangements. In a typical run, performed with a silver foil, the actual numbers observed are shown in Table 6.1, together with the statistical errors, calculated as in Section 6.2. The last column

TABLE 6.1

Geiger and Marsden's Experiments: Typical Counting Run, Silver Foil

Scattering angle $\theta°$	Counts recorded ΔQ	Counts per min	Corrected for decay ($\Delta Q'$)	Product $\Delta Q' \sin^4 \frac{1}{2}\theta$
150	95 ± 10	4.75	6.95	6.0 ± 0.6
135	115 ± 11	5.7	8.35	6.1 ± 0.6
120	130 ± 12	6.5	9.5	5.3 ± 0.5
105	200 ± 14	10.0	14.6	5.8 ± 0.4
75	570 ± 24	28.5	41.9	5.8 ± 0.3
60	1380 ± 37	69.0	101	6.3 ± 0.2
			(Weighted mean value)	6.0 ± 0.1

shows the values of the product $\Delta Q \sin^4 \frac{1}{2}\theta$, which should be constant according to the Rutherford expression. It is evident that there is no significant departure of the individual data from the mean value.

A summary of Geiger and Marsden's data for a gold foil, covering the widest range of angles investigated in two separate experiments, is shown in Table 6.2. Here there are somewhat wider fluctuations in the product $\Delta Q \sin^4 \frac{1}{2}\theta$ but, in view of the enormous range in counting rates involved, the agreement between theory and experiment may be considered excellent. The results indicate that the Coulomb law of force is obeyed by alpha particles scattered by gold nuclei between angles of a few degrees and angles near 180°, where a head-on collision occurs. The closest distance of approach (d) in a head-on collision is estimated by equating the original kinetic energy of the particle to the electrostatic potential energy at distance d

$$\tfrac{1}{2}mv_0^2 = \frac{Z_1 Z_2 e^2}{[4\pi\varepsilon_0]\, d}. \qquad [6.3.8]$$

Inserting the numerical values

$$Z_1 = 2 \text{ for He} \qquad Z_2 = 79 \text{ for Au}$$

Kinetic energy: $\tfrac{1}{2}mv_0^2 = 5 \text{ MeV} = 8.0 \times 10^{-13} \text{ J}$

we find that $d = 4.5 \times 10^{-14}$ m approximately.

This distance is much smaller than the estimated size of the gold atom, as found, for example, by x-ray analysis of the metal. It appears that the Coulomb law holds for alpha

TABLE 6.2
Geiger and Marsden's Experiments: Collected Data for a Gold Foil

Scattering angle $\theta°$	Counts per min corrected $\Delta Q'$	Product $\Delta Q' \sin^4 \frac{1}{2}\theta$
150	33.1	28.8
135	43.0	31.2
120	51.9	29.0
105	69.5	27.5
75	211	29.1
60	477	29.8
45	1435	30.8
37.5	3300	35.3
30	7800	35.0
22.5	27300	39.6
15	132000	38.4
Small angles:		
30	3.1	0.014
22.5	8.4	0.012
15	48.2	0.014
10	200	0.0115
7.5	607	0.011
5	3320	0.012

particles traveling inside the atomic volume. It follows that the positively charged nucleus of the atom is very small and that the extranuclear electrons have little effect on the alpha-particle trajectories.

Other aspects of the Rutherford scattering formula were tested experimentally. The incident alpha particles were slowed down by being passed through thin sheets of mica and the results of scattering experiments with these particles showed that the amount of back-scattering is inversely proportional to the fourth power of the speed v_0. Some attempt was made in 1913 to relate the scattering cross section to the nuclear charge of the target $(Z_2 e)$, but at that time the atomic number Z had not been identified with the number of elementary charges of the nucleus. In due course Moseley's work on x-ray spectra (Section 4.8) and the Bohr theory of the atom showed that the nuclear charge must indeed be Ze and this deduction was checked independently by Chadwick in 1920. Alpha-particle scattering by the elements copper, silver, and platinum was studied in detail, with the result that the scattering was found to be proportional to the quantity Z_2^2. Later it was found that at very close distances of approach, of the order of 10^{-14} m, the Rutherford formula is not obeyed precisely by alpha particles scattered by light elements. Some modification of the Coulomb law of interaction is therefore indicated; this is to be expected if there are specifically nuclear forces which act on the alpha particle at very short distances from the target nucleus.

6.4 The Elementary Bohr Theory of the Atom

The great achievement of the Rutherford group in establishing the existence of a small positively charged nucleus in each atom cannot be overestimated. The immediate problem for atomic theory lay in discovering the correct prescription of the possible electron orbits about the nucleus. In 1912 Nicholson showed that the angular momentum of a "planetary" electron should change by a definite amount whenever it emitted or absorbed radiant energy. The quantum law of spectroscopy [Equation (4.4.1)] was known to be accurate in several examples, including the infrared spectra of molecules. The combination of these ideas enabled Niels Bohr to propound the first partially successful theory of atomic structure in 1913.

(a) The Bohr postulates

In a series of papers between 1913 and 1915 Bohr outlined a semiclassical theory of orbital electrons which accounted for the spectrum of the hydrogen atom and certain other phenomena in atomic physics. Bohr's arguments were by no means straightforward, but in 1915 he reduced the basic assumptions of his theory to a few postulates, which may be restated as follows:

(i) each electron in an atom revolves about the nucleus in a fixed orbit satisfying the condition that the angular momentum is an integral multiple of the quantum unit $\hbar$;

(ii) an electron does not radiate while occupying one of the quantized orbits, but light is emitted or absorbed when an electron changes from one orbit to another, the angular frequency of the radiation (ω_{mn}) being given by Equation (4.4.1)

$$\hbar\omega_{mn} = W_m - W_n.$$

Here W_m and W_n are interpreted as the net energies of the orbital electrons, although, strictly speaking, each W value refers to the total energy of the atomic system (nucleus plus electrons). However, Bohr's theory is usually applied to single-electron systems, so the calculation of W depends chiefly on the determination of individual electron energies.

It is noteworthy that Bohr made no attempt to describe the process whereby electrons are assumed to change from one orbit to another. Moreover, the basic postulate of fixed orbits for electrons is contrary to the classical electromagnetic theory, since any electron which is accelerated should radiate energy away, and the continual loss of energy would cause the electron to fall into the nucleus. The theory remains classical, nonetheless, in the sense that details of the electron motions are worked out mechanically, in close analogy with the system of planets revolving about the Sun.

(b) The single-electron case

If Bohr's basic postulates are accepted, the calculation of orbit characteristics is straightforward for a single electron (charge $-e$, mass m) in a circular orbit. The angular momentum of the electron about the central nucleus is

$$mvr = n\hbar, \qquad [6.4.1]$$

where v is the orbital speed, r is the orbital radius, and n is a positive integer.

In a single-electron atom we can ignore all interactions except the Coulomb force between the electron and the nucleus (of charge $+Ze$), which is assumed to be so massive compared with the electron that its motion about their common center of mass is negligible. The centripetal force on the electron is

$$\frac{mv^2}{r} = \frac{Ze^2}{[4\pi\varepsilon_0]r^2}, \qquad [6.4.2]$$

whence

$$mv^2r = \frac{Ze^2}{[4\pi\varepsilon_0]}.$$

Elimination of the speed v from Equations (6.4.1) and (6.4.2) yields the radius immediately

$$r = \frac{n^2 \hbar^2 [4\pi\varepsilon_0]}{Ze^2 m}.$$

In the hydrogen atom ($Z = 1$) the first orbit ($n = 1$) has a radius

$$r_1 = 5 \times 10^{-11} \text{ m approximately},$$

which is a realistic answer. Moreover, the speed v can be derived from Equations (6.4.1) and (6.4.2) in the form

$$v = \frac{Ze^2}{[4\pi\varepsilon_0]n\hbar}$$

which has a value of about 2.2×10^6 m/sec for the first hydrogen orbit. Higher orbits evidently possess lower electron speeds, so we are justified in employing nonrelativistic expressions for energy and momentum, provided that the atomic number Z is not too great. However, the innermost electrons in heavy atoms possess speeds in the relativistic region.

The energy of the single electron is then found by summing the kinetic and potential energies, the sum being negative for any bound electron and expressed as W_n for the nth orbit. On this energy scale, the zero corresponds to the case of a slow electron at an infinite distance from the nucleus and the negative W values are often referred to as *binding energies* of the electron; they are evidently identical with the ionization potentials (in energy units) of Section 4.4. We find the net energy in the nth orbit to be

$$W_n = \tfrac{1}{2}mv^2 - \frac{Ze^2}{[4\pi\varepsilon_0]r}$$

$$= \tfrac{1}{2}mv^2 - mv^2$$

$$= -\tfrac{1}{2}mv^2,$$

that is,

$$W_n = -\frac{\tfrac{1}{2}mZ^2e^4}{[4\pi\varepsilon_0]^2 n^2 \hbar^2}. \qquad [6.4.3]$$

This result can be checked against the experimental data by calculating the first ionization potential of atomic hydrogen, that is, the value of W_1 for $Z = 1$, which turns out to be -13.6 eV, in agreement with experiment (Figure 4.7). The energies of the hydrogen states are given generally as

$$W_n = -\frac{13.6}{n^2} \text{ eV}$$

and the first excitation potential is found by calculating the energy required to raise the atom from its ground state ($n = 1$) to the first excited state ($n = 2$); we obtain

$$13.6(1 - \tfrac{1}{4}) = 10.2 \text{ eV}.$$

This quantum energy corresponds to a wavelength of 1200 Å, in the ultraviolet region. No spectral lines of hydrogen in this area were known in 1913, but in 1914 Lyman discovered a series of lines which represent transitions from various excited states to the ground state of hydrogen.

A precise test of the theory is obtained by comparing the wavelengths of observed spectral lines with the theoretical values. According to the quantum condition of Equation (4.4.1), the angular frequency of any line emitted or absorbed when the electron changes from the nth to the mth orbit is given by the expression

$$\hbar\omega_{mn} = W_m - W_n = \frac{mZ^2e^4}{2\hbar^2[4\pi\varepsilon_0]^2}\,(1/n^2 - 1/m^2). \qquad [6.4.4]$$

The corresponding *wavenumber* (reciprocal wavelength) is

$$1/\lambda_{mn} = \frac{mZ^2e^4}{4\pi c\hbar^3[4\pi\varepsilon_0]^2}\,(1/n^2 - 1/m^2), \qquad [6.4.5]$$

which is similar to Rydberg's relation [Equation (4.4.3)]. Various series of spectral lines are obtained by taking the quantum number n to be 1, 2, 3, . . . , and so forth, in turn, with the m values equal to $(n+1)$, $(n+2)$, . . . , and so forth, for each value of n. The different hydrogen series are distinguished by the names of their discoverers as follows:

$n = 1, m = 2, 3, 4, \ldots$ Lyman (ultraviolet)

$n = 2, m = 3, 4, 5, \ldots$ Balmer (visible)

$n = 3, m = 4, 5, 6, \ldots$ Paschen (infrared)

$n = 4, m = 5, 6, 7, \ldots$ Brackett (infrared).

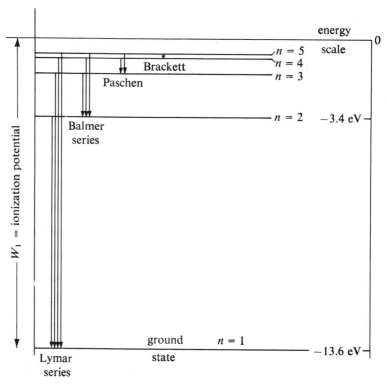

FIGURE 6.7 *The energy levels of the hydrogen atom as determined by experiment and the Bohr theory. Different series of spectral lines are obtained as the atom changes from various higher levels to different lower levels, represented by n = 1 for the Lyman series, n = 2 for the Balmer series, and so on.*

The entire scheme is shown on an energy-level diagram in Figure 6.7; all the predicted lines are observed and the wavelengths agree with the theory to within 1%.

(c) Refinements of the theory

The simple Bohr theory requires several refinements before its results can be fully tested against the highly accurate spectroscopic data. In the first place, we have assumed the nucleus to be so massive that it does not move, but in fact it should revolve around the center of mass with a small kinetic energy of its own. It turns out that in calculating the total energy of the system the electron mass m should be replaced by the *reduced mass* of the electron-nucleus system, which is

$$\mu = \frac{Mm}{M + m}, \qquad [6.4.6]$$

where M is the nuclear mass.

Substitution of μ for m in Equation (6.4.5) causes a correction of the order of 1 part in 1840 for hydrogen of mass number 1, and this difference is quite detectable in wavelength measurements. We can express Equation (6.4.5) for any mass number in terms of a *Rydberg constant* R_M as follows:

$$1/\lambda_{mn} = R_M(1/n^2 - 1/m^2),$$

where

$$R_M = R_\infty \frac{M}{M + m}$$

and R_∞ (the Rydberg constant for infinite nuclear mass) is given correctly by the Bohr theory

$$R_\infty = \frac{mZ^2e^4}{4\pi c\hbar^3[4\pi\varepsilon_0]^2}.$$

With the inclusion of the nuclear-mass correction, the theory is competent to account for all the mean wavelengths of atomic hydrogen lines, but the *fine structure* of the spectral lines remains unexplained. Bohr considered the possibility of the electron revolving in elliptical orbits, and quantum rules for this situation were devised by Sommerfeld. In the non-relativistic approximation, elliptical orbits have the same total energy as circular orbits of the same quantum number n—the levels are said to be "degenerate," with more than one type of motion having the same total energy. This degeneracy is removed when the electrons are treated as relativistic particles, as was shown by Sommerfeld, who was able to explain the fine structure of the spectral lines of hydrogen in this way. The *hyperfine* structure of the hydrogen ground state, mentioned in Section 4.4, has to be explained as a result of the very small magnetic interaction between the electron and the nucleus; this type of interaction is often important in determining the structure of spectral lines emitted by heavy atoms.

The nuclear-mass correction in hydrogen leads to detectable differences in wavelength between the spectral lines of "light" hydrogen (of mass number 1) and *deuterium* or "heavy" hydrogen (of mass number 2). This fact resulted in the discovery of deuterium by Urey, Brickwedde, and Murphy in 1932. These workers used the spectroscopic method to detect the presence of "heavy water," D_2O, in water extracted from electrolytic tanks. Since the separation of line wavelengths is of the order of 1 part in 4000, high-resolution techniques were necessary to distinguish the faint deuterium lines close to the much stronger lines of light hydrogen.

6.5 Extensions of the Bohr Theory

(a) Complex atoms

The original theory of Bohr was successful in accounting for the energy levels of hydrogen, deuterium, and certain systems containing a single electron, such as the ions He(+) and Li(++). However, no progress was made with the details of electron motions in other atoms, because the problem of dealing with more than one electron in the field of the nucleus could not be solved exactly. The general form of Rydberg's relation [Equation (4.4.3)] was better understood, but there was no explanation for the existence of prominent doublets in the spectra of alkali metals such as sodium and potassium. The theory provided no real guidance toward solving the problem of predicting the *strengths* of spectral lines; rules were formulated concerning those atomic transitions which are "forbidden" or strongly inhibited, but no explanation for these rules was forthcoming.

On the other hand, there is no doubt that the limited success of the Bohr theory gave great stimulus to research and provided a possible basis for discussing many atomic phenomena. In particular, it supplied a description of the main features of x-ray line spectra, mentioned in Section 4.8; we obtain complete agreement with the Bohr concept of electron orbits if we identify successive quantum numbers $n = 1, 2, 3, \ldots$, and so forth, with the successive $k, l, m, \ldots$ shells of Figure 4.22. Normally, all the inner shells of a heavy atom are filled with electrons and x-ray line emission occurs only when an inner shell has been ionized, the "hole" being filled with an electron from a higher shell. Thus the transitions of Figure 4.22 correspond to changes of single electrons from orbit to orbit. In general, the energy changes are difficult to calculate because of the complex interactions between electrons in the various shells. However, the K series of x-ray lines is caused by transitions to the innermost orbit ($n = 1$), where the nuclear field is dominant, and the Bohr theory can be applied approximately to this series.

Neglecting the subshell structure which is shown in Figure 4.22, we may consider the emission of a $K\alpha$ line by the atom as being due to an electron falling from the $n = 2$ shell to the $n = 1$ shell. Initially the inner shell has one electron missing and we may think of the "hole" as moving in the field of the nucleus. Such a hole acts like a particle of the same mass as the missing particle, but of opposite charge, since in an electric field the hole moves in the opposite direction to the particles themselves. Thus the $K\alpha$ transition corresponds to the motion of a hole from the inner $n = 1$ shell to the $n = 2$ shell. The energy released in the process is simply the difference in hole energies, which are the same as single-particle values, and we have, for $K\alpha$ lines,

$$\hbar\omega = W_2 - W_1$$

with

$$W_1 = -\frac{mZ'^2e^4}{2\hbar^2[4\pi\varepsilon_0]^2}\,(1/1^2)$$

and

$$W_2 = -\frac{mZ''^2e^4}{2\hbar^2[4\pi\varepsilon_0]^2}\,(1/2^2),$$

where Z' and Z'' are the nuclear charge numbers effective in the two different shells.

In the $n = 1$ (k) shell, the effective nuclear charge number Z' should be very nearly equal to the full charge number Z; but in the $n = 2$ (l) shell the nuclear charge is screened to some extent by the electrons of the inner shell. Examination of the periodic table shows that the first electron shell is full at $Z = 2$ (He), so it presumably contains two electrons and Z'' should be less than Z by about 2. Averaging the nuclear charge numbers in the initial and final shells, we can write an approximate expression for the angular frequency of the $K\alpha$ line

$$\omega = \frac{me^4}{2\hbar^3[4\pi\varepsilon_0]^2}(Z - a)^2(1/1^2 - 1/2^2), \qquad [6.5.1]$$

where a is a constant of the order of one unit.

This is precisely Moseley's law for the variation of frequency with atomic number [Equation (4.8.1)], with the constant of proportionality given by the Bohr theory.* It will be appreciated that the $K\beta$ lines, which are due to electron transitions from the $n = 3$ (m) shell to the $n = 1$ (k) shell, do not have the same value of the "screening parameter" a as the $K\alpha$ lines; also the higher x-ray lines such as those in the L and M series do not necessarily obey the simple relations outlined here.

(b) Orbital magnetic moments

A result of the Bohr theory which gives some insight into the behavior of quantum systems is the quantization of the *magnetic moment* of an electron orbit consequent upon the quantization of angular momentum [Equation (6.4.1)]. The magnetic moment of the current loop formed by a circular electron orbit is proportional to the angular momentum, as may be seen from the relation

$$\text{Magnetic moment} = \text{Current} \times \text{Area}$$

$$= \frac{ev}{2\pi r} \times \pi r^2$$

$$= \frac{evr}{2},$$

where v is the speed of the electron at radius r.

Now, by the Bohr postulate,

$$mvr = n\hbar$$

so that, for an orbit with quantum number n, the magnetic moment is

$$\mu_n = n\frac{e\hbar}{2m}. \qquad [6.5.2]$$

Thus orbital moments should be integral multiples of a basic unit, called the *Bohr magneton*, with the value

$$\mu_B = \frac{e\hbar}{2m} = 9.27 \times 10^{-24} \text{ Jm}^2/\text{weber}.$$

It might be expected that this result should have direct applications in the theory of paramagnetism, which is due to atoms and ions possessing permanent magnetic moments of the order of a few Bohr magnetons. Actually experimental data do not agree, in general, with the predictions of the Bohr theory. Nevertheless, we can use the magneton concept to obtain a valuable picture of the "normal" Zeeman effect, which was considered in this way by Debye and Sommerfeld in 1916. The magnetic moment of the electron orbit may

* Note that relativistic corrections become important in the Moseley relation when Z exceeds about 50.

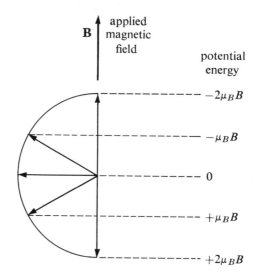

FIGURE 6.8 *Schematic diagram representing the "spatial quantization" of a magnetic moment vector μ in the Bohr theory. If the magnitude of the moment is 2 Bohr magnetons, the vector can take up only 5 possible orientations relative to the applied field* **B**, *namely, those in which the potential energy is quantized in units of $\mu_B B$.*

be represented by an axial vector μ and its potential energy (U) in an external magnetic field **B** is given by the classical expression

$$U = -\mu \mathbf{B}.$$

If the vector μ can take up *any* orientation relative to the applied field **B**, a continuous range of U values is obtained. In quantum theory, on the other hand, the quantization of both energy and magnetic moment leads to the concept of *spatial quantization*, according to which the vector μ can adopt only certain angles relative to the field. These angles are fixed by the condition that the component of the magnetic moment along the field direction must be quantized in accordance with the rule

$$\mu_z = m_n \mu_B, \qquad\qquad [6.5.3]$$

where μ_z is the component parallel to the field, which is assumed to act along the z axis and m_n is a "magnetic" quantum number which can take only the values

$$n, (n - 1), \ldots, 1, 0, -1, \ldots, (-n).$$

The situation for an orbit with $n = 2$ is shown in Figure 6.8 but, in view of later developments of the theory, the diagram must be regarded as purely schematic. It serves as a model for calculating the energy levels of the electron in an applied magnetic field, since the potential energy of interaction should be given by the expression

$$U = -\mu \mathbf{B} = -m_n \mu_B B. \qquad\qquad [6.5.4]$$

This energy is additional to the main energy of the orbital electron in the Coulomb field of the nucleus and it has the effect of splitting each principal energy level into a series of equally spaced substates, corresponding to the different possible values of m_n. The number of substates is therefore $(2n + 1)$, according to the rules of spatial quantization.

If, now, an electron changes from one orbit to another while the atom is in a magnetic field B, there may be, in addition to the large energy change due to a change in the principal quantum number n, a small energy change due to alteration in the value of m_n. If, for example, m_n changes by 1 during the transition, the magnetic energy change is

$$\Delta U = \pm \mu_B B \quad \text{(for } \Delta m_n = \mp 1\text{)}.$$

In the absence of a magnetic field, the energy of the quantum emitted or absorbed is written $\hbar \omega_0$, so with the field applied the quantum energy should be

$$\hbar \omega = \hbar \omega_0 \pm \mu_B B.$$

Substitution of $\dfrac{e\hbar}{2m}$ for the symbol μ_B then yields the angular frequency

$$\omega = \omega_0 \pm \frac{eB}{2m} \qquad \text{for} \qquad \Delta m_n = \mp 1.$$

If there is no change in the magnetic quantum number m_n, there is no change in frequency, so in addition to the doublet splitting of the spectral lines an undeviated line may be present.

These results are identical with those obtained in Section 4.2 from the classical theory of Larmor and Lorentz and they agree with observations made on elements like neon and mercury. However, the Bohr theory cannot account for the "anomalous" Zeeman effect exhibited, for example, by the spectrum of sodium. Moreover, it is evident that the "normal" Zeeman doublet is explained only if we impose the arbitrary rule $\Delta m_n = \pm 1$. If the magnetic quantum number could change by two or more units, extra lines would be observed besides the Zeeman doublets and triplets. In fact many elements do show extra lines but these lines do not have the characteristic Larmor spacing $\Delta \omega = \dfrac{eB}{2m}$ predicted by the theory.

(c) The Stern–Gerlach experiment

A remarkable test of the idea of spatial quantization was provided in a classic experiment performed by Stern and Gerlach in 1921. A beam of neutral atoms is passed through an evacuated region between two specially designed magnetic pole faces which set up a strongly inhomogeneous field transverse to the beam. The field exerts a deflecting force on the magnetic moments of the moving atoms, a force which is proportional to the field gradient $\dfrac{\partial B}{\partial z}$, where the z axis is taken to be transverse to the beam (Figure 6.9). This follows from the relation

$$F_z = -\frac{\partial U}{\partial z} = -\frac{\partial}{\partial z}(-\mu_z B)$$

$$= \mu_z \frac{\partial B}{\partial z}.$$

Now, according to classical physics, the magnetic moment vectors of the atoms can be oriented in any way relative to the field; therefore there should be a continuous range of deflections on either side of the original beam direction. The effect of spatial quantization is entirely different, in that the vectors can adopt only certain angles of orientation and the components μ_z must all be multiples of the Bohr magneton. According to the quantum theory, therefore, the beam should be split into $(2n + 1)$ different beams, each one corresponding to a certain value of the magnetic quantum number m_n. In practice each beam

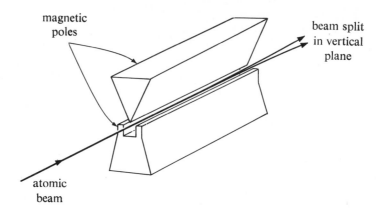

FIGURE 6.9   *Outline of the Stern-Gerlach apparatus, in which a beam of neutral silver atoms passes through a region between specially shaped magnetic poles. These set up a highly inhomogeneous field which exerts a transverse force on the atoms, causing deflection in the vertical plane.*

is broadened to some extent after deflection because of the Maxwellian distribution of atom speeds in the original beam, but if splitting can be clearly demonstrated the quantum number *n* follows directly.

Stern and Gerlach found that a beam of silver atoms does divide when it is passed through an inhomogeneous magnetic field; *two* separate beams are produced and this effect must be interpreted in terms of spatial quantization. At the same time, doubt is cast on the validity of the Bohr system of quantum numbers, since the value of *n* for silver atoms is apparently $\frac{1}{2}$. This and other experimental results showed that, while the principal quantum number *n* undoubtedly fixes the energy levels in hydrogenlike atoms and defines the main electron shells correctly, it does *not* determine the angular momentum of individual electrons. Moreover, the Stern–Gerlach experiment indicates the existence of electron variables which can take two values only. In due course this result led to the recognition of *electron spin* as an extra angular-momentum variable, with an associated magnetic moment.

(d) Gyromagnetic effects

A further test of the Bohr magneton concept is supplied by the *gyromagnetic effect*, detected by Einstein and de Haas in 1915. If the angular momentum of orbital electrons fixes the magnetic moment per atom in an element like iron, a change in the state of magnetization in a specimen of iron should result in a rotational impulse being given to the specimen. If the iron is suitably suspended inside a solenoid which carries the magnetizing current, a slight rotational recoil is detectable when the current is switched on. The experimental results may be expressed in terms of the ratio

$$\frac{\Delta M}{\Delta G} = \frac{\text{Magnetic moment acquired}}{\text{Angular momentum of recoil}}.$$

For *N* orbital electrons in the specimen, with their magnetic moments aligned by the magnetizing field, we should have

$$\Delta M = Nn\,\frac{e\hbar}{2m} \qquad \text{[from Equation (6.5.2)],}$$

where *n* is the Bohr quantum number.

At the same time, the change in angular momentum is

$$\Delta G = Nn\hbar$$

so that

$$\frac{\Delta M}{\Delta G} = \frac{e}{2m},$$

according to the Bohr theory of orbital electrons.

More generally, we write the ratio as

$$\frac{\Delta M}{\Delta G} = g\frac{e}{2m},$$ [6.5.5]

where the *gyromagnetic factor* (*g*) should be exactly one for orbital electrons. Measurements carried out with a wide range of ferromagnetic materials have yielded values of *g* very close to two. The gyromagnetic effect has also been detected in paramagnetic materials by Sucksmith and others; various *g* values are found, but there is no agreement between experiment and the simple theory of orbiting electrons.

An effect inverse to the gyromagnetic effect was discovered by Barnett in 1914. If a cylindrical specimen of some ferromagnetic material is rotated rapidly about its own axis, it exhibits a magnetic moment, due presumably to the extra angular momentum imparted to the atomic electrons by the rotation. The effect can be used to yield an estimate of the *g* factor and once more values close to two are obtained for metals like iron. These results, together with those from the Einstein–de Haas effect, suggest that the basic ideas of the electron theory are sound, but no successful theory of magnetism can be based on orbital motions alone; it is necessary to take into account the intrinsic *spin* momentum of the electron in order to explain these results and those of Stern and Gerlach.

FOR FURTHER READING

Early history of radioactivity:

A. ROMER, *The Restless Atom* (Science Study Series, Doubleday and Co., New York, 1960).

A. S. EVE, *Rutherford* (Cambridge University Press, New York, 1939).

Experiments on radioactivity:

E. RUTHERFORD, J. CHADWICK, and C. D. ELLIS, *Radiations from Radioactive Substances* (Cambridge University Press, New York, 1930).

Geological dating:

P. M. HURLEY, *How Old is the Earth?* (Science Study Series, Doubleday and Co., New York, 1959).

The Bohr theory:

N. BOHR, *The Theory of Spectra and Atomic Constitution* (Cambridge University Press, New York, 1924) 2nd ed.

PROBLEMS FOR CHAPTER 6

DATA REQUIRED:

No. of molecules per kilomole: $N^* = 6.0 \times 10^{26}$

Electron rest-mass energy: $m_0c^2 = 0.51$ MeV

Electron specific charge: $e/m_0 = 1.76 \times 10^{11}$ C/kg

Proton specific charge: $e/M_0 = 9.6 \times 10^7$ C/kg

Ratio of proton to electron mass: $M_0/m_0 = 1836$

Planck's constant: $h = 6.6 \times 10^{-34}$ J sec

$$\hbar = 1.05 \times 10^{-34} \text{ J sec}$$

6.1. A Geiger counter placed close to a beta-ray source recorded the following counting rates C (corrected for background effects) when different thicknesses (t) of copper foil were inserted between the source and the counter:

t (mm)	0	0.125	0.25	0.375	0.50	0.625	0.75	1.0	1.25	1.5
C	35	20	12	7.8	5.4	3.5	2.5	1.8	1.8	1.7

(in thousands of counts per min)

Plot a graph of ln C against the thickness to show that:

(i) an appreciable number of gamma rays is probably emitted from the source;

(ii) when the gamma-ray background is subtracted from the data, the absorption of beta-rays in copper is roughly exponential;

(iii) hence calculate an effective absorption coefficient [μ in Equation (4.9.3)] for the beta rays in copper.

6.2 Alpha particles from a radioactive source pass through an evacuated region in which they traverse a distance of 0.05 m in a magnetic field B applied perpendicular to the beam, immediately followed by a distance of 0.2 m between parallel plates. With an electrostatic field of 8×10^4 V/m applied between the plates and *no* magnetic field, a deflection of 0.35 mm was recorded where the particles left the plates. This deflection was exactly cancelled by a field $B = 10^{-2}$ weber/m²; calculate the speed of the alpha particles and their specific charge. (Assume that the angular deflection in the magnetic field is small; a non-relativistic treatment is sufficiently accurate).

6.3 Beta particles of kinetic energy 0.6 MeV are ejected *in vacuo* from a source into a velocity-selector system which consists of two parallel plates between which an electrostatic field of 3×10^5 V/m is maintained and a transverse magnetic field B is superposed (Section 3.3.e). The undeviated rays pass through a slit and carry on in the same magnetic field B until they strike a screen placed perpendicular to their original direction at 0.5 m from the edge of the plates. Calculate the deflection of the beam due to field B, as measured on the screen.

6.4(a) The nuclide U²³³ has a half-life of 1.6×10^5 years. Calculate its decay constant (λ) and hence find the mean number of disintegrations per second in a pure sample of U²³³ with mass 1 mg.

(b) A possible sequence of emitted particles in the $(4n + 1)$ radioactive series starting at U²³³ is as follows: $\alpha\alpha\beta\alpha\alpha\alpha\beta\alpha\beta$. Identify each nuclide in the sequence.

6.5 Assume that the intrinsic probability of a particle emitted from a source reaching a Geiger counter is p. Then the chances of recording N particles in the counter from a total of Y particles emitted are given by the *binomial* frequency distribution

$$P(N) = \binom{Y}{N} p^N (1 - p)^{Y-N},$$

where

$$\binom{Y}{N} = \frac{Y!}{N!\,(Y - N)!}.$$

Set up a moment-generating function of the type shown in Equation (6.2.2) and calculate the mean and variance in the values of N.

6.6 Observations on the mean activity (a) of a certain radioactive sample at various times (t) yielded the data:

t (sec)	0	10	20	30	60	100	200
a (counts/sec)	5000	410	35	13	7.5	5.0	1.8

Plot a semilogarithmic graph to show that there are two activities present; estimate the decay constant of each.

6.7 Assuming that the isotopes of uranium were equally abundant when the Earth was formed, estimate the age of the Earth with the aid of the following information:

$$\text{Half-life of } U^{238} = 4.5 \times 10^9 \text{ yr}$$

$$\text{Half-life of } U^{235} = 7.1 \times 10^8 \text{ yr}$$

Present abundance ratio of U^{238} to $U^{235} = 140:1$.

6.8 Suppose that a radioactive body A decays at a mean rate λ_1 per atom per second to give a body B, which in turn decays at a mean rate λ_2 per atom per second to give C, which is stable. Prove that, if at time $t = 0$,

$$N_A = \text{number of } A \text{ atoms present} = N_0,$$

$$N_B = \text{number of } B \text{ atoms present} = 0,$$

$$N_C = \text{number of } C \text{ atoms present} = 0,$$

then at any subsequent time t the numbers of B and C atoms will be given by the relations

$$N_B = \frac{\lambda_1 N_0}{(\lambda_2 - \lambda_1)} \left[\exp(-\lambda_1 t) - \exp(-\lambda_2 t) \right]$$

$$N_C = \frac{N_0}{(\lambda_2 - \lambda_1)} \{ \lambda_2 [1 - \exp(-\lambda_1 t)] - \lambda_1 [1 - \exp(-\lambda_2 t)] \}.$$

6.9(a) Set up the problem of the motion of a charged particle in a fixed Coulomb field of force as a differential equation in (r, φ) coordinates, by use of the angular-momentum condition

$$v_0 h_0 = vh = r^2 \frac{d\varphi}{dt}$$

and the conservation-of-energy relation

$$\text{Total energy:} \quad E = \tfrac{1}{2} m v_0^2 = U(r) + \tfrac{1}{2} m \left[\left(\frac{dr}{dt} \right)^2 + r^2 \left(\frac{d\varphi}{dt} \right)^2 \right],$$

where $U(r)$ stands for the potential energy of the charged particle at distance r from the center of force.

(b) Hence show that the scattering angle θ, related to the final value (φ_m) of φ by $\theta = \pi - 2\varphi_m$, is determined by the equation

$$\theta = \pi - 2 \int \frac{dr}{\left[r^4/h_0^2 - r^2 - \dfrac{2r^4}{mv_0^2 h_0^2} U(r) \right]^{1/2}}.$$

(c) Use this expression to derive the Rutherford scattering formula for the case $U(r) \propto r^{-1}$.

6.10 Calculate the differential scattering cross section as a function of the scattering angle θ for a charged particle scattered by an *inverse-cube* field of force. Use your result to test Geiger and Marsden's data. Do the experimental data distinguish clearly between the inverse-cube and inverse-square fields of force?

6.11 Protons are accelerated in a cyclotron to a kinetic energy of 10 MeV and are then used to bombard a gold target. Find

(i) the magnetic field B required to keep the protons in an orbit of radius 0.8 m;

(ii) the closest distance of approach by the protons to nuclei of gold ($Z = 79$).

6.12 In an early experiment Geiger and Marsden found the following figures for the number (N) of alpha particles back-scattered at a fixed angle by *thick* foils made of different metals, the atomic numbers of which are given:

N:	62	67	63	34	27	14.5	10.2	3.4
Metal	Pb	Au	Pt	Sn	Ag	Cu	Fe	Al
Z	82	79	78	50	47	29	25	13

Show that, if Rutherford's scattering formula is correct so far as the variation of scattering with Z number is concerned, the penetration of alpha particles through different metals varies with atomic number approximately according to the relation:

$$\text{Thickness of metal penetrated} \propto Z^{-\frac{1}{4}}.$$

6.13 A negative muon of rest-mass 207 times that of the electron is captured by a carbon atom ($Z = 6$, $A = 12$) and may be assumed to revolve in an orbit within the Bohr electron orbits. Calculate the binding energy of the muon in the $n = 1$ state, also the wavelength of radiation emitted when the particle passes from its $n = 2$ orbit to the $n = 1$ orbit.

6.14 The "Pickering" spectral lines emitted by the ions of helium, He($+$), are caused by transitions to the $n = 4$ level from higher levels and the general pattern is similar to that of the Balmer series in hydrogen. Show that *alternate* lines of the Pickering series almost coincide with the Balmer lines. Also calculate the difference in wavelength between the red line of Balmer ($n = 2$, $m = 3$, $\lambda = 6563$ Å) and the corresponding line of the Pickering series, due to the nuclear-mass correction.

6.15 Find the difference in quantum energies between the nth and $(n + 1)$th Bohr orbit in a single-electron atom when n is large. Hence show that the angular frequency of radiation emitted or absorbed when the electron changes from one orbit to the other is equal to the mean angular velocity in the two orbits, as calculated in the Bohr theory. (This is one of the arguments for Bohr's Correspondence principle, according to which classical behavior may be expected as the electron orbits reach very high quantum numbers, equivalent to the condition $h \to 0$.)

6.16 Assuming that the magnetic moment of a paramagnetic material is due to N electron orbits, each with $n = 1$ and intrinsic moment 1 Bohr magneton, also that the probability of different magnetic energies [Equation (6.5.4)] in a field B is given by the Boltzmann rule, calculate the total magnetic moment (M) as a function of the temperature T.

Compare the quantum result with the *classical* expression found by assuming that the magnetic moments can take any orientation in the field, namely, Langevin's result

$$M = N\mu_B[\coth \chi - 1/\chi],$$

where $\chi = \mu_B B/kT$.

6.17 Calculate the rotational impulse given to a cylindrical iron specimen of mass M when it is fully magnetized parallel to the axis. Assume that $g = 2$ and the atomic mass number $A = 55$. Hence show that the maximum observable change in angular velocity ($\Delta\omega$) is obtained by making the cylinder as thin as possible; estimate $\Delta\omega$ for a cylinder of radius 1 mm.

6.18 In a Stern–Gerlach experiment, a beam of silver atoms ($A = 108$) of mean velocity 700 m/sec passes between magnetic poles 0.1 m long, producing a field with the transverse field gradient $\dfrac{dB}{dz} = 2.5 \times 10^3$ weber/m³. Assuming that the deflection of each component of the beam is due to an effective magnetic moment of 1 Bohr magneton per atom, find the net separation of the two components as they emerge from the field region.

❦❦❦❦❦❦❦❦❦❦❦❦❦❦❦❦❦❦❦❦❦❦❦❦❦❦❦❦❦❦❦❦❦❦❦

CHAPTER VII

QUANTUM MECHANICS

Despite the initial success of the Bohr theory, and other developments of the original quantum theory of Planck, it became increasingly evident in the early 1920's that many features of atomic physics cannot be described in semiclassical terms. The discovery and interpretation of the Compton effect in 1923 stressed the photon aspect of radiation but the necessary connection between the wave and corpuscle treatments remained elusive. Shortly after this discovery de Broglie suggested that beams of "particles" should exhibit wave properties, the effective wavelength being inversely proportional to the momentum per particle. This idea was widely accepted, but it was not until 1927 that full experimental confirmation was obtained, by Davisson and Germer and by G. P. Thomson.

The initial development of quantum mechanics stemmed from the problem of calculating the probabilities of transitions between various atomic states. The theory was put in the form of matrix algebra by Heisenberg, Born, and Jordan, whose ideas expressed a new philosophy of physical interpretation. Briefly, quantum mechanics is concerned only with the calculation of observable quantities: detailed mechanical models are regarded as misleading and unnecessary. An alternative approach, explored by Schrödinger in 1926, led to a system of wave mechanics based on de Broglie's hypothesis, and this system admits of more direct interpretation than matrix mechanics. In wave mechanics an atomic state is described by a function Ψ, which is related to the probability of the atom being in such a state. An important consequence of any form of quantum mechanics is the "uncertainty" principle, stated by Heisenberg in 1927, limiting the accuracy with which physical measurements can be carried out. The principle stresses the essentially statistical nature of the new quantum theory, which cannot predict the exact behavior of any atomic system but is confined to the calculation of probabilities, such as the transition probabilities of Heisenberg's matrix mechanics.

While the quantum-mechanical scheme was still being worked out, many difficulties in atomic theory were removed by Uhlenbeck and Goudsmit's hypothesis that the electron possesses intrinsic angular momentum or "spin." The entire periodic classification of the chemical elements could be understood with the aid of the spin variables and Pauli's exclusion principle. The incorporation of electron spin into a fully relativistic theory of particles was achieved in 1928 by Dirac, whose treatment of the electron was particularly significant in that it predicted the existence of an antiparticle, in this case the positron.

Among the many applications of quantum mechanics to systems containing several particles, the most general are the laws governing the statistical behavior of large assemblies. A new form of statistics was discovered in 1924 by Bose and Einstein, who treated all similar particles in an assembly as strictly indistinguishable. The special properties of particles which are indistinguishable and obey Pauli's exclusion principle were expressed in the Fermi-Dirac statistics of 1926. Under suitable conditions, both these forms of quantum statistics can be replaced approximately by the classical Boltzmann scheme, but the quantum theory is essential in dealing with problems such as the behavior of photons in an enclosure and electrons in a metal.

7.1 de Broglie Waves

The Compton effect shows clearly that a photon has linear momentum (p) which is related to the energy (E), the frequency (v), and the wavelength (λ) by the expressions

$$p = \frac{E}{c} = \frac{hv}{c} = \frac{h}{\lambda},$$ [7.1.1]

where c is the velocity of light.

In itself this equation expresses the dual nature of radiation, which exhibits both corpuscular properties linked to the quantity p and wave effects characterized by the quantity λ.

In 1923 de Broglie suggested that the wavelength-momentum relation

$$p\lambda = h$$ [7.1.2]

should apply to all forms of matter and energy, including entities normally considered as particles, for example, electrons and protons. The proper linear momentum of a "particle" is given by Equation (5.6.6)

$$p = mv = \frac{m_0 v}{(1 - v^2/c^2)^{1/2}},$$

where m_0 is the rest-mass of the particle and v is the magnitude of the particle's velocity relative to the measuring apparatus. We can therefore calculate the de Broglie wavelength λ associated with a beam of particles of speed v. For electrons of low kinetic energy (up to 100 eV) λ is a few Ångstroms, similar to the wavelength of x rays, so diffraction effects should be observable when electron beams encounter crystal lattices or other suitable gratings.

(a) Experimental investigations

Experimental verification of the de Broglie relation for electrons was obtained, after lengthy investigations, by Davisson and Germer in 1927. A beam of electrons was directed from an electron "gun" on to a nickel block which contained several large crystals presenting their (111) planes perpendicular to the beam. The electrons scattered at various angles were detected and several strong diffraction maxima were observed, at angles depending on the bombarding energy and the crystal orientation. For example, with a beam of energy 54 eV incident on the (111) plane, a maximum was found at an angle of 50° to the beam in those azimuthal planes which were perpendicular to the rows of nickel atoms on the crystal face (Figure 7.1).

Nickel is known to possess a face-centered cubic lattice with lattice constant $a = 3.52$ Å. A beam perpendicular to the (111) face encounters a close-packed array of atoms similar to any one layer of the structure shown in Figure 4.17. Many of the diffraction maxima observed in electron scattering can be attributed to surface effects, so we have to consider

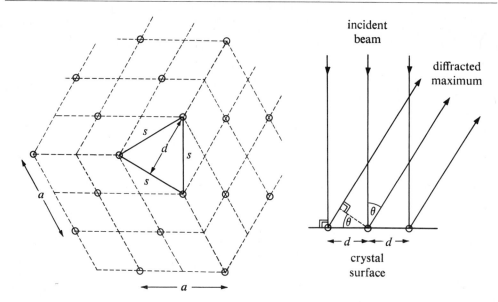

FIGURE 7.1　*Left: View of a face-centered cubic lattice taken perpendicular to the (111) planes, in which the atoms form a close-packed layer with interatomic distance s, the distance between successive rows being d. Right: In Davisson and Germer's experiment a beam of electrons was incident normally on the (111) surface of a nickel crystal and diffracted maxima were observed at angles θ to the incident beam.*

the diffraction of waves at a layer which is equivalent to three sets of line gratings at 120° to each other. In any plane perpendicular to one particular row of atoms, the spacing between successive rows (d) is found to be (from Figure 7.1)

$$d = \frac{\sqrt{3}}{2}\, s,$$

where s is the interatomic spacing.
In a face-centered cubic lattice, the interatomic spacing is

$$s = \frac{a}{\sqrt{2}},$$

hence

$$d = a\sqrt{\tfrac{3}{8}} = 2.15 \,\text{Å in nickel.}$$

The condition for a first-order diffraction maximum to be observed at angle θ to the incident beam is derived also from Figure 7.1,

$$\lambda = d \sin \theta$$

so that the effective wavelength for 54 eV electrons is

$$\lambda = 2.15 \sin 50° = 1.65 \,\text{Å.}$$

For comparison, the de Broglie relation yields

$$\lambda = \frac{h}{p} = \frac{h}{(2mK)^{1/2}},$$

where K is the kinetic energy (for nonrelativistic particles). Substitution of the appropriate figures gives

$$\lambda = 1.67 \text{ Å}.$$

Davisson and Germer obtained satisfactory agreement between theory and experiment with several surface-scattered electron beams in the energy region between 15 eV and 300 eV. In addition, certain diffraction maxima were found which corresponded to scattering from successive layers of atoms in the nickel crystal. It is important to note that the calculated layer separations did *not* agree exactly with the results of x-ray analysis: this effect is attributed to a change in wavelength as the electrons penetrated the metallic lattice. We can correct for this change by introducing an effective refractive index (n_e) for electrons, by the methods of Section 3.3.b. If K is the kinetic energy per particle and the change in potential at the metal surface is $-\Delta V$, we find the relation

$$n_e = \frac{\sin \theta_0}{\sin \theta} = \frac{v}{v_0} = \sqrt{\frac{K + e \, \Delta V}{K}} \qquad [7.1.3]$$

and this is also the ratio of the de Broglie wavelengths outside and inside the metal.

Not only are diffraction effects found with electron beams scattered from crystal surfaces but also with beams transmitted through thin metallic films. In 1927 G. P. Thomson observed that a transmitted beam is attended by a series of concentric diffracted beams which produce rings on a photographic plate. These rings correspond to the various spots which are produced by Laue diffraction (Figure 4.13) and are apparently rotated about the axis of the beam to make rings, an effect due to the polycrystalline nature of the metal film. It was also found that electron diffraction occurs when a beam is scattered from a ruled grating at grazing incidence. In 1930 Estermann and Stern tested the de Broglie relation with beams of neutral hydrogen and helium atoms scattered from the face of a lithium fluoride crystal. More recently, intense beams of slow neutrons have become available from nuclear reactors, and the analysis of materials by neutron diffraction has been developed into a powerful technique capable of revealing details, such as the positions of hydrogen atoms in a lattice, which were previously unknown.

(b) Standing-wave systems

A simple theoretical application of de Broglie's relation shows that it is consistent with the Bohr quantization condition for electron orbits in a hydrogenlike atom. If we assume that an electron wave "occupies" (in some sense) an orbit of radius r, the condition for standing waves to be set up is for the circumference to be an integral multiple of the wavelength (Figure 7.2)

$$2\pi r = n\lambda, \qquad \text{where } n = 1, 2, 3, \ldots,$$

that is,

$$2\pi r = \frac{nh}{mv}$$

or

$$mvr = n\hbar \qquad [\text{Equation (6.4.1)}].$$

However, it is *not* correct in quantum mechanics to regard the Bohr number n as an angular-momentum number. Nor is it possible to develop a mechanical model of electron standing-wave systems in an atom, since, as we have emphasized, the wave aspects of particle motion are to be interpreted statistically. In the diffraction experiments, for example, the interpretation is similar to that of Taylor's experiment with photons (Section 4.6): the wave model yields the *probability* of individual particles arriving at a given point when the beam

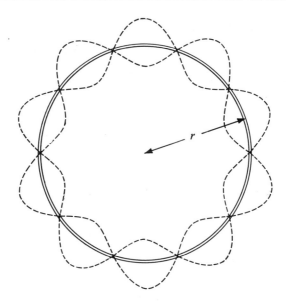

FIGURE 7.2   *Schematic diagram of the way in which de Broglie waves might be arranged to produce standing waves around the circumference of a circle of radius r.*

has traversed the diffraction grating or other scattering material. Accordingly the wave pattern for an electron in an atom has to be determined by a complete analysis of the situation with a particle in a Coulomb field and the results have to be regarded as statistical patterns only.

More generally, the de Broglie hypothesis is highly significant in providing a new approach to the problem of determining the energy levels of an atomic system. The method may be illustrated by the modes of a vibration of a stretched string (Figure 7.3), which are fixed

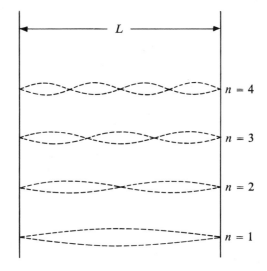

FIGURE 7.3   *Different modes of vibration of a string stretched between fixed ends distance L apart. The number n is the number of antinodes in the length L.*

by the condition that each end must be a node in the standing wave. The distance between successive nodes is always $\frac{1}{2}\lambda$, so, if L is the length of the string, this must be an integral multiple of $\frac{1}{2}\lambda$

$$L = n\frac{\lambda}{2} \quad \text{with } n = 1, 2, 3, \ldots .$$

A similar situation exists in de Broglie waves whenever a particle is confined within a distance L in one dimension. Different "modes of vibration" correspond to different wavelengths, different momenta, and therefore different energies. For the nth "mode," the wavelength is

$$\lambda = \frac{2L}{n}$$

and

$$p = \frac{h}{\lambda} = n\frac{h}{2L}$$

so that, in the nonrelativistic approximation, the kinetic energy K is given by the relation

$$K = \frac{p^2}{2m} = \frac{n^2 h^2}{8mL^2}. \qquad [7.1.4]$$

The energy levels of a particle in such a situation are therefore fixed by the boundary conditions imposed on the de Broglie waves. On the other hand, if the particle were free to move without constraint, the energy would be not quantized but would be continuously variable, as in classical mechanics.

(c) Wave mechanics

In order to put the scheme of wave mechanics into Schrödinger's form, we must generalize the foregoing method by the inclusion of a potential energy function, which is dependent on the position of the particle. In one dimension we may write the potential energy as $U(x)$ and the total energy (E) as the sum of the kinetic and potential terms

$$E = K(p) + U(x)$$

or

$$K(p) = E - U(x).$$

We then write down a second-order differential equation to represent the wave motion in one dimension

$$\frac{\partial^2 \Psi}{\partial x^2} - \frac{1}{u^2}\frac{\partial^2 \Psi}{\partial t^2} = 0, \qquad [7.1.5]$$

where u is the wave velocity (to be distinguished from the particle's proper speed v) and $\Psi(x, t)$ is a wave function varying in position and time. The function Ψ may correspond to traveling waves in some cases or it may describe standing waves in cases where the boundary conditions are suitable. In the latter event, we may separate the x and t variables, writing a solution

$$\Psi(x, t) = \psi(x) \exp(\pm i\omega t), \qquad [7.1.6]$$

where ω is the angular frequency of the wave motion.
The spatial function $\psi(x)$ then obeys the equation

$$\frac{d^2\psi}{dx^2} + \kappa^2\psi = 0 \qquad [7.1.7]$$

with the "wave number" parameter

$$\kappa = \frac{\omega}{u} = \frac{2\pi}{\lambda} = \frac{p}{\hbar}.$$ [7.1.8]

In this way we obtain the time-independent form of Schrödinger's wave equation in one dimension, since the substitution of κ^2 yields a term involving the total energy and the potential energy

$$\frac{d^2\psi}{dx^2} + \frac{2m}{\hbar^2}\,[E - U(x)]\psi = 0.$$ [7.1.9]

Different types of potential energy function $U(x)$ lead to different kinds of solution $\psi(x)$. It is often found that solutions exist in closed form and for each specific solution there is a definite energy value E. Following German usage, we call each energy value an *eigenvalue* of the variable E and the corresponding function $\psi(x)$ is the *eigenfunction* for that particular energy level.

Although this wave-mechanical routine is normally successful in determining energy levels in an atomic system, there remains the question of the significance to be attached to the function $\psi(x)$. Equation (7.1.9) shows that $\psi(x)$ is similar to a sinusoidal function wherever E exceeds the potential energy U, that is, where the particles are free, in the classical sense. However, we may not disregard situations where E is less than U, although here the wave interpretation is no longer valid. In general, a complete solution is achieved only when $\psi(x)$ is finite, regular, and continuous over the entire region from $x = -\infty$ to $x = +\infty$, or, in a three-dimensional problem, over the whole of space. Each complete solution $\psi(x, y, z)$ is a *state function* describing the state of the atomic system; the amplitude of this function is related to the probability of a particle being detected at any chosen point, when the system is in the appropriate state. Born's interpretation of the state function is that the *square* of its modulus at any point

$$|\psi(x, y, z)|^2 \equiv \psi^*(x, y, z)\,\psi(x, y, z)$$ [7.1.10]

is the "probability density" function, that is, the probability per unit volume of the particle being at the point (x, y, z). This principle enables us to impose a condition of normalization for any one particle, since the total probability is unity if we integrate over all space

$$\iiint \psi^*(x, y, z)\,\psi(x, y, z)\,dx\,dy\,dz = 1.$$ [7.1.11]

Born's interpretation serves to emphasize that a particle cannot be precisely located, even when it is confined within a known volume. Where the particle is free in the classical sense, the state function spreads with varying amplitude over the entire accessible volume. The degree of spread depends, in general, on the mass per particle (m) and is greatest for small values of the mass, since the wavelength is inversely proportional to the momentum. One result of this general principle is that electrons cannot be located by experimental methods inside any kind of atom. On the other hand, atoms themselves are much more massive than electrons and can be located with fair precision, for example by x rays in crystal analysis. Macroscopic objects possess very short de Broglie wavelengths so a classical description of the motion of such objects is accurate enough for all ordinary purposes. These considerations emphasize the need for a more careful definition of the limitations which quantum mechanics imposes on the accuracy of physical measurements, since these limitations distinguish the new mechanics most strikingly from classical mechanics.

7.2 Heisenberg's Uncertainty Principle

In 1927 Heisenberg showed that quantum mechanics embodies a very general rule which relates the uncertainty in the position coordinate of a particle to the uncertainty in its momentum, measured in the same direction. In other words, the errors in measurement of position are necessarily correlated with errors in measurement of momentum. A similar "uncertainty" relation exists between the energy of a system and the time during which it is observable in that energy state.

To begin with, we may consider a perfectly uniform de Broglie wave of sinusoidal shape, characterized by a definite wavelength (λ) and extending over the entire range of possible position coordinates (x) in one dimension. Since the wavelength is precisely fixed and de Broglie's relation [Equation (7.1.2)] expresses the momentum (p_x) in terms of wavelength, there can be no uncertainty in the momentum and we can write

$$\Delta p_x = 0.$$

On the other hand, such a wave exhibits no variation in amplitude over the entire range of x, so the probability of locating the particle is essentially the same everywhere, that is, the error (Δx) in position coordinates is effectively infinite. Thus we make the momentum determination sharp at the cost of rendering the position determination completely uncertain.

(a) A wave packet in one dimension

In order to locate a particle with some accuracy, some variation in the amplitude of its de Broglie wave must be introduced, and this can only be done by superimposing waves of different wavelength Thus Δx can be reduced only at the expense of increasing the uncertainty in momentum (Δp_x). For example, assume that two cosine waves of different wavelength are added together, the first being represented by the function

$$f_1(x) = A \cos \kappa x,$$

where

$$\kappa = \frac{2\pi}{\lambda} \quad \text{as in Equation (7.1.8)}$$

and A is the amplitude of the cosine function. The second wave is represented by

$$f_2(x) = A \cos (\kappa + \Delta\kappa)x$$

and the sum of the two functions is (approximately)

$$f_1(x) + f_2(x) = 2A \cos \kappa x \cos (\tfrac{1}{2}\Delta\kappa\, x),$$

provided that $\Delta\kappa$ is small.

The sum of the cosines represents a wave in which the amplitude is reduced to zero at regular intervals along the x axis (Figure 7.4). The distance between successive nodes in such a wave is denoted by Δx, as giving an approximate value for the error in location of the particle, although the model is by no means realistic. To find Δx, we note that the amplitude vanishes on either side of the origin $x = 0$ when the second cosine term in the product vanishes, that is, when

$$\tfrac{1}{2}(\tfrac{1}{2}\Delta\kappa\, \Delta x) = \pm\tfrac{1}{2}\pi$$

thus

$$\Delta x = \frac{2\pi}{\Delta\kappa}.$$

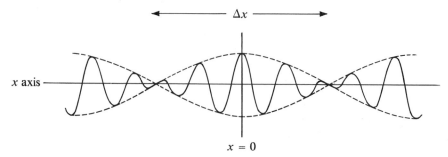

FIGURE 7.4   *Wave pattern obtained by adding together two sinusoidal waves of slightly different wavelength. The amplitude is reduced to zero at regular intervals of Δx along the x axis.*

At the same time, the uncertainty in momentum (Δp_x) is obtained directly from de Broglie's relation

$$\Delta p_x = \frac{h}{2\pi} \Delta \kappa = \hbar \, \Delta \kappa$$

so that the product $\Delta x \Delta p_x$ becomes, very approximately,

$$\Delta x \Delta p_x \approx h. \tag{7.2.1}$$

The foregoing treatment is not satisfactory because the wave of Figure 7.4 still varies regularly on a large scale, but the result correctly indicates an inverse relationship between the uncertainties in momentum and position. A more useful model is obtained by adding together many waves of slightly different wavelength. For example, Figure 7.5 shows the result of adding four cosine waves of the same amplitude; it is clear that the maximum amplitude of the sum must occur at the origin $x = 0$. As the number of waves is increased, the wave is confined to the region close to the origin and forms a "wave packet," the spread of which depends on the range of wavelengths comprised in the components added together.

Summation of a continuous range of wavelengths may be performed by means of Fourier integrals, which supply reciprocal relations between the function $f(x)$, which represents the disturbance when all the components are added, and the function $g(\kappa)$, which expresses the distribution of component wavelengths in terms of the parameter $\kappa = 2\pi/\lambda$. Thus, for distributions continuous over the whole range of x and κ, we have the reciprocal relations

and

$$\left.\begin{aligned} f(x) &= \frac{1}{(2\pi)^{1/2}} \int_{-\infty}^{\infty} g(\kappa) \exp{(i\kappa x)} \, d\kappa \\[2mm] g(\kappa) &= \frac{1}{(2\pi)^{1/2}} \int_{-\infty}^{\infty} f(x) \exp{(-i\kappa x)} \, dx \end{aligned}\right\} \tag{7.2.2}$$

Here we need to find the function $f(x)$ when the distribution $g(\kappa)$ corresponds to a series of wavelengths grouped narrowly about a mean value. It is convenient to adopt a Gaussian type of function for $g(\kappa)$, with the peak of the distribution set at some value $\kappa = \kappa_0$, as in Figure 7.6,

$$g(\kappa) = A \exp{[-a(\kappa - \kappa_0)^2]}, \tag{7.2.3}$$

where A is an arbitrary constant and a is a parameter which fixes the spread of the distribution. In order to express the spread in κ values in terms of a, we define $\Delta \kappa$ as the root-mean-square deviation from the mean value κ_0 and calculate $(\Delta \kappa)^2$ by the methods of

cosine-wave components

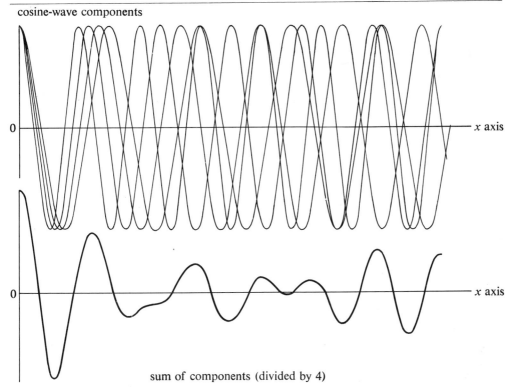

sum of components (divided by 4)

FIGURE 7.5 *The addition of four cosine waves of equal amplitude but slightly different wavelength produces a disturbance of maximum amplitude at the origin.*

Section 2.3, as follows:

$$(\Delta\kappa)^2 = \frac{\int_0^\infty (\kappa - \kappa_0)^2 g(\kappa)\,d\kappa}{\int_0^\infty g(\kappa)\,d\kappa}.$$

The integral in the denominator can be replaced by the full integral over values from $-\infty$ to $+\infty$, provided that $g(\kappa)$ is negligible near the origin (as in Figure 7.6), and we have, from Equation (2.3.4),

$$\int_{-\infty}^\infty g(\kappa)\,d\kappa = A\sqrt{\frac{\pi}{a}}$$

(independent of κ_0, since the area under the curve does not depend on the position of the peak). Under the same conditions, we find from Equation (2.3.5)

$$\int_{-\infty}^\infty (\kappa - \kappa_0)^2 g(\kappa)\,d\kappa = \frac{A}{2}\sqrt{\frac{\pi}{a^3}}$$

so that the mean square deviation from the mean is

$$(\Delta\kappa)^2 = \frac{1}{2a}.$$

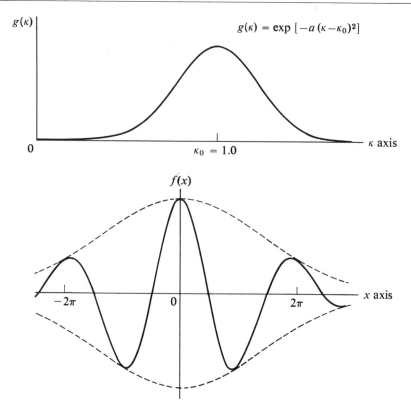

FIGURE 7.6   *Above: the function* $g(\kappa)$ *represents a distribution in wavelengths, expressed in terms of*

$\kappa = \dfrac{2\pi}{\lambda}$ *as a Gaussian function of the form:* $g(\kappa) = exp\,[\,-a(\kappa - \kappa_0)^2]$. *Below: the result of*

Fourier synthesis is to make a wavepacket represented by: $f(x) \propto cos\,\kappa_0 x\;exp\left(-\dfrac{x^2}{4a}\right)$

The spatial function obtained by adding together the wavelengths represented by the function $g(\kappa)$ is then

$$f(x) = \frac{A}{(2\pi)^{\frac{1}{2}}} \int_{-\infty}^{\infty} \exp\left[-a(\kappa - \kappa_0)^2 + i\kappa x\right] d\kappa$$

$$= \frac{A}{(2\pi)^{\frac{1}{2}}} \exp\left(i\kappa_0 x - \frac{x^2}{4a}\right) \int_{-\infty}^{\infty} \exp\left\{-a\left[\kappa - \left(\kappa_0 + \frac{ix}{2a}\right)\right]^2\right\} d\kappa,$$

where the terms independent of κ have been taken in front of the integral, which is a constant factor (independent of x). Thus the variable part of $f(x)$ is confined to the exponential term in front of the integral

$$f(x) \propto \exp\left(i\kappa_0 x\right) \exp\left(-\frac{x^2}{4a}\right) \qquad\qquad [7.2.4]$$

and the real part of this function is a cosine curve with the amplitude varying according to the Gaussian term, as in Figure 7.6. This result is independent of the value of κ_0, so we could make κ_0 very large and have many oscillations within the localized wave packet. The effective spread in distance of these waves may be expressed, as before, in terms of the root-mean-square deviation from the origin. If this is done with the function of Equation (7.2.4), we find

$$(\Delta x)^2 = 2a$$

and the product $(\Delta x)^2(\Delta \kappa)^2 = 1$.

However, following Born's interpretation of the de Broglie waves, we should argue that the probability of locating the particle depends on the *square* of the function $f(x)$, that is,

$$|f(x)|^2 \propto \exp\left(-\frac{x^2}{2a}\right).$$

With this function representing the envelope of the wave packet, we find that the mean square deviation from the origin is

$$(\Delta x)^2 = a$$

and

$$(\Delta x)^2(\Delta \kappa)^2 = \tfrac{1}{2}.$$

The exact value of the product $(\Delta x \Delta \kappa)$ depends on the exact form of the function $g(\kappa)$, but we see that, in the wave-packet model, the product in the uncertainties of x and κ, expressed as root-mean-square deviations, is

$$\Delta x \Delta \kappa \approx 1, \qquad\qquad [7.2.5]$$

or, in terms of the linear momentum $p_x = \hbar\kappa$,

$$\Delta x \Delta p_x \approx \hbar.$$

Heisenberg showed quite generally that the product $\Delta x \Delta p_x$ must always exceed $\tfrac{1}{2}\hbar$, except in the lowest state of a harmonic oscillator, where the product is equal to $\tfrac{1}{2}\hbar$. The correlation of errors applies only to measurements made in the same direction, so in three dimensions we obtain the following uncertainty relations

$$\left.\begin{array}{ll} \Delta x \Delta p_x \geqslant \tfrac{1}{2}\hbar & \Delta x \Delta p_y \geqslant 0 \\ \Delta y \Delta p_y \geqslant \tfrac{1}{2}\hbar & \text{and so forth.} \\ \Delta z \Delta p_z \geqslant \tfrac{1}{2}\hbar & \end{array}\right\} \qquad [7.2.6]$$

(b) Indeterminacy

The physical basis of Heisenberg's principle was stressed by Bohr in a series of arguments designed to show that the fundamental indeterminacy is due to the necessary interaction between the system observed and the apparatus used to detect it. For example, if we want to measure the position of an electron accurately, we can illuminate it with some form of short-wavelength radiation; however, de Broglie's relation shows that the shorter the wavelength used the greater is the momentum per photon. Owing to the Compton effect, there must be appreciable recoil of the electron and the momentum will be rendered increasingly uncertain as the position is made more precise.

Suppose, for example, that we use light of wavelength λ to illuminate the electron and we detect the scattered light by means of a microscope (Figure 7.7). If the light is incident along the axis of the microscope objective, which subtends an angle of 2θ at the object, we can estimate the resolving power in terms of λ and θ. Abbé's experiments with ruled gratings of spacing d showed that the rulings can be distinguished under the microscope if at least one diffracted beam enters the objective, in addition to the central undeviated beam. Thus, under the conditions depicted in Figure 7.7, the minimum distance resolved in the focal plane is

$$d = \frac{\lambda}{\sin\theta}$$

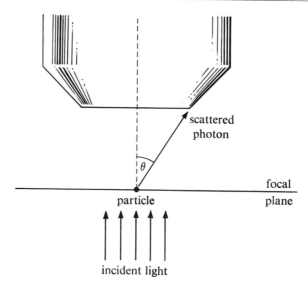

FIGURE 7.7 *Bohr's argument about the uncertainty in position of an electron located by means of a microscope using incident light of wavelength λ. The resolving power of the microscope depends on the maximum angle of collection (θ) of light scattered by the particle.*

and we may write the error in locating a particle approximately as

$$\Delta x \approx \frac{\lambda}{\sin \theta}.$$

If we consider the Compton scattering process (Section 5.6), also for light entering the objective at angle θ to its original direction, the momentum per photon is h/λ', where λ' is the wavelength of the scattered photon. The transverse component of the momentum of the scattered photon is necessarily equal to the transverse momentum imparted to the electron at the collision, so we can estimate the error in electron momentum (in the focal plane) as

$$\Delta p_x \approx \frac{h}{\lambda'} \sin \theta.$$

If the wavelength is not too short, the change in wavelength is very small, so that $\lambda = \lambda'$ approximately, and

$$\Delta x \Delta p_x \approx h \qquad \text{[Equation (7.2.1)]}.$$

Bohr showed that the same type of result is always obtained when allowance is made for the disturbance applied to an observed particle by the measuring device. Moreover, it is necessary to invoke the uncertainty principle if interference experiments like that of Taylor (Section 4.6) are to receive a consistent interpretation. It is therefore unrealistic to invent precise models of electron behavior within atoms because any experimental process which could locate an electron would involve a large momentum change and the electron would almost certainly change its state.

Adoption of Heisenberg's principle therefore changes the basis of theoretical mechanics, since the behavior of individual particles is always, to some extent, indeterminate. This principle does not prevent us from calculating excitation energies and other atomic properties, but it does impose limitations on the degree of accuracy with which changes of state can be predicted. It is not possible to say what a single atom will do, but the behavior of a large number of atoms can be predicted on a statistical basis. In this connection the law of radioactive decay (Section 6.2) furnishes a clear example of random processes occurring in an atomic system. Given the details of the initial and final states in a radioactive change, we can, in principle, calculate the probability of change per unit time, but no further details are provided by the theory and the sequence of observed changes is completely random.

(c) Energy-time relations

Heisenberg's principle applies not only to position and momentum coordinates but also to the energy and time variables. The correlation may be derived in outline by considering the classical kinetic energy of a particle

$$E = \tfrac{1}{2}mv^2 = \frac{p^2}{2m}$$

and finding the uncertainty in E

$$\Delta E = \frac{p}{m}\Delta p = v\,\Delta p.$$

If v is interpreted as the recoil velocity of an electron irradiated with light, the uncertainty in position (Δx) is related to the time of observation (Δt) by the equation

$$\Delta x = v\,\Delta t.$$

Hence

$$\Delta E\,\Delta t = \Delta x\,\Delta p \approx \hbar \qquad \text{from Equation (7.2.5).}$$

The energy-time relation emerges directly if we consider a de Broglie wave varying in time with angular frequency ω. If there is only a single frequency involved, the energy is fixed precisely by Planck's relation

$$E = \hbar\omega$$

so that $\Delta E = 0$. But this precise measurement requires an infinite time of observation, to ensure beyond doubt that the wave amplitude is in fact constant, hence $\Delta t \to \infty$. If we have only a finite time for measurements, or if we set up a pulse in the form of a wave packet, the uncertainty ($\Delta\omega$) in angular frequency is related to the time uncertainty (Δt) by the equation

$$\Delta\omega\,\Delta t \approx 1 \qquad\qquad [7.2.7]$$

as may be shown by Fourier analysis of the wave packet. Thus

$$\Delta E\,\Delta t \approx \hbar. \qquad\qquad [7.2.8]$$

This result is of special importance in the theory of spectroscopic linewidths and in nuclear physics. If a certain excited state has a very short mean lifetime, represented by Δt, it follows that there is a considerable uncertainty, ΔE, in a single energy determination. Many energy levels of high excitation are found to be "broad," in the sense that there is an appreciable spread in the observed energies of transition to other states. The observed width in the energy level can then be used to estimate the mean lifetime, from Equation (7.2.8). Recently it has become feasible for measurements of the energy spread (ΔE) of certain nuclear gamma rays to be carried out over different periods of observation (Δt), which are of the order of the mean lifetime of the excited state. Wu and her collaborators* have shown that, when the period Δt is reduced, the energy spread increases in such a way

* C. S. Wu, Y. K. Lee, N. Benczer-Koller, and P. Simms, *Phys. Rev. Letters*, **5**, 432 (1960).

that the product $\Delta E \, \Delta t$ is approximately constant. Moreover, the *natural* line widths observed in the sharply defined gamma rays emitted by Fe^{57}, Ir^{191} and other isotopes are in agreement with Equation (7.2.8).

The linewidth problem can be described classically in terms of an oscillating charge subject to *radiation damping*, an effect due to the loss of energy by the charge to the electromagnetic field. The charge is supposed to oscillate freely, commencing at time $t = 0$, and the equation of motion is

$$\frac{d^2x}{dt^2} + \Gamma \frac{dx}{dt} + \omega_0^2 x = 0,$$

where ω_0 is the proper angular frequency for undamped motion and Γ is the damping factor, which may be calculated from the theory of oscillating charges (Section 4.1). The equation can be solved by means of a complex exponential function

$$x = A \exp\left(-\tfrac{1}{2}\Gamma t\right) \exp\left(\pm i\omega' t\right), \qquad [7.2.9]$$

where $\omega'^2 = (\omega_0^2 - \Gamma^2/4)$ and A is an arbitrary amplitude. The solution represents an oscillation of angular frequency ω' with amplitude decaying exponentially according to the term $\exp\left(-\tfrac{1}{2}\Gamma t\right)$.

The rate at which energy is radiated from an oscillating charge is proportional to the square of the amplitude, as may be seen from Equations (4.1.11) and (4.1.13). The motion represented by Equation (7.2.9) corresponds to a rate of emission varying as $\exp\left(-\Gamma t\right)$, so that the rate drops to e^{-1} of its former value in time

$$\tau = \frac{1}{\Gamma}.$$

In terms of quantum mechanics, each excited state has a mean lifetime τ and the probability of decay per unit time is given by the reciprocal Γ, which corresponds to the radioactive decay constant (λ) in Equation (6.2.7).

The influence of the damping term on the spectrum of emitted frequencies is to introduce a spread about the mean value ω', that is, a line-broadening effect. This result may be worked out directly from Fourier integrals involving time t and angular frequency ω

$$\left. \begin{aligned} f(t) &= \frac{1}{(2\pi)^{1/2}} \int_{-\infty}^{\infty} g(\omega) \exp\left(i\omega t\right) d\omega \\[2mm] g(\omega) &= \frac{1}{(2\pi)^{1/2}} \int_{-\infty}^{\infty} f(t) \exp\left(-i\omega t\right) dt \end{aligned} \right\} \qquad [7.2.10]$$

Here we need to analyze the time function of Equation (7.2.9) into its frequency components. Accordingly we substitute

$$f(t) = A \exp\left(-\tfrac{1}{2}\Gamma t\right) \exp\left(i\omega' t\right)$$

for $t \geqslant 0$, into the second integral, and obtain

$$g(\omega) = \frac{A}{(2\pi)^{1/2}} \int_0^{\infty} \exp\left\{[-\tfrac{1}{2}\Gamma + i(\omega' - \omega)]t\right\} dt$$

$$= \frac{A}{(2\pi)^{1/2}} \left| \frac{\exp\left(-\tfrac{1}{2}\Gamma t\right) \exp\left[i(\omega' - \omega)t\right]}{i(\omega' - \omega + i\Gamma/2)} \right|_0^{\infty}$$

$$= \frac{iA}{(2\pi)^{1/2}(\omega' - \omega + i\Gamma/2)}.$$

This expression represents the complex amplitude of the frequency function equivalent to the damped oscillation $f(t)$. In order to find the intensity (I) as a function of frequency, we square the modulus of $g(\omega)$, multiplying $g(\omega)$ by its complex conjugate $g^*(\omega)$ to obtain

$$I(\omega) = g^*(\omega)g(\omega)$$

$$= \frac{-iA}{(2\pi)^{\frac{1}{2}}(\omega' - \omega - i\Gamma/2)} \frac{iA}{(2\pi)^{\frac{1}{2}}(\omega' - \omega + i\Gamma/2)}$$

$$= \frac{A^2}{2\pi[(\omega' - \omega)^2 + \frac{1}{4}\Gamma^2]} . \qquad [7.2.11]$$

The resultant function is plotted in Figure 7.8 against angular frequency. It is a conventional resonance curve with a peak at $\omega = \omega'$ and a resonance width depending on Γ. On either side of the peak the function falls to half the peak value at

$$\omega = \omega' \pm \tfrac{1}{2}\Gamma$$

so that the full width at half-maximum can be written

$$\Delta\omega = \Gamma \qquad \text{in angular frequency units.}$$

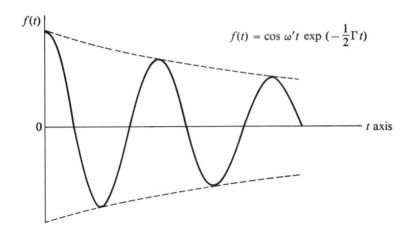

$$f(t) = \cos \omega't \exp\left(-\frac{1}{2}\Gamma t\right)$$

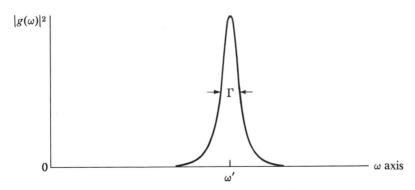

FIGURE 7.8 *Above: the function $f(t)$ represents a damped oscillation, the amplitude of which decreases exponentially according to the relation: $f(t) \propto exp\,(-\frac{1}{2}\Gamma t)$. Below: the intensity of Fourier components of the same oscillation plotted against the angular frequency: the resonance curve has width Γ (at half maximum).*

We showed that the mean lifetime of the excited state for energy loss is given by the relation

$$\Delta t = \tau = \frac{1}{\Gamma}$$

so that the product $(\Delta\omega\Delta t)$ becomes

$$\Delta\omega\Delta t = 1.$$

If we multiply the equation throughout by $\hbar$, the resonance width becomes $(\hbar\Gamma)$ in energy units and we have

$$\tau(\hbar\Gamma) = \hbar \qquad\qquad [7.2.12]$$

which is consistent with Equation (7.2.8).

If the period of observation is curtailed, as in Wu's experiments, the Fourier integral has to be taken over the appropriate time limits and it is found that the resonance curve is broadened as the time interval is reduced. The results are generally in agreement with Equation (7.2.8), although the parameters ΔE and Δt cannot be defined so simply in such cases. The chief value of the classical Equation (7.2.12) lies in its exact specification of the time and energy variables.

7.3   The Hamiltonian and Schrödinger's Equations

The development of quantum mechanics took place historically through the wave mechanics of Schrödinger, based on the work of de Broglie, and simultaneously through the matrix mechanics of Heisenberg, Born, and Jordan. The latter scheme was concerned chiefly with the literal observables of an atomic system, such as the spectral lines obtained in transitions between pairs of states, but it was adapted to yield energy levels in certain cases. The two approaches were unified in the work of Dirac, who based quantum mechanics on the classical mechanics of Poisson and Hamilton, with a new interpretation of Hamilton's "canonical" variables.

(a) Hamiltonian mechanics*

In a simple mechanical system, the Hamiltonian function for a particle is the sum of its kinetic energy (K), which depends on the momentum (p), and the potential energy (U), which varies with position:

$$H = K(p_x, p_y, p_z) + U(q_x, q_y, q_z),$$

where p_x, p_y, p_z are the momentum components and q_x, q_y, q_z are position coordinates. If the suffices are replaced by $j = 1, 2, 3$, we may write the Hamiltonian in the form

$$H = \sum_j \frac{p_j^2}{2m} + U(q_j) \qquad\qquad [7.3.1]$$

for a nonrelativistic particle of constant mass m. The classical equations of motion are then

$$\frac{dq_j}{dt} = \frac{\partial H}{\partial p_j} \quad \text{and} \quad \frac{dp_j}{dt} = \frac{-\partial H}{\partial q_j}. \qquad\qquad [7.3.2]$$

* See, for example, R. B. Lindsay and H. Margenau, *Foundations of Physics* (Dover Publications, New York, 1957) Chap. 3.

For example, the Hamiltonian of a simple harmonic oscillator of angular frequency ω is [compare Equation (2.4.3)]

$$H = \frac{p^2}{2m} + \tfrac{1}{2}m\omega^2 q^2 \qquad [7.3.3]$$

for motion in one dimension only. The equations of motion then yield

$$\frac{dq}{dt} = \frac{p}{m} = v \text{ (the instantaneous velocity)} \quad \text{and} \quad \frac{dp}{dt} = -m\omega^2 q,$$

that is, the force is proportional to the displacement q and is opposite to the displacement in direction.

In quantum mechanics the formal Hamiltonian expression is retained in problems where a classical analog exists, as in the harmonic oscillator. However, the variables q_j and p_j are no longer treated as quantities with numerical values but as *operators* acting on the state function Ψ.* The link between the operator calculus and Heisenberg's matrices was provided by the noncommutative algebra of operators and matrices. Here we shall confine our attention to operators and work out some of their simpler properties. For example, if we apply the operator $\partial/\partial q$ to the function $(q\Psi)$ we obtain

$$\frac{\partial}{\partial q}(q\Psi) = \Psi + q\frac{\partial \Psi}{\partial q}$$

or

$$\left(\frac{\partial}{\partial q}q - q\frac{\partial}{\partial q}\right)\Psi = \Psi.$$

If the function Ψ is elided, the remainder is the operator identity

$$\frac{\partial}{\partial q}q - q\frac{\partial}{\partial q} = 1. \qquad [7.3.4]$$

It is possible to base quantum mechanics on the fundamental axiom that there are certain properties of the q_j and p_j operators which lead to *commutation relations* such as

$$q_j p_j - p_j q_j = i\hbar, \qquad [7.3.5]$$

which is equivalent to writing the operator identity

$$p_j = -i\hbar \frac{\partial}{\partial q_j}. \qquad [7.3.6]$$

Equation (7.3.5) applies only to variables with the same suffix j. Other pairs of q and p operators obey the relation

$$q_j p_k - p_k q_j = 0 \qquad \text{for} \quad j \neq k$$

and are said to "commute" with each other.

The commutation relations [Equation (7.3.5)] between q and p operators lead directly to uncertainty relations between pairs of variables and the relations have been quoted previously [Equation (7.2.6)]. It follows that the introduction of Planck's constant in the commutation relations is the essential step which distinguishes classical mechanics from the new mechanics embodying the uncertainty principle. It also follows that we can regain classical results by letting the constant $\hbar$ tend to zero in expressions obtained by quantum mechanics (the Correspondence principle of Bohr, employed in Section 4.5).

* R. B. Lindsay and H. Margenau, *Foundations of Physics* (Dover Publications, New York, 1957) Chap. 9.

(b) *Angular-momentum operators*

In the scheme of operator calculus, angular-momentum operators possess certain special properties which may be derived directly from Equation (7.3.5). The orbital angular-momentum vector **G** is defined classically as the vector product of the linear momentum **p** and the radius vector **r** from the axis of rotation

$$\mathbf{G} = \mathbf{r} \times \mathbf{p}$$

with the three components (in terms of coordinates x, y, z)

$$\left. \begin{aligned} G_x &= yp_z - zp_y \\ G_y &= zp_x - xp_z \\ G_z &= xp_y - yp_x \end{aligned} \right\} \qquad [7.3.7]$$

The commutation relation for a pair of components, say G_x and G_y, can be worked out with the aid of Equation (7.3.5), care being taken to keep all noncommuting factors in the correct order throughout the calculation

$$\begin{aligned} G_x G_y - G_y G_x &= (yp_z - zp_y)(zp_x - xp_z) - (zp_x - xp_z)(yp_z - zp_y) \\ &= p_z z(yp_x - xp_y) + zp_z(xp_y - yp_x) \\ &= i\hbar G_z. \end{aligned} \qquad [7.3.8]$$

Two similar relations are obtained by cyclic permutation of the x, y, and z terms.

The magnitude of the angular momentum can be obtained, in certain cases, by finding the eigenvalues of the squared vector G^2. Since G^2 is an operator acting on the state-function Ψ, we have to consider the product

$$G^2\Psi.$$

It may happen that this product can be written in the form

$$G^2\Psi = \hbar^2 C\Psi,$$

where C is a number and the constant $\hbar^2$ is introduced because $\hbar$ is the quantum of angular momentum. If such a relation exists, we say that $\hbar^2 C$ is an eigenvalue of the operator G^2; physically, this means that $\hbar^2 C$ is an observable value of the squared orbital angular momentum.

In order to find the operator form of G^2, we must express this physical variable in Cartesian coordinates. In terms of the operators G_x, G_y, and G_z, we have

$$\begin{aligned} G^2 &= G_x^2 + G_y^2 + G_z^2 \\ &= (yp_z - zp_y)^2 + (zp_x - xp_z)^2 + (xp_y - yp_x)^2, \end{aligned}$$

which can be put in differential form with the aid of Equation (7.3.6)

$$\begin{aligned} G^2 &= -\hbar^2\left[\left(y\frac{\partial}{\partial z} - z\frac{\partial}{\partial y}\right)^2 + \left(z\frac{\partial}{\partial x} - x\frac{\partial}{\partial z}\right)^2 + \left(x\frac{\partial}{\partial y} - y\frac{\partial}{\partial x}\right)^2\right] \\ &= -\hbar^2\left[(x^2 + y^2 + z^2)\left(\frac{\partial^2}{\partial x^2} + \frac{\partial^2}{\partial y^2} + \frac{\partial^2}{\partial z^2}\right) - x^2\frac{\partial^2}{\partial x^2} - y^2\frac{\partial^2}{\partial y^2} - z^2\frac{\partial^2}{\partial z^2} \right. \\ &\quad \left. - 2\left(x\frac{\partial}{\partial x} + y\frac{\partial}{\partial y} + z\frac{\partial}{\partial z}\right) - 2xy\frac{\partial}{\partial x}\frac{\partial}{\partial y} - 2yz\frac{\partial}{\partial y}\frac{\partial}{\partial z} - 2zx\frac{\partial}{\partial z}\frac{\partial}{\partial x}\right]. \end{aligned}$$

This expression can be simplified by use of the Laplacian operator

$$\nabla^2 = \frac{\partial^2}{\partial x^2} + \frac{\partial^2}{\partial y^2} + \frac{\partial^2}{\partial z^2}$$

and the relations

$$r^2 = x^2 + y^2 + z^2$$

where

$$x = r \sin\theta \cos\varphi, \qquad y = r \sin\theta \sin\varphi, \qquad z = r \cos\theta,$$

whence

$$\frac{\partial}{\partial r} = \frac{x}{r}\frac{\partial}{\partial x} + \frac{y}{r}\frac{\partial}{\partial y} + \frac{z}{r}\frac{\partial}{\partial z}.$$

Also

$$\left(x\frac{\partial}{\partial x}\right)^2 = x\frac{\partial}{\partial x}x\frac{\partial}{\partial x} = x^2\frac{\partial^2}{\partial x^2} + x\frac{\partial}{\partial x}, \qquad \text{and so forth,}$$

so that

$$\left(r\frac{\partial}{\partial r}\right)^2 = \left(x\frac{\partial}{\partial x} + y\frac{\partial}{\partial y} + z\frac{\partial}{\partial z}\right)^2$$

$$= x^2\frac{\partial^2}{\partial x^2} + y^2\frac{\partial^2}{\partial y^2} + z^2\frac{\partial^2}{\partial z^2} + x\frac{\partial}{\partial x} + y\frac{\partial}{\partial y} + z\frac{\partial}{\partial z}$$

$$+ 2xy\frac{\partial}{\partial x}\frac{\partial}{\partial y} + 2yz\frac{\partial}{\partial y}\frac{\partial}{\partial z} + 2zx\frac{\partial}{\partial z}\frac{\partial}{\partial x}.$$

The squared angular momentum is therefore represented by the quantum-mechanical operator

$$G^2 = -\hbar^2\left[r^2\nabla^2 - \left(r\frac{\partial}{\partial r}\right)^2 - \left(r\frac{\partial}{\partial r}\right)\right].$$

Now in spherical polar coordinates (r, θ, φ) the Laplacian operator takes the form

$$\nabla^2 = \frac{\partial^2}{\partial r^2} + \frac{2}{r}\frac{\partial}{\partial r} + \frac{1}{r^2\sin\theta}\frac{\partial}{\partial\theta}\left(\sin\theta\frac{\partial}{\partial\theta}\right) + \frac{1}{r^2\sin^2\theta}\frac{\partial^2}{\partial\varphi^2}$$

so that

$$r^2\nabla^2 = \left(r\frac{\partial}{\partial r}\right)^2 + r\frac{\partial}{\partial r} + \Lambda(\theta, \varphi),$$

where $\Lambda(\theta, \varphi)$ is an operator containing only θ and φ terms. Thus the squared angular momentum becomes

$$G^2 = -\hbar^2\Lambda(\theta, \varphi) = -\hbar^2\left[\frac{1}{\sin\theta}\frac{\partial}{\partial\theta}\left(\sin\theta\frac{\partial}{\partial\theta}\right) + \frac{1}{\sin^2\theta}\frac{\partial^2}{\partial\varphi^2}\right]. \qquad [7.3.9]$$

This result is of great importance in the theory of quantized angular momenta.

(c) The Schrödinger equations

The Hamiltonian H is itself to be regarded as an operator because it is usually a function of the q and p variables, or of quantities like G^2. Provided that the expression for H does not include time t explicitly, we can immediately set up Schrödinger's *time-independent* wave equation. We operate on the state function ψ with H and impose the requirement that the equation

$$H\psi = E\psi \qquad [7.3.10]$$

is valid for any eigenvalue of the total energy E. In other words, if a solution of this equation exists with a numerical value E, that value must be an observable energy of the system. Since H is a function of the operators q_j, p_j the equation is frequently written

$$H\left(q_j, -i\hbar \frac{\partial}{\partial q_j}\right)\psi = E\psi, \qquad [7.3.11]$$

where the differential operator replaces p_j according to Equation (7.3.6). In the non-relativistic approximation, Equation (7.3.1) yields

$$H = \sum_j \frac{p_j^2}{2m} + U(q_j)$$

$$= -\frac{\hbar^2}{2m} \sum_j \frac{\partial^2}{\partial q_j^2} + U(q_j)$$

$$= -\frac{\hbar^2}{2m} \nabla^2 + U(q_j)$$

and the Schrödinger equation becomes

$$\nabla^2 \psi + \frac{2m}{\hbar^2}[E - U(q_j)]\psi = 0. \qquad [7.3.12]$$

This is a three-dimensional generalization of Equation (7.1.9), which was derived directly from the de Broglie relation.

In many cases the form of $U(q_j)$ is such that solutions take the character of eigenfunctions and to each solution there corresponds an eigenvalue E. The wave-mechanical method is therefore directly applicable to problems where definite energy levels are known to exist. However, in other problems involving transitions between states, it is necessary to find out how the state function changes in time. So far we have been concerned with state functions ψ which describe stationary states of the system. Now we revert to functions Ψ which vary in time and space.

We first consider a de Broglie wave traveling in one dimension and represented by the wave function

$$\Psi = A \exp\left[\frac{2\pi i}{\lambda}(x - ut)\right], \qquad [7.3.13]$$

where A is an arbitrary amplitude, λ is the de Broglie wavelength, and u is the wave velocity, as in Equation (7.1.5). This wave travels to the right along the conventional x axis. In terms of the parameters ω (the angular frequency) and $\kappa = 2\pi/\lambda$, the wave function is

$$\Psi = A \exp[i(\kappa x - \omega t)]$$

so that

$$\frac{\partial \Psi}{\partial t} = -i\omega\Psi.$$

Multiplying both sides by $\hbar$, and putting $\hbar\omega = E$, we have

$$i\hbar \frac{\partial \Psi}{\partial t} = E\Psi, \qquad [7.3.14]$$

that is, the total energy operator is equivalent to $i\hbar(\partial/\partial t)$ when applied to Ψ. It follows that the rate of change of Ψ is given by the Hamiltonian operator applied to Ψ

$$i\hbar \frac{\partial \Psi}{\partial t} = H\left(q_j, -i\hbar \frac{\partial}{\partial q_j}\right)\Psi,$$ [7.3.15]

which is Schrödinger's *time-dependent* equation for state functions which vary in time and space.

The sign of the operator in Equation (7.3.14) is in fact undetermined because we could have considered a wave traveling in the opposite direction, which yields the same equation with a minus sign. The physical consequences, however, are precisely the same when the theory is applied to transitions, since the probability depends on the *square* of the appropriate terms involving H. For the same reason, the probability of transition one way between a pair of states is exactly the same as the probability for the reverse process, if the same stimulus is responsible. For example, stimulated emission of light from an excited state to the ground state of an atom proceeds at the same rate as the absorption process from ground to excited state; this idea was used by Einstein in his derivation of the Planck distribution law for blackbody radiation (Section 4.5).

(d) Heisenberg's equation of motion

Equation (7.3.15) provides information about the rate of change of the state function Ψ but this is of limited application where physical variables (operators) are concerned. Heisenberg's scheme enables us to find the rate of change of any operator (f) from its algebraic relations with the Hamiltonian operator H. In Heisenberg's mechanics, H acts as the total differential operator $i\hbar(d/dt)$ and this operator can be applied to the product $f\Psi$

$$i\hbar \frac{d}{dt}(f\Psi) = i\hbar \frac{df}{dt}\Psi + i\hbar f \frac{d\Psi}{dt},$$

thus, in operator form,

$$Hf\Psi = i\hbar \frac{df}{dt}\Psi + fH\Psi.$$

Elision of the state function yields Heisenberg's equation

$$i\hbar \frac{df}{dt} = [Hf - fH].$$ [7.3.16]

It follows that any operator which commutes with the Hamiltonian function has zero rate of change, that is, it is a constant of the motion. For example, the momentum operator p commutes with the Hamiltonian of a single particle in any field-free situation, so the linear momentum is necessarily constant.

An important example of this general result is the motion of a particle in a *central* field of force, in which the potential energy U is a function only of the distance (r) of the particle from the center of force. The nonrelativistic Hamiltonian may be written

$$H = \frac{G^2}{2\mathscr{I}} + U(r),$$

where $\mathscr{I}$ stands for the effective moment of inertia about the center. Equation (7.3.9) shows that the squared angular momentum (G^2) is represented by operators involving θ and φ only, which necessarily commute with the independent radius variable r. Also G^2

commutes with itself, therefore it commutes with the Hamiltonian and the orbital angular momentum is constant for any central field, as in classical mechanics.

7.4 Particle in a Rectangular Potential Well

(a) *Solution of Schrödinger's equation*

Many problems in atomic and nuclear physics are concerned with particles which are confined in a narrow compass, for example the particles within a nucleus. If the forces acting on such a particle are of very short range, the potential energy of the particle changes rapidly with distance and in an extreme case we may imagine the form of $U(x, y, z)$ to be a double step function in the shape of a "potential well," for example, a one-dimensional well of the form shown in Figure 7.9, where $U = 0$ for $-\tfrac{1}{2}L \leqslant x \leqslant \tfrac{1}{2}L*$ and $U = U_0$ for $x < -\tfrac{1}{2}L$ and for $x > \tfrac{1}{2}L$. We assume that U_0 is large and positive and we need to find the energy levels of a particle bound in the well, that is, we impose the condition $E < U_0$.

The time-independent Schrödinger equation in one dimension is

$$\frac{d^2\psi}{dx^2} + \frac{2m}{\hbar^2}(E - U)\psi = 0$$

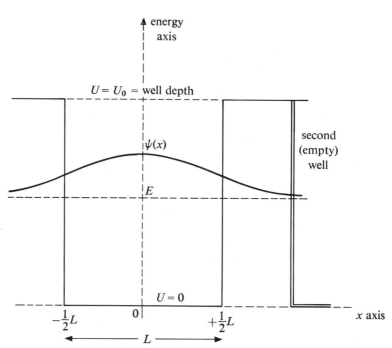

FIGURE 7.9 *The state function $\psi(x)$ obtained for a particle in a rectangular potential well of width L and depth U_0 is found by fitting the sinusoidal function inside the well to exponential functions on either side. If a second well is brought up from one direction, the exponential functions may overlap into the empty well to an appreciable extent.*

* We take $U = 0$ for convenience *inside* the well, but identical results are obtained if $U = 0$ outside the well and $U = -U_0$ inside it.

and in the central region where $U = 0$ we may write

$$\frac{d^2\psi}{dx^2} + \kappa^2\psi = 0 \quad \text{where} \quad \kappa^2 = \frac{2mE}{\hbar^2}$$

with the general solution

$$\psi = A \cos \kappa x + B \sin \kappa x,$$

where A and B are amplitudes which remain undetermined. If we impose the condition that the state-function ψ is to be symmetrical about the origin, we put $B = 0$ and retain the cosine term only. This means that the state is of *even parity*, that is, its state function does not change sign when the coordinate x changes sign. Alternatively we could put $A = 0$ and employ the sine function, which is of *odd parity* because it changes sign when $(-x)$ is substituted for $(+x)$.

Outside the potential well, the Schrödinger equation involves U_0 and may be written

$$\frac{d^2\psi}{dx^2} - \mu^2\psi = 0, \quad \text{where} \quad \mu^2 = \frac{2m(U_0 - E)}{\hbar^2}$$

with the general solution

$$\psi = C \exp(\mu x) + D \exp(-\mu x).$$

For a bound particle, the state function must decrease to zero amplitude as the distance from the well increases on either side, so we immediately choose the following solutions:

$$\text{when} \quad x < -\tfrac{1}{2}L, \quad \psi = C \exp(\mu x)$$
$$\text{when} \quad x > \tfrac{1}{2}L, \quad \psi = D \exp(-\mu x).$$

The entire range of x has been arbitrarily divided into three regions for the purpose of analysis, and these regions are separated by discontinuities in the potential; but the state function itself must be regular and continuous everywhere. We therefore apply the condition that ψ is continuous in magnitude and gradient at the boundaries $x = \pm\tfrac{1}{2}L$. With even-parity functions we obtain the relations (at $x = -\tfrac{1}{2}L$),

$$A \cos(\tfrac{1}{2}\kappa L) = C \exp(-\tfrac{1}{2}\mu L),$$
$$\kappa A \sin(\tfrac{1}{2}\kappa L) = \mu C \exp(-\tfrac{1}{2}\mu L),$$

whence

$$\tan(\tfrac{1}{2}\kappa L) = \mu/\kappa$$

and an identical equation is found at $x = \tfrac{1}{2}L$. In terms of the energies E and U_0, the equation becomes

$$\tan\left(\tfrac{1}{2}L\sqrt{\frac{2mE}{\hbar^2}}\right) = \sqrt{\frac{U_0 - E}{E}}, \qquad [7.4.1]$$

which is a transcendental equation for E and has to be solved by numerical methods when all the other factors are known. In the limit when U_0 is very large compared with E, we find a simple solution, since

$$\tan(\tfrac{1}{2}\kappa L) \to \infty,$$

whence $\tfrac{1}{2}\kappa L = \pm[n + \tfrac{1}{2}]\pi$, with $n = 0, 1, 2, 3, \ldots$, and so forth. The energy levels can then be expressed by the formula

$$E = \frac{(2n + 1)^2\hbar^2\pi^2}{2mL^2} = \frac{(2n + 1)^2h^2}{8mL^2}. \qquad [7.4.2]$$

The alternative odd-parity solutions are obtained similarly. At $x = -\frac{1}{2}L$,

$$-B \sin \left(\tfrac{1}{2}\kappa L\right) = C \exp \left(-\tfrac{1}{2}\mu L\right)$$
$$\kappa B \cos \left(\tfrac{1}{2}\kappa L\right) = \mu C \exp \left(-\tfrac{1}{2}\mu L\right)$$

whence

$$\cot \left(\tfrac{1}{2}\kappa L\right) = -\mu/\kappa$$

or, in terms of the energies,

$$\cot \left(\tfrac{1}{2}L\sqrt{\frac{2mE}{\hbar^2}}\right) = -\sqrt{\frac{U_0 - E}{E}}. \qquad [7.4.3]$$

In the limit when U_0 is very large compared with E, we have

$$\tfrac{1}{2}\kappa L = \pm n\pi, \qquad \text{with} \quad n = 1, 2, 3, \ldots, \text{and so forth,}$$

since the root $n = 0$ is ruled out by the condition that ψ must actually vary over the accessible region. The energy levels for odd-parity state functions are then given by the formula

$$E = \frac{n^2\hbar^2\pi^2}{\tfrac{1}{2}mL^2} = \frac{(2n)^2 h^2}{8mL^2}. \qquad [7.4.4]$$

Combining this result with Equation (7.4.2), we see that the single expression of Equation (7.1.4) includes all the results and that the energy levels alternate in parity, starting with the lowest even-parity state and counting upwards. For an infinitely deep well the state functions are similar to those for vibration of a string between fixed ends (Figure 7.3). When the well has finite depth the amplitude of ψ decreases exponentially with distance on either side of the well proper. According to Born's interpretation of the state function, this means that there is always a small but finite probability of the particle being outside the well, a situation which is impossible in classical mechanics. If a second well, which initially is empty, exists close to the first well, as shown in Figure 7.9, there is always a possibility of the particle transferring from one well to the other. This phenomenon of "barrier penetration" is characteristic of quantum systems and has been observed experimentally with electrons and nuclear particles.

(b) The conservation of parity

The analysis of the simple rectangular-well problem has shown that, although we started with a potential function which is symmetrical about the origin, two types of state function exist with different symmetry properties. Moreover, we have assigned even or odd parity to all the energy levels of the system. It may be enquired whether this division of energy levels into two classes is generally valid. Deeper analysis indicates that the character of the Hamiltonian is important in this connection. In all ordinary classical examples, the Hamiltonian function is invariant when we change the sign of one spatial coordinate, for example, the x coordinate. Under such conditions the parity of each state function is fixed, either odd or even, and all states can have definite parity assigned to them.

Changing the sign of one spatial coordinate is equivalent to a reflection of the system in a plane mirror and, as we have stated, this operation does not normally change the Hamiltonian. Of course, a single mirror reflection does change right-handed rotations into left-handed rotations and vice versa. However, if we postulate that the sense of rotation is an accidental characteristic, depending on the point of view, there is no reason to doubt the conservation of parity in each energy state of a system. On the other hand, if certain particles are always associated with a definite sense of rotation, it is no longer possible to maintain the invariance of the Hamiltonian under reflection. Recently it has been discovered that the so-called "weak interactions" do not obey the parity-conservation principle and, in the case of beta decay at least, this property is ascribed to the special properties of neutrinos and antineutrinos. However, in all the Coulomb and stronger interactions which are responsible for the structure of atoms and nuclei the Hamiltonian is believed to be invariant under reflection, to a high degree of accuracy. We shall therefore continue to assign definite parity to atomic and nuclear states in the following applications of the theory.

7.5 The Linear Harmonic Oscillator

(a) Solution of Schrödinger's equation

An exact solution can be obtained for Schrödinger's equation in the case where a particle has the same Hamiltonian as the classical harmonic oscillator, namely,

$$H = \frac{p^2}{2m} + \tfrac{1}{2}m\omega^2 q^2. \qquad \text{[Equation 7.3.3]}$$

This corresponds to a potential well of parabolic shape in one dimension, extending over the entire range of q variables (Figure 7.10). The rules for transformation into quantum

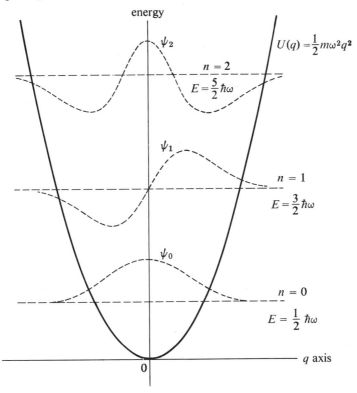

FIGURE 7.10 *The parabolic potential well for a particle whose motion corresponds to that of a classical harmonic oscillator in one dimension. The first three energy levels and their state functions $\psi_n(q)$ are shown.*

mechanics then yield the Schrödinger equation

$$\frac{d^2\psi}{dq^2} + \frac{2m}{\hbar^2}(E - \tfrac{1}{2}m\omega^2 q^2)\psi = 0. \tag{7.5.1}$$

In this problem there are no strict boundary conditions, such as those we employed in the rectangular well, but we can fix the eigenvalues of E by obtaining solutions of Equation (7.5.1) in closed analytical form.

First we note that, if q is large, we have the equation

$$\frac{d^2\psi}{dq^2} - \frac{m^2\omega^2}{\hbar^2}q^2\psi \approx 0$$

with the approximate solution (neglecting terms of power less than 2)

$$\psi = \exp(-\alpha q^2)$$

where

$$\alpha = \frac{m\omega}{2\hbar}.$$

If we adopt the exponential function as an asymptotic solution for large values of q, we may expect the full solution to be of the form

$$\psi = f(q)\exp(-\alpha q^2), \tag{7.5.2}$$

where the function $f(q)$ has yet to be determined. If Equation (7.5.2) is differentiated twice it yields

$$\frac{d^2\psi}{dq^2} = \exp(-\alpha q^2)\left[\frac{d^2f}{dq^2} - 4\alpha\frac{df}{dq} - 2\alpha f + 4\alpha^2 q^2 f\right].$$

This expression is substituted into Equation (7.5.1) and after some simplification we obtain a differential equation for $f(q)$

$$\frac{d^2f}{dq^2} - 4\alpha q\frac{df}{dq} + (\kappa^2 - 2\alpha)f = 0,$$

where we have written

$$\kappa^2 = \frac{2mE}{\hbar^2}.$$

This second-order differential equation is then solved by series, that is, we substitute an expression of the form

$$f(q) = \sum_{n=0} a_n q^{n+c}$$

together with

$$\frac{df}{dq} = \sum_{n=0}(n+c)a_n q^{n+c-1}$$

and

$$\frac{d^2f}{dq^2} = \sum_{n=0}(n+c)(n+c-1)a_n q^{n+c-2}.$$

In these expressions c is a constant, which may be found from the "indicial equation." If the series is to be a valid solution for all q, the net coefficient of any power of q, when all terms are collected on the left-hand side of the equation, must vanish. In particular, the lowest power of q which can appear on the left-hand side is q^{c-2} (for $n = 0$) and the coefficient of this term is

$$c(c - 1)a_0 = 0$$

so that $c = 0$ or $c = 1$.

Retaining the factor c, we can collect all terms with the power q^{n+c} and put the coefficient equal to zero, thus:

$$(n + c + 2)(n + c + 1)a_{n+2} - 4\alpha(n + c)a_n + (\kappa^2 - 2\alpha)a_n = 0$$

a general equation relating alternate coefficients a_n in the series solution. The ratio of alternate coefficients is found directly

$$\frac{a_{n+2}}{a_n} = \frac{4\alpha(n + c + \frac{1}{2}) - \kappa^2}{(n + c + 2)(n + c + 1)}. \qquad [7.5.3]$$

By successive use of this ratio we can find any coefficient a_n in terms of a_0 (for $c = 0$) or of a_1 (for $c = 1$). It is therefore possible to build up several series $f(q)$ which satisfy the Schrödinger equation when multiplied by $\exp(-\alpha q^2)$. However, closed solutions are obtained only when the series $f(q)$ terminates to form a polynomial expression. Since the series can terminate at any value of n we find an infinity of polynomial solutions, each of which provides an eigenfunction for the system. The eigenvalues are derived from Equation (7.5.3) by imposing the condition that the series terminate at the nth term, that is, $a_{n+2} = 0$, or

$$4\alpha(n + c + \tfrac{1}{2}) - \kappa^2 = 0$$

whence

$$\frac{2m\omega(n + c + \tfrac{1}{2})}{\hbar} = \frac{2mE}{\hbar}$$

or

$$E = (n + c + \tfrac{1}{2})\hbar\omega \quad \text{with} \quad c = 0 \quad \text{or} \quad 1.$$

Without loss of generality we may write the energy result

$$E = (n + \tfrac{1}{2})\hbar\omega \quad \text{with} \quad n = 0, 1, 2, \ldots, \text{and so forth.} \qquad [7.5.4]$$

The eigenvalues of E are therefore very similar to those assumed by Planck (Section 4.3) for harmonic oscillators in equilibrium with blackbody radiation, but the quantum-mechanical treatment introduces an extra term amounting to $\frac{1}{2}\hbar\omega$. This *zero-point energy* is a consequence of the uncertainty principle and it reflects the impossibility of a quantum system being in a state of no motion. In actual systems, the zero-point energy plays an important role in the theory of liquid helium's behavior at very low temperatures, but usually it is negligible compared with other energy terms.

(b) The eigenfunctions

The state function ψ_n for any eigenvalue E corresponding to a quantum number n is the product of $\exp(-\alpha q^2)$ and a polynomial $f_n(q)$, called Hermite's polynomial of order n. If $n = 0$, we have simply $f_0(q) = a_0$ (constant) and ψ_0 is a Gaussian function centered at the origin. The probability of locating the particle per unit distance is given by

$$\psi_0^2 = a_0^2 \exp(-2\alpha q^2)$$

and we can find the value of a_0 from the normalization condition [Equation (7.1.11)] adapted to this one-dimensional problem

$$\int_{-\infty}^{\infty} \psi^2 \, dq = a^2 \int_{-\infty}^{\infty} \exp(-2\alpha q^2) \, dq = 1.$$

The integral is found from Equation (2.3.4) and we deduce that

$$a_0 = \left(\frac{2\alpha}{\pi}\right)^{1/4}.$$

Likewise we can set up the wave function for the first excited state $n = 1$

$$\psi_1 = a_1 q \exp\left(-\alpha q^2\right)$$

which is normalized by the equation

$$a_1^2 \int_{-\infty}^{\infty} q^2 \exp\left(-2\alpha q^2\right) dq = 1$$

yielding

$$a_1 = \left(\frac{32\alpha}{\pi}\right)^{1/4}.$$

The next excited state ($n = 2$) is characterized by the function

$$\psi_2 = a_0'(1 - 4\alpha q^2) \exp\left(-\alpha q^2\right),$$

where the constant a_0' necessarily differs from the a_0 worked out for the lowest state. In this way we can build up a complete list of state functions for the various states, the polynomials $f_n(q)$ being derived from the recursion relation [Equation (7.5.3)]. The first three functions are shown schematically in Figure 7.10. It is clear from the nature of the series $f_n(q)$ that the parity of the functions alternates between even and odd in successive states, the parity always being the same as the parity of the quantum number n.

(c) The Uncertainty relation

The expression for zero-point energy prescribed by the quantum theory of a harmonic oscillator may be used to determine a precise limit for the product $(\Delta q \Delta p)$ appearing in Heisenberg's uncertainty relations. The spread of the ground-state function ψ_0 is a measure of the uncertainty in determinations of the particle position. The mean square deviation of the particle from the origin $q = 0$ is taken to be the mean square error in q measurements, that is,

$$(\Delta q)^2 = \frac{\displaystyle\int_{-\infty}^{\infty} q^2 \psi_0^2 \, dq}{\displaystyle\int_{-\infty}^{\infty} \psi_0^2 \, dq}$$

since ψ_0^2 represents the probability of locating the particle per unit distance along the q axis. By the methods of Section 2.3, we find

$$(\Delta q)^2 = \frac{\displaystyle\int_{-\infty}^{\infty} q^2 \exp\left(-2\alpha q^2\right) dq}{\displaystyle\int_{-\infty}^{\infty} \exp\left(-2\alpha q^2\right) dq} = \frac{1}{4\alpha}$$

$$= \frac{\hbar}{2m\omega}.$$

To this spread in position there corresponds a spread in momentum; the mean square deviation in momentum $(\Delta p)^2$ can be found directly from the energy eigenvalue in the ground state

$$E = \tfrac{1}{2}\hbar\omega = \frac{(\Delta p)^2}{2m} + \tfrac{1}{2}m\omega^2(\Delta q)^2$$

whence

$$(\Delta p)^2 = \tfrac{1}{2}m\hbar\omega.$$

This result shows that the zero-point energy is equally divided, on the average, between kinetic and potential energy, as in a classical oscillator. The product of the mean square deviations in displacement and momentum is

$$(\Delta q)^2(\Delta p)^2 = \tfrac{1}{4}\hbar^2$$

whence

$$\Delta q\,\Delta p = \tfrac{1}{2}\hbar. \qquad\qquad\qquad [7.5.5]$$

Thus for the ground state we obtain a precise value for the product of root-mean-square deviations in q and p. In any other state of the system, the product is necessarily larger, so in general we write

$$\Delta q\,\Delta p \geqslant \tfrac{1}{2}\hbar$$

in agreement with Equation (7.2.6).

7.6 Particle in a Central Field of Force

(a) Solution of Schrödinger's equation

In Section 7.3 we showed that the square of the angular momentum of a particle about the origin of coordinates is represented in quantum mechanics by a combination of angle-variable operators. It follows that, in a central field, where the potential energy varies only with the radius r, the angular momentum is constant in magnitude. We now find what values the angular momentum can take, by direct analysis of the appropriate Schrödinger equation

$$\nabla^2\psi + \frac{2M}{\hbar^2}\,[E - U(r)]\psi = 0,$$

where M stands for the particle mass.

In spherical polar coordinates the Laplacian operator is

$$\nabla^2 = \frac{\partial^2}{\partial r^2} + \frac{2}{r}\frac{\partial}{\partial r} + \frac{1}{r^2}\Lambda(\theta, \varphi),$$

where

$$\Lambda(\theta, \varphi) = \frac{1}{\sin\theta}\frac{\partial}{\partial\theta}\left(\sin\theta\frac{\partial}{\partial\theta}\right) + \frac{1}{\sin^2\theta}\frac{\partial}{\partial\varphi^2}$$

$$= -\frac{G^2}{\hbar^2} \quad \text{[by Equation (7.3.9)]}$$

if G^2 is the square of the angular momentum about the center of force.

It is now assumed that the state function $\psi(r, \theta, \varphi)$ may be expressed as the product of three separate functions

$$\psi(r, \theta, \varphi) = R(r)\,\Theta(\theta)\,\Phi(\varphi)$$

which enables us to solve the equation successively for Φ, Θ, and R. We substitute this product into the Schrödinger equation and multiply throughout by r^2 to obtain

$$\Theta\Phi\left[r^2\frac{d^2R}{dr^2} + 2r\frac{dR}{dr} + \frac{2Mr^2}{\hbar^2}(E - U)R\right] + R\,\Lambda(\theta,\,\varphi)\Theta\Phi = 0$$

which is divided by $R\Theta\Phi$ so that the variables are separated

$$\frac{1}{R}\left(r^2\frac{d^2R}{dr^2} + 2r\frac{dR}{dr}\right) + \frac{2Mr^2}{\hbar^2}(E - U) + \frac{1}{\Theta\Phi}\Lambda(\theta,\,\varphi)\Theta\Phi = 0. \qquad [7.6.1]$$

If we can find an appropriate solution for the angle functions $\Theta\Phi$, in the form

$$\Lambda(\theta,\,\varphi)\Theta\Phi = -C\Theta\Phi,$$

where C is constant, then two results follow:
  (i) the eigenvalues of $\Lambda(\theta,\,\varphi)$ are given by $-C$,
  (ii) the radial part of the equation becomes

$$\frac{1}{R}\left(r^2\frac{d^2R}{dr^2} + 2r\frac{dR}{dr}\right) + \frac{2Mr^2}{\hbar^2}(E - U) = C \qquad [7.6.2]$$

(where M stands for the mass of the particle).
  We therefore have to discover possible solutions for the angle-variable equation

$$\frac{1}{\Theta\Phi}\Lambda(\theta,\,\varphi)\Theta\Phi = -C,$$

or

$$\frac{1}{\Theta\sin\theta}\frac{d}{d\theta}\left(\sin\theta\frac{d\Theta}{d\theta}\right) + \frac{1}{\Phi\sin^2\theta}\frac{d^2\Phi}{d\varphi^2} = -C.$$

A proper solution requires that the function $\Phi(\varphi)$ be periodic at intervals of 2π rad, that is, the function must vary in azimuth somewhat as shown in Figure 7.2, except that we are concerned here only with the angular variation. Evidently Φ must be a sinusoidal function of φ and it is convenient to write Φ in the imaginary exponential form

$$\Phi = \exp(\pm im\varphi), \qquad [7.6.3]$$

where m is an integer. Thus

$$\frac{d^2\Phi}{d\varphi^2} = -m^2\Phi$$

and the equation in θ variables becomes

$$\frac{1}{\sin\theta}\frac{d}{d\theta}\left(\sin\theta\frac{d\Theta}{d\theta}\right) + C\Theta - \frac{m^2\Theta}{\sin^2\theta} = 0. \qquad [7.6.4]$$

The variable is changed from from θ to $\cos\theta$, which is written μ

$$\mu = \cos\theta$$
$$-d\mu = \sin\theta\,d\theta$$

and the equation becomes

$$\frac{d}{d\mu}\left[(1 - \mu^2)\frac{d\Theta}{d\mu}\right] + C\Theta - \frac{m^2\Theta}{1 - \mu^2} = 0.$$

Simplification of this equation is achieved by the substitutions

$$\Theta = (1 - \mu^2)^{m/2} g(\mu)$$

$$\frac{d\Theta}{d\mu} = -m\mu(1 - \mu^2)^{m/2-1}g + (1 - \mu^2)^{m/2}\frac{dg}{d\mu}$$

$$\frac{d^2\Theta}{d\mu^2} = -m(1 - \mu^2)^{m/2-1}g + m(m - 2)\mu^2(1 - \mu^2)^{m/2-2}g$$

$$- 2m\mu(1 - \mu^2)^{m/2-1}\frac{dg}{d\mu} + (1 - \mu^2)^{m/2}\frac{d^2g}{d\mu^2}.$$

After division by $(1 - \mu^2)^{m/2-1}$ we obtain

$$(1 - \mu^2)^2\frac{d^2g}{d\mu^2} - 2m\mu(1 - \mu^2)\frac{dg}{d\mu} + m(m - 2)\mu^2 g - m(1 - \mu^2)g$$

$$+ 2m\mu^2 g - 2\mu(1 - \mu^2)\frac{dg}{d\mu} + C(1 - \mu^2)g - m^2 g = 0$$

and further simplification yields

$$(1 - \mu^2)\frac{d^2g}{d\mu^2} - 2\mu(m + 1)\frac{dg}{d\mu} + (C - m - m^2)g = 0. \qquad [7.6.5]$$

This is a form of Legendre's equation and the associated Legendre polynomial solutions are found by solving in series

$$g(\mu) = \sum_{k=0} b_k \mu^{c+k},$$

where the constant c is to be found from the indicial equation. Substitution of this series into Equation (7.6.5) and selection of the coefficients of μ^{c-2} (for $k = 0$) yields directly

$$c(c - 1)b_0 = 0$$

so that $c = 0$ or $c = 1$. We can adopt $c = 0$ without loss of generality and proceed to find the recursion relation between pairs of b_k coefficients by taking all the coefficients of μ^k on the left-hand side of the equation

$$(k + 2)(k + 1)b_{k+2} - k(k - 1)b_k - 2k(m + 1)b_k + (C - m - m^2)b_k = 0$$

whence

$$\frac{b_{k+2}}{b_k} = \frac{k(k + 2m + 1) - (C - m - m^2)}{(k + 2)(k + 1)}$$

$$= \frac{(k + m)(k + m + 1) - C}{(k + 2)(k + 1)}. \qquad [7.6.6]$$

This recursion relation shows that solutions in closed form are obtained when the numerator vanishes, that is, the series terminates at the kth term if $b_{k+2} = 0$ and

$$C = (k + m)(k + m + 1),$$

where k and m are integers. The sum of these numbers is usually written l and we have the result

$$C = l(l + 1), \qquad \text{where} \quad l = 0, 1, 2, \ldots, \text{and so forth.} \qquad [7.6.7]$$

(b) Spherical harmonics and parity

It is conventional to write the product of angle functions, $\Theta\Phi$, as a spherical harmonic function specified by l and m numbers. Instead of using both signs of m in Equation (7.6.3) we write only the positive solution and then let m take negative values in the specification of the function

$$Y_{l,m}(\theta, \varphi) = \Theta(\varphi)\Phi(\varphi)$$

$$= (1 - \mu^2)^{m/2} \exp(im\varphi) \sum_{k=0}^{l-m} b_k \mu^k$$

$$= P_l^m(\cos \theta) \exp(im\varphi), \qquad [7.6.8]$$

where $P_l^m(\cos \theta)$ is the "associated Legendre polynomial" of order l and m in $\mu = \cos \theta$. When a particular value of l is chosen, the number m can take the integral values

$$m = l, (l - 1), \ldots 1, 0, -1, \ldots (-l + 1), (-l). \qquad [7.6.9]$$

In many applications this m number is written m_l to indicate that it is related to the quantum number l.

The normalization of the spherical harmonics is achieved by integrating over the entire range of angle variables, and for a single particle we may write

$$\int_{\theta=0}^{\pi} \int_{\varphi=0}^{2\pi} Y^*_{l,m} Y_{l,m} \sin \theta \, d\theta \, d\varphi = 1,$$

where the factor $(\sin \theta \, d\theta \, d\varphi)$ is the element of volume

$$dV = r^2 \sin \theta \, dr \, d\theta \, d\varphi$$

with the radial terms omitted. Alternatively the normalization condition may be expressed in Legendre polynomials

$$2\pi \int_{-1}^{1} [P_l^m(\cos \theta)]^2 \, d(\cos \theta) = 1,$$

where the factor 2π arises from the integration over φ. With the aid of the recursion relation [Equation (7.6.6)] and Equation (7.6.7) for constant C, we derive the following expressions for the first few normalized spherical harmonic functions:

$$l = 0, m = 0 \qquad Y_{0,0} = \frac{1}{\sqrt{4\pi}}$$

$$l = 1, m = 1 \qquad Y_{1,1} = \sqrt{\frac{3}{8\pi}} \sin \theta \exp(i\varphi)$$

$$l = 1, m = 0 \qquad Y_{1,0} = \sqrt{\frac{3}{4\pi}} \cos \theta$$

$$l = 1, m = -1 \qquad Y_{1,-1} = \sqrt{\frac{3}{8\pi}} \sin \theta \exp(-i\varphi)$$

$$l = 2, m = \pm 2 \qquad Y_{2,\pm 2} = \sqrt{\frac{15}{32\pi}} \sin^2 \theta \exp(\pm 2i\varphi)$$

$$l = 2, m = \pm 1 \qquad Y_{2,\pm 1} = \sqrt{\frac{15}{18\pi}} \sin \theta \cos \theta \exp(\pm i\varphi)$$

$$l = 2, m = 0 \qquad Y_{2,0} = \sqrt{\frac{5}{16\pi}} (1 - 3\cos^2 \theta).$$

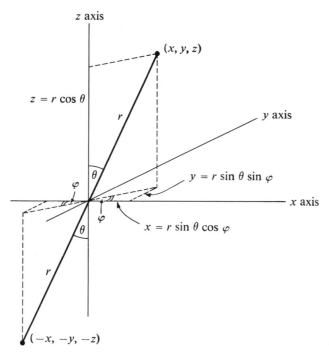

FIGURE 7.11 *The parity of a state function in three dimensions is found by reversing the coordinates of a point* (x, y, z) *to make* $(-x, -y, -z)$. *This is equivalent to changing from* (r, θ, φ) *to* $(r, \pi - \theta, \pi + \varphi)$ *in polar coordinates.*

It is important to derive the parity of these functions, because they are employed in numerous applications of the Schrödinger equation to problems in atomic and nuclear physics. Use of spherical polar coordinates requires that we modify the general concept of parity introduced in Section 7.4. Instead of changing the sign of one coordinate, we change the sign of all three Cartesian coordinates, substituting $(-x, -y, -z)$ for (x, y, z), and find the effect of this transformation on the sign of the state function. From Figure 7.11 we see that the transformation is equivalent, in polar coordinates, to substituting $(r, \pi - \theta, \pi + \varphi)$ for (r, θ, φ). If this criterion is applied to the spherical harmonic functions listed previously, it is found that all the functions with even l have parity, all those with odd l have odd parity. Thus the simple rule emerges that any spherical harmonic of order l has parity $(-1)^l$, where "$+1$" stands for even and "-1" for odd.

(c) Spatial quantization of angular momentum

Another important physical consequence of the solution of Schrödinger's equation in spherical harmonics is that the operator $\Lambda(\theta, \varphi)$ has eigenvalues

$$-C = -l(l + 1) \qquad \text{(from Equation 7.6.7)}.$$

By Equation (7.3.9), the eigenvalues of the squared angular momentum are given by

$$G^2 = \hbar^2 l(l + 1) \qquad [7.6.10]$$

so that the magnitude of the orbital angular momentum is

$$|G| = \hbar\sqrt{l(l + 1)}. \qquad [7.6.11]$$

Thus the l number characterizing the spherical harmonic function for a particular state determines the angular momentum as well as the parity. However, it remains to be found what values of the angular momentum are *observable*; that is, in view of the spatial quantization concept, introduced in Section 6.5, what component the angular momentum may have in any specified direction.

This question may be answered by taking one particular component of the angular momentum, say G_z, in operator form and applying this operator to the spherical-harmonic function $Y_{l,m}(\theta, \varphi)$ in order to determine the eigenvalues of G_z. Each eigenvalue then corresponds to an observable value of G_z. From Equations (7.3.6) and (7.3.7) we have

$$G_z = xp_y - yp_x$$

$$= -i\hbar\left(x\frac{\partial}{\partial y} - y\frac{\partial}{\partial x}\right).$$

Now from the standard relations between Cartesian and spherical polar coordinates

$$\left.\begin{aligned} z &= r\cos\theta \\ y &= r\sin\theta\sin\varphi \\ x &= r\sin\theta\cos\varphi \end{aligned}\right\} \qquad [7.6.12]$$

we deduce that

$$\frac{\partial}{\partial\varphi} = \frac{\partial x}{\partial\varphi}\frac{\partial}{\partial x} + \frac{\partial y}{\partial\varphi}\frac{\partial}{\partial y} + \frac{\partial z}{\partial\varphi}\frac{\partial}{\partial z}$$

$$= -r\sin\theta\sin\varphi\frac{\partial}{\partial x} + r\sin\theta\cos\varphi\frac{\partial}{\partial y}$$

$$= -y\frac{\partial}{\partial x} + x\frac{\partial}{\partial y}$$

and

$$G_z = -i\hbar\frac{\partial}{\partial\varphi}. \qquad [7.6.13]$$

Applying this operator to the state function for any central force situation, we obtain

$$G_z\psi = G_z R(r)\,\Theta(\theta)\,\Phi(\varphi)$$

$$= -i\hbar\frac{\partial}{\partial\varphi}[R(r)\,\Theta(\theta)\,\Phi(\varphi)]$$

$$= -i\hbar R(r)\,\Theta(\theta)\frac{\partial}{\partial\varphi}[\exp(im\varphi)]$$

$$= m\hbar\psi. \qquad [7.6.14]$$

Thus the eigenvalues of G_z are integral multiples of $\hbar$, since the quantum number m takes the values

$$m = l,\,(l-1),\,\ldots,\,1,\,0,\,-1,\,\ldots(-l),$$

that is, $(2l + 1)$ different values.

In this way we obtain a more precise formulation of the idea of spatial quantization, differing in detail from the earlier notions of the Bohr theory (Section 6.5). In quantum mechanics, the orbital angular momentum is characterized by a quantum number l and is represented by a vector of magnitude $\hbar\sqrt{l(l+1)}$, while its component in any specified direction is an integral multiple of the basic unit $\hbar$. The diagram of Figure 7.12 illustrates

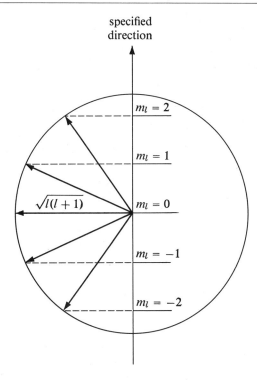

FIGURE 7.12 *The spatial quantization of orbital angular momentum in quantum mechanics is represented schematically by a vector of length $\sqrt{l(l+1)}$ which has components $m_l = l, l-1, \ldots, 1, 0, -1, \ldots, -l$ in any specified direction. The diagram has been drawn for $l = 2$.*

the new concept of spatial quantization and is to be compared with the Bohr version in Figure 6.8.

The new rules derived for orbital angular momentum are obeyed by all forms of angular momentum, except insofar as the introduction of electron spin and half-odd integral quantum numbers has the effect of altering the possible m values. Thus, if the total angular momentum of a system is denoted by the number J, its magnitude is $\hbar\sqrt{J(J+1)}$ and its component in any specified direction is given by $m_J\hbar$, where m_J takes the values

$$m_J = J, (J-1), \ldots (-J+1), (-J). \qquad [7.6.15]$$

This is a general rule, which includes the rule worked out for orbital angular momentum [Equation (7.6.9)]: in future the m number related to orbital motion will be written m_l where confusion is likely to arise.

7.7 The Hydrogenlike Atom

The method developed in the previous section for dealing with a particle in a central field of force may be used to find the energy levels in a single-electron atom. However, the theory is still subject to two severe limitations. The Schrödinger wave equation is not relativistically invariant and it takes no account of the intrinsic angular momentum of the electron, usually called the "spin" of the particle. With these limitations, the quantum-mechanical treatment leads to the same result as the Bohr theory, with, however, new significance attached to the quantum numbers. Here we shall develop the theory as it applies to two particles of any mass interacting according to the Coulomb law of force. The results are therefore relevant, subject to the limitations mentioned, to a nucleus-plus-electron system (the hydrogenlike atom) and to a positron-plus-electron system (called *positronium*) and to various dual combinations of charged mesons with nuclei and electrons.

(a) Schrödinger's equation for two interacting particles

First we have to set up the Schrödinger equation for two particles in coordinates moving with their common center of mass. In general coordinates, the momentum of any particle is the sum of its momentum relative to the center of mass and a fraction of the total momentum ($\mathbf{P}$) measured in the general frame. Thus for two masses m_1 and m_2 we may write the separate momenta as

$$\mathbf{p}_1 = \boldsymbol{\pi}_1 + \frac{m_1 \mathbf{P}}{m_1 + m_2}$$

$$\mathbf{p}_2 = \boldsymbol{\pi}_2 + \frac{m_2 \mathbf{P}}{m_1 + m_2},$$

where $\boldsymbol{\pi}_1$ and $\boldsymbol{\pi}_2$ are the components relative to the center of mass. These components are necessarily equal and opposite, in order that we may satisfy the condition

$$\mathbf{p}_1 + \mathbf{p}_2 = \mathbf{P} \text{ (the total momentum)}$$

so
$$\boldsymbol{\pi}_1 + \boldsymbol{\pi}_2 = 0.$$

In the general frame, the nonrelativistic Hamiltonian function takes the form

$$H = \frac{p_1^2}{2m_1} + \frac{p_2^2}{2m_2} + U(r),$$

where, for a central force, the potential energy U depends only on the distance between the particles (r). Substitution of the expressions for $\mathbf{p}_1$ and $\mathbf{p}_2$ leads to the result

$$H = \frac{\pi_1^2}{2m_1} + \frac{\pi_2^2}{2m_2} + \frac{(\boldsymbol{\pi}_1 + \boldsymbol{\pi}_2)\mathbf{P}}{m_1 + m_2} + \frac{P^2}{2(m_1 + m_2)} + U(r)$$

or, since $\boldsymbol{\pi}_1 + \boldsymbol{\pi}_2 = 0$,

$$H = \frac{(m_1 + m_2)\pi^2}{2m_1 m_2} + \frac{P^2}{2M} + U(r), \qquad [7.7.1]$$

where the total mass $M = m_1 + m_2$ and

$$\pi = |\boldsymbol{\pi}_1| = |\boldsymbol{\pi}_2|.$$

Therefore the kinetic energy is the sum of the system's kinetic energy as a whole ($P^2/2M$) and the internal or "reduced" energy

$$\left(\frac{m_1 + m_2}{2m_1 m_2}\right)\pi^2 = \frac{\pi^2}{2\mu}, \qquad [7.7.2]$$

where the "reduced mass" is

$$\mu = \frac{m_1 m_2}{m_1 + m_2}.$$

In the quantum theory we translate the reduced energy into operator form by writing

$$\pi = -i\hbar \frac{\partial}{\partial r}$$

so that the one-dimensional Schrödinger equation becomes

$$H\psi = E'\psi$$

or

$$-\frac{\hbar^2}{2\mu}\frac{\partial^2\psi}{\partial r^2} + \frac{P^2}{2M}\,\psi + U(r)\psi = E'\psi.$$

The observed total energy of the system is denoted by E' and is the sum of the internal energy (E) and eigenvalues of the external energy $(P^2/2M)$. The latter term cancels the $(P^2/2M)$ term on the left and we have the *reduced* Schrödinger equation

$$-\frac{\hbar^2}{2\mu}\frac{\partial^2\psi}{\partial r^2} + U(r)\psi = E\psi$$

which may be generalized to make the three-dimensional equation

$$\nabla^2\psi + \frac{2\mu}{\hbar^2}[E - U(r)]\psi = 0, \qquad [7.7.3]$$

where r is still the distance between the particles. The same result may be obtained by direct transformation of the Laplacian operator from general into center-of-mass coordinates.

(b) *Solution of the Schrödinger equation*

In a hydrogenlike atom, where the nuclear mass is denoted by M and the electron mass by m, we have the reduced mass

$$\mu = \frac{Mm}{M + m}$$

and the potential energy

$$U(r) = -\frac{Ze^2}{[4\pi\varepsilon_0]r}.$$

In spherical polar coordinates, the Laplacian operator is

$$\nabla^2 = \frac{\partial^2}{\partial r^2} + \frac{2}{r}\frac{\partial}{\partial r} + \frac{1}{r^2}\Lambda(\theta, \varphi)$$

and we showed in Section 7.6 that, for a central force, with

$$\psi = R(r)\,\Theta(\theta)\,\Phi(\varphi)$$

the angle-variable functions are spherical harmonics with the property

$$\Lambda(\theta, \varphi)Y_{l,m} = -l(l + 1)Y_{l,m}.$$

The radial equation in $R(r)$ therefore becomes [see Equation (7.6.1)]

$$\frac{d^2R}{dr^2} + \frac{2}{r}\frac{dR}{dr} + R\left\{\frac{2\mu E}{\hbar^2} + \frac{2\mu Ze^2}{[4\pi\varepsilon_0]\hbar^2 r} - \frac{l(l + 1)}{r^2}\right\} = 0. \qquad [7.7.4]$$

The asymptotic form of the function $R(r)$ as r becomes very large may be found by neglecting all terms involving r^{-1} and r^{-2}, which leaves

$$\frac{d^2R}{dr^2} + \frac{2\mu E}{\hbar^2}R \approx 0.$$

From this equation it follows that, when the net energy E is positive, the functions $R(r)$ are periodic in r and these solutions correspond to classical free particles with a continuous distribution of energies. In classical mechanics such particles would describe hyperbolic orbits with the nucleus (assumed to be massive) in the near focus.

The only *discrete* eigenvalues of the energy are obtained when E is negative, that is, the particle is "bound" to the nucleus in the classical sense. We then write

$$\kappa^2 = -\frac{2\mu E}{\hbar^2}$$

and adopt the asymptotic solution

$$R(r) \approx \exp(-\kappa r) \qquad \text{for } r \text{ large.}$$

The full solution is supposed to take the form

$$R(r) = u(r) \exp(-\kappa r),$$

where $u(r)$ is a function of the radius which is to satisfy the conditions of regularity imposed on all state functions. In Equation (7.7.4) we substitute

$$\frac{dR}{dr} = -\kappa u \exp(-\kappa r) + \frac{du}{dr} \exp(-\kappa r)$$

$$\frac{d^2R}{dr^2} = \kappa^2 u \exp(-\kappa r) - 2\kappa \frac{du}{dr} \exp(-\kappa r) + \frac{d^2u}{dr^2} \exp(-\kappa r)$$

and obtain, after simplification,

$$\frac{d^2u}{dr^2} + 2\left(\frac{1}{r} - \kappa\right)\frac{du}{dr} + u\left\{\frac{2\mu Ze^2}{[4\pi\varepsilon_0]\hbar^2 r} - \frac{2\kappa}{r} - \frac{l(l+1)}{r^2}\right\} = 0.$$

This equation may be solved in series to find a closed expression for $u(r)$

$$u(r) = \sum_{\rho=0} b_\rho r^{c+\rho},$$

where the constant c is to be determined by taking the coefficients of the lowest power of r, namely, r^{c-2},

$$b_0[c(c-1) + 2c - l(l+1)] = 0,$$

that is,

$$c(c+1) = l(l+1).$$

The solutions for c are $c = l$ and $c = -l - 1$. Of these the latter is ruled out by the condition that $u(r)$ must not diverge at the origin $r = 0$. We therefore adopt $c = l$ and find a recursion relation between the b_ρ coefficients by taking the coefficients of $r^{l+\rho-1}$

$$(l + \rho + 1)(l + \rho)b_{\rho+1} + 2(l + \rho + 1)b_{\rho+1} - 2\kappa(l + \rho)b_\rho$$

$$+ \frac{2\mu Ze^2}{[4\pi\varepsilon_0]\hbar^2} b_\rho - 2\kappa b_\rho - l(l+1)b_{\rho+1} = 0.$$

The ratio of successive coefficients is

$$\frac{b_{\rho+1}}{b_\rho} = \frac{2\kappa(l + \rho + 1) - \dfrac{2\mu Ze^2}{[4\pi\varepsilon_0]\hbar^2}}{(l + \rho + 2)(l + \rho + 1) - l(l+1)}. \qquad [7.7.5]$$

This result shows that we can adopt closed solutions in polynomial form (the "Laguerre polynomials") by arranging for the series to terminate at the pth power in r

$$b_{p+1} = 0$$

if

$$2\kappa(l + p + 1) = \frac{2\mu Z e^2}{[4\pi\varepsilon_0]\hbar^2} .$$

This equation yields the energy eigenvalues

$$E = -\frac{\mu Z^2 e^4}{2[4\pi\varepsilon_0]^2\hbar^2} \frac{1}{(l + p + 1)^2} , \qquad [7.7.6]$$

the same as Bohr's result, corrected for the finite nuclear mass, if we write Bohr's quantum number (n) as

$$n = l + p + 1.$$

Since the number p can take integral values from 0 upwards, the quantity $(n - l)$ is equal to 1, 2, 3, . . . , and so forth. In other words, if the *principal* quantum number n is given, the angular momentum number l adopts the values 0, 1, 2, . . . $(n - 1)$. Such a rule had been worked out in the semiclassical theory of elliptical orbits, but here the derivation is direct instead of empirical. Moreover, the present treatment shows that the number n determines the *energy* of the system, independent of the value of l (for single-electron atoms). In this approximation, therefore, the energy levels are degenerate, with different electron states having the same energy. In more complicated atoms, the mutual electron interactions have the effect of removing this degeneracy, with the result that the energy depends on l as well as n.

(c) State functions

The significance of the *radial* quantum number p may be discovered by examining the properties of the radial functions $R(r)$ which are solutions of Equation (7.7.4). We have shown that

$$R(r) = u(r) \exp(-\kappa r),$$

where $u(r)$ is a polynomial expression (the Laguerre polynomial) and

$$\kappa^2 = -\frac{2\mu E}{\hbar^2} = \frac{2\mu}{\hbar^2} \frac{\mu Z^2 e^4}{2[4\pi\varepsilon_0]^2\hbar^2 n^2} .$$

Thus for a particular value of n we may write

$$\kappa_n = \frac{\mu Z e^2}{[4\pi\varepsilon_0]\hbar^2 n} . \qquad [7.7.7]$$

This parameter is expressed conveniently in terms of the radius (r_1) of the first hydrogen orbit in Bohr's theory (Section 6.4), corrected for the finite nuclear mass

$$r_1 = \frac{[4\pi\varepsilon_0]\hbar^2}{\mu e^2} = 5.29 \times 10^{-11} \text{m}.$$

Thus, for any nuclear charge Z and quantum number n,

$$\kappa_n = \frac{Z}{n r_1} .$$

The Laguerre functions are found from the series recursion relation [Equation (7.7.5)] and the (non-normalized) radial functions for the first few states are written as $R_{n,l}$ below

$$n = 1, l = 0, \rho = 0 \qquad R_{1,0} = b_0 \exp{(-\kappa_1 r)}$$

$$n = 2, l = 0, \rho = 1 \qquad R_{2,0} = b_0'(1 - \kappa_2 r) \exp{(-\kappa_2 r)}$$

$$n = 2, l = 1, \rho = 0 \qquad R_{2,1} = b_1' \kappa_2 r \exp{(-\kappa_2 r)}$$

$$n = 3, l = 0, \rho = 2 \qquad R_{3,0} = b_0''\left(1 - 2\kappa_3 r + \frac{2\kappa_3^2 r^2}{3}\right) \exp{(-\kappa_3 r)}$$

$$n = 3, l = 1, \rho = 1 \qquad R_{3,1} = b_1'' \kappa_3 r(1 - \tfrac{1}{2}\kappa_3 r) \exp{(-\kappa_3 r)}$$

$$n = 3, l = 2, \rho = 0 \qquad R_{3,2} = b_2''(\kappa_3 r)^2 \exp{(-\kappa_3 r)}.$$

These functions are plotted, with arbitrary amplitudes, as dependent on the parameter Zr/r_1 in Figure 7.13. It is clear from the behavior of the curves and from the occurrence of ρ in the series that the number ρ represents the number of radial nodes in each case, that is, the number of points between zero and infinity where $R(r)$ vanishes.

The normalization of the complete state functions $\psi(r, \theta, \varphi)$ for the hydrogenlike atom follows from Equation (7.1.11), expressed in spherical polar coordinates

$$\int_{r=0}^{\infty} \int_{\theta=0}^{\pi} \int_{\varphi=0}^{2\pi} \psi^*(r, \theta, \varphi)\, \psi(r, \theta, \varphi)\, r^2 \sin\theta \, dr \, d\theta \, d\varphi = 1. \qquad [7.7.8]$$

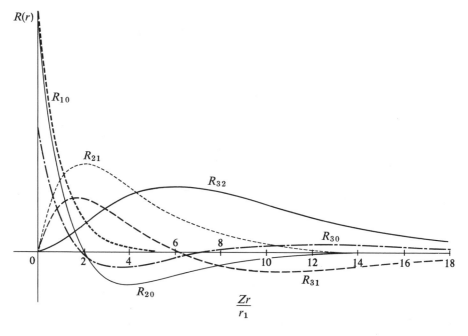

FIGURE 7.13 *The radial functions $R_{n,l}(r)$ plotted (with arbitrary amplitude) against $\frac{Zr}{r_1}$ for the cases $n = 1, 2,$ and 3.*

The angle variables are represented by spherical harmonic functions $Y_{l,m}(\theta, \varphi)$ which obey the condition

$$\int_{\theta=0}^{\pi} \int_{\varphi=0}^{2\pi} Y_{l,m}^*(\theta, \varphi)\, Y_{l,m}(\theta, \varphi)\, \sin\theta\, d\theta\, d\varphi = 1.$$

The radial functions must therefore satisfy the condition

$$\int_{r=0}^{\infty} [R_{n,l}(r)]^2\, r^2\, dr = 1.$$

For example, the lowest state ($n = 1$, $l = 0$) yields

$$b_0^2 \int_0^{\infty} \exp(-2\kappa_1 r)\, r^2\, dr = 1$$

whence

$$b_0 = (4\kappa_1^3)^{1/2} = 2\left(\frac{Z}{r_1}\right)^{3/2}$$

and the complete state function, written as $\psi_{n,l,m}(r, \theta, \varphi)$, is

$$\psi_{1,0,0} = R_{1,0}(r)Y_{0,0}(\theta, \varphi)$$

$$= \frac{b_0}{\sqrt{4\pi}} \exp(-\kappa_1 r). \qquad [7.7.9]$$

In this way we can obtain functions for all states denoted by the quantum numbers n, l, m and find the following:

$$\psi_{1,0,0} = \frac{1}{\sqrt{\pi}}\left(\frac{Z}{r_1}\right)^{3/2} \exp\left(-\frac{Zr}{r_1}\right),$$

$$\psi_{2,0,0} = \frac{1}{\sqrt{8\pi}}\left(\frac{Z}{r_1}\right)^{3/2}\left(1 - \frac{Zr}{2r_1}\right) \exp\left(-\frac{Zr}{2r_1}\right),$$

$$\psi_{2,1,\pm 1} = \frac{1}{4\sqrt{\pi}}\left(\frac{Z}{r_1}\right)^{3/2} \frac{Zr}{2r_1} \exp\left(-\frac{Zr}{2r_1}\right) \sin\theta \exp(\pm i\varphi),$$

$$\psi_{2,1,0} = \frac{1}{\sqrt{8\pi}}\left(\frac{Z}{r_1}\right)^{3/2} \frac{Zr}{2r_1} \exp\left(-\frac{Zr}{2r_1}\right) \cos\theta,$$

$$\psi_{3,0,0} = \frac{1}{\sqrt{27\pi}}\left(\frac{Z}{r_1}\right)^{3/2}\left(1 - \frac{2Zr}{3r_1} + \frac{2Z^2 r^2}{27 r_1^2}\right) \exp\left(-\frac{Zr}{3r_1}\right),$$

$$\psi_{3,1,\pm 1} = \frac{2}{9\sqrt{\pi}}\left(\frac{Z}{r_1}\right)^{3/2} \frac{Zr}{3r_1}\left(1 - \frac{Zr}{6r_1}\right) \exp\left(-\frac{Zr}{3r_1}\right) \sin\theta \exp(\pm i\varphi),$$

$$\psi_{3,1,0} = \frac{2\sqrt{2}}{9\sqrt{\pi}}\left(\frac{Z}{r_1}\right)^{3/2} \frac{Zr}{3r_1}\left(1 - \frac{Zr}{6r_1}\right) \exp\left(-\frac{Zr}{3r_1}\right) \cos\theta,$$

$$\psi_{3,2,\pm 2} = \frac{1}{18\sqrt{\pi}}\left(\frac{Z}{r_1}\right)^{3/2}\left(\frac{Zr}{3r_1}\right)^2 \exp\left(-\frac{Zr}{3r_1}\right) \sin^2\theta \exp(\pm 2i\varphi),$$

$$\psi_{3,2,\pm 1} = \frac{1}{9\sqrt{\pi}}\left(\frac{Z}{r_1}\right)^{3/2}\left(\frac{Zr}{3r_1}\right)^2 \exp\left(-\frac{Zr}{3r_1}\right) \sin\theta \cos\theta \exp(\pm i\varphi),$$

$$\psi_{3,2,0} = \frac{1}{9\sqrt{6\pi}}\left(\frac{Z}{r_1}\right)^{3/2}\left(\frac{Zr}{3r_1}\right)^2 \exp\left(-\frac{Zr}{3r_1}\right)(1 - 3\cos^2\theta).$$

It is evident that the variation of ψ with r, θ, and φ is extremely complicated, except for states with $l = 0$, which possess spherical symmetry, and which have radial functions like those of Figure 7.13, labeled $R_{1,0}$, $R_{2,0}$, and $R_{3,0}$.

The probability of locating the electron in a hydrogenlike atom is given by the three-dimensional "probability density," expressed in spherical polar coordinates,

$$|\psi|^2 \, dV = |\psi|^2 \, r^2 \sin \theta \, dr \, d\theta \, d\varphi.$$

The function $|\psi|^2$ does not vary with the angle φ so all the distributions are symmetrical about the z axis, that is, about the line $\theta = 0$. The variation with angle θ, when a fixed radius is adopted, may be shown in the form of polar diagrams of $|\psi|^2$ plotted against θ, as in Figure 7.14. Here the length of any radius from the center is proportional to the probability of locating the electron per unit solid angle. The curves shown are for $l = 2$, and more complex shapes are found as the value of l increases.

In states possessing spherical symmetry, the probability of locating the electron per unit

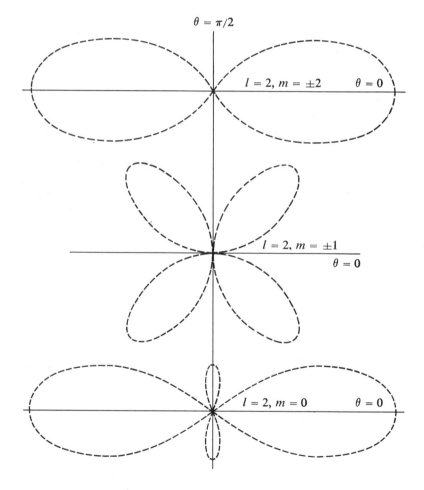

FIGURE 7.14 *The function $|\psi|^2$ plotted against angle θ in polar form (with r fixed) for $l = 2$, which yields three different angular distributions.*

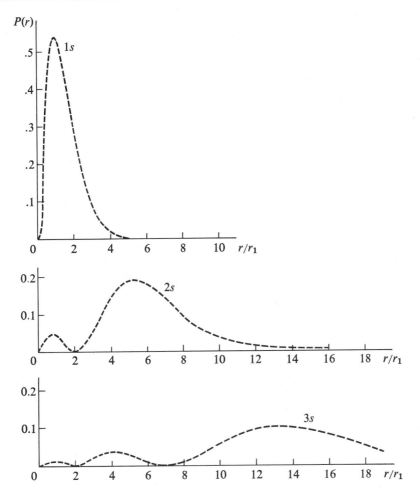

FIGURE 7.15 *The normalized probability function P(r) plotted against r/r₁ for states of the hydrogen atom with spherical symmetry (l = 0) and n = 1, 2, and 3.*

interval in radius r is obtained by integrating $|\psi|^2\,dV$ over all angles

$$P(r)\,dr = \int_{\theta=0}^{\pi}\int_{\varphi=0}^{2\pi}|\psi|^2\,r^2\sin\theta\,dr\,d\theta\,d\varphi$$

$$= 4\pi[R(r)]^2 r^2\,dr.$$

Here $4\pi r^2\,dr$ represents the volume of a spherical shell between radii r and $(r + dr)$, which is multiplied by $[R(r)]^2$ to yield the probability as a function of radius. In Figure 7.15 we plot $P(r)$ as the normalized probability against the ratio r/r_1 for the three states $n = 1, 2$, and 3, all with $l = 0$. In the usual chemical notation, electrons with $l = 0$ are denoted by "s," so the radial distribution curves are labeled $1s$, $2s$, and $3s$, respectively. It is interesting to note that each curve contains n maxima, in positions which correspond, very roughly, with the radii of the Bohr orbits. However it should be emphasized that the three peaks of the $3s$ electron distribution correspond in energy with a *single* orbit radius in the Bohr theory. In general the quantum-mechanical treatment yields results which are far removed from the semiclassical concept of orbiting electrons.

7.8 Electron Spin and the Exclusion Principle

A major shortcoming of the Schrödinger theory of hydrogenlike atoms is its failure to account for the fine structure of spectral lines, including those of hydrogen. Sommerfeld's semiclassical treatment of 1916 showed that a relativistic theory of electrons is necessary, but an extra factor in the problem became important with the discovery of electron "spin." Several lines of evidence converged to indicate that an electron possesses intrinsic angular momentum and that this is a two-valued quantum variable. In 1925 Uhlenbeck and Goudsmit suggested that this intrinsic momentum has observable values $\pm\frac{1}{2}\hbar$. In the Stern-Gerlach experiment, for example, the neutral silver atoms might have spin momentum only, due to the single valence electron in each atom, and the observed splitting of the beam into two components could be explained.

It is to be emphasized that, although the eigenvalues of the observed spin momentum of an electron are $\pm\frac{1}{2}\hbar$, the *change* in angular momentum from one state to the other is necessarily $\hbar$, which remains the indivisible unit of angular momentum. Thus all changes in the electron configuration of an atom involve angular-momentum changes which are multiples of $\hbar$, whether orbital or spin momentum is subjected to alteration.

(a) Pauli matrices

The identification of electron spin immediately raised the problem of incorporating this new type of variable with the scheme of dynamical operators outlined in Section 7.3. Unlike the other variables in the Hamiltonian function, the spin momentum cannot be replaced by a differential operator. Pauli tackled this problem by writing a new angular momentum vector $\mathbf{G}_s$ in the form

$$\mathbf{G}_s = \tfrac{1}{2}\hbar\boldsymbol{\sigma}, \qquad [7.8.1]$$

where $\boldsymbol{\sigma}$ is a three-component variable with certain special properties. In the first place, the component of $\boldsymbol{\sigma}$ in any specified direction, say the "z" or third direction, must have eigenvalues ± 1, since the observed values of G_s are $\pm\frac{1}{2}\hbar$. If, therefore, σ_3 operates on a two-valued state function ψ which is composed of ψ_+ (representing the condition in which the eigenvalue is $+1$) and ψ_- (representing the condition with eigenvalue -1), we have

$$\left. \begin{array}{l} \sigma_3\psi_+ = +\psi_+ \\ \sigma_3\psi_- = -\psi_- \end{array} \right\} \qquad [7.8.2]$$

These two equations are conveniently replaced by a single matrix type of equation

$$\sigma_3\psi = \pm\psi, \qquad [7.8.3]$$

where ψ stands for the one-column matrix $\begin{pmatrix} \psi_+ \\ \psi_- \end{pmatrix}$

and σ_3 is represented by the 2×2 matrix $\begin{pmatrix} 1 & 0 \\ 0 & -1 \end{pmatrix}$

The other two components of **σ** are found from the particular commutation relations obeyed by these operators. Since $\mathbf{G}_s$ is an angular momentum vector, we suppose that it satisfies the same relations as **G** in Equation (7.3.8), for example,

$$G_{s1}G_{s2} - G_{s2}G_{s1} = i\hbar G_{s3}$$

or, in terms of the σ variables,

$$\sigma_1\sigma_2 - \sigma_2\sigma_1 = 2i\sigma_3 \tag{7.8.4}$$

and two other relations obtained by cyclic permutation. We also suppose that all three components of **σ** have unit magnitude, that is, their squares are identical with the unit matrix (I)

$$\sigma_3^2 = \begin{pmatrix} 1 & 0 \\ 0 & -1 \end{pmatrix}\begin{pmatrix} 1 & 0 \\ 0 & -1 \end{pmatrix} = \begin{pmatrix} 1 & 0 \\ 0 & 1 \end{pmatrix} = I.$$

Likewise

$$\sigma_1^2 = \sigma_2^2 = I.$$

With the aid of these assumptions we can derive several algebraic relations between the components of **σ**. For example, if we multiply Equation (7.8.4) on the left by σ_1, we find

$$\sigma_1^2\sigma_2 - \sigma_1\sigma_2\sigma_1 = 2i\sigma_1\sigma_3,$$

that is,

$$\sigma_2 - (2i\sigma_3 + \sigma_2\sigma_1)\sigma_1 = 2i\sigma_1\sigma_3 \text{ [from Equation (7.8.4)]}$$

whence

$$\sigma_2 - 2i\sigma_3\sigma_1 - \sigma_2 = 2i\sigma_1\sigma_3$$

or

$$\sigma_3\sigma_1 = -\sigma_1\sigma_3 = i\sigma_2 \tag{7.8.5}$$

and two similar relations obtained by cyclic permutation. These relations show that the **σ** components "anticommute" with each other. This property is characteristic of operators representing particles of spin $\frac{1}{2}\hbar$.

Pauli showed that the following three 2×2 matrices satisfy the conditions established:

$$\sigma_1 = \begin{pmatrix} 0 & 1 \\ 1 & 0 \end{pmatrix} \qquad \sigma_2 = \begin{pmatrix} 0 & -i \\ i & 0 \end{pmatrix} \qquad \sigma_3 = \begin{pmatrix} 1 & 0 \\ 0 & -1 \end{pmatrix}. \tag{7.8.6}$$

Any other 2×2 matrices must be linear combinations of these three basic matrices with the unit matrix. The Pauli matrices possess the essential property that the component of **σ** in any direction relative to the three chosen axes has eigenvalues ± 1, so that the observed spin momentum is always $\pm\frac{1}{2}\hbar$. For example, suppose that we choose a direction specified by the three numbers (λ, μ, ν) which are the direction cosines, defined, for any point (x, y, z) on the line, by the equations

$$\lambda = \frac{x}{r}, \quad \mu = \frac{y}{r}, \quad \nu = \frac{z}{r}.$$

Then the component of **σ** in this direction is represented by the expression

$$\sigma(\lambda, \mu, \nu) = \lambda\sigma_1 + \mu\sigma_2 + \nu\sigma_3$$

$$= \lambda\begin{pmatrix} 0 & 1 \\ 1 & 0 \end{pmatrix} + \mu\begin{pmatrix} 0 & -i \\ i & 0 \end{pmatrix} + \nu\begin{pmatrix} 1 & 0 \\ 0 & -1 \end{pmatrix}$$

$$= \begin{pmatrix} \nu & \lambda - i\mu \\ \lambda + i\mu & -\nu \end{pmatrix}.$$

The square of this matrix is obtained by the standard rules of matrix multiplication

$$[\sigma(\lambda, \mu, \nu)]^2 = \begin{pmatrix} \nu & \lambda - i\mu \\ \lambda + i\mu & -\nu \end{pmatrix} \begin{pmatrix} \nu & \lambda - i\mu \\ \lambda + i\mu & -\nu \end{pmatrix}$$

$$= \begin{pmatrix} \lambda^2 + \mu^2 + \nu^2 & 0 \\ 0 & \lambda^2 + \mu^2 + \nu^2 \end{pmatrix}$$

$$= \begin{pmatrix} 1 & 0 \\ 0 & 1 \end{pmatrix} = I.$$

Thus the eigenvalues of the expression $\sigma(\lambda, \mu, \nu)$ are always ± 1.

The vector $\boldsymbol{\sigma}$ has properties similar to those described for the angular momentum of orbital motion in Section 7.6. The magnitude of the vector is found from the sum

$$|\sigma|^2 = \sigma_1^2 + \sigma_2^2 + \sigma_3^2$$

whence

$$|\mathbf{G}_s| = \hbar\sqrt{\tfrac{3}{4}} = \hbar\sqrt{\tfrac{1}{2}(\tfrac{1}{2} + 1)}. \qquad [7.8.7]$$

Thus in applications involving spatial quantization of the spin angular momentum, $\mathbf{G}_s$ for one electron can be represented by a vector of length $\hbar\sqrt{\tfrac{1}{2}(\tfrac{1}{2} + 1)}$, with components $\pm\tfrac{1}{2}\hbar$ along any specified direction. This scheme is similar to that of Figure 7.12 except that the vector has only two possible orientations. If there are *two* electrons with their spins parallel, the total spin angular momentum is represented by a vector denoted by $S = 1$ (in units of $\hbar$), with magnitude $\hbar\sqrt{2}$ and components $m_S\hbar$, where m_S takes the values

$$m_S = S, (S - 1), \ldots (-S) = 1, 0, -1. \qquad [7.8.8]$$

This rule may be generalized to cover the spins of any number of electrons. In all atomic states, S is used to denote the total spin and L denotes the total orbital angular momentum, the same rules of quantization being employed throughout [see Equation (7.6.15)].

(b) Pauli's Exclusion principle

With the aid of the spin formalism, Pauli, Thomas, and others were able to bring spin into the structure of quantum mechanics and to explain a wide range of phenomena, including the anomalous Zeeman effect. Even before Uhlenbeck and Goudsmit explicitly recognized spin as a variable, Pauli's work on the structure of complex atoms had shown that, in any many-electron system, each electron state is uniquely specified by four quantum numbers. Moreover, different electrons have different sets of numbers and this is the basis of the famous Exclusion principle: in any closed system, no two electrons can have the same set of numbers, denoted (in the case of an atom) by n, l, m_l, and m_s. Of these four numbers, three are established in a hierarchy by the Schrödinger theory of Section 7.7, which assigned the following properties:

n the principal quantum number of Bohr, which fixes the energy of a hydrogenlike atom and denotes the main shell in a complex atom;

l the orbital angular momentum number, which adopts the values $0, 1, 2, \ldots (n - 1)$;

m_l a "magnetic" quantum number, defining the component of the orbital angular momentum in any specified direction and taking the values $l, (l - 1), \ldots, 1, 0, -1, \ldots (-l)$. In addition, we now have the spin component, denoted by m_s and taking the values $\pm\tfrac{1}{2}$ only.

The introduction of m_s effectively doubles the number of electronic states allowed by the Schrödinger theory and it solves a long-standing difficulty encountered by the Bohr theory. It is well known that the element helium, with two electrons outside the nucleus, is outstandingly stable from the chemical point of view and also possesses the highest ionization potential (W_0) of any element (Figure 4.7). These facts could be explained if both extra nuclear electrons are accommodated in the first ($n = 1$) shell, but the relations between these two electrons remained obscure in the earlier theory. According to Pauli's principle, the two electrons are characterized by opposite spins in the ground state of helium and the total angular momentum (spin and orbital) is zero. On this basis the essential properties of helium atoms were worked out by Heisenberg in 1926.

With the aid of the four quantum numbers previously defined we can show that the entire structure of the periodic table of chemical elements is explicable in terms of Pauli's principle. The various electron states in an atom are filled in turn, and every time a shell or subshell is completed (as in helium) the chemical properties undergo significant changes. For example, the "inert" gases above helium always possess a full complement of eight electrons in the outer "valence" shell or subshell.*

In spectroscopic notation the different subshells (or the electrons in the subshells) are identified by a number n (having values 1, 2, 3, . . . , and so forth) and a letter (s, p, d, f, g, h, . . . , and so forth) which indicates the value of l (0, 1, 2, 3, 4, 5, . . . , respectively). The full sequence of subshells is then obtained by writing down all the l values in each main shell; for each value l there are ($2l + 1$) components m_l, hence $2(2l + 1)$ total states when spin is taken into account. In any main shell the total possible number of electrons is

$$\sum_{l=0}^{n-1} 2(2l + 1) = 2n^2$$

giving the sequence 2, 8, 18, 32, 50, . . . , when $n = 1, 2, 3, 4, 5, ...$ The division of these numbers into subshells is shown in Table 7.1.

If the sequence of chemical elements were formed by filling subshells in the above order, we should have a periodic table with 2, 8, 18, 32, 50, . . . elements in the successive rows. The first two rows are indeed filled according to this scheme and the chemical behavior of all the lightest elements (up to $Z = 18$) depends directly on the number of electrons in the outer or valence shell. Beyond this region the classification becomes more complex (see Appendix II) with three transition series and the group of rare earths breaking the similarity of elements falling in the same column.

The occurrence of the transition series depends on the way in which the energy of an electron in a particular subshell varies with the quantum numbers n and l and the atomic number Z. The energy relations of the different subshells are shown schematically in Figure 7.16, where the sequence in order of energy is plotted against Z. It is seen that when all the lower subshells are filled the energy sequence is indeed the sequence of Table 7.1; however, in the case of incomplete shells, the mutual interactions of the electrons cause electrons of high angular momentum to possess higher energy than those of low angular momentum and this effect can result in overlapping of levels belonging to different main shells. For example, in a light atom the $3d$ energy level lies above the $4s$ level so that it is possible for the $4s$ state to be occupied while the $3d$ subshell is still empty. If further electrons are added, they enter the $3d$ state but the difference between $3d$ and $4s$ energies decreases and it is difficult to predict the configuration which possesses the lowest energy.

* Recently, regular chemical compounds of "inert" gases have been produced, notably fluorides of krypton, xenon, and radon.

TABLE 7.1
Electron Shells and Subshells

Shell	Quantum numbers				Sub-	Number of
x-ray letter	n	l	m_l	m_s	shell	electrons
"k"	1	0	0	$\pm\frac{1}{2}$	$1s$	2
"l"	2	0	0	$\pm\frac{1}{2}$	$2s$	2⎫ 8
		1	1, 0, −1	$\pm\frac{1}{2}$	$2p$	6⎭
"m"	3	0	0	$\pm\frac{1}{2}$	$3s$	2⎫
		1	1, 0, −1	$\pm\frac{1}{2}$	$3p$	6⎬ 18
		2	2, ... −2	$\pm\frac{1}{2}$	$3d$	10⎭
"n"	4	0	0	$\pm\frac{1}{2}$	$4s$	2⎫
		1	1, ... −1	$\pm\frac{1}{2}$	$4p$	6⎪ 32
		2	2, ... −2	$\pm\frac{1}{2}$	$4d$	10⎬
		3	3, ... −3	$\pm\frac{1}{2}$	$4f$	14⎭
"o"	5	0	0	$\pm\frac{1}{2}$	$5s$	2⎫
		1	1, ... −1	$\pm\frac{1}{2}$	$5p$	6⎪
		2	2, ... −2	$\pm\frac{1}{2}$	$5d$	10⎬ 50
		3	3, ... −3	$\pm\frac{1}{2}$	$5f$	14⎪
		4	4, ... −4	$\pm\frac{1}{2}$	$5g$	18⎭

With these considerations in mind, we can interpret the structure of the fourth row of the periodic table. The element $Z = 18$ (argon) has eight electrons in the $3p$ subshell and the comparatively wide gap between this level and the $3d$-$4s$ levels indicates that the element has high ionization potential (W_0) besides being chemically inert. The next electron enters the $4s$ subshell because this has slightly lower energy than the $3d$ level; two electrons can be accommodated in $4s$ and we find that the elements $Z = 19$ (K) and $Z = 20$ (Ca) resemble sodium and magnesium, respectively. After this the "inner" $3d$ subshell begins to fill and there is a sequence of ten transition metals ending at $Z = 30$ (Zn) before the $4p$ subshell is occupied appreciably. The metals from $Z = 22$ (Ti) to 29 (Cu) are characterized by variable valence, because electrons can change from the "inner" $3d$ level to the "valence" $4s$ level with little alteration in energy. When ionized, the atoms of these elements retain unbalanced electrons in the $3d$ subshell, with the result that the ions possess magnetic moment, that is, they exhibit paramagnetic behavior, unlike the ions of alkalis and alkaline-earth metals. Most of the transition metals have two electrons in the $4s$ subshell in the ground state, but there are two exceptions (Cr and Cu) which retain only one $4s$ electron as the valence electron.

A second series of transition metals occurs in the fifth row of the table and a third series occurs in the sixth row. A remarkable illustration of the effects of filling "deep" subshells is afforded by the 15 rare-earth elements or *lanthanides* ranging from $Z = 57$ (La) to $Z = 71$ (Lu). These elements are extremely similar in chemical behavior, also in ionization potential (Figure 4.7), because the outer subshells ($6s$ and $5d$) usually contain three electrons,

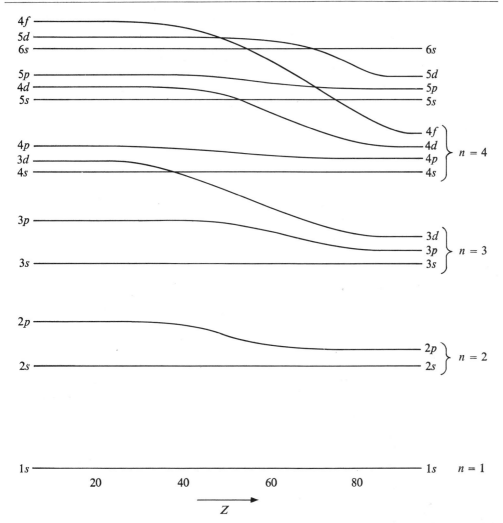

FIGURE 7.16 *For each subshell the electron energy is plotted against the atomic number Z in order to show how the sequence of subshells on the energy scale changes with the increasing number of electrons.*

while the next subshells (5s and 5p) contain eight electrons always. The progression from La to Lu corresponds to the successive addition of electrons to the 4f subshell, which is so deep-seated that it has very little effect on the element's behavior. A rather similar situation exists among the *actinide* elements occurring in the seventh row of the table.

The Pauli Exclusion principle is not only successful in explaining the electronic structure of atoms but is also applicable wherever particles of spin $\frac{1}{2}\hbar$ are concerned. For example, neutrons and protons within a nucleus separately obey the Pauli principle, which therefore has a profound effect on the particles' behavior and on the properties of nuclear states. Deeper analysis reveals that the fundamental significance of Pauli's principle lies in the *symmetry* properties of the state function describing a number of particles, in particular the behavior of the function when two particles are exchanged. Particles obeying Pauli's principle (electrons, neutrons, protons, and related particles) are described by an *anti-symmetrical* function which changes sign when exchange occurs. This type of function vanishes when two particles occupy the same substate, a result in accordance with Pauli's Exclusion principle.

Not all particles obey Pauli's principle, however. The behavior of an assembly of photons is described by the Planck distribution function, which is derived (in Section 7.15) on the assumption that any number of photons can occupy the same energy state. It is believed that certain particles, the mesons possessing zero spin, are similar to photons in their symmetry properties, that is, they are described by a *symmetrical* state function which does not change sign when two particles are exchanged. All particles are allotted to one or other of these symmetry categories.

7.9 Relativistic Quantum Mechanics

(a) The Klein-Gordon equation

The successful representation of electron spin by Pauli's matrices showed the way to many advances in quantum mechanics. However, the theory was still inadequate to deal with fast-moving particles, because Schrödinger's equation is not relativistic in form, that is, it is not invariant under a Lorentz transformation. In order to derive a relativistic wave equation we can adopt a Hamiltonian obtained from Equation (5.6.5), namely, for a free particle of rest mass m_0 and momentum p we write

$$H = (p^2c^2 + m_0^2c^4)^{\frac{1}{2}}. \qquad [7.9.1]$$

A state function of some kind (ψ) may then be introduced so that H^2 has eigenvalues E^2, where

$$H^2\psi = E^2\psi.$$

If, now, we replace the term E by the operator $i\hbar(\partial/\partial t)$ as in Equation (7.3.14) and the momentum by its operator equivalent

$$p^2 = p_x^2 + p_y^2 + p_z^2$$
$$= -\hbar^2\nabla^2$$

we obtain the differential equation

$$\nabla^2\psi - \frac{1}{c^2}\frac{\partial^2\psi}{\partial t^2} = \frac{m_0^2c^2\psi}{\hbar^2} = \mu^2\psi, \qquad [7.9.2]$$

where

$$\mu = \frac{m_0c}{\hbar}.$$

The reciprocal of the parameter μ is a characteristic length depending on the rest mass of the particles described by the equation.

In this way we obtain the *Klein-Gordon equation* for free particles of rest mass m_0. It bears a close resemblance to Maxwell's electromagnetic field equations apart from the right-hand term involving m_0. Indeed we can regard Equation (7.9.2) as a general field equation which reduces to Maxwell's form when the rest mass m_0 vanishes. The *type* of particle described depends on the nature of the function ψ. In the case of photons ψ is replaced by a vector field or vector potential and it follows that Equation (7.9.2) stands for three separate equations. In terms of quantum mechanics, this is equivalent to describing particles of spin $\hbar$ ($S = 1$), with state functions which have three components, in general. Alternatively we could use a scalar function ψ and this would correspond to particles without spin. Various possible theories were investigated by Pauli* and others, and it was shown that Equation (7.9.2) is the general equation for a field which is quantized in the form of particles of rest mass m_0. This result provides an essential link between the concepts of classical field theory and quantum mechanics.

(b) Dirac's equation

In 1928 Dirac pointed out that there are several difficulties in applying the second-order Klein-Gordon equation to electrons and he proposed instead to set up a relativistic equation of first order in H. The simplest linear equation involving all three momentum operators p_x, p_y, and p_z and the rest mass m_0 is

$$H\psi = c[\alpha_1 p_x + \alpha_2 p_y + \alpha_3 p_z + \beta m_0 c]\psi = E\psi, \qquad [7.9.3]$$

where α_1, α_2, α_3, and β are operators which have to satisfy suitable conditions. The energy E stands for the total energy of the free particle and it is convenient to write this as

$$E = p_0 c, \qquad [7.9.4]$$

where p_0 has the dimensions of momentum. The Dirac equation then takes the form

$$[p_0 - (\boldsymbol{\alpha}\,\mathbf{p}) - \beta m_0 c]\psi = 0, \qquad [7.9.5]$$

where the scalar product is used for the expression

$$\alpha_1 p_x + \alpha_2 p_y + \alpha_3 p_z.$$

If we multiply Equation (7.9.5) from the left by the expression

$$[p_0 + (\boldsymbol{\alpha}\,\mathbf{p}) + \beta m_0 c]$$

and impose the conditions

$$\alpha_1^2 = 1 \quad \alpha_2^2 = 1 \quad \alpha_3^2 = 1 \quad \beta^2 = 1$$

and also

$$\left.\begin{array}{ll} \alpha_1\alpha_2 + \alpha_2\alpha_1 = 0 & \alpha_1\beta + \beta\alpha_1 = 0 \\ \alpha_2\alpha_3 + \alpha_3\alpha_2 = 0 & \alpha_2\beta + \beta\alpha_2 = 0 \\ \alpha_3\alpha_1 + \alpha_1\alpha_3 = 0 & \alpha_3\beta + \beta\alpha_3 = 0 \end{array}\right\} \qquad [7.9.6]$$

then we find that

$$(p_0^2 - p^2 - m_0^2 c^2)\psi = 0,$$

that is,

$$\left(\frac{E^2}{c^2} - p^2 - m_0^2 c^2\right)\psi = 0$$

which is equivalent to the Klein-Gordon equation (7.9.2). Thus Dirac's equation is consistent with the general field equation provided that the α and β operators have unit magnitude and anticommute with each other. We have seen in Section 7.8 that the 2×2 Pauli matrices satisfy these conditions and this suggests that the α and β operators might be represented as matrices.

* W. Pauli, Rev. Mod. Phys., **15**, 175 (1943).

Dirac showed that a suitable representation of the α and β operators is obtainable in 4×4 matrices, acting upon a four-component state function ψ, which may be written

$$\begin{pmatrix} \psi_1 \\ \psi_2 \\ \psi_3 \\ \psi_4 \end{pmatrix}$$

Thus the Dirac equation is equivalent to four simultaneous equations involving the components of ψ. Dirac's matrices can be expressed as

$$\alpha_i = \rho_1 \Sigma_i \qquad \beta = \rho_3, \qquad\qquad [7.9.7]$$

where ρ_1 and ρ_3 are 4×4 matrices which anti-commute with each other but commute with the three Σ matrices ($i = 1, 2, 3$). The latter are 4×4 expansions of the Pauli spin matrices

$$\Sigma_i = \left(\begin{array}{c|c} \sigma_i & 0 \\ \hline 0 & \sigma_i \end{array} \right)$$

which possess the same properties as the σ's [Equations (7.8.4) and (7.8.5)]. For example, if we write

$$\rho_1 = \begin{pmatrix} 0 & 0 & 1 & 0 \\ 0 & 0 & 0 & 1 \\ 1 & 0 & 0 & 0 \\ 0 & 1 & 0 & 0 \end{pmatrix} \quad \text{and} \quad \rho_3 = \begin{pmatrix} 1 & 0 & 0 & 0 \\ 0 & 1 & 0 & 0 \\ 0 & 0 & -1 & 0 \\ 0 & 0 & 0 & -1 \end{pmatrix}$$

we find that

$$\alpha_1 = \begin{pmatrix} 0 & 0 & 0 & 1 \\ 0 & 0 & 1 & 0 \\ 0 & 1 & 0 & 0 \\ 1 & 0 & 0 & 0 \end{pmatrix} \qquad \alpha_2 = \begin{pmatrix} 0 & 0 & 0 & -i \\ 0 & 0 & i & 0 \\ 0 & -i & 0 & 0 \\ i & 0 & 0 & 0 \end{pmatrix}$$

$$\alpha_3 = \begin{pmatrix} 0 & 0 & 1 & 0 \\ 0 & 0 & 0 & -1 \\ 1 & 0 & 0 & 0 \\ 0 & -1 & 0 & 0 \end{pmatrix} \qquad \beta = \rho_3.$$

These four matrices possess the essential property of anticommuting with each other, but they are not a unique set and the Dirac equation can be put into different forms.

The special properties of Dirac's equation do not depend on the particular representation employed but emerge directly from a study of the Hamiltonian

$$H = c[(\alpha \mathbf{p}) + \beta m_0 c]. \qquad\qquad [7.9.8]$$

The rate of change of any operator f is given by Equation (7.3.16)

$$i\hbar \frac{df}{dt} = [Hf - fH].$$

For a particle moving in a central field of force, we can find the rate of change of the x component of the *orbital* angular momentum, namely,

$$G_x = yp_z - zp_y,$$

from

$$i\hbar \frac{dG_x}{dt} = H(yp_z - zp_y) - (yp_z - zp_y)H.$$

With the aid of the basic commutation relations [Equation (7.3.5)]:

$$yp_y - p_y y = i\hbar$$
$$zp_z - p_z z = i\hbar$$

we obtain

$$\frac{dG_x}{dt} = -c(\alpha_2 p_z - \alpha_3 p_y)$$

which does not vanish. In other words, the orbital angular momentum of the Dirac particle is *not* constant.

However, if we combine orbital momentum suitably with spin momentum, it is possible to find a quantity which is conserved. The first component of the generalized spin operator $\boldsymbol{\Sigma}$ is

$$\Sigma_1 = \begin{pmatrix} \sigma_1 & 0 \\ \hline 0 & \sigma_1 \end{pmatrix}$$

and we can establish the properties

$$\left. \begin{array}{l} \Sigma_1 \Sigma_2 = -\Sigma_2 \Sigma_1 = i\Sigma_3 \\ \Sigma_1 \Sigma_3 = -\Sigma_3 \Sigma_1 = -i\Sigma_2 \end{array} \right\} \qquad \text{from Equation (7.8.5).}$$

The rate of change of Σ_1 is then obtained from the relation

$$i\hbar \frac{d\Sigma_1}{dt} = H\Sigma_1 - \Sigma_1 H$$

$$= c\rho_1[(\Sigma_1 p_x + \Sigma_2 p_y + \Sigma_3 p_z)\Sigma_1 - \Sigma_1(\Sigma_1 p_x + \Sigma_2 p_y + \Sigma_3 p_z)]$$

$$= -2ci\rho_1[\Sigma_3 p_y - \Sigma_2 p_z]$$

or

$$\tfrac{1}{2}\hbar \frac{d\Sigma_1}{dt} = \rho_1 c(\Sigma_2 p_z - \Sigma_3 p_y) = c(\alpha_2 p_z - \alpha_3 p_y).$$

Thus we find that the combination $(G_x + \tfrac{1}{2}\hbar\Sigma_1)$ possesses the property

$$\frac{d}{dt}(G_x + \tfrac{1}{2}\hbar\Sigma_1) = 0, \qquad [7.9.9]$$

that is, $(G_x + \tfrac{1}{2}\hbar\Sigma_1)$ is constant in time. Similar results obtain for two other components of $\mathbf{G}_l$. It is therefore necessary to combine the orbital momentum $\mathbf{G}_l$ with spin momentum

$$\mathbf{G}_s = \tfrac{1}{2}\hbar\boldsymbol{\Sigma}$$

if we are to retain the principle of conservation of angular momentum.

We therefore write the total angular momentum of a Dirac particle as

$$\mathbf{G} = \mathbf{G}_l + \mathbf{G}_s \qquad [7.9.10]$$

and the quantity **G** obeys the rules of spatial quantization worked out previously for orbital and spin momentum. Thus for the quantum number j^* (denoting the total angular momentum of a single electron) the magnitude of **G** is $\hbar\sqrt{j(j+1)}$ and its component in any specified direction is $m_j\hbar$, where

$$m_j = j, (j-1), \ldots (-j). \qquad \text{[see Equation (7.6.15)]}$$

For an even number of Dirac particles the total angular momentum number J is an integer, while for an odd number of particles J must be half of an odd integer.

The theory may be extended to deal with a particle of spin $\frac{1}{2}\hbar$ moving in an electromagnetic field. Two important results emerge:

(i) in a magnetic field **B** there is an interaction with potential energy

$$\frac{e\hbar}{2m_0} (\mathbf{\Sigma B}) = \frac{e}{m_0} (\mathbf{G}_s\mathbf{B}) \qquad [7.9.11]$$

and this is interpreted as being due to an intrinsic magnetic moment, of magnitude $\dfrac{e\hbar}{2m_0}$, linked to the spin;

(ii) in a Coulomb field, there is an energy term depending on "spin-orbit" interaction, proportional to the scalar product $(\mathbf{G}_l\mathbf{G}_s)$, and this causes particle states of different j to have different energies even when they have the same (n, l) numbering.

Both these effects are of major importance in the theory of atomic states (Section 7.10) and their magnetic interactions (Section 7.14). Here we note that the magnetic moment associated with electron spin is one Bohr magneton, according to the Dirac theory. This is twice the value which would be expected from the angular momentum $(\frac{1}{2}\hbar)$ if the original Bohr theory (Section 6.5) applied. In other words, the gyromagnetic factor [Equation (6.5.5)] for electron spin is 2, whereas the orbital motion yields $g = 1$; we see that the phenomenon of spin is needed to account for experimental results on the gyromagnetic effect (Section 6.5).

(c) Antiparticles

The most striking feature of the Dirac equation, apart from the intrinsic spin of the particles described, is the fact that the state function ψ must consist of four components, because of the 4×4 matrix operators acting on the function. Thus the equation represents four linear equations rather than one. Analysis shows that this feature is due to the two possible spin states of the particle ("spin up" and "spin down" in the usual parlance) combined with two possible energy states, positive and negative. The latter characteristic is a direct consequence of the relativistic form of the Dirac equation and the quadratic form of the Hamiltonian

$$H = (p^2c^2 + m_0^2c^4)^{1/2}. \qquad \text{[Equation (7.9.1)]}$$

Obviously this equation has negative roots as well as positive roots; consequently negative energies appear in any relativistic theory of particles.

In classical physics the negative energy states of a particle are not accessible because they are separated from the positive energy states by a gap which is twice the rest-mass energy of the particle (Figure 7.17). Since energy changes are assumed to take place by small continuous amounts, it is possible to regard the negative energy states as inaccessible. In quantum theory, on the other hand, there is always a possibility of discontinuous changes in

---

* Symbols l, s, j will be retained for single-electron quantum numbers, L, S, J standing for many-electron states.

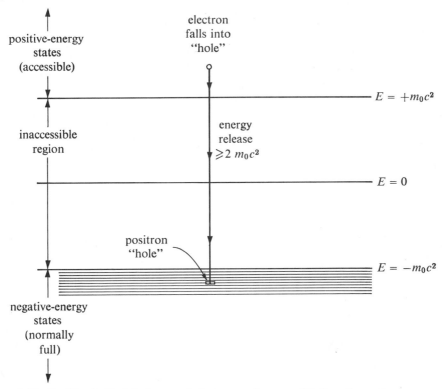

FIGURE 7.17 *In Dirac's "hole" theory of electron-positron annihilation the positron appears as a "hole" in the otherwise filled negative energy states. When an electron falls into the "hole" both particles disappear and the energy released must exceed twice the rest-mass energy of an electron.*

energy amounting to more than $2m_0c^2$ and these enable a particle of rest mass m_0 to make transitions into negative energy states or out of them.

Dirac attempted to meet the serious objections raised against his theory because of the negative energy difficulty with a simple but bold working hypothesis. If all the negative energy states for electrons are filled, we have a "sea" of occupied states which is not detectable because no transitions into it can occur, by virtue of Pauli's principle. Suppose that one electron makes the transition from the negative energy sea into a vacant positive energy state (a process which requires at least $2m_0c^2 = 1.02$ MeV energy). This electron becomes observable as a "proper" electron and at the same time there is a "hole" left in the negative energy states. Such a "hole" behaves like an ordinary electron except that it moves the opposite way in electromagnetic fields, that is, it acts like a positive charge. The hole is very "unstable" in the presence of positive energy electrons, one of which may easily fall into it, filling the "sea" again and liberating at least 1.02 MeV energy. This fantasy is a possible way of describing the phenomena of pair creation and annihilation (Section 4.9). In pair creation the incident gamma ray spends its energy in raising an electron from the negative sea to a positive level and the hole left behind is the positron. The positron is annihilated when an electron falls into the hole and the energy released appears as two gamma rays (Figure 7.17). The surprising thing is the success of this hypothesis in predicting the existence of the positron some years before the particle was identified and in giving correctly the probabilities of the creation and annihilation processes. The "hole" theory of positrons has also been applied successfully to other cases of interaction between electrons and photons, notably the Compton effect.

The "hole" theory is important in that it provided the first concept of the types of particle now known as *antiparticles*. These bear the same relations to their "proper" particles as the positron does to the negatively charged electron, that is, their charges are opposite in sign, but the masses, spins and symmetry properties are the same. An antiparticle may combine with its opposite number to release energy in considerable amounts; conversely, it requires much energy for a pair of particles to be created. For example, the creation of a proton-antiproton pair in laboratory experiments requires the absorption of about 6×10^9 eV (6 GeV) energy from a single particle incident upon the target. Proton beams of this energy are available from synchrotron accelerators, which can therefore be used for the purpose of studying the properties of antiprotons produced artificially.

It is believed that all types of particle possess antiparticles, although the detailed relations between them have to be studied carefully in each case. The antineutron is a particularly intriguing particle because it cannot be distinguished from a proper neutron by charge. However, these particles do possess magnetic moment, which is related to the $\frac{1}{2}\hbar$ spin, but is "anomalous" in the sense that it cannot be explained by the Dirac theory alone. The neutron proper has a *negative* moment, that is, its vector is directed oppositely to the spin vector; it follows that the antineutron is to be distinguished by having a *positive* magnetic moment, that is, parallel to the spin. A more difficult question concerns the existence of particles (neutrinos) with no charge and no rest mass; evidently the relations between neutrinos and antineutrinos require further elucidation, despite the supposition that all particles of spin $\frac{1}{2}\hbar$ obey Dirac's equation (see Section 10.7).

7.10 Single-Electron States

(a) Spectroscopic notation

In Section 7.8 we found that the structure of atoms can be interpreted in terms of Pauli's Exclusion principle and four quantum numbers (n, l, m_l, m_s) specified for each electron in a complex atom. We have also seen that the Dirac equation describes particles of spin $\frac{1}{2}\hbar$ and that the spin momentum must be combined with the orbital momentum to form a conserved quantity **G** for such particles. The total angular momentum **G** for one electron is characterized by a quantum number j with components specified by a number m_j, which ranges in value from j to $-j$. We now assume that the Dirac theory may be applied to single-electron states of atoms and these states have to be defined with their appropriate quantum numbers.

In the first place, we need to know the relations between the quantum number j and the orbital number l for a single electron. If l is given, we know that m_l takes the values

$$l, (l-1), \ldots, 1, 0, -1, \ldots, (-l).$$

Since $m_s = \pm\frac{1}{2}$, we can combine m_l with m_s in all possible ways to find the possible components m_j in a specified direction. We obtain

(for $m_s = +\frac{1}{2}$) $\qquad (l + \frac{1}{2}),(l - \frac{1}{2}), \ldots, (-l + \frac{1}{2})$

and

(for $m_s = -\frac{1}{2}$) $\qquad (l - \frac{1}{2}), \ldots, (-l - \frac{1}{2}).$

These numbers may be regrouped as follows:

$$m_j = (l + \tfrac{1}{2}), (l - \tfrac{1}{2}), \ldots, (-l + \tfrac{1}{2}), (-l - \tfrac{1}{2})$$

and

$$m_j = \qquad (l - \tfrac{1}{2}), \ldots, (-l + \tfrac{1}{2}).$$

The two groups correspond to j values of $(l + \tfrac{1}{2})$ and $(l - \tfrac{1}{2})$, respectively. We deduce that the combination of orbital momentum with spin for a single electron leads, in general, to two values of j, namely $j = l \pm \tfrac{1}{2}$. The only exception to this rule is the case $l = 0$, where $j = \tfrac{1}{2}$ is the sole possibility.

A hydrogenlike atom with one electron outside the nucleus therefore possesses a multiplicity of states which are specified in terms of the j values. This specification is more important than the detailed description in terms of l, m_l, m_s because the energy of a state depends on the value of j, but we have seen that the two descriptions are necessarily equivalent. Each state is denoted by a spectroscopic symbol

$$n^p X_j,$$

where n is the principal quantum number, p is the "multiplicity," which is $(2s + 1)$, where s stands for the total spin number ($s = \tfrac{1}{2}$ for one electron), X is a letter to denote the value of l, being S for $l = 0$, P for $l = 1$, D for $l = 2$, F for $l = 3, \ldots$. It should be noted that p is intended to indicate the number of j values for a given group of states, but the number quoted may be misleading occasionally, for example in S states $j = \tfrac{1}{2}$ always but p is written 2 nevertheless.

With the aid of the spectroscopic notation we can set out the states of a one-electron atom in order:

n	l	j	Notation
1	0	$\tfrac{1}{2}$	$1^2 S_{1/2}$
2	0	$\tfrac{1}{2}$	$2^2 S_{1/2}$
	1	$\tfrac{1}{2}$	$2^2 P_{1/2}$
		$\tfrac{3}{2}$	$2^2 P_{3/2}$
3	0	$\tfrac{1}{2}$	$3^2 S_{1/2}$
	1	$\tfrac{1}{2}$	$3^2 P_{1/2}$
		$\tfrac{3}{2}$	$3^2 P_{3/2}$
	2	$\tfrac{3}{2}$	$3^2 D_{3/2}$
		$\tfrac{5}{2}$	$3^2 D_{5/2}$

This specification is somewhat different from that used to enumerate the state functions of a hydrogenlike atom in Section 7.7, but both specifications are important; here we are concerned to find the correct number of states which are observable when the degeneracy of levels (featured in both the Bohr and Schrödinger theories) is removed.

(b) Spin-orbit interaction

The relation between l and j for a single electron can be illustrated by a vector model which employs the concept of spatial quantization in a simplified form. If the value of l is given, we can think of the angular momentum $\mathbf{G}_l$ as a vector in a particular direction (Figure 7.18). The spin momentum $\mathbf{G}_s$ can take only two possible orientations relative to $\mathbf{G}_l$ and so $\mathbf{G}_s$ is drawn parallel or antiparallel to $\mathbf{G}_l$, corresponding to the two j values: $j = l + \tfrac{1}{2}$ and $j = l - \tfrac{1}{2}$. This picture is not precise, but it enables us to visualize the origin of an interaction which depends on the scalar product $(\mathbf{G}_l \mathbf{G}_s)$—the *spin-orbit interaction*

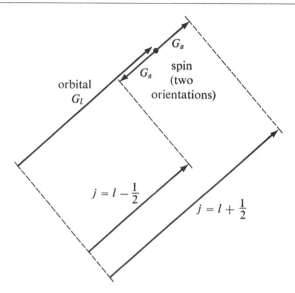

FIGURE 7.18 *According to the simple vector model of angular momentum, the total angular momen-tum number (j) for a single electron takes two possible values ($l \pm \frac{1}{2}$) because of the two possible orientations of the spin vector ($\mathbf{G}_s$) relative to the orbital momentum vector ($\mathbf{G}_l$).*

mentioned in Section 7.9. The interaction energy can be calculated precisely for a hydrogen-like atom by Dirac's theory, but first we make a semiclassical estimate of the effect in order to obtain its order of magnitude.

The single electron is supposed to orbit round the nucleus (of charge $+ Ze$) and to carry its intrinsic magnetic moment $\mathbf{\mu}$, which is, according to the Dirac theory,

$$\mathbf{\mu} = - \frac{e\hbar}{2m}\, \mathbf{\Sigma} = - \frac{e}{m}\, \mathbf{G}_s. \qquad [7.10.1]$$

In circulating about the nucleus the electron experiences an effective magnetic field $\mathbf{B}'$ due to its high speed in the electric field of the nucleus. The existence of $\mathbf{B}'$ is a relativistic effect, but we can estimate the field by thinking of the electron as stationary with the nucleus revolving round it. The field at the electron due to the current loop formed by the nucleus moving in a circle of radius r is

$$\mathbf{B}' = \frac{Ze[\mathbf{r} \times \mathbf{v}]}{[4\pi\varepsilon_0]c^2 r^3}$$

where $\mathbf{v}$ is the instantaneous velocity of the nucleus. The orbital momentum of the electron in its proper orbit is

$$\mathbf{G}_l = m[\mathbf{r} \times \mathbf{v}],$$

where $\mathbf{v}$ is taken to be the same as before, so the effective field acting upon the electron is

$$\mathbf{B}' = \frac{Ze}{[4\pi\varepsilon_0]mc^2 r^3}\, \mathbf{G}_l. \qquad [7.10.2]$$

The interaction energy between the electron's intrinsic magnetic moment and the effective field $\mathbf{B}'$ is then

$$\Delta E = - \mathbf{\mu}\mathbf{B}' = \frac{Ze^2}{[4\pi\varepsilon_0]m^2 c^2 r^3}\, (\mathbf{G}_l\mathbf{G}_s).$$

This expression is of the correct form in G_l and G_s but it is hardly reliable for exact calculations because of the term r^3 in the denominator. It is difficult to estimate the appropriate mean value of r^3 for states in which G_l is appreciable, owing to the nonspherical probability distributions in these cases (see Figure 7.14). Accordingly it is customary to write the spin-orbit interaction in the form

$$\Delta E = a(G_l \, G_s), \qquad [7.10.3]$$

where a is an appropriate constant.

However, we may use the semiclassical result to yield an order-of-magnitude estimate by considering the lowest Bohr orbit ($n = 1$) in a hydrogenlike atom. Such an orbit has radius

$$r_1 = \frac{\hbar^2[4\pi\varepsilon_0]}{mZe^2} \qquad \text{from Equation (6.4.2)}$$

so that we find

$$\Delta E \approx \frac{Z^4 e^8 m}{[4\pi\varepsilon_0]^4 c^2 \hbar^6} (G_l G_s). \qquad [7.10.4]$$

We can simplify the expression by introducing a dimensionless constant

$$\alpha = \frac{e^2}{c\hbar[4\pi\varepsilon_0]} \qquad [7.10.5]$$

which is called the *fine-structure constant* and has the numerical value $\alpha = \frac{1}{137}$ very nearly. The product of spin and orbital angular momentum is approximated as

$$(G_l G_s) \approx \tfrac{1}{2}\hbar^2$$

and we find that

$$\Delta E \approx \tfrac{1}{2}mc^2 Z^4 \alpha^4$$

which for hydrogen ($Z = 1$) has the value

$$\Delta E \approx 7 \times 10^{-4} \text{ eV}.$$

If this is compared with the ionization potential for hydrogen (13.6 eV) it is obvious that the spin-orbit interaction has little effect on the positions of the main energy levels in a simple atom. On the other hand, the magnitude of the effect is such that it might be detectable as a splitting of levels which were previously supposed to be degenerate, for example, the main levels of hydrogen. In this connection, it should be noted that Equation (7.10.4) indicates that ΔE varies rapidly with Z and, although the nuclear charge Ze is probably screened to a considerable extent in heavy atoms, one would expect the spin-orbit effects to increase as Z increases.

(c) The Dirac fine structure

A precise value of ΔE for hydrogenlike atoms may be derived from the theory of Dirac. The result of a long calculation* is that the eigenvalues for the total energy of a single electron in the field of a massive nucleus are given by the expression

$$E = \frac{m_0 c^2}{1 + \dfrac{Z^2 e^4}{(4\pi\varepsilon_0)^2 c^2 \hbar^2 [v + \sqrt{(j + \tfrac{1}{2})^2 - \alpha^2 Z^2}]^2}} \qquad [7.10.6]$$

where m_0 is the rest mass of the electron, v is a quantum number taking values $0, 1, 2, \ldots$, j is the quantum number for total angular momentum. The expression may be expanded,

---

* P. A. M. Dirac, *The Principles of Quantum Mechanics* (Oxford Univ. Press, New York, 1958) 4th ed., Sec. 72.

with the aid of the binomial theorem, to give

$$E = m_0 c^2 - \frac{m_0 Z^2 e^4}{2(4\pi\varepsilon_0)^2 \hbar^2 [\nu + \sqrt{(j + \frac{1}{2})^2 - \alpha^2 Z^2}]^2} + \frac{3 m_0 Z^4 e^8}{8(4\pi\varepsilon_0)^4 c^2 \hbar^4 [\nu + \sqrt{(j + \frac{1}{2})^2 - \alpha^2 Z^2}]^4} \cdots$$

Since the constant α is approximately $\frac{1}{137}$ we can neglect αZ compared with $(j + \frac{1}{2})$ in a light atom and the second term in the expansion is very nearly

$$- \frac{m_0 Z^2 e^4}{2(4\pi\varepsilon_0)^2 \hbar^2 n^2}, \qquad \text{where} \quad n = \nu + j + \frac{1}{2},$$

that is, we have Bohr's expression with the principal quantum number n. Since the number ν takes the values 0, 1, 2, ... and j takes the values $\frac{1}{2}, \frac{3}{2}, \frac{5}{2}, \ldots$, the n sequence is 1, 2, 3, ... as in the theories of Bohr and Schrödinger. It is clear, therefore, that, to a first approximation, the energy of a Dirac particle, given by Equation (7.10.6), is its rest-mass energy *minus* the binding energy in the Coulomb field of the nucleus.

In order to find the small corrections of order α^2 in the energy E we reintroduce the $\alpha^2 Z^2$ in the second term, expand this term binomially, and collect the appropriate expressions from the second and third terms

$$E = m_0 c^2 - \frac{m_0 Z^2 e^4}{2(4\pi\varepsilon_0)^2 \hbar^2 n^2} \left[1 - \frac{\alpha^2 Z^2}{2n(j + \frac{1}{2})} \right]^{-2} + \frac{3 m_0 Z^4 e^4 \alpha^2}{8(4\pi\varepsilon_0)^2 \hbar^2 n^4} \cdots$$

$$= m_0 c^2 - \frac{m_0 Z^2 e^4}{2(4\pi\varepsilon_0)^2 \hbar^2 n^2} \left[1 + \frac{\alpha^2 Z^2}{n} \left(\frac{1}{j + \frac{1}{2}} - \frac{3}{4n} \right) \cdots \right]. \qquad [7.10.7]$$

The correction term of order α^2 therefore depends on j as well as n; thus each Bohr level in the hydrogenlike atom is split into a number of levels equal to the number of different j values. In this way the spin-orbit interaction removes some of the degeneracy predicted for these levels, but examination of the sequence of states shows that degeneracy remains because each j value, except the highest in each group, belongs to a pair of different states.

The magnitude of the relativistic corrections including the spin-orbit effect, as given by the Dirac theory, can be found by isolating the correction term

$$\Delta E = - \frac{m_0 Z^2 e^4}{2(4\pi\varepsilon_0)^2 \hbar^2 n^2} \frac{\alpha^2 Z^2}{n} \left(\frac{1}{j + \frac{1}{2}} - \frac{3}{4n} \right)$$

$$= - \frac{1}{2} m_0 c^2 Z^4 \alpha^4 \frac{1}{n^3} \left(\frac{1}{j + \frac{1}{2}} - \frac{3}{4n} \right).$$

Thus for the lowest state of hydrogen ($Z = 1, n = 1, j = \frac{1}{2}$)

$$\Delta E = - \frac{m_0 c^2 \alpha^4}{8} \approx -2 \times 10^{-4} \, \text{eV},$$

that is, minus one-quarter of the semiclassical estimate. This state is necessarily single (to the degree of accuracy given by this approximation) and the shift in energy is difficult to detect. However, we may apply the theory to find the splitting of the first excited state ($n = 2$) which should divide into two levels:

$$n = 2, \quad j = \frac{1}{2} \, (2 \, {}^2S_{1/2}, 2 \, {}^2P_{1/2}) \, \Delta E_{1/2} = -(5/8) \frac{m_0 c^2 \alpha^4}{16}$$

$$n = 2, \quad j = \frac{3}{2} \, (2 \, {}^2P_{3/2}) \qquad \Delta E_{3/2} = -(1/8) \frac{m_0 c^2 \alpha^4}{16}.$$

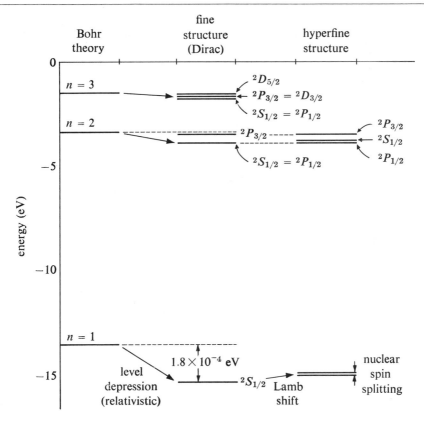

FIGURE 7.19 *Energy levels of the hydrogen atom. Left: the three lowest states according to the Bohr-Schrödinger theory. Center: fine structure with spin-orbit interaction according to the Dirac theory (all shifts and splittings enhanced by 10^4). Right: hyperfine effects in the two lowest states (enhanced by 10^4).*

The difference between these values is

$$\Delta E_{3/2} - \Delta E_{1/2} = \frac{m_0 c^2 \alpha^4}{2 \times 16} = 4.5 \times 10^{-5} \text{ eV}$$

corresponding to a radiofrequency difference of about 11,000 Mc/sec. With the aid of these calculations we can make a diagram of the fine structure of hydrogen levels (Figure 7.19) in which the splitting has been magnified by a factor of 10^4. It is noteworthy that all the levels are slightly depressed by relativistic effects below the values given by the simple Bohr theory and that the lowest levels always have the lowest values of j. In other words the spin-orbit interaction energy is largest in the positive sense when the vectors $\mathbf{G}_l$ and $\mathbf{G}_s$ are parallel (largest j). This result confirms the sign of the semiclassical interaction of Equation (7.10.3), although the simple treatment does not give the correct result for the absolute energy shifts.

(d) Hyperfine effects

Experimental tests of the fine-structure effects predicted for hydrogen by the Dirac theory are difficult to carry out because the transition between the ground state and the $n = 2$ states (where the splitting is greatest) produces lines in the far ultraviolet region (the Lyman series). In addition there are complicating factors due to interactions not dealt with in the Dirac theory. We have mentioned in Section 4.4 that the ground state of hydrogen is split by the magnetic interaction between the electron and the proton which forms the nucleus. This "hyperfine" splitting is of the order of 6×10^{-6} eV, about one order of magnitude smaller than the "fine" spin-orbit splitting.

In addition to the nuclear interaction effect (which is appreciable only in the ground state) there are subtle differences between energy levels observed, especially by radio-frequency methods, and those predicted theoretically. In 1947 Lamb and Retherford discovered that the $2^2S_{1/2}$ and $2^2P_{1/2}$ states of hydrogen are not degenerate, as was previously supposed. It appears that the $^2S_{1/2}$ state is shifted upwards slightly relative to the $^2P_{1/2}$ state, the transition being characterized by a radiofrequency of 1060 Mc/sec, about one tenth of the spin-orbit splitting between $j = \frac{1}{2}$ and $j = \frac{3}{2}$ levels. In addition the $1^2S_{1/2}$ state is raised by 8130 Mc/sec above the Dirac value. The origin of the "Lamb shift" is to be sought in the details of interaction between an electron and the electromagnetic field. Normally the electron is regarded as a point charge which can react with external fields and also, presumably, with its own field. Unfortunately the latter interaction always leads mathematically to an infinite self-energy of the particle (Section 4.1). In a new scheme of quantum electrodynamics formulated by Tomonaga, Schwinger, and others, the infinite energy terms are subtracted systematically from the interaction and it is found that certain small terms remain, notably an effect due to the zero-point motion of the particle* (Section 7.5). This small effect accounts for the Lamb shift almost exactly, not only in hydrogen but also in deuterium and ionized helium (He^+). In addition the new quantum electrodynamics predicts a small change in the electron's intrinsic magnetic moment from the Dirac value of one Bohr magneton. The theoretical value becomes

$$\mu = \mu_B \left[1 + \frac{e^2}{2\pi\hbar c (4\pi\varepsilon_0)} \right] = \frac{e\hbar}{2m}\left(1 + \frac{\alpha}{2\pi}\right). \qquad [7.10.8]$$

The discrepancy between the magnetic moment and the Bohr magneton has been measured.

The results of experiments performed on the Lamb shift between $^2S_{1/2}$ and $^2P_{1/2}$ states and on the magnetic moment of the electron are in impressive agreement with the quantum theory of interaction. In 1958 Lamb gave a list of comparisons between theory and experiment and this is shown in Table 7.2. We see from these data that even the simplest atom, that of hydrogen, is rich in subtle effects requiring the most elaborate analysis. In general

TABLE 7.2
Tests of Quantum Electrodynamics (Lamb)

	Theory	*Experiment*
Electron Magnetic Moment in μ_B	1.001160	$1.001165 \pm .000011$
Lamb Splittings in Mc/sec		
$2\,^2S_{1/2} - 2\,^2P_{1/2}$ in H	$1058.03 \pm .15$	$1057.77 \pm .10$
in D	$1059.38 \pm .15$	$1059.00 \pm .10$
in He^+	14056.8 ± 3.0	14040.2 ± 4.5
$3^2S_{1/2} - 3\,^2P_{1/2}$ in H	315.3	315 ± 1

* V. F. Weisskopf, Rev. Mod. Phys., **21**, 305 (1949).

the Dirac theory is taken to be the main guide to the structure of single-electron levels, since spin-orbit interaction is the most important feature of many atomic states.

(e) Alkali metals

We can apply the theory of single-electron states to other systems besides the hydrogen-like atoms. For example, the atoms of alkali metals each possess a single electron outside a set of complete shells and the excited states are due almost entirely to single-electron excitations. The mutual interactions between the valence electron and the inner electrons have two principal effects. Firstly, the inner electrons screen the outer electron from the nuclear charge to some extent, as discussed in Section 4.8. Secondly, the energy of the outer electron, and therefore of the atomic state as a whole, depends on the orbital angular momentum number l as well as on the Bohr number n, as indicated by Figure 7.16. It is not possible to predict the energy levels without elaborate calculations, but we can make a general outline by using the classification of states developed for the hydrogenlike atoms, also the general pattern of spin-orbit effects indicated by the Dirac theory.

As an example, we consider the states of the sodium atom which are shown diagrammatically in Figure 7.20. The single valence electron is normally in the 3s subshell, so the

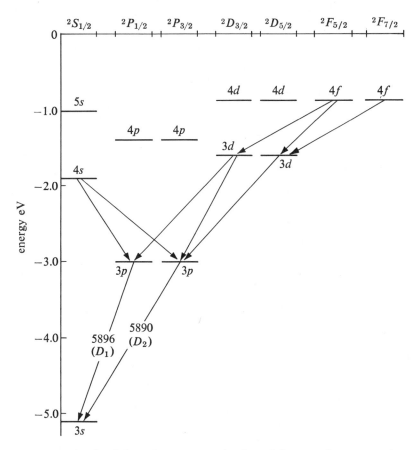

FIGURE 7.20 *Energy levels of the sodium atom and a few of the optical transitions between these levels: the wavelengths of the two main "D" lines are shown in Ångstroms. All the P, D, F, ... states are split by spin-orbit interaction into pairs.*

ground state is denoted by $3^2S_{1/2}$ and various degrees of excitation take the electron into the $3p$, $3d$, $4s$, $4p$, $4d$, $4f$ subshells, and so forth. The energy relations of these levels are complex, as indicated in Figure 7.16, but the spin-orbit splitting of the p, d, f, ... levels, and so forth, is regular. In practice the different types of state are depicted in different columns to reduce confusion among the various transitions which are possible. It will be observed in Figure 7.20 that transitions between P and S states and between P and D states are allowed, also those between D and F states; but no transition occurs between S and D states or between P and F states. This feature is ascribed to the operation of selection rules, which are discussed in Section 7.13.

(f) X-ray spectra

The single-electron description of atomic states is also applicable to the important energy levels operative in the x-ray spectra of heavy elements. In Section 4.9 the relations between x-ray lines and photoelectric absorption edges were described, and in Section 6.5 the Bohr theory was used to give an account of Moseley's law. It was supposed that removal of

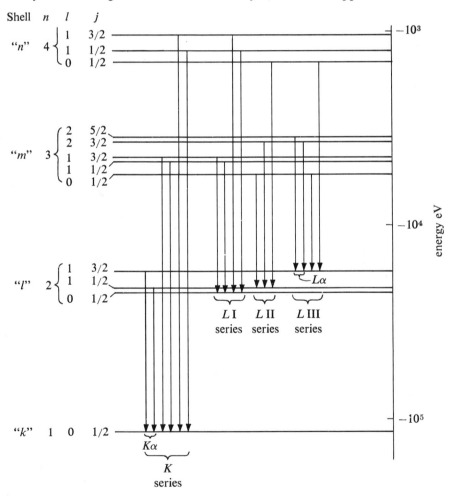

FIGURE 7.21 *X-ray levels of the uranium atom on a logarithmic energy scale, showing the possible transitions between states and the fine structure of x-ray lines.*

an electron from an inner shell leads in due course to capture by this shell of an electron from one of the outer shells; and this process may be regarded as the transfer of a "hole" from the inner to the outer shell. The effective energy of the hole is the same as that of a single particle in the same shell, so the Bohr theory may be applied in its simple form with some success. The theoretical expression [Equation (6.5.1)] provides an adequate account of the experimental data for the K series of lines if fine-structure effects are ignored. However, there remain several problems of interpretation in connection with the higher series of lines and these necessarily involve fine structure.

If we continue to regard the initial and final states in a x-ray transition as due to the "hole" moving in the field of the nucleus, it should be possible to classify the states in the same way as single-electron states. Moreover, in a heavy atom like uranium, the sequence of subshell levels is regular, according to Figure 7.16. We therefore expect the sequence of states, modified by the spin-orbit interaction, to be as follows: $1\ ^2S_{1/2}$, $2\ ^2S_{1/2}$, $2\ ^2P_{1/2}$, $2\ ^2P_{3/2}$, $3\ ^2S_{1/2}$, $3\ ^2P_{1/2}$, $3\ ^2P_{3/2}$, $3\ ^2D_{3/2}$, $3\ ^2D_{5/2}$, ..., with spacings which are dependent on the complex mutual interactions of electrons. Figure 7.21 shows experimental results for uranium, the energies being plotted on a logarithmic scale to render the details evident in higher shells. This diagram may be compared with the purely schematic Figure 4.22 to emphasize the differences in scale between the separations of main shells. As one proceeds upwards from the "k" to the "l," "m," and "n" shells (in x-ray notation) the separations become smaller and the extra complexity introduced by spin-orbit effects eventually causes the groups to overlap. The transitions between states shown in Figure 7.21 obey the same selection rules as transitions in the sodium atom (Figure 7.20).

7.11 Many-Electron States

Where the states of an atom can be described in terms of the single-electron classification, we have to consider the quantum numbers n, l, and j of the electron (or hole) responsible. The total angular momentum number j is obtained directly by compounding the orbital and spin momenta, and the spin-orbit interaction has relatively little effect on the energy. However, there are many atoms in which the excited states are due to changes in configuration by many electrons, belonging, in some cases, to different subshells. The classification of states then becomes a matter of great difficulty.

(a) L-S and j-j coupling

The immediate problem in classifying many-electron states is to decide how the angular momentum of a number of electrons is compounded from the separate orbital and spin momenta. Here the spin-orbit interaction plays a very important role. If the interaction is strong, so that the constant a in Equation (7.10.3) is large, each individual electron tends to retain its own j value and the total angular momentum (characterized by the quantum number J) is made up of contributions from the various electronic j values. Such a situation is called *j-j coupling* and it obtains chiefly in heavy elements, where the spin-orbit interaction becomes dominant. In the light elements, where the spin-orbit interaction has little effect, the total angular momentum J is made up of the total orbital angular momentum (characterized by number L) and the total spin momentum (denoted by S) of the contributing electrons. This is called *Russell-Saunders* coupling or *L-S coupling*, and in this situation it is legitimate to use the same spectroscopic notation as in single electron states, that is, we denote a state by

$$^\rho X_J,$$

where $\rho = 2S + 1$ (the multiplicity), X stands for the letters S $(L = 0)$, P $(L = 1)$, and so forth, and J denotes the total angular momentum. Instead of the Bohr number in front of the spectroscopic symbol it is frequently convenient to write the electronic configuration responsible for the state. For example, if we have two $2p$ electrons combined to form a $^3P_0$ state, this is written

$$(2p)^2 \, ^3P_0.$$

In both j-j and L-S coupling, it is necessary to frame a rule whereby the total angular momentum is given when two known angular momentum vectors are added together. Suppose that we have two particles in j-j coupling, with one particle contributing angular momentum characterized by the number j_1 and the other contributing j_2, where $j_1 \geqslant j_2$. In any specified direction, the components of these two angular momenta are

$$m'_j = j_1, \quad (j_1 - 1), \ldots, (-j_1),$$

$$m''_j = j_2, \quad (j_2 - 1), \ldots, (-j_2).$$

Provided that there are no restrictions on the particles' angular momenta, the components (m_J) of the *combined* angular momentum take the values

$$m_j = (j_1 + j_2), (j_1 + j_2 - 1), \ldots, (-j_1 + j_2), (j_1 + j_2 - 1), \ldots,$$
$$(-j_1 + j_2), (-j_1 + j_2 - 1), \ldots, (j_1 - j_2), \ldots, (-j_1 - j_2)$$

and these can be regrouped to give all the components of the J values: $J = (j_1 + j_2)$, $(j_1 + j_2 - 1), \ldots (j_1 - j_2)$. Thus, in this example, there are $(2j_2 + 1)$ different J values produced by addition of the two angular momenta. This type of result is characteristic of quantum-mechanical rules for adding vectors (see Figure 7.18).

(b) Two-electron systems

If we confine our attention to light elements, we can describe the ground states and some of the excited states with the aid of the spectroscopic notation and the energy levels of Figure 7.16. To begin with, we consider simple cases of two-electron excitation, occurring in elements like helium and calcium. The simplest two-electron system is in fact that of positronium, where a positron and an electron combine very briefly to form definite two-electron states before the particles annihilate each other with the emission of photons. The binding energy of positronium may be calculated directly from Equation (7.7.6) if we substitute $Z = 1$ and the reduced mass $\mu = \frac{1}{2}m$, that is, one-half of the electron mass, because the two particles have the same rest-mass. The ground state $n = 1$ then has a binding energy

$$W_1 = - \frac{me^4}{4(4\pi\varepsilon_0)^2\hbar^2} = -6.8 \text{ eV},$$

that is, one-half of the ionization potential of hydrogen.

However, we have neglected the effects of the particles' spin. In the ground state, $l = 0$ for each particle (since $n = 1$) so $L = 0$. The components of spin are $m_s = \pm\frac{1}{2}$ and these can be added together in four ways to form

$$m_S = 1 \quad 0 \quad 0 \quad -1$$

which are regrouped in two sets belonging to $S = 0$ and $S = 1$

$$S = 0 \quad m_S = 0,$$
$$S = 1 \quad m_S = 1 \quad 0 \quad -1.$$

Two possible ground states therefore appear, written

$$\text{for} \quad S = 0 \quad (1s)^2 \, {}^1S_0,$$
$$\text{for} \quad S = 1 \quad (1s)^2 \, {}^3S_1.$$

The difference in energy has to be calculated by the methods of quantum electrodynamics and experiment provides a delicate test of the theory, as is shown by the comparison,

Frequency difference between ${}^1S_0$ and ${}^3S_1$ states of positronium

Theory	Experiment
2.0337×10^5 Mc/sec	$(2.0338 \pm 0.0004) \times 10^5$ Mc/sec.

This figure corresponds to a very small energy difference, negligible compared with the binding energy, which is, in turn, very much smaller than the total energy released when the particles annihilate each other.

The two lowest states of positronium may be detected by studies of the annihilation radiation from slow positrons. It is found that the ${}^1S_0$ state leads to the emission of two photons in opposite directions, the mean lifetime being very short, of the order of 10^{-10} sec. The ${}^3S_1$ state, on the other hand, cannot produce two photons, if angular momentum is to be conserved, and the emission of three photons is a slower process with a mean lifetime of about 10^{-7} sec. These lifetimes may be modified considerably by the type of material in which the annihilation takes place.

If we compare the lowest states of positronium with those of the helium atom, a profound difference is immediately apparent. The ground state of helium is denoted by $(1s)^2 \, {}^1S_0$ and there is no sign of a ${}^3S_1$ state nearby. This can be understood as due to the Exclusion principle forbidding the two $1s$ electrons to have the same m_s value, which would be necessary for the $S = 1$ state (spins parallel). On the other hand, it is perfectly possible for a ${}^3S_1$ state to be formed with one electron in the $1s$ subshell and one in the $2s$ subshell. Indeed, the first excited state of the helium atom is the "triplet" state, $(1s)(2s) \, {}^3S_1$. This state is the first in the series of triplet states, which are characterized by parallel electron spins ($S = 1$) and which are distinguished from the singlet states ($S = 0$), as seen in Figure 7.22.

The different types of state formed by the two electrons of helium may be enumerated as follows:

Singlets: $S = 0$ throughout

Configuration:	$(1s)^2$	$L = 0$	${}^1S_0$
	$(1s)(2s)$	$L = 0$	${}^1S_0$
	$(1s)(2p)$	$L = 1$	${}^1P_1$
	$(1s)(3s)$	$L = 0$	${}^1S_0$
	$(1s)(3p)$	$L = 1$	${}^1P_1$
	$(1s)(3d)$	$L = 2$	${}^1D_2.$

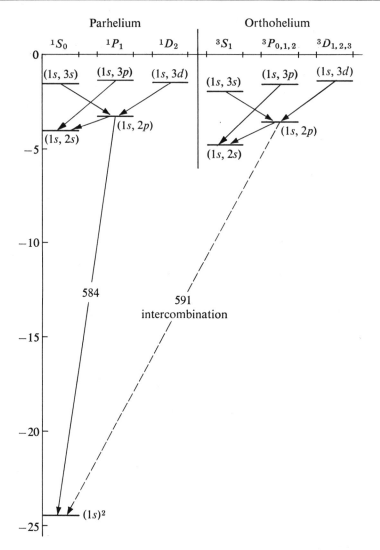

FIGURE 7.22 *Energy levels of the helium atom, divided into singlet states (parhelium) and triple states (orthohelium). The triplet levels are so close together that they are effectively singlets. The wavelengths of the two main transitions to the ground state are marked in Ångstroms.*

In the triplet series, we have $S = 1$ throughout and we have to discover the possible J values produced when a given orbital L combines with a spin S. The method used to find J when j_1 and j_2 are given for two electrons may be used here, or we may employ the simple vector model of Figure 7.18, which is generalized in Figure 7.23. If L is larger than S we can visualize the vector representing L as fixed and the spin vector S is then supposed to take up $(2S + 1)$ different orientations relative to L. In this way we find the $(2S + 1)$ different values of J to be

$$J = |L + S|, |L + S - 1|, \ldots, |L - S|.$$

On the other hand, if S is greater than L, we find

$$J = |S + L|, |S + L - 1|, \ldots, |S - L|.$$

[7.11.1]

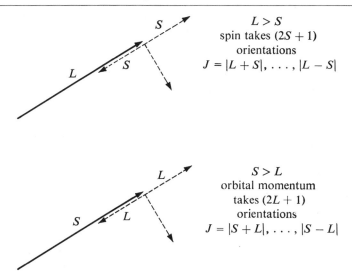

$L > S$
spin takes $(2S + 1)$
orientations
$J = |L + S|, \ldots, |L - S|$

$S > L$
orbital momentum
takes $(2L + 1)$
orientations
$J = |S + L|, \ldots, |S - L|$

FIGURE 7.23 *In Russell-Saunders coupling, the total orbital momentum (denoted by number L) and the total spin (denoted by S) combine to form the total angular momentum J. Above: for L > S, the possible J values are given by the simple vector model as J = |L + S|, ..., |L − S|. Below: for S > L, the possible values are J = |S + L|, ..., |S − L|.*

With the aid of these rules, we find the triplet states as follows:

Triplets: $S = 1$ throughout

Configuration:	$(1s)(2s)$	$L = 0$	$^3S_1$
	$(1s)(2p)$	$L = 1$	$^3P_0 \, ^3P_1 \, ^3P_2$
	$(1s)(3s)$	$L = 0$	$^3S_1$
	$(1s)(3p)$	$L = 1$	$^3P_0 \, ^3P_1 \, ^3P_2$
	$(1s)(3d)$	$L = 2$	$^3D_1 \, ^3D_2 \, ^3D_3$.

In fact the triplet substates are so close together in helium that they are regarded as effectively single states.

Examination of the helium term scheme in Figure 7.22 shows that optical transitions between states are confined almost entirely within the singlet or within the triplet terms. This is due to an optical selection rule which forbids a change of spin number S in the electric-dipole approximation (Section 7.13). The rule is so effective in helium that there are practically two separate spectroscopic series, called the "parhelium" (singlet) and "orthohelium" (triplet) lines. However, the *intercombination* line representing the transition between the ground state ($^1S_0$) and second orthohelium state ($^3P_1$) has been observed at a wavelength of 591 Å, although the transition is very feeble compared with the "allowed" lines. The existence of this line is due to the spin-orbit interaction which is present in all elements, and, as the atomic number of the element increases, the increased interaction causes intercombination lines to become more and more prominent. For example, in mercury (Figure 4.10), the general structure of spectral lines is similar to that in helium but the first intercombination line (at a wavelength of 2537 Å) is extremely strong, if not so strong as the other "resonance" line at 1849 Å.

(c) Ground states in complex atoms

Where more than two electrons are involved in excited states, the configurations may be very complicated, but it is often possible to pick out the ground state. Suppose, for example, that we consider the elements in the second row of the periodic table of chemical elements (Appendix II), ranging from $Z = 3$ (Li) to $Z = 10$ (Ne). It is clear that lithium is similar in properties to sodium (Figure 7.20) and has the ground state $2s\,^2S_{1/2}$. Likewise the element beryllium has two $2s$ electrons in the outer shell and its ground state is similar to that of helium, being written $(2s)^2\,^1S_0$. Boron has one electron in the $2p$ subshell and, in accordance with the general properties of doublet states split by the spin-orbit interaction, the lower state of the ^2P pair is the one with $j = \frac{1}{2}$, so the ground state is $2p\,^2P_{1/2}$.

The case of carbon, with two ^2P electrons in its outer subshell, requires some elucidation. If Russell-Saunders coupling is operative, we must combine all the possible m_l values to make m_L in all possible ways consistent with Pauli's principle; at the same time, the m_s values must be combined to make m_S. Then the appropriate L and S combinations have to be isolated and the spectroscopic terms discovered. We start by writing down all the possible combinations of m_l and m_s for a single $2p$ electron

$$m_l = 1 \quad 0 \quad -1 \quad 1 \quad 0 \quad -1,$$
$$m_s = \tfrac{1}{2} \quad \tfrac{1}{2} \quad \tfrac{1}{2} \quad -\tfrac{1}{2} \quad -\tfrac{1}{2} \quad -\tfrac{1}{2}.$$

The respective components have to be added two at a time in such a way that the same combination is not repeated (otherwise Pauli's principle would be violated). This gives a total of 15 values of m_L with their corresponding m_S values:

$$m_L = 1^+ \quad 0^+ \quad 2^* \quad 1^* \quad 0^* \quad -1^+ \quad 1^+ \quad 0^+ \quad -1^+ \quad 0 \quad -1^* \quad -2^* \quad 1^+ \quad 0^+ \quad -1^+,$$
$$m_S = 1 \quad 1 \quad 0 \quad 0 \quad 0 \quad 1 \quad 0 \quad 0 \quad 0 \quad 0 \quad 0 \quad 0 \quad -1 \quad -1 \quad -1.$$

We pick out the highest value of L (namely 2) and write it down with the corresponding maximum value of S (namely 0)

$$L = 2 \qquad S = 0, \quad \text{that is, the state } {}^1D_2.$$

Allowing for spatial quantization this particular term accounts for five combinations (m_L, m_S) and these are marked by an asterisk above. The next term picked out is

$$L = 1 \qquad S = 1, \quad \text{that is, the states } {}^3P_0\ {}^3P_1\ {}^3P_2$$

and these account for nine different combinations, marked $+$ above. There remains only the single combination $\quad L = 0 \qquad S = 0, \quad \text{that is, the state } {}^1S_0.$

The results of this analysis are several states, all of which are made up by the two $2p$ electrons of carbon (or any similar element). The theory does not enable us to decide which of these is the actual ground state, but empirical rules have been devised to meet the need. According to *Hund's rules*, states with the highest multiplicity form the lowest grouping in energy and, as we have seen in the single-electron cases, spin-orbit interaction causes the lowest J value to lie lowest in energy within a multiplet. In agreement with these rules the ground state of the carbon atom is $(2p)^2\,^3P_0$.

It is instructive to consider the same problem with j-j coupling operative. Here the two $2p$ electrons have to be treated in terms of j and m_j only and we have seen that the possible j values in this subshell are $j = \frac{1}{2}$ and $\frac{3}{2}$. The electron configurations are three in number and are written

$$(\tfrac{1}{2}, \tfrac{1}{2}) \qquad (\tfrac{1}{2}, \tfrac{3}{2}) \qquad (\tfrac{3}{2}, \tfrac{3}{2}).$$

In the first configuration, the electrons must have different m_j values, by Pauli's principle, so we write

$$m_j' = +\tfrac{1}{2} \quad m_j'' = -\tfrac{1}{2} \quad m_J = 0 \quad J = 0.$$

The second configuration covers the possibilities

$$m'_j = +\tfrac{1}{2} \quad -\tfrac{1}{2} \qquad m''_j = \tfrac{3}{2} \quad \tfrac{1}{2} \quad -\tfrac{1}{2} \quad -\tfrac{3}{2}$$

and, since Pauli's principle imposes no restrictions here, we have

$$m_J = 2 \quad 1 \quad 0 \quad -1 \quad 1 \quad 0 \quad -1 \quad -2$$

dividing into two levels characterized by $J = 2$ and $J = 1$. The third configuration has, for each electron,

$$m_j = \tfrac{3}{2} \quad \tfrac{1}{2} \quad -\tfrac{1}{2} \quad -\tfrac{3}{2}$$

and these have to be added without repetition of any combination. The result is

$$m_J = 2 \quad 1 \quad 0 \quad 0 \quad -1 \quad -2$$

dividing into two levels with $J = 2$ and $J = 0$.

The net result of the *j-j* coupling scheme is five different J values, which are necessarily the same as those obtained by Russell-Saunders coupling. However, the groupings of the levels are entirely different, as may be seen in Figure 7.24, where the energy levels are plotted on an arbitrary scale against the degree of spin-orbit interaction, represented by the parameter a of Equation (7.10.3). When $a = 0$, there is no spin-orbit interaction and the triplet P levels of Russell-Saunders coupling coincide. As the value of a increases, the P states separate in such a way that the level with $J = 0$ remains the lowest (as in the carbon

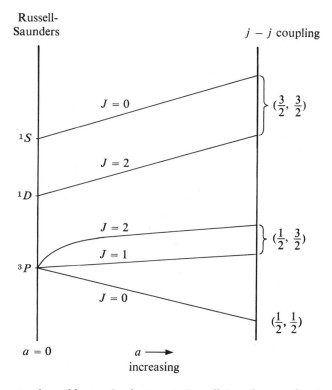

FIGURE 7.24 *The states formed by two 2p electrons in Russell-Saunders coupling (on the left) and in j–j coupling (on the right). The spin-orbit interaction constant a increases from left to right. The energy scale is entirely arbitrary.*

atom) and approaches the $(\frac{1}{2}, \frac{1}{2})$ level of *j-j* coupling. The remaining ^3P states go over into the two $(\frac{1}{2}, \frac{3}{2})$ states of the *j-j* scheme, while the upper two $(\frac{3}{2}, \frac{3}{2})$ states correspond with the ^1S and ^1D pair. The actual situation in many complex atoms can be described as "intermediate coupling," somewhere between pure Russell-Saunders and pure *j-j* coupling.

The next element above carbon is nitrogen, the atoms of which possess three $2p$ electrons in the outer shell. In Russell-Saunders coupling the ground state is $(2p)^3\,{}^4S_{3/2}$ and the alternative $(\frac{1}{2}, \frac{1}{2}, \frac{3}{2})$ configuration yields $J = \frac{3}{2}$ as the ground state. When we come to oxygen, with four $2p$ electrons, the summation of all possible (m_l, m_s) combinations gives exactly the same results as in carbon, as may be seen by considering that the combinations of four electrons out of six are the same as those of two holes in the same subshell. Thus the lowest terms are ^3P, ^1D, and ^1S in Russell-Saunders coupling. Hund's rule operates as before, but the spin-orbit interaction is of opposite sign for holes, relative to electrons, so the lowest state is the one with *maximum J* in the ^3P multiplet, that is, the ground state is $(2p)^4\,{}^3P_2$. A similar situation obtains in fluorine, where the five $2p$ electrons are equivalent to a single hole in the subshell and the lowest multiplet is necessarily ^2P. The inverted spin-orbit interaction then yields a $^2P_{3/2}$ ground state. In neon the shell is full and the lowest state is automatically $^1S_0$.

In many-electron states it is often important to know the parity of the system and in this connection the electron configuration is significant. If, for example, we have an *odd* number of p electrons, each with $l = 1$ and therefore odd parity, the net result is always odd. An *even* number of p electrons, or any number of s or d electrons, leads to even total parity. If, therefore, we sum all the electronic l values of the configuration, the parity is the same as that of the sum, independent of the L value attached to the state. Thus the ground state of nitrogen, $(2p)^3\,{}^4S_{3/2}$, has odd parity. The single-electron states, of course, always have the same parity as the l number, as shown in Section 7.6.

7.12   The Theory of Transitions

(a) Matrix elements

So far we have dealt chiefly with eigenvalue problems concerning state functions which vary with spatial coordinates but not in time. The "stationary states" of quantum mechanics are described by the eigenfunctions and no radiation or absorption occurs while the atom is in such a state. However, it is important to be able to handle transitions between different states and to work out which transitions are favored, which are inhibited or forbidden. This branch of atomic theory could not be developed without the aid of *perturbation* theory, which is based on the time-dependent Schrödinger equation of Section 7.3. For a state function which varies in space and time we have the rate of change in time given by Equation (7.3.14)

$$i\hbar\,\frac{\partial \Psi}{\partial t} = H\Psi,$$

that is, the Hamiltonian operator is equivalent to $i\hbar\,\dfrac{\partial}{\partial t}$. We can revert to the time-independent equation by substituting

$$\Psi(t, x, y, z) = \psi(x, y, z) \exp\left(-\frac{iEt}{\hbar}\right)$$

when we obtain

$$E\psi = H\psi.$$

However, this is only one out of many possible solutions and a more general solution is found by substituting a linear combination of eigenfunctions ψ_m, each with an amplitude A_m and the eigenvalue E_m

$$\Psi(t, x, y, z) = \sum_m A_m \psi_m \exp\left(-\frac{iE_m t}{\hbar}\right), \qquad [7.12.1]$$

where the amplitude A_m is assumed to be real. Schrödinger interpreted the condition represented by this equation as being similar to the excitation of a complex note in a string when several different frequencies are sounded simultaneously. In a single-electron atom we can proceed to find the probability density function

$$|\Psi|^2 = \Psi^* \Psi$$

$$= \sum_m A_m^2 |\psi_m|^2 + \sum_{m \neq n} \left\{ A_m A_n \left[\psi_m^* \psi_n \exp \frac{i(E_m - E_n)t}{\hbar} + \psi_m \psi_n^* \exp \frac{i(E_n - E_m)t}{\hbar} \right] \right\}.$$

Such an expression gives a picture of the intercombination frequencies as "beats" between the fundamental frequencies of oscillation. The intercombination terms vary with time according to the function $\exp(\pm i\omega_{mn}t)$ where the angular frequencies are defined directly by Bohr's relation (Section 6.4)

$$\omega_{mn} = \frac{E_m - E_n}{\hbar}.$$

We also find from this elementary argument that the transition or intercombination terms are related to products of the state functions ($\psi_m^* \psi_n$ and $\psi_m \psi_n^*$). Averaged over any considerable time, however, the mean values of the oscillatory functions reduce to zero and the probability attached to each squared eigenfunction depends on the square of the amplitude A_m.

A more detailed treatment of the problem of transitions brings in perturbation theory. Here we shall be concerned with one particular result of the time-dependent theory.[†] We assume that a system is in a state a at time $t = 0$, then we apply a perturbing interaction energy which is supposed to be small compared with the original unperturbed Hamiltonian H_0, that is, we write

$$H = H_0 + H',$$

where H' stands for the small perturbing interaction. We deduce that the probability of finding the system in another state b at time t depends on the square of the *matrix element* of the operator H' for the transition from state a to state b. This matrix element may be written H'_{ab}, or, in Dirac's notation,

$$\langle a |H'| b \rangle \equiv \int \psi_b^* H' \psi_a \, dV, \qquad [7.12.2]$$

where the complex state functions are supposed to be normalized within some specified volume. The integration is taken over the entire volume of normalization, usually over the whole of space for functions which vanish at large distances. The probability of transition per unit time, P_{ab}, is proportional to the squared modulus of the matrix element H'_{ab}:

$$P_{ab} \propto |H'_{ab}|^2.$$

The matrices formed by H'_{ab} have the "Hermitian" property that each element is the complex conjugate of the element for the reverse transition

$$H'_{ab} = H'^*_{ba}.$$

[†] See L. I. Schiff, *Quantum Mechanics* (McGraw-Hill Book Co., New York, 1955) 2nd ed., Chap. VIII.

Thus, for the same perturbation H', the probabilities of forward and reverse transitions are the same,

$$P_{ab} = P_{ba},$$

a principle which has been used in Section 4.5.

Matrix elements may be calculated in many cases where the interaction H' is known and their values are important in predicting the strengths of different transitions. However, it is often even more significant to find situations in which the matrix elements vanish identically, that is, the transition is forbidden. These cases give rise to *selection rules* which are of immense value in applications of the theory.

(b) Orthogonality

The existence of selection rules is intimately related to the *orthogonality* of the state functions which are solutions of the Schrödinger equation. The property of orthogonality may be demonstrated by writing down the equation twice, for the eigenfunctions ψ_b^* and ψ_a, with eigenvalues E_b and E_a, respectively,

$$\nabla^2 \psi_b^* + \frac{2m}{\hbar^2}(E_b - U)\psi_b^* = 0,$$

$$\nabla^2 \psi_a + \frac{2m}{\hbar^2}(E_a - U)\psi_a = 0.$$

We multiply the first equation by ψ_a, the second by ψ_b^*, and subtract

$$\psi_a \nabla^2 \psi_b^* - \psi_b^* \nabla^2 \psi_a + \frac{2m}{\hbar^2}(E_b - E_a)\psi_b^* \psi_a = 0.$$

The expression is then integrated over the whole of space (on the assumption that the functions vanish at sufficiently large distances) and we obtain

$$\int (\psi_a \nabla^2 \psi_b^* - \psi_b^* \nabla^2 \psi_a)\, dV = \frac{2m}{\hbar^2}(E_a - E_b)\int \psi_b^* \psi_a\, dV.$$

The left-hand side may be transformed into a surface integral by means of Green's theorem and becomes

$$\int (\psi_a \operatorname{grad} \psi_b^* - \psi_b^* \operatorname{grad} \psi_a)\, d\mathbf{A},$$

where $d\mathbf{A}$ represents the element of surface area as a vector. For all state functions which decrease rapidly with distance the surface integral vanishes, so we conclude that

$$(E_a - E_b)\int \psi_b^* \psi_a\, dV = 0. \qquad [7.12.3]$$

Provided that E_a and E_b are actually different for the two eigenfunctions ψ_a and ψ_b^*, that is, the states are nondegenerate, we find from Equation (7.12.3) that

$$\text{either} \qquad\qquad a = b$$

$$\text{or} \qquad\qquad \int \psi_b^* \psi_a\, dV = 0.$$

The latter equation is known as the orthogonality condition and it applies to all the functions derived in Section 7.5 and Section 7.6. For example, the spherical harmonics of

Section 7.6 are shown to satisfy the condition as follows. We have the relation between $Y_{l,m}(\theta, \varphi)$ and the Legendre polynomial

$$Y_{l,m}(\theta, \varphi) = P_l^m(\cos \theta) \exp (im\varphi).$$

Integrating first over φ, we know that

$$\int_{\varphi=0}^{2\pi} \exp (-im'\varphi + im\varphi) \, d\varphi = 0 \quad \text{unless} \quad m = m'$$

so that

$$\int_{\theta=0}^{\pi} \int_{\varphi=0}^{2\pi} Y_{l',m}^* Y_{l\,m} \, d(\cos \theta) \, d\varphi = 2\pi \int_{-1}^{1} P_{l'}^m(\cos \theta) \, P_l^m(\cos \theta) \, d(\cos \theta)$$

and the properties of Legendre polynomials ensure that the θ integral vanishes unless $l = l'$.[†] Thus the product of spherical harmonics $(Y_{l',m'}^* \, Y_{l,m})$ vanishes when integrated over the full range of angles unless both $m = m'$ and $l = l'$.

(c) Parity selection rules

Reverting to the matrix elements of the perturbing interaction H', we see that unless H' varies in spatial (or spin) coordinates there can be no change from a given state a, because all matrix elements for transitions to other states b vanish automatically. In practice H' varies with displacement, radius, or angle in some way and different types of variation lead to different selection rules for "allowed" transitions. Usually these rules are based on the variations in spin or angle coordinates, but one very general rule may be deduced concerning changes in *parity*. We assume that the Hamiltonian is strictly scalar so that each physical state is described by a function of either odd or even parity (Section 7.4). Whatever the parity of the individual functions may be, the integrand in H_{ab}', namely,

$$\psi_b^* H' \psi_a \equiv f(x, y, z),$$

must itself be of even parity, otherwise the integral over the whole of space vanishes. This effect may be seen by reversing the coordinates (x, y, z) to make $(-x, -y, -z)$ or by replacing (r, θ, φ) with $(r, \pi - \theta, \pi + \varphi)$, as in Figure 7.11. If the integrand $f(x, y, z)$ changes sign on reversal of coordinates the contributions to the integral from similar regions on opposite sides of the origin must cancel out and the entire integral vanishes. We deduce that the integrand must have *even* parity for a transition to occur between states a and b.

This result may be applied as follows. If H' includes spatially dependent terms which are *scalar* throughout, that is, independent of spatial direction, the functions ψ_b^* and ψ_a must be of the same parity (both even or both odd) to ensure an even-parity integrand in Equation (7.12.2). In such cases the transition causes *no* change in parity and the parity selection rule is written "No."

In other cases, H' is itself scalar but the spatially dependent part is a *polar vector*, such as the radius vector $\mathbf{r}$. Such a quantity possesses intrinsically odd parity, since the reversal of coordinates changes the sign of $\mathbf{r}$, and nonvanishing matrix elements are obtained only if ψ_b^* and ψ_a have different parity, that is, the selection rule for transitions is "Yes."

Instead of a polar vector, the interaction H' may include an *axial vector*, such as the angular momentum $\mathbf{G} = \mathbf{r} \times \mathbf{p}$. The vector product of two polar vectors, each of which possesses odd parity, is itself of even parity. This may readily be appreciated because the sign of $\mathbf{G}$ depends only on the sense of rotation, which is unchanged when we reverse both

---

[†] See, for example, H. Margenau and G. M. Murphy, *The Mathematics of Physics and Chemistry* (Van Nostrand Co. Princeton, 1956) 2nd ed., Vol I, Sec. 3.6.

r and **p**. If the perturbation involves an axial vector, therefore, the matrix elements vanish unless the final and original states have the same parity and the selection rule is "No."

Finally we may consider the case where H' involves a *pseudoscalar* quantity, such as the scalar product of a polar and an axial vector, which changes sign on reversal of coordinates. Such quantities are rarely encountered in classical physics (one example is the potential in a magnetic field) but they are of some significance in particle interactions and where they exist the parity selection rule is "Yes."

7.13 Electromagnetic Transitions and Selection Rules

(a) Electric-dipole selection rules

The most important selection rules in atomic physics are those for electromagnetic radiation emitted or absorbed by an atom. The processes of absorption and stimulated emission must obey the same rules because the corresponding matrix elements have the same absolute magnitude for the same pair of states [Equation (7.12.2)]. The process of spontaneous emission can be dealt with in two ways, either by making a semiclassical calculation of the energy emitted (along the lines of Section 4.1.c) or by considering the exchange of energy between the atom and the photons of the radiation field, which is treated as an assembly of harmonic oscillators. Both treatments lead to the conclusion that stimulated and spontaneous emission must obey the same selection rules for the same kind of radiation mechanism. The most important mechanism is the electric-dipole process, described classically in Section 4.1, and the selection rules for this kind of radiation will now be considered.

Suppose that radiant energy is absorbed by the interaction of an electromagnetic wave with a single electron which is bound to a fixed atom. The interaction may be described semiclassically in terms of field variables, the most important term being the electric-dipole interaction energy

$$H' = -(\mathbf{p}\mathscr{E}) = +e(\mathbf{r}\mathscr{E}), \qquad [7.13.1]$$

where **p** stands for the instantaneous dipole moment of the single electron at radius **r**, that is, $\mathbf{p} = -e\mathbf{r}$, and $\mathscr{E}$ is the electric field vector of the incident wave. This expression does not involve electron spin, so, to a first approximation, we can use the Schrödinger state functions in our study of the matrix elements. Moreover, in the absence of spin-orbit interaction, the electric-dipole interaction can affect only the electron's *orbital* momentum. This applies to any number of electrons and we derive the selection rule

$$\Delta S = 0 \qquad [7.13.2]$$

which accounts for the weakness of intercombination lines between singlet ($S = 0$) and triplet ($S = 1$) states of a light atom like helium (Figure 7.22). In heavy elements like mercury (Figure 4.10) the rule breaks down because of enhanced spin-orbit interaction. The rule is trivial for single-electron states, in which $S = \frac{1}{2}$ throughout.

The second rule which emerges from a study of the interaction Hamiltonian H' of Equation (7.13.1) is *Laporte's rule*, which is concerned with parity changes. Since H' involves the polar vector **r** the initial and final states must always be of different parity for electric-dipole transitions (Section 7.12). In the case of a single-electron state the parity is always given by $(-1)^l$ so the value of the orbital quantum number l must change by an odd number $(1, 3, 5, \ldots)$ at each transition. In multielectron states the parity is found by summing the *l* values of the electrons contributing to the state involved, which is then classified as even or odd. Laporte's rule then prohibits transitions within even states and within odd states. For example, the set of states derived from a single electron *configuration* (such as the ^3P, ^1D, and ^1S low-energy states of carbon) cannot combine with each other.

In the absence of appreciable spin-orbit interaction, we can employ the Schrödinger state functions to derive specific selection rules for the m_l and *l* numbers of single-electron states. Suppose, to begin with, that the incident electromagnetic wave is polarized with its electric vector along the *z* direction, that is, the interaction Hamiltonian is

$$H' = e\mathscr{E}_z z = e\mathscr{E}_z r \cos \theta.$$

The single-electron state functions are written

$$\psi_a = R_a(r) P_l^m(\cos \theta) \exp (im\varphi)$$
$$\psi_b^* = R_b(r) P_{l'}^{m'}(\cos \theta) \exp (-im'\varphi),$$

where *m* and *m'* stand for the m_l values of the electron. The matrix element H'_{ab} is the product of three integrals

$$H'_{ab} = e\mathscr{E}_z \int_0^\infty R_a R_b r^3 \, dr \int_{-1}^1 P_l^m P_{l'}^{m'} \cos \theta \, d(\cos \theta) \int_0^{2\pi} \exp [i(m - m')\varphi] \, d\varphi.$$

Thus the matrix element vanishes unless $m = m'$, because of the integration over φ, and, for this particular polarization, the selection rule is

$$\Delta m_l = 0. \tag{7.13.3}$$

However, the parity rule of Laporte requires that the value of *l* should change. The associated Legendre polynomials with $m = m'$ obey the following recurrence relation†:

$$(2l + 1) \cos \theta \, P_l^m = (l - m + 1)P_{l+1}^m + (l + m)P_{l-1}^m.$$

The θ integrand then becomes

$$\frac{P_{l'}^m}{2l + 1} [(l - m + 1)P_{l+1}^m + (l + m)P_{l-1}^m]$$

and the orthogonality rule for spherical harmonics (Section 7.12) ensures that the matrix element vanishes unless

$$l' = l + 1 \quad or \quad l' = l - 1,$$

that is, the selection rule for electric-dipole transitions is

$$\Delta l = \pm 1. \tag{7.13.4}$$

Another set of selection rules operates if the incident light is circularly polarized. For example, if the (xy) plane is the plane of circular polarization of the $\mathscr{E}$ vector, the interaction energy becomes

$$H' = e(\mathbf{r}\mathscr{E})$$
$$= e(x\mathscr{E}_x + y\mathscr{E}_y).$$

The term in parentheses is the real part of the expression

$$(x + iy)(\mathscr{E}_x - i\mathscr{E}_y)$$

† H. Margenau and G. M. Murphy, *The Mathematics of Physics and Chemistry* (Van Nostrand Co., Princeton, N.J., 1956) 2nd ed., Vol. I, Sec. 3.6.

in the case where the $\mathscr{E}$ vector rotates clockwise (see Section 4.2) or of the alternative expression

$$(x - iy)(\mathscr{E}_x + i\mathscr{E}_y)$$

for counterclockwise rotation of $\mathscr{E}$. Thus the matrix element is proportional to the factor

$$x \pm iy,$$

where the sign depends on the sense of the electric polarization.

We now write x and y in terms of the angle variables

$$x = r \sin \theta \cos \varphi \qquad y = r \sin \theta \sin \varphi$$

and obtain

$$x \pm iy = r \sin \theta \exp(\pm i\varphi).$$

The integral over φ becomes

$$\int_0^{2\pi} \exp[i(m - m')\varphi] \exp(\pm i\varphi)\, d\varphi$$

which vanishes unless

$$m' = m \pm 1,$$

and the selection rule is

$$\Delta m_l = \pm 1. \qquad [7.13.5]$$

The integral over θ is

$$\int_{-1}^{1} P_{l'}^{m'} P_l^m \sin \theta\, d(\cos \theta)$$

and the integrand can be transformed by the recurrence relations for $m' = m \pm 1$, namely,

$$(2l + 1)P_l^m \sin \theta = P_{l+1}^{m+1} - P_{l-1}^{m+1}$$

and

$$(2l + 1)P_l^m \sin \theta = (l + m - 1)(l + m)P_{l-1}^{m-1} - (l - m + 1)(l - m + 2)P_{l+1}^{m-1}.$$

The orthogonality relations for associated Legendre polynomials then lead to the result that the matrix element vanishes unless $l' = l \pm 1$, as before.

The selection rules for single-electron transitions are completed by consideration of possible changes in the total angular momentum number j. If angular momentum is to be conserved, the change in j has to be balanced by an opposite amount which is carried by the photon absorbed or emitted. We have seen that the photon has an effective spin of one unit ($\hbar$) and, in the electric-dipole interaction, this single unit has to be compounded with the original angular momentum (j) to form the final angular momentum (j') of the atom. Using the angular-momentum argument of Section 7.11, we see that the original vector j can be compounded three ways with a unit spin, the latter having components of 1, 0, and -1 units along the j direction. We deduce that

$$j' = j + 1, \quad j, \quad \text{or} \quad j - 1$$

except in the two special cases

$$j = 0, \qquad \text{when the final } j' = 1$$
$$j = \tfrac{1}{2}, \qquad \text{when the final } j' = \tfrac{3}{2} \text{ or } \tfrac{1}{2}.$$

Thus the j selection rule for electric-dipole transitions is written

$$\Delta j = 0, \pm 1 \qquad (\text{with } 0 \leftrightarrow 0 \text{ forbidden}). \qquad [7.13.6]$$

This result may be generalized to cover many-electron transitions, where the total angular momentum number J is involved

$$\Delta J = 0, \pm 1 \qquad (\text{with } 0 \leftrightarrow 0 \text{ forbidden}). \qquad [7.13.7]$$

We have already seen that, when spin-orbit interaction is slight, the total spin number does not change in electric-dipole transitions

$$\Delta S = 0. \qquad \text{[Equation (7.13.2)]}$$

It follows that, to the same approximation, the selection rule for the number L (valid only in Russell-Saunders coupling) is

$$\Delta L = 0, \pm 1.$$

In addition, we have the Laporte rule requiring a change in parity and forbidding changes between states of the same electron configuration.

(b) Alkali-metal spectra

With the aid of the foregoing rules, spectroscopic data obtained for many elements can be interpreted. The operation of the rules $\Delta l = \pm 1$, $\Delta j = 0, \pm 1$ has already been seen in Figure 7.20, which refers to the alkali metal sodium. As stated in Section 7.10, transitions occur only between states differing by one unit of orbital angular momentum, and the different series of spectral lines observed in sodium may be classified as follows:

Original state	Final state	Series
$n\,^2P$ ($n = 3, 4$, and so forth)	$3\,^2S$	Principal
$n\,^2S$ ($n = 4, 5$, and so forth)	$3\,^2P$	Sharp
$n\,^2D$ ($n = 3, 4$, and so forth)	$3\,^2P$	Diffuse
$n\,^2F$ ($n = 4, 5$, and so forth)	$3\,^2D$	Fundamental

These series names were given in the early history of spectroscopy and their initial letters survive in the spectroscopic notation for atomic states.

It is clear from the study of single-electron states in Section 7.10 that both the principal and sharp series found in the spectra of alkali metals consist entirely of doublet lines, due to the spin-orbit splitting of the ^2P states. The relative intensities of the lines in a doublet may be derived from the matrix elements for the transition (involving the spin appropriately) or, more directly, from a *sum rule* based on the concept of "statistical weight." We have seen that the total angular momentum denoted by the number J can be resolved into $(2J + 1)$ components, each with a separate number m_J, and that up to $(2J + 1)$ electrons can occupy the states of a multiplet J, in accordance with Pauli's Exclusion principle. We therefore assign statistical weight $(2J + 1)$ to such a state. The sum rule requires that the *sum* of intensities of all spectral lines belonging to a given initial (or final) state shall be proportional to the statistical weight of the initial (or final) state. For example, the "D" resonance lines of sodium are formed by transitions from the $^2P_{1/2}$ and $^2P_{3/2}$ states to the ground state $^2S_{1/2}$. Since the final state is common to both lines, their intensities (I_1 and I_2) are in the ratio of the statistical weights

$$\frac{I_1(D1, {}^2P_{1/2} \to {}^2S_{1/2})}{I_2(D2, {}^2P_{3/2} \to {}^2S_{1/2})} = \frac{2}{4} = \frac{1}{2}.$$

The spectral lines in the "diffuse" series of an alkali metal provide an interesting example of the operation of selection rules and the sum rule. The upper ^2D doublet states have $j = \frac{3}{2}$ and $\frac{5}{2}$, while the lower ^2P states have $j = \frac{1}{2}$ and $\frac{3}{2}$, so there are three allowed transitions, as shown in Figure 7.25. However, the observed lines appear to be doublets under low resolution and it requires high resolving power to reveal the triplet structure. For this reason the diffuse lines are sometimes called "compound doublets." The line formed by

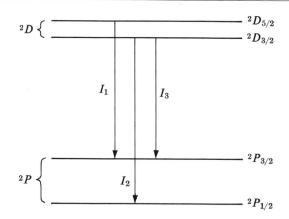

FIGURE 7.25 *Transitions between ^2D and ^2P doublet states of an alkali metal (the level splittings are greatly exaggerated). I_1, I_2, and I_3 denote the intensities of the lines produced by three allowed transitions.*

the transition $\frac{3}{2} \to \frac{3}{2}$ is in fact very weak, and the reason for this is shown by applying the sum rule. Since the three transitions end in the $^2P_{1/2}$, $^2P_{3/2}$ states, the total intensities of lines reaching these states are in the ratio 2:4 (as in the "D" lines). If, therefore, we denote the intensities of the separate lines by the symbols I_1, I_2, and I_3, where

I_1 is the intensity for the change $^2D_{5/2} \to {}^2P_{3/2}$

I_2 is the intensity for the change $^2D_{3/2} \to {}^2P_{1/2}$

I_3 is the intensity for the change $^2D_{3/2} \to {}^2P_{3/2}$

we have the relation

$$\frac{I_1 + I_3}{I_2} = 2.$$

At the same time the ratio of statistical weights for the upper states is

$$\frac{2(2\frac{1}{2}) + 1}{2(1\frac{1}{2}) + 1} = \frac{3}{2},$$

so that we have an extra relation between the intensities

$$\frac{I_1}{I_2 + I_3} = \frac{3}{2}.$$

Solution of the two equations yields

$$I_1 = 9I_3 \quad \text{and} \quad I_2 = 5I_3$$

and the ratio of intensities is

$$I_1 : I_2 : I_3 = 9:5:1.$$

It follows that the third line is very weak compared with the other two and the pair of stronger lines appears very similar to the true doublets of the principal series.

(c) More complex atoms

The single-electron selection rules for electric-dipole interaction may also be applied to x-ray transitions, with results shown in Figure 7.21 for uranium. Various schemes of nomenclature have been proposed for the different lines, but, to simplify matters, all the lines involving the basic $1\,^2S_{1/2}$ state have been labeled the "K" series, all those reaching the $2\,^2S_{1/2}$ level the "LI" series, and so on. The prominent $K\alpha$ line seen in x-ray spectra (Figure 4.19) is in fact a close doublet due to the spin-orbit splitting of the $2\,^2P$ states. In addition to the numerous lines produced by single-electron transitions, there are faint "satellite" lines due to double-electron processes of various kinds.

In "two-electron" atoms like helium (Figure 7.22) and mercury (Figure 4.10) the general selection rules are needed. The ground state is always a singlet of the type $^1S_0$ and the transitions within the singlet series include $^1P_1 \to {}^1S_0$; $^1D_2 \to {}^1P_1$; $^1F_3 \to {}^1D_2$. All these lines are necessarily single. Within the triplet series we have transitions of the types $^3P_{0,1,2} \to {}^3S_1$; $^3D_3 \to {}^3P_2$; $^3D_2 \to {}^3P_{2,1}$; $^3D_1 \to {}^3P_{2,1,0}$; and so on. Such transitions give triplets or "compound triplets" but the spacings of the triplet components may be considerable in a heavy atom like mercury. The intercombination lines which violate the (approximate) rule $\Delta S = 0$ are usually emitted in transitions to the ground state ($^1S_0$) from the ^3P group, which contains levels with $J = 0$, 1, and 2. Of these the first and last cannot be reached because of the strict rule [Equation (7.13.7)] for changes in J by electric-dipole interaction, so the intercombination line is a singlet $^1S_0 \leftrightarrow {}^3P_1$.

(d) Magnetic-dipole and electric-quadrupole interactions

Although the electric-dipole interaction is by far the most important in atomic physics, there are other forms of interaction which are detected under special circumstances. For example, we might consider the *magnetic-dipole* interaction between the magnetic field of the incident electromagnetic wave and the orbital magnetic moment of an electron. The latter is of magnitude one Bohr magneton [Equation (6.5.2)] and can be written in vector form as proportional to the orbital angular momentum $\mathbf{G}_l$

$$\mathbf{\mu} = -\frac{e}{2m}\,\mathbf{G}_l = \frac{-e}{2m}\,[\mathbf{r} \times \mathbf{p}].$$

The potential energy of interaction with the incident wave is expressed in terms of the field $\mathbf{B}$ as

$$H'' = -(\mathbf{\mu B}).$$

The magnitude of $\mathbf{B}$ is related to the magnitude of the associated electric vector $\mathscr{E}$ via the field $\mathscr{H}$, as follows:

$$|B| = \mu_0\,|\mathscr{H}| = \mu_0\sqrt{\frac{\varepsilon_0}{\mu_0}}\,|\mathscr{E}|,$$

$$= c^{-1}\,|\mathscr{E}|,$$

where μ_0, ε_0, and c refer to the permeability, permittivity, and velocity of light in free space. The order of magnitude of H'' is therefore given by the expression

$$H'' \approx \frac{erp}{2mc}\,|\mathscr{E}| = \tfrac{1}{2}e\frac{v}{c}\,r\,|\mathscr{E}|,$$

where v is the orbital speed of the electron. Compared with the H' of Equation (7.13.1), the magnetic interaction is reduced by the factor v/c. The corresponding transitions, which depend on the square of the matrix element, have intensities only v^2/c^2 times those of the electric-dipole transitions. In practice the ratio of intensities, for comparable changes in level, is of the order of 10^5. It is therefore very difficult to detect magnetic-dipole effects unless two conditions are satisfied:

(i) the transition must be forbidden for electric-dipole interaction;

(ii) the atom must be disturbed as little as possible by collisions and other influences, so that there is plenty of time for the long lifetime processes to occur.

With regard to condition (i), the selection rules for magnetic-dipole transitions differ from those for electric-dipole transitions in one important feature. Since H'' involves spatial variables only through the axial vector $\mathbf{G}_l$ the parity selection rule is "No" (Section 7.12). This has the effect of allowing transitions between members of a group of states formed by the same electron configuration. Such transitions are rarely seen in laboratory work but they are responsible for unusual lines observed in the spectra of gaseous nebulae and referred to sometimes as "nebulium" lines. In fact these lines are due to ionized oxygen and nitrogen atoms which, in the rarefied conditions obtaining in nebulae, emit lines of the magnetic-dipole character.

Another type of transition which is only observed under special conditions is the *electric-quadrupole* change, which involves no change in parity but can change the number J by 0, 1, or 2 units. Prominent lines observed in the spectra of auroral displays have been ascribed to this type of transition in neutral oxygen atoms. These lines have been produced in the laboratory and their peculiar Zeeman splittings show that they are indeed of electric-quadrupole character.

7.14 Atoms in a Magnetic Field

(a) *Splitting of energy levels*

Under normal conditions the energy levels of an atom are fixed by the electron configurations and the numbers J, L, and S which specify the states. The spin-orbit interaction is responsible for the fine structure of many states and in addition there may be hyperfine structure due to small nuclear interactions (which are different for different isotopes of the same element) or to Lamb shifts. The only remaining parameter which may influence energy levels is the "magnetic" quantum number m_J which represents the component of the total angular momentum in any preferred direction. Normally this does not have any effect because all directions are equivalent, that is, the levels are degenerate with respect to the number m_J. However, if we impose a magnetic field $\mathbf{B}$ the atom may have its angular momentum vector $\mathbf{G}$ oriented in $(2J + 1)$ different ways relative to the field direction. Each of these orientations corresponds to a definite value m_J among the series

$$J, (J - 1), \ldots , (-J)$$

and each has a distinct energy level, so that the degeneracy is removed.

The splitting of levels in a magnetic field may be observed either by direct experiments of the Stern-Gerlach type, which employ deflection of atomic beams by inhomogeneous fields, or by measurements of spectral lines (the Zeeman effect). For example, Stern and Gerlach found that beams of neutral silver atoms split into two (Section 6.5) and this observation can be understood if we suppose that these atoms are in the $5\,{}^2S_{1/2}$ ground state. Furthermore the amount of deflection agreed with the magnetic moment per atom being one Bohr magneton, which is the appropriate value for the spin of one electron (Section

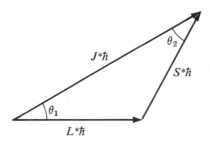

FIGURE 7.26 *Vector model representing the composition of orbital angular momentum (L*ħ) and spin (S*ħ) to form the total angular momentum (J*ħ) for a given atomic state in Russell-Saunders coupling. The effective magnetic moment can be calculated by summing the orbital and spin contributions along the J* direction.*

7.9). In general an experiment of the Stern-Gerlach type splits an atomic beam into $(2J + 1)$ components, although it is often necessary to pass the beam through a velocity selector first to improve the resolution of the apparatus.

The effective magnetic moment per atom is not, however, a simple multiple of the Bohr magneton, in general, because of the different gyromagnetic factors [g in Equation (6.5.5)] for orbital and spin momentum. In states where the only angular momentum is orbital (for example, $^1P_1$) the magnetic moment is strictly one magneton per unit angular momentum, so g is exactly one. In states where only spin momentum is present (for example $^2S_{1/2}$) the magnetic moment is very slightly greater than one magneton per spin unit ($\frac{1}{2}\hbar$), namely, from Equation (7.10.8)

$$\mu = \mu_B\left(1 + \frac{\alpha}{2\pi}\right), \qquad \text{where} \quad \alpha = \frac{1}{137}.$$

Accordingly we assume that $g = 2$ (very nearly) for spin momentum by itself. In states where orbital and spin momentum are combined to form the total angular momentum according to the rules of Russell-Saunders coupling, the effective gyromagnetic factor can be calculated with the aid of the vector model (Figure 7.18), as follows.

In Figure 7.26 the orbital angular momentum is represented by a vector $L^*\hbar$, of magnitude given by $L^* = \sqrt{L(L + 1)}$ as found in Section 7.6, and the spin momentum by a vector $S^*\hbar$ with magnitude given by $S^* = \sqrt{S(S + 1)}$. In some particular state these vectors are supposed to add up to make the total angular momentum, represented by $J^*\hbar$, with $J^* = \sqrt{J(J + 1)}$. In the vector triangle of Figure 7.26 the angles between J^* and $L^*(\theta_1)$ and between J^* and $S^*(\theta_2)$ can be calculated by the cosine rule as follows:

$$\cos\theta_1 = \frac{J^{*2} + L^{*2} - S^{*2}}{2J^*L^*}$$

and

$$\cos\theta_2 = \frac{J^{*2} + S^{*2} - L^{*2}}{2J^*S^*}.$$

The magnetic moment due to orbital momentum is one Bohr magneton per unit angular momentum, so we have a magnetic vector of magnitude $L^*\mu_B$ along the L^* direction. The magnetic vector due to the spin is of magnitude $2S^*\mu_B$ (very nearly) along the S^* direction. In order to find the total magnetic vector along the J^* direction, we add the components of the orbital and spin moments in this direction and obtain

$$\mu_J = L^*\mu_B \cos\theta_1 + 2S^*\mu_B \cos\theta_2$$

$$= \mu_B\left[\frac{J^{*2} + L^{*2} - S^{*2}}{2J^*} + \frac{J^{*2} + S^{*2} - L^{*2}}{J^*}\right]$$

$$= \mu_B\left[\frac{3J^{*2} + S^{*2} - L^{*2}}{2J^*}\right].$$

The gyromagnetic factor g for such a state is then

$$g = \frac{\mu_J}{J^*\mu_B} = 1 + \frac{J^{*2} + S^{*2} - L^{*2}}{2J^{*2}}$$

$$= 1 + \frac{J(J+1) + S(S+1) - L(L+1)}{2J(J+1)}. \qquad [7.14.1]$$

This is also called the Landé splitting factor and it assumes the correct limiting values $g = 2$ for $L = 0$, $J = S$, and $g = 1$ for $S = 0$, $J = L$. The effective moment per atom is readily expressed in terms of the angular momentum number J as follows:

$$\mu_J = J^*g\mu_B = g\mu_B\sqrt{J(J+1)}. \qquad [7.14.2]$$

When we wish to calculate the potential energy of the magnetic moment in an applied field B, however, we apply the rules of spatial quantization (Section 7.6) and employ the components of angular momentum $(m_J\hbar)$ instead of the magnitude of the angular momentum vector $(J^*\hbar)$. Since the effective magnetic moment per unit of angular momentum is $g\mu_B$, the energy in the field for some particular component m_J is

$$\Delta E = -m_J g\mu_B B. \qquad [7.14.3]$$

This formula yields the splitting of any energy level denoted by numbers L, S, and J in Russell-Saunders coupling.

(b) The Zeeman effect

With the aid of the level-splitting formula and the electromagnetic selection rules of Section 7.13, we can work out the details of Zeeman splitting for any spectral line. As an example, we consider the prominent "D" lines of sodium, which are emitted by transitions from the $3\,{}^2P$ states to the ground state $(3\,{}^2S)$ of the atom (Figure 7.20). In a magnetic field B applied along the direction $0z$, the energy levels each split into $(2J + 1)$ components and the transitions between the split levels are governed by the single-electron selection rules

$$\Delta j = 0, \pm 1 \quad \text{and} \quad \Delta l = \pm 1,$$

also

$$\Delta m_j = 0 \qquad \text{for electric polarization parallel to } 0z \text{ ("}\pi\text{" polarization)}$$

$$\Delta m_j = \pm 1 \qquad \text{for circular polarization in the } xy \text{ plane ("}\sigma\text{" polarization).}$$

The two latter rules are generalizations from the rules for the number m_l [Equations (7.13.3) and (7.13.5)] which are valid in electric-dipole interaction.

In the field B the ground state splits into two levels with spacings given by Equation (7.14.3) with $g = 2$, that is,

$$\Delta E_0 = \pm\tfrac{1}{2}2\mu_B B = \pm\mu_B B. \qquad [7.14.4]$$

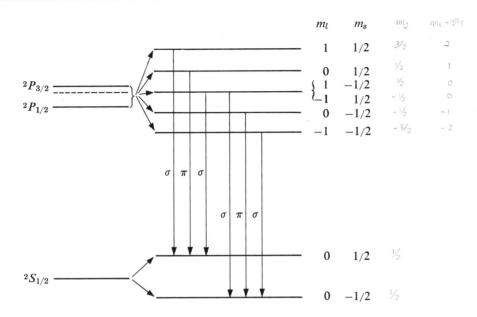

m_l	m_s	m_j	$m_l - 2m_s$
1	1/2	3/2	2
0	1/2	1/2	1
1	−1/2	1/2	0
−1	1/2	−1/2	0
0	−1/2	−1/2	−1
−1	−1/2	−3/2	−2
0	1/2	1/2	
0	−1/2	1/2	

FIGURE 7.27 *Zeeman splitting of the "D" lines of sodium in a moderate magnetic field. The ground state divides into two magnetic substates and the $^2P_{1/2}$ state likewise (with a lower g factor), while the $^2P_{3/2}$ state divides into four substates. As a result the D_1 line splits into 4 lines and the D_2 into 6. (The magnetic splittings are greatly exaggerated.)*

The lower of the ^2P states, namely the $^2P_{1/2}$ state, has

$$g = 1 + \frac{\frac{1}{2} \cdot 1\frac{1}{2} + \frac{1}{2} \cdot 1\frac{1}{2} - 2}{2 \cdot \frac{1}{2} \cdot 1\frac{1}{2}} = \frac{2}{3}$$

so the energy splitting in the field is

$$\Delta E_{1/2} = \pm\frac{1}{2} \cdot \frac{2}{3}\mu_B B.$$

The upper state, $^2P_{3/2}$, has

$$g = 1 + \frac{1\frac{1}{2} \cdot 2\frac{1}{2} + \frac{1}{2} \cdot 1\frac{1}{2} - 2}{2 \cdot 1\frac{1}{2} \cdot 2\frac{1}{2}} = \frac{4}{3}$$

so the energy splitting is

$$\Delta E_{3/2} = (\pm\tfrac{3}{2}, \pm\tfrac{1}{2})\tfrac{4}{3}\mu_B B.$$

The pattern of energy levels is shown in Figure 7.27 with the splittings exaggerated relative to the separation between the states in zero field. The selection rules operate in such a way that the lower (D_1) line divides into four components, and the upper (D_2) line into six components. In terms of angular frequency, the degree of splitting for the D_1 line is given by

$$\hbar\omega = \hbar\omega_0 + (\Delta E_{1/2} - \Delta E_0)$$

or

$$\omega = \omega_0 \pm (\tfrac{2}{3}, \tfrac{4}{3})\frac{\mu_B B}{\hbar} = \omega_0 \pm (\tfrac{2}{3}, \tfrac{4}{3})\frac{eB}{2m}.$$

In $(eB/2m)$ units, the frequency splitting is $\pm\frac{2}{3}$ for "π" lines and $\pm\frac{4}{3}$ for "σ" lines. Similar calculations show that, in the splitting of the D_2 line, the frequency differences are $\pm\frac{1}{3}$ for "π" lines and ± 1 and $\pm\frac{5}{3}$ for "σ" lines. These patterns are observed experimentally in moderate magnetic fields and were originally ascribed to "anomalous" Zeeman effects.

The "normal" Zeeman effect was explained on classical lines in Section 4.2 and was used to illustrate the concept of spatial quantization in the Bohr theory (Section 6.5). It remains to be seen how this comparatively simple pattern arises, since it is clear that single-electron transitions lead to complex patterns, in general. If we consider the strong "resonance" line of a two-electron atom like helium (Figure 7.22), this is formed by transitions between the first accessible singlet state ($^1P_1$) and the ground state ($^1S_0$). In a magnetic field the ground state is unaffected while the upper $^1P_1$ state is split into three with the energy separations of the outer two given by Equation (7.14.3):

$$\Delta E_1 = \pm \mu_B B \qquad \text{(since } g = 1\text{)}.$$

The selection rules are

$$\Delta m_J = 0 \qquad \text{for ``}\pi\text{'' polarization}$$

$$\Delta m_J = \pm 1 \qquad \text{for ``}\sigma\text{'' polarization}$$

so the line of unchanged frequency (ω_0) is polarized in the direction $0z$ (the field direction) and is not observed along this direction. The two outer lines are separated by the Larmor frequency $\left(\Delta \omega = \dfrac{eB}{2m}\right)$ from the central line and are circularly polarized in the xy plane.

If the light is viewed at right angles to the field the outer components are both plane polarized with the electric vector perpendicular to the field (see Section 4.2). We see that the classical result happens to be correct in this case because no electron spin is involved, so the "normal" Zeeman effect can occur only in transitions between singlet states.

(c) The Paschen-Back effect

In strong magnetic fields, the normal Zeeman effect is modified by terms quadratic in the field B but the triplet pattern of lines remains. "Anomalous" effects, such as those seen in the sodium D lines, are changed more radically and approximate finally to a simple triplet. This change in pattern is called the *Paschen-Back effect* and is due to a breakdown in the coupling of orbital and spin momenta to form the total angular momentum. Normally the ^2P states of sodium are split by the spin-orbit interaction [Equation (7.10.3)] which is essentially a magnetic coupling of spin and orbital motion. In a very powerful magnetic field, the Zeeman energy splitting becomes comparable with the spin-orbit splitting and in this region the external field dominates the situation. In classical terms, the **L** and **S** vectors are no longer coupled to form **J** precessing about the field **B** and the **L** and **S** vectors precess *independently* about **B** instead. The ^2P states then split as a whole into six levels (Figure 7.28) characterized by independent m_l and m_s numbers

$$m_l = 1 \qquad \text{with} \qquad m_s = \pm \tfrac{1}{2}$$
$$ 0 \qquad \text{with} \qquad m_s = \pm \tfrac{1}{2}$$
$$ -1 \qquad \text{with} \qquad m_s = \pm \tfrac{1}{2}.$$

The effective magnetic moment along the field direction is simply the sum of m_l and $2m_s$ Bohr magnetons, so the energy splitting is

$$\Delta E' = (m_l + 2m_s)\mu_B B. \qquad [7.14.5]$$

It is evident from this expression and from Figure 7.28 that the two middle levels almost coincide and in strong fields the system approximates to five levels. The ground state is split into two as before [Equation (7.14.4)] and the transitions are governed by the

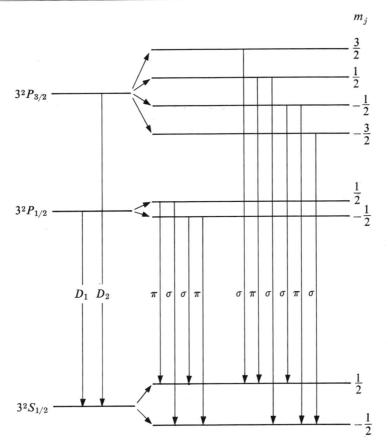

FIGURE 7.28 *The Paschen-Back effect for the sodium "D" lines in very strong magnetic fields. The* ²*S ground state is still divided into two magnetic substates but the* ²*P states form a total of five levels in the limit when orbital and spin vectors become completely uncoupled. The net result is 6 transitions coalescing into a triplet of lines in the strong-field limit.*

single-electron rules for electric-dipole interaction (Section 7.13), namely,

$$\Delta m_l = 0, \pm 1 \qquad \Delta m_s = 0.$$

The consequence of these rules is that there are six possible transitions which coalesce into three different frequencies in the limit when Equation (7.14.5) is valid. Thus the final result resembles the normal Zeeman effect.

7.15 Quantum Statistics

When we try to deal with assemblies containing numerous particles in an effort to predict the properties of matter in bulk, we have to introduce statistical methods because of our ignorance concerning the behavior of individual particles. To some extent the behavior of a large assembly does not depend on detailed knowledge, as is shown by the many applications of Boltzmann statistics (Section 2.2) to problems in classical physics. However, the assumptions made in deriving the Boltzmann expression [Equation (2.2.10)] require further examination and the methods of Section 2.2 are also open to objections on mathematical grounds. When the principles of quantum mechanics are adopted, new types of statistics are needed and the Boltzmann formulation is seen as an approximation to the more fundamental theory.

(a) Bosons and fermions

In the first place, the assembly of identical particles was treated in Section 2.2 as though the particles in different energy states are distinguishable in some way. In many problems the particles may be "localized," for example an within atom or a nucleus, so that each differs in situation from a similar particle localized elsewhere. In a true assembly, however, all the particles are similarly situated and it is axiomatic in quantum mechanics that identical particles are quite indistinguishable from each other. This principle has the effect of replacing the Boltzmann scheme by a new type of statistics, due to Bose and Einstein. Particles obeying the Bose-Einstein statistics include photons and all spinless particles, such as alpha particles and He^4 atoms in the ground state. These particles are called *bosons*.

A severe restriction on statistical behavior is evident in the case of particles like electrons, neutrons, and protons, which obey Pauli's Exclusion principle (Section 7.8). Since the various energy states can be occupied by no more than one particle each, at low temperatures the states are filled up to a level (the *Fermi energy*) which depends on the number of particles present. This type of behavior is described by the Fermi-Dirac statistics and particles exhibiting such behavior are often called *fermions*. Quantum mechanics therefore divides all elementary systems into two classes according to which form of statistics applies.

In order to illustrate the different types of statistical behavior we may cite an example due to Cowan,* who published a treatment of the problem in 1957. Suppose that we have three energy states, labeled 1, 2, and 3, and two particles to be distributed among them.

TABLE 7.3
Arrangements of Two Particles in Three Different States.

State	Boltzmann 1	2	3	Bose-Einstein 1	2	3	Fermi-Dirac 1	2	3
Arrangements	x	y	—	x	x	—	x	x	—
	y	x	—						
	x	—	y	x	—	x	x	—	x
	y	—	x						
	—	x	y	—	x	x	—	x	x
	—	y	x						
	xy	—	—	xx	—	—			
	—	xy	—	—	xx	—			
	—	—	xy	—	—	xx			
Totals		9			6			3	

* R. D. Cowan, Am. J. Phys., **25**, 463 (1957).

Under the different assumptions of Boltzmann, Bose-Einstein, and Fermi-Dirac statistics, we shall find three different numbers for the *complexions*, which is the number of possible distributions. If, for example, we adopt the Boltzmann approach, the particles are distinguishable in some way (and can be labeled x, y) and there are nine different ways of assigning them to states, as shown in Table 7.3. In Bose-Einstein statistics, the particles are no longer distinguishable (so are labeled x) and only six different arrangements are allowed. In Fermi-Dirac statistics the particles remain indistinguishable and no more than one can occupy a single state, so the number of arrangements is three.

(b) Equilibrium distributions

It is clear that the three different methods for enumerating the complexions of an assembly of similar particles must lead to different energy distributions, especially at low temperatures, where the Fermi-Dirac scheme, in particular, yields results greatly at variance with the other schemes. In order to set up a method for determining the correct distributions, we assume that the distribution of energy states available is known and can be represented by the function

$$f(\varepsilon)\, d\varepsilon,$$

where $f(\varepsilon)$ denotes the number of states per unit energy interval at the energy value ε.

Alternatively we may divide the energy spectrum discontinuously into groups so that f_i represents the number of states with the energy ε_i. If, now, there are N particles available, they are distributed among the states in such a way that N_i of them are in the energy state ε_i. We wish to find the equilibrium value of N_i. As stated in Section 2.2, there are usually two overriding conservation conditions

$$\sum_i N_i = N,$$

$$\sum_i N_i \varepsilon_i = E \text{ (the total energy of the assembly).}$$

In Cowan's treatment* we confine our attention to the N_i particles of energy ε_i which have to be divided among the f_i energy states. This is equivalent to setting the particles in the array of states in all possible ways consistent with the rules being observed. The following results are found:

(i) In Fermi-Dirac statistics, the particles are indistinguishable but if they *were* labeled in some way, we should find that the first of the N_i particles could go into f_i states, the second into $(f_i - 1)$ states, and so on. The number of arrangements of distinguishable particles is therefore

$$f_i(f_i - 1)(f_i - 2) \cdots (f_i - N_i + 1) \qquad \text{if} \qquad f_i > N_i.$$

If the correct number of arrangements of indistinguishable particles is W_i, we can make them distinguishable and obtain all the distinguishable arrangements by permuting all the N_i particles among themselves, which can be done in $N_i!$ ways, hence

$$W_i N_i! = \frac{f_i!}{(f_i - N_i)!}$$

or

$$W_i = \frac{f_i!}{N_i!\,(f_i - N_i)!}. \qquad [7.15.1]$$

* For an alternative treatment, see R. B. Lindsay and H. Margenau, *Foundations of Physics* (Dover Publications, New York 1957) Sec. 9.16.

The same result is found if we simply calculate the number of ways in which the N_i filled states can be selected from f_i states.

(ii) In Bose-Einstein statistics, we follow a similar routine with distinguishable particles at first. The first particle has f_i possible locations and, when this particle has been placed in a state or "cell," the next particle can go either into one of the $(f_i - 1)$ remaining cells or to the "left" or "right" of the first particle in its cell (since the latter two locations produce different arrays with distinguishable particles). Thus the second particle has $(f_i + 1)$ different possible locations, the third has $(f_i + 2)$, and so on. In this way the number of different arrays of distinguishable particles is found to be

$$f_i(f_i + 1)(f_i + 2) \cdots (f_i + N_i - 1).$$

As before we remove the distinguishability of the particles and divide by $N_i!$ to obtain the number of complexions

$$W_i = \frac{(f_i + N_i - 1)!}{N_i!\,(f_i - 1)!}. \qquad [7.15.2]$$

In either the Fermi-Dirac or the Bose-Einstein schemes the total number of arrangements for the entire assembly is obtained by multiplying together all the W_i expressions

$$W = \prod_i W_i$$

and this can be written

$$W = \prod_i \frac{f_i(f_i - \delta)(f_i - 2\delta) \cdots [f_i - (N_i - 1)\delta]}{N_i!}, \qquad [7.15.3]$$

where the parameter δ is introduced to distinguish between the two systems. In Fermi-Dirac statistics, $\delta = 1$: and in Bose-Einstein statistics: $\delta = -1$. We immediately find the logarithm of W in Equation (7.15.3)

$$\ln W = \sum_i \{\ln f_i + \ln (f_i - \delta) + \ldots + \ln [f_i - (N_i - 1)\delta] - \ln N_i!\}. \qquad [7.15.4]$$

If the value of one particular N_i increases by 1, the change in $\ln W$ becomes

$$\Delta(\ln W) = \ln (f_i - N_i\delta) - \ln (N_i + 1)$$

and the corresponding change in the entropy S is (from Section 2.2)

$$\Delta S = k\,\Delta(\ln W).$$

We have to find the most probable distribution subject to the conservation conditions (total number N and total energy E), so with the Lagrange multipliers $(-\alpha)$ and $(-\beta)$ we introduce a new function S'. The variation in this function for unit increase in N_i is then given by the expression

$$\Delta\left(\frac{S'}{k}\right) = \Delta(\ln W) - \alpha\Delta\left(\sum_i N_i\right) - \beta\Delta\left(\sum_i N_i\varepsilon_i\right)$$

$$= \ln (f_i - N_i\delta) - \ln (N_i + 1) - \alpha - \beta\varepsilon_i$$

and for maximum entropy this must vanish. Hence at equilibrium

$$N_i = \bar{N}_i \quad \text{and} \quad \frac{f_i - N_i\delta}{N_i + 1} = \exp (\alpha + \beta\varepsilon_i)$$

or, since $\bar{N}_i$ is large compared with 1 if the density of states is high, we have effectively

$$\bar{N}_i = \frac{f_i}{\exp(\alpha + \beta\varepsilon_i) + \delta}. \qquad [7.15.5]$$

By substituting $\delta = 0$ we revert to the Boltzmann type of distribution

$$\bar{N}_i = f_i \exp(-\alpha) \exp(-\beta\varepsilon_i)$$

which, with suitable normalization, yields the same results as Equation (2.2.6). Further analysis shows that the parameter α is related to the free energy of the assembly; Problem (2.16) is an example indicating that, for positive free energy, the parameter α must be negative. The parameter β corresponds to a temperature factor, which is constant throughout a mixed assembly at equilibrium; in Section 2.2 we found that

$$\beta = \frac{1}{kT},$$

where k is Boltzmann's constant and T is the absolute temperature.

Taking these results over into the general statistical expression of Equation (7.15.5), we have the equilibrium value of N_i, namely,

$$\bar{N}_i = \frac{f_i}{\exp\left(\alpha + \dfrac{\varepsilon_i}{kT}\right) + \delta} \qquad [7.15.6]$$

with

$$\delta = 1 \text{ (Fermi-Dirac)}, \quad 0 \text{ (Boltzmann)}, \quad -1 \text{ (Bose-Einstein)}.$$

The parameter δ has a profound effect on the behavior of $\bar{N}_i$ in the low-energy region, as may be seen by plotting $\bar{N}_i/f_i$ as a function of ε_i/kT with different values of α and δ. In Figure 7.29 this is done with $\alpha = -1$ and $\delta = 1, 0$ and -1; the graphs diverge markedly for $\varepsilon_i < 3kT$ approximately, with the Fermi-Dirac curve lower than the Boltzmann line, and the Bose-Einstein ordinate tends to infinity as ε_i approaches kT. The same kind of result is found with $\alpha = -0.1$ except that the divergence between the three curves is less marked in the region $\varepsilon_i \approx 3kT$ and the Bose-Einstein ordinate tends to infinity as ε_i approaches $0.1\,kT$. In all curves of this kind the effect of the parameter δ is negligible for $\varepsilon_i \gg kT$.

The degree of importance attached to the differences between the three statistical expressions depends ultimately on the value of the parameter α. If we temporarily regard the temperature T as fixed, we can substitute the expression

$$-\alpha = \frac{\zeta}{kT}, \qquad [7.15.7]$$

where ζ is a characteristic energy of the assembly for this particular value of T. Then we find that for values of the energy $\varepsilon_i \gg \zeta$ the three curves almost coincide. Also, if ζ/kT is smaller than, say, 10^{-2}, the quantum expressions can be replaced by the classical expression over a wide range of ε_i/kT values. This result justifies the application of classical statistics to many problems such as the velocity distribution of molecules in a gas (Section 2.3). On the other hand, if the ratio ζ/kT is large, the quantum effects are extremely important in determining the behavior of the assembly. For example, in helium gas at very low temperatures the value of ζ/kT is such that the Bose-Einstein statistics has to be applied to the

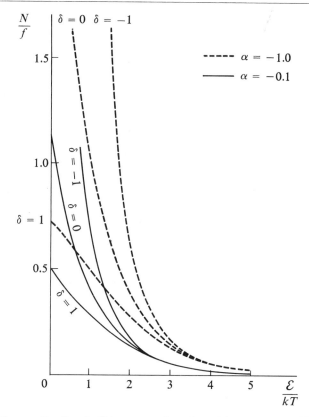

FIGURE 7.29 *The "occupation fraction" (mean number of particles per state, N/f) plotted against the energy ratio ε/kT for three kinds of statistics, denoted by $\delta = +1$ (Fermi-Dirac), $\delta = 0$ (Boltzmann), and $\delta = -1$ (Bose-Einstein). The two sets of curves were calculated for $\alpha = -1.0$ and -0.1.*

problem of fixing the equation of state. Likewise for "free" electrons in a metal, the effective specific heat is much less than that for classical particles because the Fermi-Dirac theory applies.

(c) The photon assembly

One special case of great importance, namely an assembly of photons, has yet to be considered. These particles are supposed to obey the Bose-Einstein rules but, in applying the statistical treatment to radiation in an enclosure, we must remember that photons are emitted and absorbed by the atoms of the walls. The number of photons is therefore not fixed, unlike the number (N) of particles in the assembly previously considered. This means that the first Lagrange multiplier ($-\alpha$) is not required, although we retain the second multiplier ($-\beta$) to maintain conservation of the total photon energy. The distribution of photons at equilibrium then becomes (with $\alpha = 0$)

$$\bar{N}_i = \frac{f_i}{\exp\left(\dfrac{\varepsilon_i}{kT}\right) - 1}.$$

For a photon of angular frequency ω, the energy is

$$\varepsilon = \hbar\omega$$

and in an assembly of photons in an enclosure we may replace the factor f_i by the continuous distribution in frequency of Equation (4.3.6), which represents the density of states per unit angular frequency interval

$$n(\omega) = \frac{\omega^2}{\pi^2 c^3}.$$

The energy distribution of photons in an enclosure is therefore given by the expression

$$F(\omega)\,d\omega = \frac{\hbar\omega\omega^2\,d\omega}{\pi^2 c^3\left[\exp\left(\dfrac{\hbar\omega}{kT}\right) - 1\right]}$$

which is Planck's result [Equation (4.3.10)]. The statistical derivation given here is free from some of the theoretical difficulties attending the methods of Section 4.3.

FOR FURTHER READING

Fundamentals:

P. A. M. DIRAC, *The Principles of Quantum Mechanics* (Oxford University Press, New York, 1958) 4th ed.

R. B. LINDSAY and H. MARGENAU, *Foundations of Physics* (Dover Publications, New York, 1957).

Applications:

L. I. SCHIFF, *Quantum Mechanics* (McGraw Hill Book Co., New York, 1955) 2nd ed.

N. F. MOTT and I. SNEDDON, *Wave Mechanics and its Applications* (Oxford University Press, New York, 1948).

Electron Diffraction:

R. BEECHING, *Electron Diffraction* (Methuen Monographs, J. Wiley & Sons, New York, 1950) 3rd ed.

Spectra:

G. HERTZBERG, *Atomic Spectra and Atomic Structure* (Dover Publications, New York, 1944) 2nd ed.

PROBLEMS FOR CHAPTER 7

DATA REQUIRED:

Planck's constant:	$h = 6.6 \times 10^{-34}$ J sec
	$\hbar = 1.05 \times 10^{-34}$ J sec
Elementary charge:	$e = 1.6 \times 10^{-19}$ C
Electron rest-mass:	$m = 9.1 \times 10^{-31}$ kg
Neutron rest-mass:	$M_n = 1.67 \times 10^{-27}$ kg
Velocity of light in vacuo:	$c = 3.0 \times 10^8$ m/sec
Gravitation constant:	$G = 6.6 \times 10^{-11}$ mks
Coulomb force constant:	$\dfrac{1}{4\pi\varepsilon_0} = 9 \times 10^9$ mks

1 Angstrom (Å) $= 10^{-10}$ m

Boltzmann's constant: $\qquad\qquad k = 1.4 \times 10^{-23}$ J/°K

7.1. Calculate the de Broglie wavelengths for:

(a) a neutron of speed 10^3 m/sec

(b) an electron of speed 10^8 m/sec

(c) an automobile of mass 1500 kg and speed 30 m/sec

7.2. A beam of electrons of mean energy 40 eV falls perpendicularly on the (100) face of a nickel crystal, which is a face-centered cubic structure of lattice constant $a = 3.52$ Å. At what angles to the incident beam will diffracted maxima occur (i) in vertical planes perpendicular to the cubic axes? (ii) in planes at 45° to the cubic axes?

7.3. A beam of "thermal" neutrons (of mean energy 0.025 eV) is incident on the face of a crystal which consists effectively of reflecting planes 2.2 Å apart. Calculate the angles of incidence at which strong Bragg reflections occur, assuming that the wavelength inside the crystal is the same as that outside.

7.4. Calculate the effective refractive index for electrons of kinetic energy 40 eV entering a metallic crystal where the mean potential energy per electron is -10 eV (relative to the situation outside the crystal). If strong Bragg reflection is observed in first order at an angle of incidence of 45° what is the distance between successive reflecting layers?

7.5. Given that the total energy (E) of a particle is

$$E = \frac{p^2}{2m} + U(x)$$

and writing $E = h\nu$, where ν is the effective frequency of the de Broglie waves, show that the group velocity of the waves $\left[\partial \nu / \partial \left(\frac{1}{\lambda} \right) \right]$ is equal to the particle's proper velocity (v).

7.6. (a) Suppose that the wave function

$$\Psi = A \exp i(\kappa x - \omega t)$$

represents a traveling de Broglie wave in one dimension with $|A|^2$ denoting the mean number of particles per unit volume, show that the particle flux F (the number crossing unit area per second) is

$$F = \frac{\hbar}{m} |A|^2 \kappa.$$

(b) Use the flux expression to find the reflection coefficient (R) and transmission coefficient (T) for a de Broglie wave of energy E encountering a potential barrier of height U_0, where $E > U_0$. Assume that the barrier occurs at $x = 0$ and for $x < 0$ write $U = 0$, and

$$\Psi = \exp [i(\kappa x - \omega t)] + \alpha \exp [-i(\kappa x + \omega t)],$$

for $x > 0$ write $U = U_0$, $\Psi = \beta \exp [i(\kappa_0 x - \omega t)]$. Adjust Ψ to be continuous at $x = 0$, solve for α and β, and derive the coefficients

$$R = |\alpha|^2, \qquad T = \frac{\kappa_0}{\kappa} |\beta|^2.$$

7.7. Estimate the lowest possible energy of an electron in a deep potential well if the width of the well is 2.5 Å in one dimension. Suppose that the electron had to be located physically inside the well to an accuracy of 0.2 Å; what effect would the appropriate incident radiation have on the electron's state?

7.8. Estimate the minimum *binding* energy of an electron confined inside a nucleus of diameter $D = 5 \times 10^{-15}$ m. Compare this energy with (i) the gravitational potential energy, (ii) the electrostatic potential energy of the electron at the same distance D from a proton. Can you draw any conclusions about the possible existence of electrons within nuclei?

7.9. Show that the Fourier synthesis of waves of constant amplitude and all angular frequencies from zero up to a maximum value ω_0 yields a time function of intensity

$$F(t) = |f(t)|^2 \propto \frac{\sin^2 \left(\frac{1}{2}\omega_0 t\right)}{t^2}.$$

Deduce a relation between the "bandwidth" ω_0 and the width of the time pulse represented by $F(t)$.

7.10. The gamma-ray line emitted by the nuclide Ir^{191} has mean energy 129 keV and the measured width of the line at half-maximum intensity is 4.6×10^{-6} eV. Estimate (a) the mean lifetime of the excited state emitting this line,

(b) the relative velocity of source and observer which is required to give a first-order Doppler shift equal to the measured linewidth.

7.11. (a) With the aid of Equation (4.1.11) show that the instantaneous rate of energy radiation from a classical oscillating dipole is

$$\frac{2}{3} \frac{e^2 \langle a \rangle^2}{[4\pi\varepsilon_0]c^3},$$

where e is the magnitude of the oscillating charge, and $\langle a \rangle$ stands for the acceleration of the charge.

(b) Find the mean rate of energy loss as a function of the energy of the oscillator and hence find the *radiation damping* width Γ of Equation (7.2.9).

(c) Calculate the value of this "natural" linewidth for an optical transition of wavelength 6000 Å.

7.12. Use the operator form for the components of orbital angular momentum $\mathbf{G} = \mathbf{r} \times \mathbf{p}$ to establish the identity $\mathbf{G} \times \mathbf{G} = i\hbar\mathbf{G}$

in quantum mechanics.

7.13. Show that for a central-force Hamiltonian of the form

$$H = \frac{G^2}{2\mathscr{I}} + U(r)$$

any particular component (say, G_z) of the orbital angular momentum commutes with H and is therefore a constant of the motion.

7.14. (a) Find the energy eigenvalues for a rigid rotator of rotational inertia $\mathscr{I}$ if the Hamiltonian is

$$H = \frac{G^2}{2\mathscr{I}} \qquad \text{(no potential energy term).}$$

(b) Assuming that the rotator is suitably charged so that electric dipole radiation is possible, show that the selection rules for this radiation are

$$\Delta J = \pm 1,$$

where J is the quantum number.

(c) Hence work out the sequence of spectral lines emitted by polar molecules of rotational inertia $\mathscr{I}$ in a "rotational" band.

7.15. In certain molecular states, the electronic energy is modified by the presence of rotational *fine structure* so that we may write, for two particular states,

$$E_1 = \hbar\omega_1 + \hbar B_1 J(J+1)$$
$$E_2 = \hbar\omega_2 + \hbar B_2 J(J+1)$$

$\left\{ \begin{array}{l} \text{where } B_1 \text{ and } B_2 \text{ are} \\ \text{rotational constants.} \end{array} \right.$

The optical selection rules are $\Delta J = 0, \pm 1$ giving rise to three sets of lines. Show that these spectral lines crowd together to form a "head" on the low-frequency side of the basic angular frequency ($\omega_1 - \omega_2$), by plotting the line frequencies against the original value of J in the transition ("Fortrat's diagram").

7.16. Show that for an infinitely deep potential well between limits $x = 0$ and $x = L$ in one dimension the normalized state function for a single particle is

$$\psi_n = \sqrt{\frac{2}{L}} \sin \left(\frac{n\pi x}{L} \right),$$

where n is a quantum number taking values 1, 2, ...

7.17. Suppose that an electron moves in the region between two deep potential wells, as represented in Figure 7.30, where the central region is of width $2a$ at potential U_0 and the wells are each of width b. Show that for even-parity functions $\psi = A \cos \kappa x$ (in each well region) and $\psi = B \cosh \mu x$ (in the central region) the solution is

$$\kappa^2 = \mu^2 \tanh^2(\mu a) \tan^2(\kappa b)$$

and that, if b is small, we find

$$E < U_0 - \frac{\hbar^2}{2mb^2}.$$

Also show that, for odd-parity functions,

$$E > U_0 - \frac{\hbar^2}{2mb^2}.$$

Hence discuss the effects of parity on the binding together of a single-electron molecule such as H_2^+.

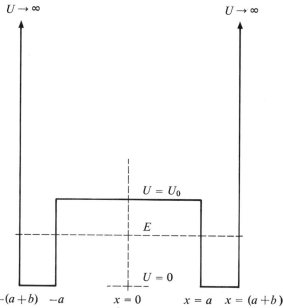

FIGURE 7.30 *Two deep potential wells, each of width b, are separated by a region of potential U_0 and width 2a. Assuming that $E < U_0$, solutions are to be found for (i) even-parity functions, (ii) odd-parity functions.*

7.18. Calculate by numerical methods the well depth (U_0) for a particle of mass 1.67×10^{-27} kg in a rectangular well of width 3×10^{-15} m in one dimension, given that its binding-energy $(U_0 - E)$ is 2 MeV for the lowest state $(n = 1)$.

7.19. Show by direct substitution that the eigenfunctions for the lowest three states of a particle in a one-dimensional parabolic potential well (equivalent to a linear harmonic oscillator) satisfy the orthogonality relation

$$\int_{-\infty}^{\infty} \psi_a(q)\psi_b(q)\, dq = 0 \qquad \text{unless } a = b.$$

7.20. Set up the Schrödinger equation for a particle in a three-dimensional parabolic well, represented by the function $U(r) = \frac{1}{2}m\omega^2 r^2$. Show that the equation separates into three linear equations in x, y, and z, respectively; hence establish the energy eigenvalues as

$$E = (n + 1\tfrac{1}{2})\hbar\omega \quad \text{with } n = 0, 1, 2, \ldots .$$

Also solve the equation in spherical polar coordinates and show that

$$E = (l + v + 1\tfrac{1}{2})\hbar\omega,$$

where l is the orbital angular momentum quantum number and v takes the values $0, 1, 2, \ldots$.

7.21. With the aid of the Schrödinger state function for the hydrogen atom in its ground state

$$\psi_{1,0,0} = \frac{1}{\sqrt{\pi r_1^3}} \exp\left(-\frac{r}{r_1}\right),$$

calculate (a) the mean distance, (b) the root mean square distance, (c) the most probable distance, between electron and nucleus, in terms of the Bohr radius r_1.

7.22. Express the Bohr orbital speed and Bohr energy of a particle in the nth state of a hydrogenlike atom in terms of the fine structure constant

$$\alpha = \frac{e^2}{[4\pi\epsilon_0]c\hbar} = \frac{1}{137}.$$

Hence estimate the value of the atomic number Z at which the electron energy in the inner-most orbit $(n = 1)$ is seriously affected by relativistic corrections (putting $v/c = 0.25$).

7.23. Show that Pauli spin operators of the form

$$\tfrac{1}{2}(\sigma_1 \pm i\sigma_2)$$

act on a two-component state function in such a way that the direction of spin is reversed.

7.24. Show that the Klein-Gordon equation (7.9.2) admits static spherically-symmetrical solutions of the form
$$\psi(r) = \text{const } r^{-1} \exp\left(-\mu r\right)$$
where
$$\mu = \frac{m_0 c}{\hbar}.$$

(This expression is employed in Yukawa's "meson theory" of nuclear forces.)

7.25. Use the Dirac Hamiltonian

$$H = [c(\boldsymbol{\alpha} \cdot \mathbf{p}) + \beta m_0 c^2]$$

and Equation (7.3.16) to demonstrate that the proper velocity of a Dirac particle can be expressed as
$$\mathbf{v} = c\boldsymbol{\alpha},$$

where $\boldsymbol{\alpha}$ is the (polar) vector composed of the three α operators.

7.26. Make a semiclassical estimate of the nuclear-spin splitting in the ground state of hydrogen by finding the magnetic interaction energy between the field of the circulating electron ($n = 1$ orbit) and the magnetic moment of the central proton (of magnitude 1.4×10^{-26} A m²).

7.27. Enumerate the possible combinations of the orbital and spin components (m_L and m_S) for three electrons in the $2p$ subshell, assuming that Russell-Saunders coupling is valid. Isolate the separate spectroscopic terms and use Hund's rule to establish the ground state of the nitrogen atom as $^4S_{3/2}$. Also treat the problem in j-j coupling and draw a diagram to illustrate the correspondence of states with the same J values in Russell-Saunders and j-j coupling.

7.28. Show that the *magnetic potential* due to a small dipole of moment **M** at the origin is given, at any point denoted by radius vector **r**, by the expression

$$\varphi = \frac{(\mathbf{Mr})}{4\pi\mu_0 r^3},$$

where μ_0 is the free-space permeability. Use this expression to find the total potential energy of two magnetic dipoles **M** and **M**′ separated by the radius **r** and show that the *force* between the dipoles is, in general, noncentral.

7.29. Examine Figure 4.10 (the level diagram for mercury) and decide the most probable configurations of states which are reached by the "resonance" lines of wavelengths 1849 Å and 2537 Å from the ground state, which is supposed to be $(6s)^2\,{}^1S_0$. How do these resonance lines appear when the mercury atoms are in a magnetic field?

7.30. Use the electric-dipole selection rules to specify the three allowed transitions between a doublet ^2F and a doublet ^2D state in an alkali metal (the "fundamental" series). Denoting the intensities by I_1, I_2, and I_3 find the ratios of these, with the aid of the sum rule.

7.31. The electric-quadrupole interaction between an electromagnetic wave and an atom involves terms proportional to

$$x^2 \quad y^2 \quad z^2 \quad xz \quad xy \quad yz.$$

Show, by consideration of the matrix elements as integrals over the angle variables θ and φ, that the selection rules for single-electron electric-quadrupole transitions are

$$\Delta m_l = 0, \pm1, \pm2 \qquad \Delta l = 0, \pm2.$$

7.32. Assuming that the difference between the $2\,{}^2S_{1/2}$ and $2\,{}^2P_{1/2}$ states in atomic hydrogen is about 1000 Mc/sec in zero magnetic field, estimate the least field which would cause magnetic substates of these levels to overlap.

7.33. With the aid of the vector model of Figure 7.26 show that the eigenvalues of the spin-orbit interaction energy of Equation (7.10.3), namely,

$$\Delta E = a(\mathbf{G}_l\,\mathbf{G}_s),$$

are given by the expression

$$\tfrac{1}{2}a\hbar^2[J(J+1) - L(L+1) - S(S+1)]$$

for Russell-Saunders coupling. Hence calculate the value of the constant $a\hbar^2$ (in energy units) for the 3^2P states of sodium, given that the wavelengths of the "D" lines are 5890 and 5896 Å, respectively. What magnetic field strength is required to make the magnetic splitting of the ^2P states comparable with the spin-orbit interaction?

7.34. What is the energy difference between the two spin states of an electron in an applied magnetic field of 10^{-1} weber/m² and what frequency of radiation corresponds to this energy difference?

7.35. A proton changes its spin from "up" to "down" in the Earth's magnetic field, of strength 5×10^{-5} weber/m², and the observed frequency of signals emitted is 2100 c/sec. What is the magnetic moment of the proton:

(i) in Bohr magnetons $\left(\dfrac{e\hbar}{2m}\right)$?

(ii) in nuclear magnetons $\left(\dfrac{e\hbar}{2M}\right)$ (where $M = 1.67 \times 10^{-27}$ kg)?

7.36. A beam of neutral copper atoms, each in the electron configuration $(3d)^{10}(4s)^1$, emerges from an oven at effective temperature 1000°K and passes through a slit into a transverse inhomogeneous magnetic field of gradient $\left(\dfrac{dB}{dz}\right) = 10^3$ weber/m³. If the field region is 0.2 m long, determine the pattern made by the atoms on a screen placed at the end of the field.

CHAPTER VIII

৵৵৵৵৵৵৵৵৵৵৵৵৵৵৵৵ ৵৵৵৵৵৵৵৵৵৵৵৵৵৵৵৵৵

THE QUANTUM THEORY
OF SOLIDS

Quantum mechanics provides a method for theoretical treatment of atomic systems, for calculating their energy levels and for predicting the probability of transition from one state to another. When we consider the properties of matter in bulk, new problems arise because of the complicated interactions between atoms. Even in the gaseous phase, inter-molecular forces affect the behavior considerably, although it is possible to describe deviations from the gas laws in terms of simple two-body interactions. In the solid state, the close proximity of atoms gives rise to strong forces affecting many particles. At the same time, the fundamental rules of quantum statistics become important in dealing with the vibrations of the crystal lattice and with conduction electrons in metals. Despite intense mathematical difficulties solid-state physics has made great progress in accounting for several phenomena which received no classical explanation. Moreover its results have great practical significance and wide implications in many fields of physical research.

Particularly important is the study of magnetic effects in solids. The classical statistics of Boltzmann can be applied to assemblies of paramagnetic atoms which are not interacting strongly. The basic theory of level splitting in magnetic fields is well known and can be used directly in such cases to calculate the paramagnetic susceptibility. However, in the solid state, atoms and ions interact strongly with each other and complex behavior may be observed, notably the phenomenon of ferromagnetism. The spontaneous magnetization of metals like iron was treated phenomenologically in Weiss' theory, the prototype of many attempts to describe cooperative effects, which include the melting of solids and order-disorder transitions in alloys. Some success has been achieved in theoretical description of such effects but it is still difficult to formulate a fundamental account of the interactions responsible for them.

8.1 The Theory of Phonons

The classical theory of the specific heat of a solid was outlined in Section 2.4 where it was shown that the empirical rule of Dulong and Petit can be understood in terms of the equipartition theorem. Each atom or molecule in the solid structure is supposed to vibrate in three dimensions, with the result that the specific heat at constant volume should be $3R$ per kilomole degree. In fact most metals obey this rule at ordinary temperatures but as the temperature is reduced the specific heat falls sharply and approaches zero at the absolute zero of temperature (Figure 2.8).

(a) Einstein's theory of specific heats

The first attempt to deal with the problem of specific heats in the context of quantum theory was made in 1907 by Einstein. If the vibrational energy of the atoms is quantized and the quanta obey Bose-Einstein statistics, their energy distribution is determined by their frequency distribution and the mean energy per oscillation found by Planck [Equation (4.3.9)]. Thus for a given angular frequency (ω) we write the mean energy per mode as

$$\bar{\varepsilon} = \frac{\hbar\omega}{\exp\left(\dfrac{\hbar\omega}{kT}\right) - 1}.$$

In Einstein's theory, each atom is assigned three degrees of vibrational freedom and all atoms have the same angular frequency ω, so the mean energy per atom becomes

$$3\bar{\varepsilon} = \frac{3\hbar\omega}{\exp\left(\dfrac{\hbar\omega}{kT}\right) - 1}.$$

It should be noted that the zero-point energy of oscillation (Section 7.5) has been omitted in the above formula. The total internal energy of an assembly of N^* atoms is

$$E = 3N^*\bar{\varepsilon} = \frac{3N^*\hbar\omega}{\exp\left(\dfrac{\hbar\omega}{kT}\right) - 1}$$

and the specific heat per kilomole becomes

$$C_v = \frac{\partial E}{\partial T} = 3N^*\hbar\omega \, \frac{\hbar\omega \exp\left(\hbar\omega/kT\right)}{\left[\exp\left(\dfrac{\hbar\omega}{kT}\right) - 1\right]^2 kT^2}$$

$$= 3R\left(\frac{\hbar\omega}{kT}\right)^2 \frac{\exp\left(\hbar\omega/kT\right)}{\left[\exp\left(\dfrac{\hbar\omega}{kT}\right) - 1\right]^2}. \qquad [8.1.1]$$

A similar result is obtained by considering an assembly of oscillators with energy quantized in amounts $r\varepsilon$, where r is a positive integer and ε is a basic unit of energy (Problem 2.18).

The important feature of Einstein's result is that it reproduces in outline the behavior of observed specific heats for metals. At low temperatures the value of C_v rises sharply from zero at $T = 0$ toward a saturation value of $3R$ approached at high temperatures (Figure 8.1). The parameter $\hbar\omega$ may be regarded as adjustable but some attempts have been made to link the assumed angular frequency ω with the observed absorption bands of ionic crystals in the infrared region. However, detailed agreement with experimental data for metals is not obtained, chiefly because an Einstein curve fitted to the data at moderately low temperatures always falls too rapidly near the absolute zero. This is clearly due to the unrealistic assumption that vibrational frequencies are restricted to a single value (ω). Various modifications have been made in the assumed frequency spectrum and it is found that acoustical vibrations must be taken into account in addition to the optical terms originally considered.

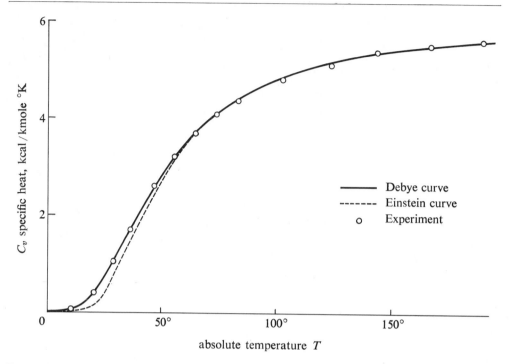

FIGURE 8.1   *The specific heat of silver at constant volume* (C_v) *plotted against the absolute temperature* (T). *The experimental points may be compared with theoretical curves derived from the Einstein theory* (*with* $\hbar\omega = 2.2 \times 10^{-21}$ *J*) *and from the Debye theory* (*with* $T_D = 210°K$).

(b) Debye's theory

A more complete theory was proposed in 1912 by Debye, who regarded the solid as a continuum in which a spectrum of acoustical frequencies operates. In modern terms, the acoustic waves are assumed to be quantized in the form of *phonons*, which are analogous to the photons of optics in that they possess energy $\hbar\omega$ and obey the Bose-Einstein rules. If the function

$$n(\omega)\, d\omega$$

represents the phonon spectrum, that is, the number of phonon vibrations per unit volume of the solid between angular frequencies ω and ($\omega + d\omega$), the total energy density of the phonon assembly is

$$\frac{E}{V} = \int_0^\infty n(\omega)\, \frac{\hbar\omega\, d\omega}{\exp\left(\dfrac{\hbar\omega}{kT}\right) - 1}.$$

Assuming that the function $n(\omega)$ can be determined, it is possible to calculate the internal energy and the specific heat of the solid.

Mechanical vibrations traveling in a solid may be divided into two principal kinds, longitudinal and transverse, possessing different velocities (c_1 and c_2, respectively). Debye proposed to adopt for both types of wave the frequency distribution for waves in an enclosure given by Rayleigh and Jeans (Section 4.3). For the longitudinal waves we write

$$n_1(\omega) \propto \frac{\omega^2}{2\pi^2 c_1^3} \qquad\qquad \text{from Equation (4.3.6).}$$

For transverse waves, possessing two polarizations, the distribution is

$$n_2(\omega) \propto \frac{2\omega^2}{2\pi^2 c_2^3}$$

and Debye's theory combines the expressions to make

$$n(\omega) = A(c_1^{-3} + 2c_2^{-3})\frac{\omega^2}{2\pi^2},$$

where A is a normalization constant. This expression diverges at high frequencies, as in the classical theory of blackbody radiation, but Debye introduced a "cutoff" or maximum angular frequency ω_D, which depends on the material under consideration. The phonon spectrum is then of the form shown by a continuous line in Figure 8.2. The cutoff is necessary to make the total number of vibrational modes finite. As in classical physics, the total number of modes must be three times the number of atoms present, so for N^* atoms the normalization condition is

$$\int_0^\infty n(\omega)\, d\omega = \frac{3N^*}{V},$$

that is,

$$\frac{A}{2\pi^2}(c_1^{-3} + 2c_2^{-3})\int_0^{\omega_D} \omega^2\, d\omega = \frac{3N^*}{V},$$

whence

$$A = \frac{18\pi^2 N^*}{V(c_1^{-3} + 2c_2^{-3})\omega_D^3}.$$

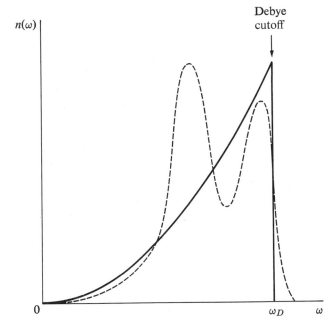

FIGURE 8.2 *The phonon frequency spectrum of a solid. The continuous line represents the spectrum assumed by Debye, with a maximum angular frequency ω_D, and the dotted line represents the result of calculations by Blackman and others.*

The internal energy of the assembly of N^* particles is

$$E = V \int_0^\infty n(\omega) \frac{\hbar\omega \, d\omega}{\exp\left(\dfrac{\hbar\omega}{kT}\right) - 1}$$

$$= \frac{AV(c_1^{-3} + 2c_2^{-3})}{2\pi^2} \int_0^{\omega_D} \frac{\hbar\omega^3 \, d\omega}{\exp\left(\dfrac{\hbar\omega}{kT}\right) - 1}$$

$$= \frac{9N^*\hbar}{\omega_D^3}\left(\frac{kT}{\hbar}\right)^4 \int_0^{\hbar\omega_D/kT} [\exp(\xi) - 1]^{-1} \xi^3 \, d\xi,$$

where ξ stands for the dimensionless parameter $\hbar\omega/kT$. The energy may also be expressed in terms of the *Debye temperature* T_D, which is defined by the equation

$$T_D = \frac{\hbar\omega_D}{k},$$

and yields

$$E = 9R \frac{T^4}{T_D^3} \int_0^{T_D/T} \xi^3 [\exp(\xi) - 1]^{-1} \, d\xi. \qquad [8.1.2]$$

In general, the integral of this equation must be evaluated by numerical methods, but in the extreme cases of high and low temperatures it can be worked out directly.

At high values of the temperature T, the upper limit of integration is small and the parameter ξ is therefore always much less than 1. The integrand becomes

$$[\exp(\xi) - 1]^{-1}\xi^3 \approx \xi^2$$

so that

$$E = 9R \frac{T^4}{T_D^3} \frac{T_D^3}{3T^3} = 3RT \text{ approximately}$$

and the specific heat $C_v = 3R$ (the classical limit). In other words, at high temperatures the phonon density is simply proportional to the absolute temperature T.

At very low temperatures, the upper limit of integration is effectively infinity, and we find

$$\int_0^\infty \xi^3 [\exp(\xi) - 1]^{-1} \, d\xi = \frac{\pi^4}{15}$$

and

$$E = \frac{9\pi^4}{15} R \frac{T^4}{T_D^3},$$

so that the specific heat is

$$C_v = \frac{36\pi^4}{15} R\left(\frac{T}{T_D}\right)^3. \qquad [8.1.3]$$

This "T^3" relation agrees closely with experimental data for a wide range of materials near the absolute zero.

The Debye theory gives a close fit with experimental results over a wide range of temperatures also, if the parameter T_D is chosen appropriately for each material (see Figure 8.2). This success is qualified, however, by the artificial assumptions made about the frequency spectrum $n(\omega)$, which is characteristic of a structureless continuum rather than of a true solid. A more satisfactory theory would start with the actual modes of vibration of a large number of atoms interacting with each other. This type of theory was initiated by Born and Kármán in 1912 and will be outlined in the next section. Here we should point out that the concept of phonons traveling through a material is of very wide application and that the Debye theory is a useful guide in many solid-state problems.

8.2 Lattice Vibrations

(a) The one-dimensional lattice

The fundamental theory of lattice vibrations is necessarily related to the crystal structure of the solid and the interactions between atoms in a three-dimensional lattice. Unfortunately, mathematical difficulties prevent a full treatment of this problem and various approximations have to be made. We consider first the vibrations of a one-dimensional chain of identical atoms spaced evenly at intervals a when the chain is in equilibrium. Thus a is the "lattice constant" and, if there are N atoms present, the length of the chain is $(N - 1)a$, which approximates to (Na) when the number N is large. We shall assume that only nearest neighbors act on each other and that the vibrations are purely harmonic, so that we can consider a model consisting of N identical masses separated from each other by identical springs (Figure 8.3).

The equation of motion of one particular atom in the chain, say the nth atom, is determined by the condition that its acceleration $(d^2 q_n/dt^2)$ depends on the net force (F_n) acting upon it. This force is provided entirely by the two neighboring springs. If q_n is the displacement of the nth atom from its equilibrium position, and q_{n+1} and q_{n-1} the displacements of the neighboring atoms, the two springs have net extensions given by the expressions

$$q_{n+1} - q_n \quad \text{and} \quad q_n - q_{n-1}.$$

If α is the force constant of each spring, the forces exerted by the two springs are

$$\alpha(q_{n+1} - q_n) \quad \text{and} \quad \alpha(q_n - q_{n-1}),$$

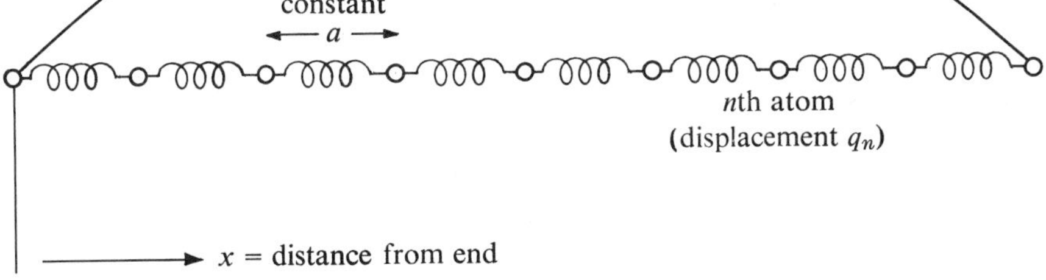

FIGURE 8.3 *Model for determining the vibrations in a one-dimensional lattice with lattice constant a. The force constant of each spring is α and the lowest frequency mode is fixed by the total length of the lattice.*

so that the net force acting upon the nth atom is

$$F_n = \alpha(q_{n+1} - q_n) - \alpha(q_n - q_{n-1}).$$

The equation of motion of this atom (of mass m) is therefore

$$m\frac{d^2 q_n}{dt^2} = \alpha(q_{n+1} + q_{n-1} - 2q_n) \qquad [8.2.1]$$

and this equation applies to all the atoms except those at the ends, which are neglected.

Now let us assume that the vibrations in this one-dimensional lattice may be represented by a traveling wave of the form

$$q_n = q_0 \exp [i(\omega t - \kappa x)],$$

where ω is the angular frequency and κ is the wave-number parameter $2\pi/\lambda$. The only points at which this equation can represent an actual displacement are those for which, on the average, $x = na$, where x is the distance along the lattice measured from one end. The displacement expressions therefore become

$$q_n = q_0 \exp \{i[\omega t - \kappa na]\}$$
$$q_{n+1} = q_0 \exp \{i[\omega t - \kappa(n + 1)a]\}$$
$$q_{n-1} = q_0 \exp \{i[\omega t - \kappa(n - 1)a]\}$$

and the equation of motion reduces to

$$m\omega^2 = -\alpha[\exp(i\kappa a) + \exp(-i\kappa a) - 2]$$
$$= \alpha[2 - 2\cos\kappa a].$$

Thus

$$\omega = \omega_0 \sin \tfrac{1}{2}\kappa a, \qquad [8.2.2]$$

where

$$\omega_0^2 = \frac{4\alpha}{m}.$$

The maximum angular frequency which can be propagated through the lattice is evidently ω_0, corresponding to the wave-number parameter κ taking the values

$$\kappa = \pm\frac{\pi}{a}. \qquad [8.2.3]$$

At these κ values, the ratio of displacements of neighboring particles in the chain is

$$\frac{q_{n+1}}{q_n} = \exp(\pm i\kappa a) = -1,$$

that is, adjacent particles oscillate out of phase with each other. This motion exhibits the shortest wavelength which is meaningful in the lattice, so the corresponding values of κ are the extreme wave-number parameters for this lattice. The range of κ values between $-\frac{\pi}{a}$ and $+\frac{\pi}{a}$ is called the *Brillouin zone* of the simple one-dimensional lattice.

A simple physical explanation for the existence of Brillouin zones is derived from the condition of Bragg reflection in any lattice. In the one-dimensional case, a wave traveling to the right is subject to a Bragg reflection, that is, reinforcement of the wave traveling in the opposite direction, whenever a multiple of the wavelength is *twice* the lattice constant

$$r\lambda = 2a \quad \text{where} \quad r = 1, 2, 3, \ldots$$

corresponding to

$$\kappa = \frac{r\pi}{a}.$$

It appears that a first-order Bragg reflection ($r = 1$) occurs at the limit of the first Brillouin zone and leads to the production of standing waves, in which neighboring particles move in antiphase.

The same conclusion is reached by consideration of the effective velocity of waves in the lattice. The *dispersion relation* [Equation (8.2.2)] shows that the phase velocity (u), given by the expression $u = \nu\lambda = \omega\kappa$, is a function of the frequency. This feature introduces a sharp distinction between the lattice as a medium for transmitting waves and a true continuum, in which the wave velocity depends only on the physical properties of the medium. The effective speed of a wave in the lattice is its *group velocity*

$$u_G = \frac{\partial \nu}{\partial(1/\lambda)} = \frac{\partial \omega}{\partial \kappa}.$$

From Equation (8.2.2) we derive the result

$$u_G = \tfrac{1}{2}a\omega_0 \cos \tfrac{1}{2}\kappa a. \qquad [8.2.4]$$

In the limit of very long waves $\kappa \to 0$ and

$$u_G \to \tfrac{1}{2}a\omega_0 = a\sqrt{\frac{\alpha}{m}},$$

whereas at the other extreme, where $\kappa = \pm\pi a$, we find

$$u_G = 0.$$

Thus at the limit of the Brillouin zone the group velocity vanishes and we obtain standing waves. The relations between ω and κ [the dispersion relation of Equation (8.2.2)] and between u_G and κ are shown in Figure 8.4.

A lattice of finite length, like the one shown in Figure 8.3, introduces a lower limit to the magnitude of κ, because, if the two ends are fixed, the *longest* wavelength produces a node at each end. Thus

$$\lambda_{\max} = 2Na \text{ approximately}$$

or

$$\kappa_{\min} = \frac{\pi}{Na} \to 0 \quad \text{as} \quad N \to \infty.$$

All modes of vibration are subject to the same boundary condition so in general we can write the wavelength as a submultiple of $\lambda_{\max}$

$$\lambda = \frac{2Na}{j}$$

where j takes the values $1, 2, 3, \ldots, N$, and the dispersion relation becomes

$$\omega = \omega_0 \sin \frac{j\pi}{2N}. \qquad [8.2.5]$$

Thus the number of different wavelengths, that is, the number of discrete κ values in the Brillouin zone, is just N, the number of atoms in the chain. The same result is obtained when

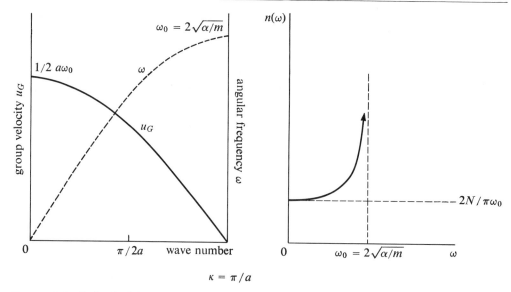

FIGURE 8.4 *Left: the "dispersion relation" (angular frequency ω plotted against the wave-number parameter κ) and the group velocity plotted against κ for a one-dimensional lattice. Right: the corresponding phonon spectrum rises to very high values as the frequency approaches the limit ω₀.*

the problem is solved by finding the eigenfunctions which satisfy the correct boundary conditions. Each of the N eigenfunctions corresponds to a discrete value of the wave-number parameter κ.

In order to derive the phonon spectrum for the one-dimensional lattice, we enumerate the values of the number j for different angular frequencies ω and proceed to the limit where j may be regarded as a continuous variable. We have, from Equation (8.2.5), the derivative

$$\frac{d\omega}{dj} = \frac{\pi\omega_0}{2N} \cos\frac{j\pi}{2N}.$$

The distribution function for angular frequencies between ω and $(\omega + d\omega)$ is

$$n(\omega)\,d\omega = \frac{dj}{d\omega}\,d\omega$$

or, using Equation (8.2.5),

$$n(\omega) = \frac{2N}{\pi(\omega_0^2 - \omega^2)^{\frac{1}{2}}}. \qquad [8.2.6]$$

The method is invalid when j reaches values close to N, that is, near the high-frequency end of the spectrum, and this fact is reflected in the divergence of the expression $n(\omega)$ at $\omega = \omega_0$. However, the formula is correct in showing the steep rise at frequencies close to the ω_0 limit, as shown in Figure 8.4. The limiting frequency ω_0 can be expressed either in terms of the force constant

$$\omega_0 = 2\sqrt{\frac{\alpha}{m}} \qquad \text{from Equation (8.2.2)}$$

or, with the aid of Equation (8.2.4), in terms of the velocity (u_0) of long waves in the medium

$$u_0 = a\sqrt{\frac{\alpha}{m}} = \tfrac{1}{2}a\omega_0.$$

It is of interest to note that at low frequencies the distribution $n(\omega)$ approaches the value $2N/\pi\omega_0$. A one-dimensional *continuum* of length (Na) would possess a frequency spectrum fixed by the condition

$$j\lambda = 2Na$$

and, if u_0 is the wave velocity in this nondispersive medium, corresponding to u_0 in the lattice, we have

$$j = \frac{2Na\omega}{2u_0\pi}$$

and

$$\frac{dj}{d\omega} = \frac{2Na}{2\pi u_0} = \frac{2N}{\pi\omega_0}.$$

Thus at low frequencies the lattice distribution $n(\omega)$ approaches the value given by the continuum (Debye) theory.

(b) Phonon spectra

Although the one-dimensional model is far from realistic for application to actual crystals, comparison with the continuum theory indicates what alterations are necessary for taking lattice properties into account. The most important feature is the change from non-dispersive to dispersive waves and the occurrence of Brillouin zones, each of which is associated with a sharp peak in the phonon frequency spectrum. Detailed calculations have been made for two-dimensional lattices by Blackman and for three-dimensional lattices by Fine and Leighton. The general outline of the phonon spectra is shown by a dotted line in Figure 8.2. Two maxima are obtained in most cases, and the higher one is followed by a sharp drop to zero. This drop provides some justification for the upper frequency limit (ω_D) introduced by Debye. Blackman showed that the correct spectrum should cause deviations from the T^3 law for specific heats at low temperatures. Although these are not large compared with other effects, such deviations have been observed. In practice, experimental data on the lattice specific heats of solids can be matched very closely by allowing the Debye temperature T_D to vary slightly with temperature, and this procedure has some theoretical backing from the results of lattice-vibration calculations.

Recently a great deal of information about phonon spectra and dispersion relations in solids has been obtained by diffraction experiments with slow neutrons. The energy distributions of neutrons diffracted at different angles may be analyzed to find the degree of inelastic scattering (scattering with loss of kinetic energy). This kind of scattering indicates the amount of interaction between neutrons and phonons. The data have been analyzed to yield both dispersion relations, of the form shown in Figure 8.4, and phonon frequency spectra for different types of wave. The spectrum for vanadium,[*] for example, exhibits two peaks somewhat like the dotted curve of Figure 8.2 and near the origin the curve approximates to a Debye spectrum. The difference between the Debye curve and the specific heat curve calculated from the experimental phonon spectrum is not very great.

Further developments in the theory of specific heats are summarized briefly below:

(i) It is necessary to take into account the fact that lattice vibrations are not strictly harmonic, as was assumed in the treatment of one-dimensional lattice. Anharmonic terms may be significant, especially at high temperatures, and they have the effect of raising the specific heat C_v above the classical value of $3R$ in certain solids;

(ii) In lattices containing more than one kind of atom, for example, a regular alternation of two types, the theory has to be modified. Born and Kármán showed that the spectrum

[*] A. T. Stewart and B. N. Brockhouse, *Rev. Mod. Phys.*, **30**, 250 (1958).

of frequencies divides into two branches, separated by a gap. The lower frequency "acoustical" branch behaves somewhat similarly to the spectrum of Figure 8.4 and the "optical" branch lies some way beyond the maximum acoustical frequency ω_0. In such cases, it is convenient to write the total lattice energy in the form

$$E = 9R \frac{T^4}{T_D^3} \int_0^{T_D/T} \xi^3 [\exp(\xi) - 1]^{-1} \, d\xi + \sum_i N^* \frac{\hbar\omega_i}{\exp\left(\dfrac{\hbar\omega_i}{kT}\right) - 1},$$

where the first term is a Debye function and the second represents a series of "Einstein" terms, each of which corresponds to a definite infrared absorption frequency. This type of expression is useful in dealing with the specific heats of ionic solids such as sodium chloride;

(iii) In metals there remains the unsolved problem of the electronic specific heat (Section 3.5). Over a wide range of temperatures the observed specific heats are in agreement with values calculated for the lattice alone. It follows that for most metals the contribution by "free" or conduction electrons must be very small. The reason for this was given by Sommerfeld, who applied Fermi-Dirac statistics to the assembly of electrons, as is described in the next section.

8.3   The Sommerfeld Theory of Metals

(a) The Fermi-Dirac distribution

The classical electron theory of metals (Section 3.5) gave a qualitative account of the conduction properties of this type of solid and some degree of quantitative agreement with the experimental data, for example in the law of Wiedemann and Franz [Equation (3.5.5)]. However, the absence of any appreciable specific heat due to the "free" electrons made the whole theory suspect, and other difficulties included the wrong sign of the Hall coefficient in metals like zinc. The specific-heat difficulty was removed in 1928 by Sommerfeld, who worked out the thermal properties of an assembly of electrons obeying Fermi-Dirac statistics (Section 7.15).

If we plot the "occupation number" [$\bar{N}_i/f_i$ of Equation (7.15.6)] for fermions against the energy ε, we obtain at low temperatures a characteristic curve resembling the full line of Figure 8.5. The probability of a state being occupied is essentially unity for nearly all energies up to the Fermi energy ζ and then falls rapidly to zero at energies slightly above ζ. The value of ζ is fixed by the normalization condition

$$\sum_i \bar{N}_i = N \text{ (the total number of particles)}$$

or $$\sum_i \frac{f_i}{\exp\left(\dfrac{\varepsilon_i - \zeta}{kT}\right) + 1} = N \qquad \text{from Equations (7.15.6) and (7.15.7)}.$$

If we replace the summation by integration over a continuous range of energies ε, we obtain

$$\int_0^\infty \frac{f(\varepsilon) \, d\varepsilon}{\exp\left(\dfrac{\varepsilon - \zeta}{kT}\right) + 1} = N, \qquad\qquad [8.3.1]$$

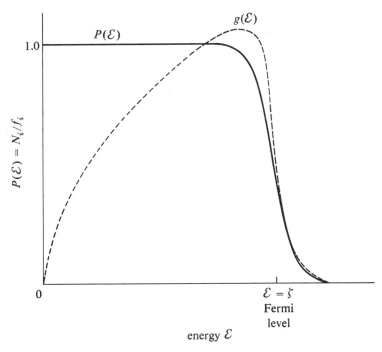

FIGURE 8.5 *The Fermi-Dirac probability function* $P(\varepsilon)$, *that is, the "occupation number"* N_i/f_i, *plotted against the energy* ε *for low temperatures where the assembly is "degenerate." The function* $g(\varepsilon)$ *represents the energy distribution of fermions in a box, as applied to electrons in a metal by Sommerfeld.*

where $f(\varepsilon)$ represents the number of states available per unit energy interval at the energy ε.

Owing to the form of the Fermi-Dirac function at low temperatures (Figure 8.5), the denominator of the integrand in Equation (8.3.1) is very nearly one at all energies below ζ and effectively infinite at nearly all energies above ζ. Thus to a high degree of accuracy we can replace the integral condition by the equation

$$\int_0^{\zeta} f(\varepsilon)\, d\varepsilon = N. \qquad [8.3.2]$$

Moreover this condition is independent of the temperature T, so that the Fermi energy ζ is defined solely by the energy distribution of states, provided that the temperature is sufficiently low. Under these conditions, which are sometimes referred to as *degeneracy* of the electron assembly, occupation of states is almost complete up to the Fermi level. A small change in temperature has the effect of raising a number of particles from states just below the Fermi level to states just above this level, but the mean energy of the assembly is hardly affected, because most of the particles remain in the filled low-energy states. Hence, provided that the value of kT is much less than the Fermi energy ζ, the specific heat should be small. The same condition may be expressed by requiring that the operating temperature T be small compared with a "Fermi temperature" T_F defined by the equation

$$\zeta = kT_F. \qquad [8.3.3]$$

(b) Calculation of the Fermi energy

The starting point of the Sommerfeld theory is the estimation of ζ, and hence of T_F, for the conduction electrons in a metal. The total number of electrons in a metal is, of course, much greater than the number of atoms, but we confine attention to the valence electrons (z per atom) which are supposed to become free in the metallic state. In most metals z has values of the order of 1, as shown by the magnitude of the Hall effect (Section 3.5). The electrons in the inner subshells of each atom are therefore regarded as tightly bound, although this assumption requires further examination where transition metals are concerned, since the incomplete inner subshells of these elements may have significant effects on their behavior.

The conduction electrons are supposed to have an energy distribution represented by the function

$$g(\varepsilon)\, d\varepsilon = f(\varepsilon)\, P(\varepsilon)\, d\varepsilon,$$

where $f(\varepsilon)$ is the distribution of states available
and $P(\varepsilon)$ is the Fermi-Dirac occupation function, that is,

$$P(\varepsilon) = \frac{1}{\exp\left(\dfrac{\varepsilon - \zeta}{kT}\right) + 1}.$$

The distribution function $f(\varepsilon)$ is found by wave mechanics in a manner analogous to the Rayleigh-Jeans treatment of waves in an enclosure (Section 4.3). Here we use the Schrödinger equation to describe particles confined in a three-dimensional "box" with impenetrable walls, that is, we neglect possible effects of the crystal lattice on the potential energy of the conduction electrons. The wave equation is written

$$\nabla^2\psi + \frac{2m}{\hbar^2}(\varepsilon - U)\psi = 0$$

with $U = 0$ for $0 \leqslant x \leqslant a$, $0 \leqslant y \leqslant a$, $0 \leqslant z \leqslant a$, and $U \to \infty$ outside the region limited by the cube of side a. Thus the wave function ψ is to vanish at the boundaries and we may write a suitable solution in Cartesian coordinates

$$\psi = C \sin\frac{l\pi x}{a} \sin\frac{m\pi y}{a} \sin\frac{n\pi z}{a},$$

where C is a normalization constant and l, m, and n are positive integers.

Substituting the solution into the wave equation, we obtain the condition

$$\frac{l^2\pi^2}{a^2} + \frac{m^2\pi^2}{a^2} + \frac{n^2\pi^2}{a^2} = \frac{2m\varepsilon}{\hbar^2} = \frac{p^2}{\hbar^2} = \kappa^2, \qquad [8.3.4]$$

where p is the momentum per particle and κ is the wave-number parameter $\dfrac{2\pi}{\lambda}$. Equation (8.3.4) represents a spherical surface of radius $\dfrac{\kappa a}{\pi}$ in the "space" for which l, m, and n are Cartesian coordinates. As in the classical Rayleigh-Jeans theory, we imagine all the types of wave with energy less than ε, or wave number less than κ, to be specified by points in a (l, m, n) unit lattice (Figure 4.5) bounded by the spherical surface. When the numbers l, m, and n are large, the lattice may be regarded as a continuum and the number of wave modes is equal to the "volume" of the positive octant in (l, m, n) space. Thus we obtain the number of states with energy less than ε

$$N(< \varepsilon) = \frac{1}{8} \frac{4\pi}{3} \frac{a^3}{\pi^3} \left(\frac{2m\varepsilon}{\hbar^2} \right)^{3/2}$$

$$= \frac{V}{6\pi^2} \kappa^3, \qquad\qquad [8.3.5]$$

where V is the proper volume of the enclosure.

A comparatively simple way of expressing this result is to find the number of states available in the "phase space" represented by the product of the proper volume V with the "volume" in momentum space appropriate to particles of momentum between 0 and some value p. If we imagine the latter to be a sphere of radius p, since all directions are equally likely, its "volume" is

$$\frac{4\pi}{3} p^3$$

and the corresponding volume of "phase space" is

$$\Phi = \frac{4\pi}{3} p^3 V. \qquad\qquad [8.3.6]$$

Equation (8.3.5) can be put in the form

$$N(< p) = \frac{V}{6\pi^2} \left(\frac{p}{\hbar} \right)^3$$

$$= \frac{\Phi}{8\pi^3 \hbar^3} = \frac{\Phi}{h^3},$$

where h is Planck's constant.

Thus for spinless particles, described by Schrödinger's equation, the number of states available is proportional to the volume of phase space occupied. If such particles obeyed the Pauli principle, and hence Fermi-Dirac statistics, the phase space accessible to each particle would correspond to that for a single state, which is an amount h^3.

Electrons, however, possess spin $\frac{1}{2}\hbar$ and for these particles (and for all known fermions) we have to allow *two* spin-states per energy state (as given by the Schrödinger equation), with the result that each particle effectively occupies $\frac{1}{2}h^3$ of phase space. The total number of states in an enclosure of volume V with energy less than ε becomes twice as great, that is, for *fermions*

$$N(< \varepsilon) = \frac{V}{3\pi^2} \left(\frac{2m\varepsilon}{\hbar^2} \right)^{3/2}. \qquad\qquad [8.3.7]$$

In order to determine the distribution function $f(\varepsilon)$, which represents the number of states per unit energy interval, we differentiate Equation (8.3.7) with respect to ε and find

$$f(\varepsilon) = \frac{V}{2\pi^2} \left(\frac{2m}{\hbar^2} \right)^{3/2} \varepsilon^{1/2}. \qquad\qquad [8.3.8]$$

This function has to be multiplied by the Fermi-Dirac probability function $P(\varepsilon)$ to give the energy distribution of particles in the enclosure

$$g(\varepsilon) = \frac{V}{2\pi^2} \left(\frac{2m}{\hbar^2} \right)^{3/2} \frac{\varepsilon^{1/2}}{\exp\left(\dfrac{\varepsilon - \zeta}{kT} \right) + 1}. \qquad\qquad [8.3.9]$$

This distribution is shown by a dotted line in Figure 8.5. It is evident that at low temperatures the Fermi-Dirac degeneracy has the effect of cutting the parabolic curve off at the Fermi energy ζ.

If, now, we assume that the Fermi temperature is high for an assembly of conduction electrons in a metal, we can apply Equation (8.3.2) to find a value for ζ, and hence for T_F, which may or may not justify the assumption made. Combination of Equation (8.3.2) with Equation (8.3.8) is equivalent to the adoption of Equation (8.3.7) with $\varepsilon = \zeta$, so for one kilomole of atoms, each contributing z electrons to the assembly, we have

$$N^*z = \frac{V}{3\pi^2}\left(\frac{2m\zeta}{\hbar^2}\right)^{3/2}$$

or the Fermi energy is

$$\zeta = \frac{\hbar^2}{2m}\left(\frac{3N^*z\pi^2}{V}\right)^{2/3}. \tag{8.3.10}$$

In a typical metal with $z = 1$

$$\frac{N^*}{V} = 8 \times 10^{28} \text{ atoms/m}^3$$

and

$$\zeta = 10^{-18}\text{J approximately}$$
$$= 6.3 \text{ eV}.$$

The Fermi temperature for such a metal is

$$T_F = \frac{10^{-18}}{1.4 \times 10^{-23}} = 70{,}000 \text{ °K}.$$

It should be noted that the proper rest-mass of the electron has been used in these calculations and that similar results are obtained for a wide variety of metals.

(c) The electronic specific heat

It appears, therefore, that owing to the extremely small mass of the electron and the high density of electrons in metals, the Fermi temperature is very high and we are justified in regarding the electron assembly as degenerate at ordinary temperatures. A precise calculation of the electronic specific heat requires a careful assessment of small energy changes in the region around the Fermi level. A rough estimate of the effect can be obtained by supposing that the fraction of electrons affected by energy changes of the order of kT is

$$\frac{kT}{\zeta}.$$

The classical specific heat of the electrons is, from Equation (3.5.12),

$$C_v^{el} = \frac{3Rz}{2} \text{ per kilomole of atoms,}$$

so a rough estimate for the Fermi-Dirac assembly might be

$$C_v^{el} \approx \frac{3Rz}{2}\frac{kT}{\zeta} = \frac{3RzT}{2T_F}.$$

An exact calculation yields, to first order in T,

$$C_v^{el} = \frac{\pi^2 RzT}{2T_F} \tag{8.3.11}$$

which is much smaller than the lattice specific heat ($3R$) at ordinary temperatures.

The electronic specific heat in metals may be detected, despite its small magnitude, in measurements carried out at very low temperatures (around 1°K). In this region the lattice specific heat varies approximately as T^3 but the electronic contribution varies as T, so there is the possibility of the latter becoming dominant. Certain anomalous effects, such as those due to paramagnetism and superconductivity, have to be avoided, but a metal like silver shows a definite linear contribution in agreement with Equation (8.3.11). When this is subtracted from the total specific heat it is found that the lattice contribution does not vary strictly as T^3, the deviations from the Debye theory being ascribed to lattice-vibration effects (Section 8.2).

(d) X-ray linewidths

The Sommerfeld account of conduction electrons in metals is valuable not only because of the light it throws on thermal behavior but also in other connections. It is possible to explore the energy distribution of electrons in various states by studying the shapes of x-ray lines emitted by the metal, especially in the long-wavelength region. For example, light elements like lithium and beryllium emit their K lines when the inner $1s$ shell is ionized and electrons pass from the valence levels to the inner shell. Such lines are appreciably broadened by the spread of electron energies in the valence (or conduction) band and to a much smaller extent by interactions affecting the inner shell. Likewise, metals like sodium and magnesium in the third row of elements in the periodic table (Appendix II) have the lines of the L III series (Figure 7.21) broadened because the electron transition is from the $3s$ conduction band to the inner $2p$ subshell. Experiments by Skinner* and others have shown that the x-ray lines of the L III series exhibit characteristic profiles, which are shown for the metals sodium, magnesium, and aluminum in Figure 8.6. The high-frequency side of the x-ray line exhibits a sharp cutoff in these materials and this is identified with the existence of the Fermi level in the conduction band, since nonconducting materials do not show such effects.

Other features of the x-ray line profiles are of interest in the theory of metals. The *width* of the line may be estimated and compared with the value of the Fermi energy calculated from Equation (8.3.10). It is evident from Figure 8.6 that the experimental resolution is not sufficient to determine the low-frequency edge of the line precisely, with the result that the zeros of the energy scales are somewhat arbitrary. Nevertheless it is clear that the width increases as we proceed along the series from sodium to aluminum and can be estimated to within ± 0.5 eV without difficulty. Skinner's estimated widths are compared with the values of ζ, calculated with $z = 1, 2$, and 3 for the metals Na, Mg, and Al, respectively,

Metal	Na	Mg	Al
Width	2.5	6.2	11.8 ± 0.5 eV
Fermi ζ	3.2	7.3	11.9 eV

From the theoretical point of view this degree of agreement between experiment and theory may be rather fortuitous, in view of later developments in the theory of metals. The shapes of the lines in Figure 8.6 do not resemble the energy distribution (dotted line) of Figure 8.5 very closely, except in the general outline of the sodium profile. Nevertheless it is satisfactory to have direct confirmation of the principal idea of the Sommerfeld theory. Confirmatory evidence has been obtained in experiments on the annihilation of positrons in metals.†

* H. W. B. Skinner, Phil. Trans. Roy. Soc. (London), **239**, 95 (1940).
† See, for example, A. T. Stewart, Can. J. Phys., **35**, 168 (1957).

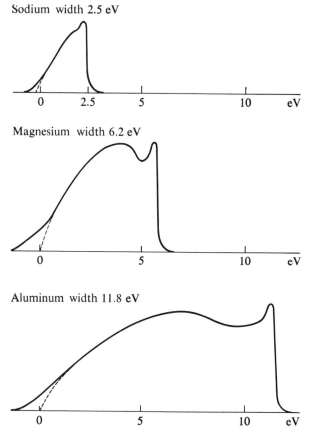

FIGURE 8.6 *Typical shapes of x-ray lines in the L III emission spectra of sodium, magnesium, and aluminum (after Skinner). The width is measured in electron volts from the assumed zero to the Fermi level in each case.*

It is also satisfactory that the electron theory requires the existence of a comparatively sharp cutoff in the energy distribution of the conduction electrons at the top of the conduction band, since this feature facilitates a definition of the electronic work function of the metal (φ). In Section 3.6 this quantity was regarded as the least energy required to remove an electron from the metal surface and it now follows that φ measures the energy gap between the Fermi level in the conduction band and the potential energy outside the metal. The quantum theory of the thermionic and photoelectric effects yields results similar to those of the classical theory at moderate temperatures, where comparatively few electrons are excited above the Fermi level (see Figure 8.5). Under these conditions the electrons of highest energy possess a distribution similar to that of Boltzmann (Figure 7.29) and the probability of thermal emission is given essentially by Richardson's relation [Equation (3.6.4)].

8.4 Conduction in Lattices

(a) General considerations

The phonon theory of solids is capable of giving a fairly complete account of the thermal properties of an ideal lattice. Sommerfeld showed that the application of Fermi-Dirac statistics to the conduction electrons of a metal explains their very small contribution to the total specific heat. However, it is necessary to apply quantum principles to *all* the constituents of a solid before a satisfactory theory of conduction can be formulated. In particular we must consider the effects of the lattice on the conduction electrons and try to find out why some elements are good conductors of heat and electricity, while others are not. One very striking fact requiring explanation is the large ratio (of the order of 10^{20}) between the electrical conductivity of a typical metal and that of an insulator. In the classical theory of Section 3.5 such phenomena received no attention, but it is clear that a detailed theory of conduction must be based on the properties of the atoms which go to make the solid.

In the classical theory electrical resistance was ascribed to the effects of electrons colliding with the atoms of the lattice, but it was found that the concept of a mean free path between such encounters cannot easily be justified. The modern theory is based on the idea that electrons move through the lattice of metallic ions like a wave moving through a regularly spaced series of obstacles. The first result of this wave theory is that, in general, a perfect lattice offers no electrical resistance at all to the motion. It is true that waves of suitable momentum and orientation must suffer Bragg reflection at certain lattice planes and, as in the theory of lattice vibrations (Section 8.2), this phenomenon causes standing waves to be set up. For each type of lattice there exist three-dimensional Brillouin zones which define electron momenta corresponding to the condition of zero group velocity. Thus electrons which have momentum very close to the boundary of a Brillouin zone cannot travel through the lattice. This feature is extremely important in the theory of conduction.

However, provided that we confine our attention to electrons far from the Brillouin boundaries, the resistance should be zero. The same result is found in the Sommerfeld theory because in that model there is no lattice to scatter the waves. It follows that the electrical resistance of actual metals must arise from *imperfections* in the lattice. These imperfections may be divided into three types:

(i) displacements of the lattice ions from their mean positions by vibrations, that is, by phonon effects;

(ii) dislocations and imperfect lattice arrays which occur even within single crystals of any metal;

(iii) impurities in a supposedly pure metal or, in the case of a disordered alloy, the mixing of atoms of different size.

From these qualitative considerations, it appears that stressed metals and alloys should have higher resistivities than pure metals in a stress-free state. Also these higher resistivities should change less with temperature than those of pure metals, in general agreement with observation.

More significantly, the resistivity of any pure metal increases markedly with increasing temperature because of the enhanced vibrations of the lattice ions. It is considered that the resistance (R) depends chiefly on interactions between the electrons and longitudinal phonons of the lattice. At high temperatures the mean phonon density is simply proportional to the absolute temperature (Section 8.1). The amount of electron scattering by phonons should therefore be proportional to T, and we expect the simple consequence

$$R \propto T \text{ provided that } T \gg T_D.$$

At temperatures below the Debye temperature, the situation is much more complex, because not all the phonon modes are excited, but it is found that the resistivity increases with T more rapidly than the linear relation, in agreement with the phonon theory. At very low temperatures, close to absolute zero, certain metals become *superconductive* as the result of phonon interactions with electrons near the Fermi level.

The *thermal* conductivity of a metal is the sum of two effects—the conductivity due to the conduction electrons and that due to phonons. Normally the electron effect is dominant and the classical conductivity formula [Equation (2.5.5)] may be used to give

$$K = \tfrac{1}{3}nmzs_v^e \bar{v}L_e = \frac{C_v^e \bar{v}L_e}{3V},$$

where V is the volume of solid per kilomole;

s_v^e is the electronic specific heat per unit mass;

C_v^e is the electronic specific heat per kilomole;

$\bar{v}$ is the mean electronic speed;

L_e is the electronic mean free path.

Now, according to Equation (8.3.11), the electronic specific heat is proportional to T at all accessible temperatures; moreover, the mean speed is almost independent of T because of the degeneracy of an electron assembly obeying Fermi-Dirac statistics. The mean free path of electrons between *phonon* interactions is inversely proportional to the mean phonon density, which is proportional to T at high temperatures. Hence in the temperature region well above the Debye temperature T_D, we expect that the thermal conductivity to vary very little. In the same region the Wiedemann-Franz ratio

$$\frac{K}{\sigma T} \quad \text{[see Equation (3.5.5)]}$$

should be constant, because the electrical conductivity σ is inversely proportional to the temperature. These general predictions of the electron-phonon theory are borne out in practice, as may be seen in the data for copper quoted in Section 3.5.

The conduction of heat by the lattice itself can be regarded as a pure phonon effect and, like the conduction of electricity, it is strongly influenced by the presence of impurities, lattice imperfections, and fluctuations in density. Debye pointed out in 1914 that the presence of *anharmonic* terms in the lattice vibrations causes density variations which scatter phonons considerably. Such variations lead to a thermal conductivity which varies inversely as the absolute temperature, in agreement with experimental data for nonmetals in the high-temperature region. Once again, the simple behavior breaks down in the low-temperature region below T_D.

b) *The single-electron theory of metallic conduction*

It appears from the foregoing survey that the modern picture of electrical and thermal conductivity is fairly complete in the temperature region above the Debye temperature. We have yet to solve the basic problem of electron conductivity and explain why certain elements are good conductors, others are semiconductors, and the rest nonconductors of electricity. We know from study of the periodic table (Appendix II) that metals occur in the left-hand columns of the table and in the transition series of elements. Atoms of these elements are characterized by a number of inner shells full of electrons and an outermost shell which usually contains one or two electrons (in the neutral atom). The outermost shell may in fact be a subshell such as the 4s subshell, which can accommodate only two electrons, by Pauli's principle (Section 7.8). This happens in the first series of transition elements, from scandium to zinc, which increase their electron numbers by adding to the incomplete 3d inner shell. On the other hand, a metal like sodium has only one electron in the 3s subshell, outside completed inner shells. The energy levels of an isolated metallic atom therefore

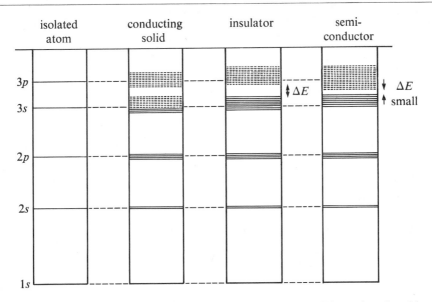

FIGURE 8.7   *The energy levels of an isolated atom (shown schematically) are broadened by strong interactions in the solid state. According to the Bloch theory of electrical conduction, the essential difference between a conductor and an insulator is the degree to which the energy bands are filled. In an insulator no conduction can occur because the top band is full and there is a considerable gap (ΔE) between this and the next vacant band; in a semiconductor the energy gap is small. Full lines indicate occupied levels; dotted lines vacant levels.*

resemble those on the left of Figure 8.7, where the full lines denote closed shells and the dotted lines represent empty subshells into which the valence electrons may be excited by optical or other means.

When a large number of metallic atoms come together to form a lattice they interact strongly with each other and this circumstance has profound effects on the atomic energy levels. The potential energy per electron is no longer represented by a single well due to nuclear attraction but many potential wells overlapping to some extent to form the pattern shown in Figure 3.14. Even if the wells are still recognizably separate, the phenomenon of barrier penetration (Section 7.4) enables electrons to migrate from one atom to another, if suitable levels are available. The latter proviso is necessary because an electron cannot enter a level which is already occupied. In this context, therefore, the entire problem of conduction resolves itself into the question whether electrons can move from atom to atom by occupying vacant levels. It is clear that the inner shells cannot contribute to conduction because these levels are normally full in all the atoms and it requires a great deal of energy to raise an electron from an inner shell to the valence (or conduction) level.

The effects of mutual interaction on the energy levels of atoms may be seen in an extreme case, where we consider the motion of a single electron in an endless series of rectangular potential wells confined to one dimension (Figure 8.8).* An *isolated* deep well of this type allows electron energies given by the expression

$$E = \frac{n^2 h^2}{8mL^2} \quad \text{with } n = 1, 2, \ldots, \qquad \text{from Equation (7.1.4)}$$

where L is the width of the well.

* R. Kronig and W. G. Penney, Proc. Roy. Soc. (London), **A130**, 499 (1931).

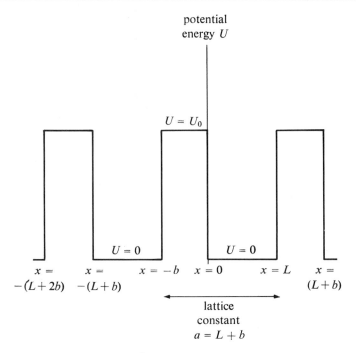

potential
energy U

$U = U_0$

$U = U_0$

$U = 0$ $U = 0$

$x =$ $x =$ $x = -b$ $x = 0$ $x = L$ $x =$
$-(L+2b)$ $-(L+b)$ $(L+b)$

lattice
constant
$a = L + b$

FIGURE 8.8 *The Kronig-Penney model for conduction in a lattice consists of an infinite series of rectangular potential wells, each of width L and depth U_0, in one dimension. The lattice constant a is the sum of L and the barrier width b.*

In the infinite series of wells which represents the crystal lattice, we impose a periodicity of "wavelength" a where

$$a = L + b$$

and L denotes the well widths (where $U = 0$) and b denotes the barrier widths (where $U = U_0$). The problem is to discover the possible energy levels ($E < U_0$) for an electron in this lattice.

According to a theorem of Bloch, the Schrödinger wave function ψ for a wave traveling through a lattice of periodicity a with wavenumber parameter κ must possess the same periodicity as the lattice, that is, if we write

$$\psi(x) = \exp(i\kappa x)\, u(x) \qquad [8.4.1]$$

then $u(x)$ is a function with periodicity a, such that

$$u(x - a) = u(x).$$

Thus
$$\psi(x - a) = \exp[i\kappa(x - a)]\, u(x - a)$$
$$= \exp(-i\kappa a)\, \psi(x). \qquad [8.4.2]$$

It follows from Equation (8.4.1) that the wave-number variable must be real, otherwise the Schrödinger function diverges for extreme values of x in the infinite lattice.

If one particular well (with $U = 0$) extends from $x = 0$ to $x = L$, as in Figure 8.8, we may write a Schrödinger solution of the form

$$\psi_1(x) = A \cos \eta x + B \sin \eta x,$$

where

$$\eta^2 = \frac{2mE}{\hbar^2}.$$

The adjacent barrier extending from $x = -b$ to $x = 0$ has a solution

$$\psi_2(x) = C \cosh \mu x + D \sinh \mu x,$$

where

$$\mu^2 = \frac{2m(U_0 - E)}{\hbar^2}.$$

The state function must be continuous in magnitude and gradient at the boundary $x = 0$, so we derive the conditions

$$A = C,$$

$$\eta B = \mu D.$$

Also, from Equation (8.4.2), with $x = L$, we obtain the relations

$$\exp(-i\kappa a)\, \psi_1(L) = \psi_2(-b)$$

and

$$\exp(-i\kappa a) \left[\frac{d\psi_1}{dx}(L)\right] = \left[\frac{d\psi_2}{dx}(-b)\right]$$

which become

$$A \cos \eta L + B \sin \eta L = \exp(i\kappa a)[C \cosh \mu b - D \sinh \mu b]$$

and

$$\frac{\eta}{\mu}[A \sin \eta L - B \cos \eta L] = \exp(i\kappa a)[C \sinh \mu b - D \cosh \mu b].$$

After elimination of A, B, C, and D (with the aid of the secular determinant) we obtain a quadratic equation

$$\exp(2i\kappa a) - \exp(i\kappa a)\left[\left(\frac{\mu}{\eta} - \frac{\eta}{\mu}\right)\sin \eta L \sinh \mu b + 2 \cos \eta L \cosh \mu b\right] + 1 = 0.$$

Multiplying this throughout by $\exp(-i\kappa a)$, we find

$$2 \cos \kappa a = \left(\frac{\mu}{\eta} - \frac{\eta}{\mu}\right)\sin \eta L \sinh \mu b + 2 \cos \eta L \cosh \mu b. \qquad [8.4.3]$$

This result may be analyzed most easily by making the barrier width (b) progressively smaller while raising the barrier height (U_0) at the same time in such a way that the limit of ($\mu^2 b$) is constant. Thus

$$\lim_{\substack{\mu \to \infty \\ b \to 0}} (\tfrac{1}{2}\mu^2 L b) = P \text{ (const)}.$$

In this limit the product μb is small, since $\mu^2 b^2 \propto Pb$ and we substitute in Equation (8.4.3)

$$\sinh \mu b \approx \mu b \qquad \text{and} \qquad \cosh \mu b \approx 1.$$

The result, for $b \to 0$, is the equation

$$\cos \kappa a = \frac{P}{\eta L} \sin \eta L + \cos \eta L. \qquad [8.4.4]$$

Since κ has to be real the limits of $\cos(\kappa a)$ are necessarily ± 1, so if we plot the right-hand function against ηL the curve's intersections with the lines ± 1 indicate the limits within

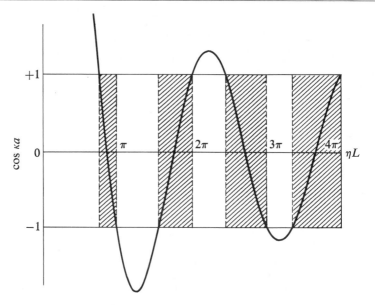

FIGURE 8.9   *The solution obtained in the Kronig-Penney treatment for high, narrow barriers leads to a graph of* cos κa *(where κ is the wave-number parameter for propagation in the lattice) against ηL where $\eta^2 = \dfrac{2mE}{\hbar^2}$. The limits of the cosine are ± 1 for κ real, and these define the allowed energy bands for conduction, shown shaded.*

which regular Schrödinger solutions are obtainable. In Figure 8.9 the graph is plotted for the special case $P = 2$ and it is seen that there are alternate "allowed" and "forbidden" regions for the parameter ηL. If $P = 0$, there are no barriers and we find

$$\kappa = \eta,$$

that is, all energy values are possible. On the other hand, if we suppose that P is very large, corresponding to deep wells effectively isolated from each other, the "allowed" regions become very narrow and the energies are restricted to values fixed by the condition

$$\eta L = \pm n\pi \qquad \text{with } n = 1, 2, 3, \ldots$$

or

$$E = \frac{n^2 h^2}{8mL^2} \qquad \text{as for one well.}$$

This model shows that the single-electron levels of an isolated deep well are broadened into continuous "allowed" energy bands when an infinite number of wells interact. It is also found that the allowed bands increase in width as the energy increases. The "forbidden" zones of energy remain, however, for all values of E so long as $P > 0$. It is seen from Figure 8.9 that the forbidden zones always commence at the abscissae

$$\eta L = \pm n\pi,$$

that is, at

$$\eta = \pm \frac{n\pi}{L}.$$

This condition, for $n = 1$, resembles the condition limiting the extent of the Brillouin zone for phonons in a one-dimensional lattice [Equation (8.2.4)]. Indeed, the same condition of Bragg reflection occurs here to define the limits of the forbidden energy regions.

An alternative approach to the problem of atomic interactions is to consider the effect of neighboring atoms on the energy levels of a given atom. For weak interactions the methods of perturbation theory (Section 7.12) are suitable and it is possible to find the energy changes in terms of the three components of the $\varkappa$ vector (which is proportional to the momentum vector **p**). The results depend on the type of lattice and on the type of original wave function (s, p, d, and so forth) adopted. For the s-type electron in a simple cubic lattice, the energy is given by the expression

$$E = E_0 - 2\gamma(\cos \varkappa_x a + \cos \varkappa_y a + \cos \varkappa_z a), \qquad [8.4.5]$$

where E_0 is a constant energy at zero interaction;

   a is the lattice constant;

   γ is an interaction term depending on the degree of overlapping between state functions.

If for this lattice we define a three-dimensional Brillouin zone in "$\varkappa$ space" by the equations

$$-\frac{\pi}{a} \leqslant \varkappa_x \leqslant \frac{\pi}{a}: \qquad -\frac{\pi}{a} \leqslant \varkappa_y \leqslant \frac{\pi}{a}: \qquad -\frac{\pi}{a} \leqslant \varkappa_z \leqslant \frac{\pi}{a}$$

which define a "cube" of side $2\pi/a$, it follows that the range of energies covered by this Brillouin zone is

$$E = E_0 \pm 6\gamma.$$

Outside this range of energies there will normally be forbidden zones which correspond to the gaps between sharp energy levels in Figure 8.7 (left-hand diagram). This theory leads to essentially the same results as the infinite one-dimensional lattice, but is more specific about the interaction effects. The inner-shell electron states are scarcely affected by interactions because the value of γ is small (little overlap of state functions). As the energy increases from one subshell to another, the effects of interactions become more pronounced and the levels are broadened more and more, as indicated schematically in Figure 8.7. To each broadened level there corresponds a Brillouin zone; if this zone is filled, no conduction is possible in the corresponding level because of the combined effects of the Pauli principle and Bragg reflection of the electrons.

The number of electron states corresponding to one Brillouin zone can be obtained directly from the phase-space theorem of Section 8.3. For the simple cubic lattice and s electrons, we have a cubic Brillouin zone of volume

$$\left(\frac{2\pi}{a}\right)^3 \qquad \text{in } \varkappa \text{ space}$$

corresponding to a volume

$$\hbar^3\left(\frac{2\pi}{a}\right)^3 = \frac{h^3}{a^3} \qquad \text{in momentum space.}$$

Thus the volume of *phase space* per unit cell of the lattice (of *proper* volume a^3) is

$$\Phi = \frac{h^3}{a^3} a^3 = h^3$$

and for N unit cells, containing N atoms (in this lattice), the phase space is $N\Phi = Nh^3$. In Section 8.3 we found that each electron, of spin $\frac{1}{2}\hbar$, can occupy an amount $\frac{1}{2}h^3$ of phase space. It follows that a single s-type Brillouin zone can accommodate $2N$ electrons, the factor 2 being due to the spin of the electron. The same conclusion is reached for all types of lattice with s-type zones.

In the Bloch single-electron theory of conduction, the essential difference between a good conductor and an insulator lies in the degree to which the Brillouin zones for the valence electrons are filled. If all the zones are full, no electron migration can occur, but if they are partly filled conduction is possible. This situation is represented in Figure 8.7 and it is clear that the operation of the Pauli principle goes far toward explaining the high ratio of conductivities between conductors and insulators. The theory is also capable of describing the properties of *semiconductors* on the assumption that these materials possess empty conduction levels with a small energy gap (ΔE in Figure 8.7) between them and the highest filled zone.

When applied to actual metals, the single-electron theory accounts immediately for the conductivity of the alkali metals and the monovalent elements copper, silver, and gold. Each atom of these elements contributes one electron to the s-type valence band, which is therefore half-full, and the metal is highly conducting. On the other hand, one expects divalent elements to be insulators, because N atoms should provide just $2N$ electrons to fill the Brillouin zone for the valence band. It is true that these elements (for example, magnesium, zinc, mercury) are poorer conductors than the monovalent elements, but there is no doubt about their metallic status. It may happen, of course, that the valence band is not quite full, because of some retention of electrons by the atoms in inner shells, and this probably does occur in the transition metals. Such an explanation does *not* account for the conductivity of elements like magnesium and zinc. In such cases it is necessary to postulate that the s-type conduction band is overlapped by higher bands, for example of the p type. Some evidence of this can be adduced from x-ray line shapes such as those shown in Figure 8.6, where the magnesium and aluminum data indicate overlapping of the s and p bands. In several of the divalent metals, for example zinc, the Hall coefficient is positive (Section 3.5) and this is interpreted as the effect of conduction by "holes" in a band which is nearly full. Vacancies in the band are filled by migrating electrons, so that the "holes" move in the opposite direction to the electrons and this has the effect of making the effective carriers of electricity positively charged. The single-electron theory can therefore explain many phenomena which were previously obscure.

(c) Collective electron effects

The single-electron theory ignores the effects of electron interactions in the conduction bands, but it is evident that, when there is a high density of conduction electrons, these interactions might be important. Mott has argued that in certain problems the specific properties of the lattice and its ions are not particularly significant—for example, metals remain conducting in the liquid state despite the absence of a well-defined lattice. In Mott's theory the transition from the nonconducting to the conducting state is a collective type of phenomenon depending on the mean interatomic spacing. Thus all elements, whatever their valence number, should become metallic if their atoms are close enough. The problem of conduction is then reduced to one of deciding the most probable structure of the solid and the degree to which *covalent* bonds can develop. If covalent bonds are present, as in carbon and other nonmetals, the mean interatomic spacing is high and conduction is rendered difficult.

A more complete collective theory of electrons in metals has been developed, chiefly by Bohm and Pines, who have studied the problem of metallic cohesion in detail. One result of their theory is to show that the single-electron model is a good approximation in practice because of "screening" effects, which limit the degree to which the electrons can interact with each other. Another result is that the electron assembly possesses well-defined frequencies of "plasma" oscillation [Equation (4.1.9)], although the energy required to excite such oscillations is considerably higher than the Fermi energy [Equation (8.3.10)]. Nevertheless, when electrons are scattered by thin metallic foils, inelastic scattering may occur with well-defined energy loss, which is ascribed to a "plasmon" excitation of energy

$$\hbar\omega_p = \hbar\sqrt{\frac{nze^2}{m\varepsilon_0}}, \qquad [8.4.6]$$

where n is the number of atoms per unit volume;
$\quad z$ is the effective valence number;
$\quad \varepsilon_0$ is the permittivity of the vacuum.

In general there is good agreement between the observed energy loss of scattered electrons and the plasmon energy calculated with the proper valence z, but there are also serious discrepancies in the transition metals.†

(d) The effective-mass concept

Further developments in the theory of conduction depend on the way in which the motion of electrons in an applied field is modified by the presence of the lattice and the existence of Brillouin zones. If an electric field of magnitude $\mathscr{E}$ is acting on an electron, of charge $-e$, the force exerted is $(-e\mathscr{E})$ and the rate of change of the parameter κ is

$$\frac{d\kappa}{dt} = \frac{1}{\hbar}\frac{dp}{dt} = -\frac{e\mathscr{E}}{\hbar}.$$

The effective velocity of the electron (v) is given by the group velocity of the de Broglie wave (as for the phonons in Section 8.2):

$$v = \frac{d\omega}{d\kappa} = \frac{1}{\hbar}\frac{dE}{d\kappa}$$

and the acceleration becomes

$$\frac{dv}{dt} = \frac{1}{\hbar}\frac{d}{dt}\left(\frac{dE}{d\kappa}\right) = \frac{1}{\hbar}\frac{d\kappa}{dt}\frac{d^2E}{d\kappa^2}$$

$$= \frac{-e\mathscr{E}}{\hbar^2}\frac{d^2E}{d\kappa^2}. \qquad [8.4.7]$$

Thus the effective mass (m^*) of the electron is given by the relation

$$m^*\frac{dv}{dt} = -e\mathscr{E}$$

or

$$\frac{1}{m^*} = \hbar^{-2}\frac{d^2E}{d\kappa^2}. \qquad [8.4.8]$$

Thus m^* depends on the relation between the energy E and the wave-number parameter κ, which is proportional to the momentum.

† D. Pines, Rev. Mod. Phys., **28**, 184 (1956).

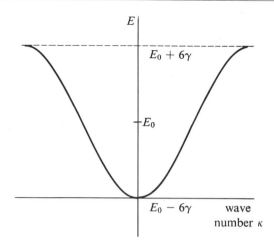

FIGURE 8.10   *The energy-wave number relation for the first Brillouin zone in a simple cubic lattice.*
The effective mass of the charge carriers depends on the value of $\dfrac{d^2E}{d\kappa^2}$ *, which varies*
throughout the band of allowed energies.

For the s-type electron in a simple cubic lattice, we had the $E - \kappa$ relation of Equation (8.4.5)

$$E = E_0 - 2\gamma(\cos \kappa_x a + \cos \kappa_y a + \cos \kappa_z a).$$

For an electron near the base of the first Brillouin zone, the factors κ_x, κ_y, and κ_z are small, so we have

$$E \approx (E_0 - 6\gamma) + \gamma a^2(\kappa_x^2 + \kappa_y^2 + \kappa_z^2)$$
$$= (E_0 - 6\gamma) + \gamma a^2\kappa^2. \qquad [8.4.9]$$

This relation may be depicted graphically as a parabolic dependence of E on κ (Figure 8.10). As the value of κ increases, the gradient of the $E - \kappa$ curve reaches a maximum value at the point represented by

$$\kappa_x = \kappa_y = \kappa_z = \frac{1}{2}\frac{\pi}{a},$$

that is, half-way up the zone. Beyond this point the gradient decreases and reaches zero at the limit of the zone, where

$$\kappa_x = \kappa_y = \kappa_z = \frac{\pi}{a} \qquad \text{see Equation (8.2.3).}$$

At the zone boundary there is an energy discontinuity before the next zone commences.
Now for electrons which are effectively free we have the classical energy-momentum relation

$$E = \frac{p^2}{2m} = \frac{\hbar^2\kappa^2}{2m}$$

so that the effective mass is

$$m^* = \hbar^2 \bigg/ \frac{d^2E}{d\kappa^2} = m.$$

For electrons near the base of the Brillouin zone, we find from Equation (8.4.9)

$$m^* = \frac{\hbar^2}{2\gamma a^2}. \qquad [8.4.10]$$

This can be greater or less than the proper value m according to the magnitude of γa^2. In alkali metals and other solids where the electrons are effectively free (and the conductivity is high) the values of m^* and m do not differ very much. On the other hand, if there are electrons in an inner shell which contribute to conduction these have a low value of γ and m^* is correspondingly high. This is the case in certain transition metals like nickel.

Application of the effective-mass concept to various problems in solid-state physics shows that it can account for several anomalous properties of the transition metals. For example, nickel atoms are normally in the electron configuration $(3d)^8(4s)^2$ and in the metallic state one expects both the $3d$ and the $4s$ electrons to contribute to conduction. It is found from x-ray studies that the $3d$ and $4s$ bands overlap, also the $3d$ band is much the narrower, in accordance with the theory of interaction. By way of contrast, the metal copper has the normal configuration $(3d)^{10}(4s)^1$ so that the $3d$ band is nonconducting and the $4s$ band produces high conductivity. In nickel the $3d$ electrons have high effective mass, because of the small value of γ, and so the Fermi energy ζ [Equation (8.3.10)] and the Fermi temperature are unusually low. The electronic specific heat C_v^{el} has therefore to be multiplied by the ratio m^*/m for these electrons. Nickel does in fact possess a very high specific heat of electronic type ($C_v \propto T$) at low temperatures. Also, in the region above the Debye temperature, the total specific heat is considerably greater than the classical value $3R$ and this effect may be electronic in origin. Such effects are not exhibited by copper.

(e) Semiconductors

The effective-mass concept is particularly important in the theory of semiconductors; these elements are characterized by a small energy gap (ΔE in Figure 8.7) between the filled valence band and the nearest vacant band, which may, in suitable circumstances, become a conduction band. An important group of semiconductors comprises the elements carbon (diamond), silicon, and germanium, all of which form stable lattices with covalent bonds between neighboring atoms and the bonds from each atom directed tetrahedrally. Thus each atom has four immediate neighbors and the lattice resembles a body-centered cubic lattice in which half the atoms are missing. In such a lattice all the electrons are effectively bound if the atoms are identical, that is, the element is in a high state of purity. Moreover, electron-lattice interactions are weak for any extra electrons which may be introduced and these electrons have long mean free paths.

The magnitude of the energy gap, ΔE, between the valence and conduction bands is 1.12 eV in pure silicon and 0.72 eV in pure germanium. At ordinary temperatures, electrons cannot be excited thermally from the valence to the conduction bands to any appreciable extent, as is shown by estimates based on the Boltzmann expression

$$\text{Probability of excitation} \approx \exp\left(-\frac{\Delta E}{kT}\right).$$

However, conduction may be stimulated in various ways:

(i) by the incidence of light — absorption of a quantum of energy greater than ΔE may give rise to *photoconduction*, which is important in the element selenium and the silver halide compounds;

(ii) by high thermal excitation — the "intrinsic" conductivity of a semi-conductor rises very sharply when the value of kT becomes comparable with the energy gap ΔE;

(iii) by the addition of impurities, which may be regarded as providing extra conduction bands in the "forbidden" region between the valence and conduction bands of the semiconducting element.

Most modern applications of semiconductors depend on the special properties obtainable by the controlled introduction of impurities into the pure elements. The impurities are of two kinds, known as "donor" atoms (which provide excess electrons) and "acceptor" atoms (which are deficient in electrons compared with the semiconductor). Thus in an element like germanium, which possesses four valence electrons per atom, impurities such as arsenic or antimony (in the next column to the right in the periodic table) are donors, while elements like gallium or indium (in the next column to the left in the periodic table) are acceptors. If donor atoms are present, the excess electrons can conduct electricity through the lattice and we have "*n*-type" germanium (with negative Hall coefficient). If acceptor atoms are present, electrons move to fill the "holes" created and the motion of the "holes" in this "*p*-type" germanium is in the opposite direction to the actual electron motions; thus the Hall coefficient in positive in such a material.

It is well known that current rectification occurs at contacts between metals and semi-conductors, for example, in selenium and copper-copper-oxide rectifiers. Similar effects take place at the contact between layers of *n*-type and *p*-type germanium or silicon. It appears that electrons in the *n*-type material tend to migrate into the *p*-type material and fill the holes provided by the acceptor atoms. This process occurs until the charge difference which is built up, making the *n*-type material positive relative to the *p*-type material, reaches such a value that further migration is prevented. At this stage the Fermi level is effectively the same throughout both layers. If, now, the two layers are connected to a battery with the *n*-type material polarized negatively and the *p* type polarized positively, electron migration is resumed and conductivity is high in the "forward" direction. If, on the other hand, the polarity is reversed, electron migration cannot exceed the small amount allowed by the intrinsic conductivity of the semiconductor. Similar mechanisms underlie the action of transistors and other semiconductor devices.

8.5 Paramagnetism of Ions and Metals

Some of the most important phenomena exhibited by metals are the magnetic properties of the transition elements, including the ferromagnetics iron, cobalt, and nickel. These phenomena are extremely complex in the metallic state and it is advantageous to study first the behavior of metallic ions in solution, where the degree of interaction is much less than in the metal and there are no effects due to conduction electrons. We have to consider the effect of an applied magnetic field on the electrons occupying the inner shells of the ions. This problem has been dealt with in Section 7.14 and it remains to relate the behavior of individual atoms to the properties of matter in bulk. Throughout this section it will be assumed that atoms and ions obey the Boltzmann statistics, but it is necessary to invoke Fermi-Dirac rules for conduction electrons in a metal, as was shown by Sommerfeld's work (Section 8.3).

(a) Diamagnetic effects

In the first place, any ion which has electrons filling closed shells around the nucleus must be in the spectroscopic state $^1S_0$ and show zero magnetic moment (if the small nuclear moment is ignored). In other words, the atomic energy state is unaffected by an applied magnetic field, to a first approximation. Nevertheless there should be an induced magnetic moment, according to the rules of classical physics, and this must be in the opposite direction to the applied field, that is, the magnetic susceptibility is negative and an assembly of such ions is *diamagnetic*. A straightforward application of the classical Larmor theorem (Section 4.2) shows that the susceptibility of N ions isolated from each other, each containing Z electrons in Bohr-type orbits, is

$$\chi_D = - \frac{NZe^2}{4\pi m} \bar{A}, \qquad [8.5.1]$$

where m is the electronic mass, $\bar{A}$ is the mean projected area of all the orbits at right angles to the field B.

In the derivation of Equation (8.5.1), it is usually assumed that the electron orbits all lie in planes perpendicular to the magnetic field B. If (x, y) denotes the position of an electron in one such orbit, the mean projected area $\bar{A}$ may be written

$$\bar{A} = \pi(\overline{x^2 + y^2}).$$

For electrons in random motion, however, the mean-square distance from the center $(\overline{r^2})$ is the sum of three squared terms

$$\overline{r^2} = \overline{x^2} + \overline{y^2} + \overline{z^2}.$$

Moreover, these three terms are equal, on the average. It follows that the area $\bar{A}$ can be expressed in terms of the quantity $\overline{r^2}$ (which can be calculated by quantum mechanics for simple atoms) as follows:

$$\bar{A} = \tfrac{2}{3}\pi \overline{r^2}.$$

The susceptibility may then be written as a sum over all electrons

$$\chi_D = - \frac{Ne^2}{6m} \sum_i \overline{r_i^2}, \qquad [8.5.2]$$

where $\overline{r_i^2}$ is the mean-square radius for the ith orbit. A similar result is obtained with the aid of quantum theory.

The simple theory of diamagnetism may be applied to the inert gases, all of which are monatomic with closed electron shells, and to the ions of alkali metals (Li^+, Na^+, and so forth) and the halogens (F^-, Cl^-, and so forth). The susceptibility per ion increases markedly with atomic number, as one would expect from Equation (8.5.1), and is not materially affected by changes in temperature. It should be noted that all assemblies of atoms and ions are capable of diamagnetic behavior, so that appropriate corrections have to be applied to experimental data when accurate results are required for the *paramagnetic* susceptibility.

(b) Paramagnetism and Curie's law

Paramagnetic behavior is observed wherever ions or atoms possess intrinsic magnetic moments, which may be detected in experiments of the Stern-Gerlach type (Section 6.5). In an applied magnetic field the moments are partially aligned, to an extent which depends on the temperature T, and the net result is a positive susceptibility (total moment **M** parallel to field **B**). In the simplest case of systems in the spectroscopic state $^2S_{1/2}$, corresponding to zero orbital moment and single-electron spin moment, there are two possible orientations of the moment vector relative to the applied field. The two possible values for the magnetic potential energy are

$$-\mu_B\left(1 + \frac{\alpha}{2\pi}\right)B \quad \text{and} \quad +\mu_B\left(1 + \frac{\alpha}{2\pi}\right)B$$

with

$$\alpha = \tfrac{1}{137} \text{ approximately} \qquad \text{from Equation (7.10.8).}$$

To a sufficient degree of accuracy, these expressions may be replaced by

$$-\mu_B B \qquad \text{and} \qquad +\mu_B B$$

and the appropriate Boltzmann probabilities are

$$\exp\left(\frac{\mu_B B}{kT}\right) \qquad \text{and} \qquad \exp\left(-\frac{\mu_B B}{kT}\right).$$

The mean magnetic moment, M, of N atoms or ions in this state is

$$M = \frac{N\mu_B[\exp(\mu_B B/kT) - \exp(-\mu_B B/kT)]}{[\exp(\mu_B B/kT) + \exp(-\mu_B B/kT)]},$$

where terms $+\mu_B$ and $-\mu_B$ in the numerator have been multiplied by the probability factors and the denominator serves to normalize the total probability to unity. The result may be written

$$M = N\mu_B \tanh\left(\frac{\mu_B B}{kT}\right). \qquad [8.5.3]$$

The same result is obtained by setting up a Boltzmann type of partition function (Section 2.2)

$$\Sigma = \sum_i \exp(-\beta\varepsilon_i) \quad \text{with} \quad \beta = \frac{1}{kT},$$

where ε_i represents the energy in the ith state. Thus for atoms in the $^2S_{1/2}$ state we write $\varepsilon = \pm\mu_B B$ and obtain

$$\Sigma = \exp(\mu_B B/kT) + \exp(-\mu_B B/kT)$$

$$= 2\cosh\left(\frac{\mu_B B}{kT}\right).$$

The mean magnetic moment for N atoms is then derived from the relation

$$M = NkT \frac{\partial}{\partial B}(\ln \Sigma)$$

$$= \frac{NkT\mu_B \sinh(\mu_B B/kT)}{kT \cosh(\mu_B B/kT)} = N\mu_B \tanh\left(\frac{\mu_B B}{kT}\right).$$

This method is readily generalized to deal with atoms in any state of total angular momentum denoted by J, since the various possible orientations give rise to energy states according to the expression

$$\varepsilon_J = -m_J g\mu_B B, \qquad \text{from Equation (7.14.3)}$$

where m_J takes the values $J, (J-1), \ldots (-J)$. The partition function is found by summation over all values of m_J and from this function various properties, in addition to the mean total magnetic moment, may be derived.

Reverting to Equation (8.5.3) for the mean magnetic moment of N ions in the $^2S_{1/2}$ state, we see that the value of M increases linearly with field B near the origin (Figure 8.11) but reaches a saturation value $N\mu_B$ in the region of high fields. In practice the saturation effects can only be detected when the absolute temperature T is very low and B is large. Under

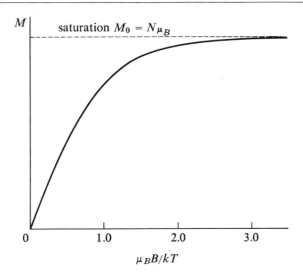

FIGURE 8.11 *The mean magnetic moment M of an assembly of atoms, each in the ${}^2S_{1/2}$ state, varies with the applied field B and the temperature T in a way indicated by the graph*

of M against the parameter $\dfrac{\mu_B B}{kT}$.

more normal conditions, M is very nearly proportional to B and the paramagnetic susceptibility χ_P is found from the relation

$$\chi_P = \left(\frac{\partial M}{\partial B}\right)_{B\to 0} = \frac{N\mu_B^2}{kT}. \qquad [8.5.4]$$

The inverse relation between paramagnetic susceptibility and the absolute temperature is a general feature of assemblies of magnetic systems which interact very little with each other. It is known as *Curie's law*, from the experimental work of Pierre Curie on the phenomenon of paramagnetism. Paramagnetic salts, in particular, obey the law very closely and are suitable for studying the more general relations involving saturation effects in the low-temperature region. In this region it is found that there are appreciable specific-heat anomalies caused by the paramagnetic ions, as may be seen from Problem 2.17.

The susceptibility of an assembly of noninteracting ions in states denoted by the angular-momentum number J is to be found from the partition function

$$\Sigma = \sum_{m_J=-J}^{J} \exp\left(\frac{m_J g\mu_B B}{kT}\right) \qquad \text{from Equation (7.14.3)}$$

with the aid of the auxiliary equation

$$M = NkT \frac{\partial}{\partial B}(\ln \Sigma),$$

that is,

$$M = \frac{NkT}{\Sigma}\frac{\partial \Sigma}{\partial B}$$

$$= \frac{Ng\mu_B}{\Sigma}\sum_{-J}^{J} m_J \exp\left(\frac{m_J g\mu_B B}{kT}\right).$$

This equation gives rise to complicated functions, known as the Brillouin functions, but the procedure may be simplified by considering only small values of the field B. The exponential terms are approximately represented by

$$\exp\left(\frac{m_J g\mu_B B}{kT}\right) \approx 1 + \frac{m_J g\mu_B B}{kT}$$

and the series become

$$\sum \approx \sum_{-J}^{J}\left(1 + \frac{m_J g\mu_B B}{kT}\right)$$

$$= 2J + 1$$

and

$$\sum_{-J}^{J} m_J \exp\left(\frac{m_J g\mu_B B}{kT}\right) = \sum_{-J}^{J} m_J\left[1 + \frac{m_J g\mu_B B}{kT}\right]$$

$$= \frac{g\mu_B B}{kT}\sum_{-J}^{J} m_J^2$$

$$= \frac{g\mu_B B}{kT}\frac{J(J+1)(2J+1)}{3}.$$

Thus in small fields the total magnetic moment is

$$M = \frac{Ng^2\mu_B^2 B}{3kT}J(J+1)$$

and the paramagnetic susceptibility becomes

$$\chi_P = \frac{\partial M}{\partial B} = \frac{Ng^2\mu_B^2}{3kT}J(J+1) \qquad\qquad [8.5.5]$$

which again involves Curie's law.

Now in a *classical* assembly of particles, each with magnetic moment μ, the result obtained from the Langevin function (Problem 6.16) is a susceptibility

$$\chi_P^{cl} = \frac{N\mu^2}{3kT}.$$

It follows that the quantum theory yields similar results if we assign to each atom or ion the effective moment

$$\mu = g\mu_B\sqrt{J(J+1)}$$

which is identical with Equation (7.14.2), derived from the vector model of atomic states.

(c) The rare-earth ions

These predictions may best be compared with experimental data for salts containing paramagnetic ions which interact very little with each other. Good examples are found among the elements of the rare-earth or lanthanide group (Appendix II) which form triply charged ions with the inner $4f$ subshell incomplete. The electron configurations are fixed by the condition that the $5s$ and $5p$ subshells must be full, and these subshells effectively screen the inner $4f$ subshell from external interactions. The number of electrons in the $4f$ subshell ranges from 0 in La^{+++} and 1 in Ce^{+++} to 13 in Yb^{+++} and 14 in Lu^{+++}.

It follows that the ions La^{+++} and Lu^{+++} display no paramagnetic effects but the thirteen intervening triply charged ions possess intrinsic moments which depend on the type of ground state. For example, Ce^{+++} is necessarily in the state $^2F_{5/2}$ and has the effective moment 2.54 Bohr magnetons, as calculated from Equation (7.14.2). We may regard Yb^{+++} as possessing a single "hole" in the $4f$ subshell, so by the rules of the spin-orbit interaction (Section 7.11) the ground state is $^2F_{7/2}$ with an effective moment of 4.54 Bohr magnetons. These predictions of the theory are in good agreement with experimental data.

The situation is more complex in the other rare-earth ions but we can evolve a general treatment, for any ion with z electrons in the $4f$ subshell, with the aid of Hund's rules for fixing the ground state. In Section 7.11 we pointed out that the state of highest multiplicity, that is, the state with the highest value of the total spin number S, is the lowest in energy for any given electron configuration. It is also found that, when different states of the *same* multiplicity are compared, the state with the highest total orbital momentum number L is the lowest in energy. If we apply these rules to the rare-earth ions in the *first half* of the group, that is, with $z = 1$ to $z = 6$, we find immediately that the maximum spin is

$$S = \tfrac{1}{2}z.$$

The maximum value of L is found by adding together the z different m_l values in such a way that Pauli's principle is obeyed and that the maximum spin is simultaneously obtained. Since $l = 3$, we find

$$L = 3 + 2 + 1 + \cdots + (4 - z)$$
$$= \tfrac{1}{2}z(7 - z).$$

The spin-orbit interaction ensures that the total angular momentum in the ground state is denoted by

$$J = L - S = \tfrac{1}{2}z(6 - z).$$

The Landé gyromagnetic factor can then be calculated

$$g = 1 + \frac{J(J + 1) + S(S + 1) - L(L + 1)}{2J(J + 1)}$$

$$= 1\tfrac{1}{2} - \frac{(L - S)(L + S + 1)}{2J(J + 1)}$$

$$= 1\tfrac{1}{2} - \frac{L + S + 1}{2(L - S + 1)} = \frac{J - S + 1}{J + 1}.$$

The effective magnetic moment per ion in Bohr-magneton units is

$$\frac{\mu}{\mu_B} = g\sqrt{J(J+1)} = \sqrt{\frac{z(6 - z)}{z(6 - z) + 2}} \, [\tfrac{1}{2}z(5 - z) + 1]. \qquad [8.5.6]$$

This formula is valid for z up to 6. The ion Eu^{+++} has $J = 0$ and therefore no magnetic moment according to this theory. For higher values of z, we work with the number (z') of "holes" in the $4f$ subshell, that is,

$$z' = 14 - z.$$

It is then found that, for values of z from 7 to 14,

$$S = \tfrac{1}{2}z' \qquad L = \tfrac{1}{2}z'(7 - z')$$

and the total angular momentum (for holes) is denoted by

$$J = L + S = \tfrac{1}{2}z'(8 - z').$$

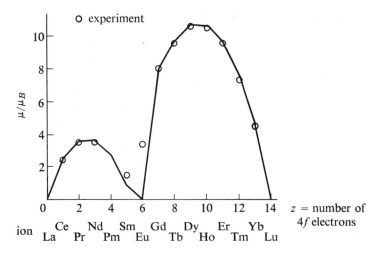

FIGURE 8.12   *The magnetic moment per ion, in Bohr magnetons, for triply charged rare-earth ions plotted against the number (z) of electrons in the (inner) 4f subshell. The theoretical predictions, based on Hund's rules, may be compared with experimental results.*

The magnetic moment in Bohr-magneton units becomes

$$\frac{\mu}{\mu_B} = \sqrt{\frac{z'(8 - z') + 2}{z'(8 - z')}} \, [\tfrac{1}{2}z'(9 - z')] \qquad\qquad [8.5.7]$$

which is valid for z' up to 7.

The results of these calculations are depicted by the full line in Figure 8.12 and it is seen that the experimental data are in close agreement, except those for $Sm^{+++}(z = 5)$ and $Eu^{+++}(z = 6)$. The discrepancies have been explained by Van Vleck, who showed that the influence of states close to the ground state is not negligible in these ions. In general, the theory is highly successful for ions of the rare-earth type.

(d) Transition-metal ions

Of more importance are the ions of the first series of transition metals, which includes the ferromagnetic elements iron, cobalt, and nickel. These ions are characterized by the incomplete $3d$ subshell which is the outermost subshell and is therefore subject to external interactions without screening. We can proceed to apply the same kind of treatment which was successful in the rare earths, and we obtain the full line of Figure 8.13. This is clearly remote from the experimental values except for the ions Mn^{++} and Fe^{+++} which have five electrons each in the $3d$ subshell. In these cases, the maximum multiplicity rule gives $S = \tfrac{5}{2}$ and this is consistent only with $L = 0$, so the ground state is $^6S_{5/2}$. All the other ions in this group have L greater than zero and all show considerable deviations from the magnetic moment calculated from Equation (7.14.2). This effect has been traced to the "quenching" of orbital momentum by the external interactions, which are always present even in dilute solutions containing the ions. The interactions are usually nonisotropic and their asymmetry causes the component of orbital momentum along any specified direction to be zero, on the average, although the *magnitude* of the orbital momentum is unaffected.

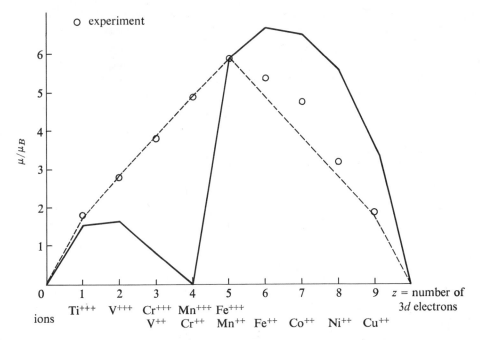

FIGURE 8.13 *The magnetic moment per ion, in Bohr magnetons, for various transition-metal ions plotted against the number (z) of electrons in the 3d subshell. The full line represents the full magnetic moment $g\sqrt{J(J+1)}$ and the dotted line the spin moment only, given by $2\sqrt{S(S+1)}$.*

Assuming that the orbital momentum is completely inoperative for these ions, we can calculate an effective magnetic moment per ion by writing

$$J_{\text{eff}} = S$$

with

$$S = \tfrac{1}{2}z \quad \text{for } 0 \leqslant z \leqslant 5,$$
$$S = \tfrac{1}{2}z' = \tfrac{1}{2}(10 - z) \quad \text{for } 5 \leqslant z \leqslant 10,$$

then

$$\frac{\mu}{\mu_B} = 2\sqrt{S(S+1)} \quad \text{since } g = 2 \text{ for pure spin.} \qquad [8.5.8]$$

This formula is represented by the dotted line in Figure 8.13 and the agreement with experimental results is much improved, although it is by no means perfect. It is evident that even comparatively weak external interactions have appreciable effect on the paramagnetic properties of the transition-metal ions.*

(e) Metallic solids

The diamagnetic and paramagnetic susceptibilities exhibited by metallic solids are complex in origin. In addition to the magnetic properties of the lattice ions, we have to take into account the "free" or conduction electrons and the energy bands which they occupy. At first sight, it would be expected that an assembly of electrons, each with spin $\tfrac{1}{2}\hbar$ and magnetic moment close to one Bohr magneton, would have a pronounced paramagnetic susceptibility given by Equation (8.5.4). However, the application of Fermi-Dirac

---

* "Quenching" effects are also detected in measurements of the gyromagnetie ratio for paramagnetic salts.

statistics yields a much smaller effect, as was first pointed out by Pauli. At ordinary temperatures, most of the electrons occupy low-energy states in the conduction band and these electrons pair off with spins opposed so that the net magnetic moment is zero. The only contribution comes from electrons near the Fermi level and we can estimate the fraction of electrons excited into higher energy states as approximately

$$\frac{kT}{\zeta} \qquad \text{as in Section 8.3.}$$

Multiplying the paramagnetic susceptibility of Equation (8.5.4) by this factor, we obtain

$$\chi_P^{el} \approx \frac{N\mu_B^2}{\zeta},$$

which is independent of temperature (in this approximation). Pauli's exact result is

$$\chi_P^{el} = \frac{3N\mu_B^2}{2\zeta} \qquad\qquad [8.5.9]$$

for N electrons, where ζ represents the true Fermi energy. In cases where the effective mass m^* is high (for example, nickel), the Fermi energy is low and there should be a correspondingly large electron-spin paramagnetism.

In addition to the spin paramagnetism, there is an orbital diamagnetism of free electrons, as was first worked out by Landau. This amounts to exactly one-third of the Pauli result above if the electrons are free, so the *net* susceptibility should be

$$\chi^{el} = \frac{N\mu_B^2}{\zeta}. \qquad\qquad [8.5.10]$$

However, the diamagnetic term is sensitive to the field in which the electrons move and the result of detailed calculations is a negative susceptibility which depends on the form of the E-κ relation in the conduction band. It turns out that the diamagnetic term, unlike the paramagnetic spin susceptibility, is inversely proportional to the effective mass, in simple cases. Thus a metal like bismuth, in which the electrons have abnormally low effective mass, exhibits very strong diamagnetism.

When the theory is applied to the simplest group of metals, the alkalis, it is found that the largest terms are the Pauli electron-spin paramagnetism, which has to be corrected for collective electron motion, and the diamagnetism of the closed-shell ions. It is possible to account in a general way for the trend of the observed total susceptibilities, which are positive and decrease steadily from lithium through caesium. However, in more complicated metals like those of the transition series, the magnetic behavior is far from systematic. Whereas the alkali susceptibilities vary little with temperature, the data for transition metals show great variations both in magnitude and in the type of behavior. In addition there are, of course, the extremely powerful effects associated with ferromagnetism. It is now clear that various types of cooperative phenomenon, including ferromagnetism, arise from the interactions between ions and electrons in metallic solids. The thermodynamic properties of cooperative effects such as phase transitions have been studied for many years but a proper statistical treatment is still rendered difficult by lack of knowledge about the details of interaction. For this reason the phenomenological approach is preferable and will be illustrated in the next section by Weiss' theory of ferromagnetism.

8.6   The Problem of Ferromagnetism

The remarkable behavior of ferromagnetic substances is of immense practical and theoretical significance. Early attempts by Weber and others to describe the process of magnetization in iron concentrated on the idea that the metal contains elementary magnets which retain magnetism permanently, except at very high temperatures. In modern terms the metal possesses a *domain* structure* such that the net effect of many domains may be zero magnetic moment, although the specimen can still be magnetized by application of a suitable external field. The specimen may also be induced with a quasipermanent magnetic moment if the metal is suitably treated. The essential problem remains the existence of spontaneous magnetization within a domain, the size of which may be considerable. This cannot be explained simply in terms of paramagnetism, because the intensity of magnetization in a ferromagnetic material is often thousands of times stronger than the intensity in any paramagnetic material.

The property of ferromagnetism is exhibited by at least four chemical elements, namely, iron cobalt and nickel, which form a group within the first transition series, and gadolinium, which belongs to the rare earths. In addition ferromagnetic alloys can be made out of transition metals like copper and manganese. It appears that the essential characteristic of ferromagnetic elements is the possession of paramagnetic ions, although this condition is clearly not sufficient to produce ferromagnetic behavior. At the same time it should be remembered that certain well-defined *compounds*, notably oxides of iron and other metals, show strongly magnetic properties. The latter group is now distinguished from the metals and described as *ferrimagnetic*, the essential difference being the lack of electrical conductivity in the oxides and other compounds.

(a)   The Weiss theory

Although it may be regarded as established that ferromagnetic behavior in metals depends on the presence of paramagnetic ions, it does not follow that these ions are the magnetic elements which combine cooperatively to give spontaneous magnetization. Experiments which have already been described in Section 6.5 yield some information about the magnetic "carriers" in the metal. For example, the gyromagnetic effect discovered by Einstein and de Haas provides a way of measuring the quantity

$$g = \frac{2m}{e}\frac{M}{G}, \qquad\qquad \text{[Equation (6.5.5)]}$$

where e/m is the specific charge of the electron;

$\quad$ M is the magnetic moment induced in the specimen;

$\quad$ G is the measured angular momentum of recoil.

Early results showed that the value of g is close to 2 for all ferromagnetic materials, and this was confirmed by Barnett's work on the inverse gyromagnetic effect, in which rotation of the specimen produces a magnetic moment. More recently it has been found necessary to distinguish between values of g measured mechanically and those obtained by resonance methods. However, the main conclusion stands: the gyromagnetic ratios agree with the idea that electron spins are the effective magnetic carriers. This is consistent with the

* See C. Kittel, Rev. Mod. Phys., **21**, 541 (1949).

"quenching" of orbital momentum which was detected in the paramagnetic ion moments of the transition metals (Section 8.5) and was ascribed to the effects of external interactions.

Adopting the hypothesis that electron spins are in some way responsible for ferromagnetic behavior, we can outline a theory which is similar to that of Weiss. It is based on the thesis that inside an assembly of interacting elementary magnets there is a strong internal field, in addition to any external field which may be present. The origin of this internal field is not immediately explored but it is assumed that its magnitude is proportional to the total magnetic moment (M) of the specimen, that is, we write

$$B = B_e + B_i,$$

where B_e is the external field;
$\qquad B_i$ is the internal field; and
$\qquad B_i = \lambda M$ (λ is a constant).

We now assume that the response of the magnetic carriers to the total field is the same as that of the assembly of atoms or ions in the $^2S_{1/2}$ state, treated in Section 8.5. According to Equation (8.5.3)

$$M = N\mu_B \tanh\left(\frac{\mu_B B}{kT}\right)$$

$$= M_0 \tanh\left(\frac{\mu_B B}{kT}\right),$$

where $M_0 = N\mu_B$, the saturation moment for N carriers, each of moment μ_B.

We have two relations linking M and B and they may be written

$$\frac{M}{M_0} = \tanh X, \qquad \text{where} \quad X = \frac{\mu_B B}{kT}$$

and

$$\frac{M}{M_0} = \frac{B - B_e}{\lambda M_0}$$

$$= \frac{kTX}{\lambda \mu_B M_0} - \frac{B_e}{\lambda M_0}.$$

Solutions of this pair of equations are found graphically by plotting M/M_0 twice against the parameter X, so that intersections of the two lines are obtained. The first equation is the characteristic curve of Figure 8.11, with a slope of unity at the origin and a saturation value $M/M_0 \to 1$ as $X \to \infty$. The second equation is represented by a straight line of gradient $\dfrac{kT}{\lambda \mu_B M_0}$ with an intercept B_e on the B axis, otherwise expressed as an intercept $\dfrac{\mu_B B_e}{kT}$ on the X axis. These lines are shown on Figure 8.14 for a finite positive value of B_e and for positive λ. It may be seen from the diagram that there is always a solution of the equations, with a positive value of M, provided that $B_e > 0$. This is true at all temperatures. An applied field B_e produces a net parallel moment and the material is paramagnetic.

However, it is also apparent from Figure 8.14 that even if B_e is zero it is possible to find a nonzero solution for M, provided that the straight line has a smaller gradient than the gradient of the curve taken at the origin, that is, provided that

$$\frac{kT}{\lambda \mu_B M_0} < 1.$$

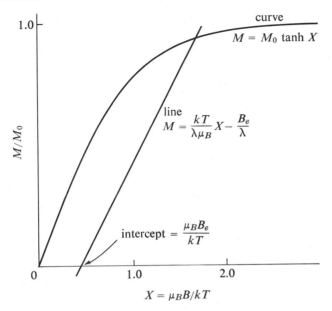

1.0

M/M_0

curve
$M = M_0 \tanh X$

line
$M = \dfrac{kT}{\lambda\mu_B} X - \dfrac{B_e}{\lambda}$

intercept $= \dfrac{\mu_B B_e}{kT}$

0   1.0   2.0

$X = \mu_B B/kT$

FIGURE 8.14 *In the Weiss treatment of ferromagnetism, the magnetic moment M is determined by the intersection of a magnetization curve (here shown for $J = \frac{1}{2}$) and a straight line with parameters fixed by the temperature, the internal field factor λ and the applied field B_e. Spontaneous magnetization can occur with $B_e = 0$ provided that the slope of the line is less than 1.*

This condition represents the occurrence of spontaneous magnetization in the specimen, which is due to the strong internal-field factor λ and can only persist at temperatures below a certain critical value. This critical temperature for the occurrence of ferromagnetism is known as the *Curie temperature* (T_c) and is given by the relation

$$kT_c = \lambda\mu_B M_0$$

or

$$T_c = \frac{N\lambda\mu_B^2}{k},$$

[8.6.1]

where N is the effective number of magnetic carriers present.

The Weiss theory is therefore initially successful in outlining a mechanism whereby ferromagnetism can exist below the Curie point, although no account has been given of the important factor λ. Estimates of N and λ are obtainable by combining the observed values of the Curie temperature with estimates of M_0 taken from the magnetic saturation moment at low temperatures. In iron it is found that $T_c = 1040°K$ and the intensity of magnetization at saturation is 220 A m²/kg at low temperatures. From the latter figure we can estimate the magnetic moment per atom directly since iron contains $\dfrac{6.0 \times 10^{26}}{55}$ atoms per kg,

$$\text{Moment per atom: } \mu = 2.02 \times 10^{-23} \text{ Am}^2$$

$$= 2.2 \, \mu_B.$$

Thus if the magnetic carriers are electron spins, as we have supposed, there are 2.2 spins effective per atom of the metal, although we have no evidence as yet concerning their location. It is noteworthy that the other ferromagnetic elements also possess fractional

Bohr-magneton numbers (1.7 for Co, 0.6 for Ni) as derived from the saturation intensities of magnetization.

The magnitude of the internal field B_i in a ferromagnetic material may be estimated from the Curie temperature, since, according to Equation (8.6.1),

$$kT_c = \lambda \mu_B (N\mu_B) = \lambda \mu_B M_0.$$

Thus the internal field at low temperatures is

$$B_i = M_0 \lambda = \frac{kT_c}{\mu_B} = 1550 \text{ weber/m}^2 \text{ for iron.}$$

This field is much larger than any which can be produced in the laboratory and also much greater than the field produced by a single atomic moment (of the order of one Bohr magneton) at typical interatomic distances (of the order of a few Ångstroms) in solids. The result serves to emphasize the fact that ferromagnetism is a collective effect due to the cooperative action of many atoms.

This cooperative action is no longer adequate to align the atomic moments spontaneously when the temperature rises above the Curie point, but the assembly is still able to respond to applied fields. Provided that the field B_e is not too great, the straight line of Figure 8.14 intersects the curve in the region where the latter is nearly straight, that is, we can write

$$\frac{M}{M_0} = \tanh X = X \text{ approximately}$$

and

$$\frac{M}{M_0} = \frac{T}{T_c} X - \frac{B_e}{\lambda M_0}.$$

The paramagnetic susceptibility is therefore

$$\chi_P = \frac{\partial M}{\partial B_e} = \frac{T_c}{\lambda(T - T_c)} \qquad [8.6.2]$$

$$= \frac{N\mu_B^2}{k(T - T_c)}. \qquad [8.6.3]$$

Comparison with Equation (8.5.4) shows that the internal-field factor λ modifies the Curie law in such a way that the susceptibility is inversely proportional to the *excess* temperature above T_c. This result is known as the Curie-Weiss law.

The elements iron, cobalt, and nickel obey the Curie-Weiss law at temperatures above their respective Curie points, although there are small discrepancies between the T_c values found from the paramagnetic behavior above T_c and those derived from ferromagnetic behavior below T_c.

In the ferromagnetic region, the theory predicts spontaneous magnetization within limited domains of the metal and it is found from Figure 8.14 that the degree of magnetization is extremely high (M is close to M_0), except for temperatures near T_c. The exact relation between M and T when *no* external field is applied is

$$\frac{M}{M_0} = \tanh X = \tanh \left(\frac{T_c}{T} \frac{M}{M_0} \right). \qquad [8.6.4]$$

This transcendental equation has solutions which can be expressed in the form of a graph of M/M_0 against T/T_c, as shown in Figure 8.15. At low values of the absolute temperature

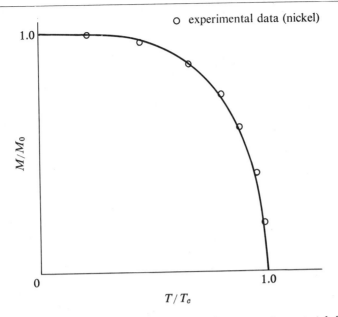

FIGURE 8.15 *The intensity of magnetization of a ferromagnetic material below its Curie temperature T_c follows a characteristic curve plotted as M/M_0 against T/T_c. Here the curve for $J = \frac{1}{2}$ may be compared with typical experimental data for nickel.*

T, the tanh function of Equation (8.6.4) is effectively unity, so that M is close to M_0. As the temperature approaches the Curie point, the ratio M/M_0 falls sharply toward zero. In this region we can make an approximation based on the first two terms of the infinite series expansion for tanh X, namely,

$$\tanh X = X - \frac{X^3}{3} \text{ approximately,}$$

whence

$$\frac{M}{M_0} = \frac{T_c}{T}\frac{M}{M_0} - \frac{T_c^3}{3T^3}\frac{M^3}{M_0^3}$$

$$\left(\frac{M}{M_0}\right)^2 = \frac{3T^3}{T_c^3}\frac{(T_c - T)}{T}$$

$$= \frac{3(T_c - T)}{T} \text{ approximately.} \qquad [8.6.5]$$

Thus the shape of the curve is approximately parabolic as it approaches the Curie point. Experimental data fit the theoretical curve fairly well over most of the ferromagnetic region, but there are significant discrepancies, especially at low temperatures.

Other ferromagnetic effects may be brought within the scope of the Weiss theory. For example, the specific heat of a ferromagnetic material rises markedly above the usual value as the temperature approaches the Curie point from below and there is a sharp drop to more normal values as the temperature passes through the critical region. The magnitude of the discontinuity in specific heat is of the order demanded by the Weiss theory. This effect is additional to the anomalously high specific heat which is characteristic of the metal nickel (Section 8.4.d).

(b) The origin of ferromagnetism

The phenomenological treatment outlined above is adequate to give a general account of ferromagnetism, but a more fundamental approach is needed to determine the *origin* of the large internal field in these materials. The magnetic carriers have not been identified, although it is evident that the assumptions made in the theory are largely justified, namely, we have effectively single electron spins which behave according to the classical Boltzmann statistics. If we adopt higher spin values, such as $S = 1$ and so forth, the agreement with experimental data in Figure 8.15 is lost. On the other hand, we cannot assume that the "free" conduction electrons of the metal are responsible for the interaction because these particles form a Fermi-Dirac assembly which is nearly degenerate (Section 8.3) and their magnetic behavior is described by the Pauli spin susceptibility [Equation (8.5.9)]. Moreover, the magnetic saturation intensity in iron shows that each atom contributes, on the average, 2.2 Bohr magnetons to the assembly. The exact electron configuration in this metal is difficult to fix by theoretical methods, but it is clear that the $4s$ conduction band can accommodate only two electrons per atom while the $3d$ subshell contains a maximum of six electrons (for iron in the ferrous state). We therefore have the double problem of explaining the occurrence of fractional Bohr-magneton numbers in the contribution of each atom and accounting for the extremely large interaction which tends to align the electron spins.

A particularly interesting case is gadolinium, which is a rare-earth element exhibiting ferromagnetic behavior below 289°K. The rare-earth ions are largely screened from each other, as explained in Section 8.5, but in a few cases the interaction seems to be sufficient to cause ferromagnetism in the low-temperature region. The saturation intensity of magnetization in gadolinium is 254 A m²/kg, equivalent to a magnetic moment per atom of

$$\mu = 7.1 \text{ Bohr magnetons.}$$

Now the number of $4f$ electrons in the triply charged gadolinium ion is 7; the ground state of the ion is denoted $^8S_{7/2}$ and the corresponding magnetic moment per ion is

$$7.94 \mu_B \text{ (calculated)} \qquad 8.0 \mu_B \text{ (observed).}$$

These results suggest that in gadolinium the ionic moments are the magnetic carriers which are responsible for ferromagnetic behavior.

The situation in the transition metals is much less clear, because the incomplete shells, for example the $3d$ subshell in the iron-cobalt-nickel group, are close in energy to the conduction band. Studies of x rays emitted by nickel indicate that the broad $4s$ conduction band overlaps the narrow $3d$ band, which, in this metal at least, contributes to conduction and produces a large electronic specific heat (Section 8.4). The actual distribution of electrons between the $3d$ and $4s$ bands has been measured by x-ray scattering experiments, with the following results for the numbers of $3d$ electrons:

Metal	Cr	Fe	Co	Ni	Cu	
No. 3d electrons	0.2	2.3	8.4	9.7	9.8	(±0.3).

These data are not conclusive, but they do suggest that there is a considerable change in structure between the Cr–Fe region and the Co–Cu region. The data are consistent with the supposition that there are effectively ten electrons in the $3d$ band of copper, which is diamagnetic and shows normal specific-heat behavior.

The metals cobalt and nickel both possess the close-packed cubic structure (Figure 4.17) in which the interaction between atoms is as strong as possible. In the ferromagnetic condition, the Bohr-magneton numbers per atom are 1.7 and 0.6, respectively. These figures suggest that the mean numbers of $3d$ electrons per atom are in fact close to 8.3 and 9.4, in agreement with the x-ray data. The magnetic moments are then due to the "holes" left in the $3d$ subshell, each "hole" contributing one Bohr magneton, and it is assumed that the $4s$ conduction electrons contribute little to the cooperative effect. This assumption is not necessarily justified, because in certain theories of ferromagnetism the conduction electrons play a vital role in the interaction.

The situation in chromium and iron is somewhat different, since these metals possess the body-centered structure, which is less compact than the close-packed (face-centered) structure. It has been argued that several electrons of the $3d$ subshell may form localized bonds between adjacent atoms, with the result that only about two electrons are free to interact cooperatively in iron and probably none in chromium. This is a possible explanation of the x-ray results and it accounts for the 2.2 Bohr magnetons per atom found in iron.

The foregoing data assume different degrees of significance in different theories of the internal field, which is required to be strong enough to align all the magnetic carriers at low temperatures. In 1928 Heisenberg and Frenkel independently proposed to explain this interaction on the basis of spin-exchange forces, such as those which are invoked to account for the covalent bonding in simple systems like the hydrogen molecule. In the normal covalent bond two electrons are engaged with spins opposed and the interaction ensures that this is a stable arrangement. On the other hand, when electron spins interact in the *same atom*, where there is a single center of force (the nucleus), the result is a parallel-spin arrangement, as illustrated by Hund's rule of maximum multiplicity (Section 7.11). According to Heisenberg, spin interactions between neighboring atoms in a lattice normally produce antiparallel spins, as in the hydrogen covalent bond, but certain special circumstances in the ferromagnetic metals cause a reversal of the pattern. On this basis Slater calculated the exchange interaction as a function of the interatomic distance and showed that the elements iron, cobalt, and nickel should be ferromagnetic whereas chromium and manganese should not. However, this theory did not explain the fractional Bohr-magneton numbers obtained from the saturation intensities of the ferromagnetic elements. Later theories have modified the mechanism of interaction considerably, notably by including the effects of the conduction electrons, but the basic idea of spin interaction remains.

In 1936 Néel pointed out that in nonferromagnetic metals the Heisenberg spin interaction should result in an ordered state in which adjacent carriers have their spins antiparallel, provided that the temperature is not too high. This condition is described as *antiferromagnetism* and is clearly one of zero total magnetic moment. However, the system possesses paramagnetic properties, with a susceptibility which rises with increasing temperature until a critical "Néel temperature" is reached. At this point the ordered state breaks down and at higher temperatures the material behaves like a normal paramagnetic substance, obeying Curie's law. Such behavior has been detected in the oxides of iron, manganese, and nickel. It is interesting to note, in view of the previous discussion of ferromagnetism, that chromium metal has been investigated by neutron-diffraction techniques, which are very useful in exploring the magnetic state of a solid, with results indicating that this element is antiferromagnetic. However, it is clear from the susceptibility data that extremely complicated conditions obtain in all the transition metals and that no simple theory is adequate to account for all the data.

FOR FURTHER READING

The solid state:

C. KITTEL, *An Introduction to Solid-State Physics* (J. Wiley & Sons, New York, 1956) 2nd ed.

Metals:

N. F. MOTT and H. JONES, *The Theory of the Properties of Metals and Alloys* (Dover Publications, New York, 1958).

Magnetism:

L. F. BATES, *Modern Magnetism* (Cambridge University Press, New York, 1961) 4th ed.

PROBLEMS FOR CHAPTER 8

DATA REQUIRED:

No. of molecules per kilomole: $N^* = 6.0 \times 10^{26}$
Boltzmann's constant: $k = 1.4 \times 10^{-23}$ J/°K
Planck's constant: $h = 6.6 \times 10^{-34}$ J sec
$\qquad\qquad\qquad\quad \hbar = 1.05 \times 10^{-34}$ J sec
Electronic charge: $e = 1.6 \times 10^{-19}$ C
Electronic rest-mass: $m = 9.1 \times 10^{-31}$ kg
Bohr magneton: $\mu_B = 9.3 \times 10^{-24}$ A m^2
Coulomb force constant: $\dfrac{1}{4\pi\varepsilon_0} = 9 \times 10^9$ mks

8.1. The specific heat of metallic silver (at.wt. 108, density 10.5×10^3 kg/m^3) at constant volume is found to be

Temperature:	6	8	10	12	14	16	°K
C_v	0.0089	0.024	0.048	0.083	0.134	0.202	kcal/kmole °K

Use Equation (8.3.11) to show that the electronic specific heat is negligible in this region (provided that the effective mass ratio m^*/m is close to 1). Test the data to see if Debye's T^3 law is obeyed and estimate the Debye temperature T_D for silver. What are the corresponding phonon energy and phonon frequency?

8.2. The specific heat of diamond varies with temperature as follows:

Temperature:	88	273	413	520	879	°K
Specific heat:	0.0025	0.104	0.222	0.303	0.441	kcal/kg °K

Devise a graphical method for testing whether these data fit the Einstein relation of Equation (8.1.1). Hence find the best value of the (optical) vibrational energy in the crystal.

8.3(a). Given that metallic sodium (at.wt. = 23) has a density of 0.97×10^3 kgm/^{3} and that each atom contributes one electron to the conduction band, find the Fermi energy for this element.

(b) Compare the Fermi energy with the plasmon energy given by Equation (8.4.6).

(c) Show that the ratio of plasmon energy to Fermi energy for a typical metal with atomic density 6×10^{28} atoms/m^3 is about 1.65.

8.4. Fast electrons scattered by thin copper foils show a characteristic energy loss of 20 eV, which is ascribed to single-plasmon excitation. Hence calculate the effective number of electrons contributed by each atom to the plasma. In what ways is this result discordant with other observations on metallic copper (at.wt. = 63.5: Density 8.9×10^3 kg/m³)?

8.5. Prove that the mean energy per particle in a Fermi-Dirac assembly at low temperature, possessing the energy distribution shown in Figure 8.5, is 0.6ζ, where ζ is the Fermi energy.

8.6. The soft x-ray lines of the K series emitted by metallic lithium were observed to have an effective width of 3.7 eV. Compare this result with the Fermi energy calculated from the lattice constant $a = 3.46$ Å for the body-centered cubic structure of this metal.

8.7. The nucleons (neutrons and protons) in a heavy nucleus may be regarded as a degenerate assembly of fermions. Given that the effective nuclear radius is

$$r = 1.4 \times 10^{-15} \sqrt[3]{A} \quad \text{m,}$$

where A is the atomic mass number, use the phase-space theorem to find the Fermi energy for a typical nucleus, the nucleon mass being 1.67×10^{-27} kg. Allow for the fact that about half of the particles are neutrons and half protons; also these two types of particle obey the Pauli Exclusion principle separately.

8.8. The observed specific heat of metallic nickel at low temperatures is as follows:

Temperature:	2	4	6	8	10	12	14	16	°K
C_v	0.004	0.008	0.013	0.018	0.024	0.030	0.038	0.048	kcal/kmole °K

Plot C_v/T against T^2 to separate the electronic specific heat from the lattice contribution, which is supposed to obey the Debye T^3 law. Hence estimate the Debye temperature T_D. Also find the Fermi temperature T_F on the assumption that each atom contributes 0.6 electron to the conduction band (as indicated by the ferromagnetic properties of the metal). Given that the atomic weight is 59 and the density is 8.9×10^3 kg/m³, calculate the effective-mass ratio m^*/m for the conduction electrons.

8.9. The effective mass of carriers in a semiconductor may be found by measurements of the "cyclotron resonance" frequency. An applied magnetic field B causes free particles to describe circular orbits with a frequency given by Equation (3.3.7). A certain specimen of germanium exhibited strong radio-frequency absorption at 23,000 Mc/sec when the applied field was 0.18 weber/m². Hence find the effective mass m^* and the ratio m^*/m. How could the method be adapted to determine the *sign* of the charge for a particular group of carriers?

8.10 (a) Solid germanium has the "diamond" lattice structure in which each atom is bound covalently to four neighboring atoms. Show that this is equivalent to a face-centered type of cubic structure with eight atoms per unit cell (in an infinite lattice).

(b) Given that germanium has at.wt. = 73, density 5.4×10^3 kg/m³ calculate the lattice constant (a) for the element, also the interatomic distance.

8.11 (a) Assuming that electron-lattice interactions are negligible in a pure semiconductor, find the radius of the lowest Bohr orbit for a single electron circulating round a donor atom in germanium, the dielectric constant ($\varepsilon/\varepsilon_0$) being 16. Compare this radius with the interatomic distance found in Problem 8.10.

(b) Also compare the binding energy of this electron to the donor atom with the observed energy difference between a typical donor level and the conduction band, which is 0.02 eV.

(c) Estimate the probability of thermal excitation for a donor electron to the conduction band at normal temperature ($T = 300°$K) and compare this probability with that of thermal excitation from the valence band of germanium, which is 0.7 eV below the conduction band.

8.12 (a) Use the classical Larmor theorem (Section 4.2) to derive the diamagnetic susceptibility of an assembly containing N electron orbits, the mean square radius being $\overline{r^2}$, and show that the result is consistent with Equation (8.5.2).

(b) The observed susceptibility of helium gas is

$$\chi_D = -1.9 \times 10^{-2} \text{ A m}^4/\text{weber kmole}$$

Estimate the root mean square radius of the $1s$ electron orbits in the helium atom.

8.13. The observed diamagnetic susceptibility of sodium *ions* is

$$\chi_D = -6.1 \times 10^{-2} \text{ A m}^4/\text{weber kmole.}$$

Calculate the Pauli and Landau spin-susceptibility terms for electrons in metallic sodium (at.wt. = 23, density $0.97 \times 10^3 \text{ kg/m}^3$) and contrast the *summed* susceptibility (ions plus electrons) with the observed value of $+16 \times 10^{-2}$ A m^4/weber kmole.

8.14 (a) Show, with the aid of Hund's rules, that the triply charged ion Cr^{+++} should have the ground state $^4F_{3/2}$.

(b) Assuming that the orbital component of the angular momentum is effectively quenched, find the precise form of the M–B relation for an assembly of Cr^{+++} ions. Compare the theoretical curve with experimental data obtained for potassium chrome alum:[*]

At $T = 1.30°$K:

Field B	0.65	0.97	1.56	2.30	weber/m²
Effective μ	1.4	2.0	2.5	2.8	μ_B

At $T = 2.0°$K:

B	0.3	0.7	1.2	1.8	2.4	3.6	4.8	weber/m²
μ_{eff}	0.4	1.0	1.7	2.15	2.5	2.8	2.9	μ_B

8.15. Determine the proper ground states for the following transition-metal ions (z is the number of $3d$ electrons):

Ion:	Ti^{+++}	V^{+++}	V^{++}	Cr^{++}	Mn^{++}	Fe^{++}	Co^{++}	Ni^{++}	Cu^{++}
z	1	2	3	4	5	6	7	8	9

Check the results against the theoretical lines of Figure 8.13, which indicate the effective magnetic moment per ion.

8.16. Calculate the saturation intensity of magnetization (per kg) and the Curie temperature for metallic cobalt (at.wt. = 59), given that the Bohr-magneton number is 1.7 per atom and the internal field (λM_0) is 940 weber/m².

8.17. The contribution of the internal field B_i to the internal energy of a specimen of moment M can be written

$$E_{\text{ferr}} = -\tfrac{1}{2}B_i M = -\tfrac{1}{2}\lambda M^2.$$

Show that the specific heat per kilomole due to this energy rises from zero at low temperatures to a peak value of $1.5R(\mu/\mu_B)$ at the Curie temperature, where (μ/μ_B) is the effective Bohr-magneton number per atom. The observed specific-heat discontinuity in nickel at the Curie point is about 2.0 kcal/kmole °K. Is this consistent with the observed saturation intensity of magnetization, which is 57.5 A m²/kg at low temperatures?

[*] W. E. Henry, Rev. Mod. Phys., **25**, 163 (1953).

❧❧❧❧❧❧❧❧❧❧❧❧❧❧❧❧❧❧❧❧❧❧❧❧❧❧❧❧❧❧❧❧❧❧

CHAPTER IX

NUCLEAR PHYSICS

The success of the nuclear model of the atom, proposed in 1911 by Rutherford and developed by Niels Bohr, served to emphasize the great difference in energy scale between atomic processes involving only the extranuclear electrons and nuclear processes proper. During the first 20 years of this century, the chief source of information about nuclei was natural radioactivity, as exhibited by the heaviest chemical elements. In 1919 Rutherford carried out some simple experiments to see if the positively charged nucleus of a light element could be disrupted by bombardment with the alpha particles emitted from a radioactive preparation. This would require the alpha particles to penetrate the Coulomb field of repulsion exerted by the nuclear charge and it was known from the scattering experiments of Geiger and Marsden that such penetration is unlikely. Nevertheless Rutherford was able to show that the element nitrogen, under alpha-particle bombardment, occasionally emitted long-range protons, probably due to the reaction

$$_7N^{14} + {_2}He^4 \rightarrow {_1}H^1 + {_8}O^{17}.$$

This hypothesis was verified by Blackett who passed many thousands of alpha particles through nitrogen in a cloud chamber and showed that certain rare forked tracks could be due only to the above reaction. In due course similar (α, p) reactions were discovered in other light elements.

Many basic discoveries were made with radioactive sources, but it was soon realized that particle accelerators would provide a much higher yield of nuclear reactions under more controllable conditions. The work of Cockcroft and Walton with an electrostatic generator reaching less than 1 MV showed the possibilities of producing many types of reaction in light nuclei. Lawrence and Livingston used the principle of repeated acceleration to attain high particle energies in the cyclotron and much effort has been devoted to extend the highest available energy, first into the 300 MeV region and now up to 30 GeV (30,000,000,000 eV). The biggest machines are used almost exclusively for producing unstable particles, which are described in the next chapter. However, a great wealth of nuclear data has been obtained with accelerators yielding particles with energies of 1 MeV or less. Important advances have been made by the development of more accurate methods for detecting particles emitted in nuclear reactions, also by using high-speed analyzers to extract information from the data obtained.

The theory of nuclear structure has not developed into a single coherent system because no complete account of the basic interactions between nucleons* has yet been given.

---

* The word *nucleon* is used generically to describe either the neutron or the proton in their roles as nuclear particles.

Despite this difficulty, several nuclear models have been evolved to account for the properties of many-nucleon systems. The strong-interaction hypothesis of Niels Bohr (1936) led to the compound-nucleus theory of nuclear reactions and to the "liquid-drop" nuclear model, which is successful in accounting for the phenomenon of fission. However, the detailed properties of individual nuclei, for example their spins and moments, were not explained until the "individual-particle" hypothesis was revived in the *shell model* of Mayer and Jensen (1948). This model has been modified to take certain collective properties of nuclei into account and present nuclear theories are concerned largely with the relations between different models of nuclear structure.

9.1 Particle Accelerators

Whereas the extranuclear electrons in an atom can be rearranged or removed by supplying energies of the order of a few electron volts, several million electron volts are usually needed to remove a nucleon from a nucleus. Such energies are indeed available in the rays emitted by natural radioactive materials, but the development of nuclear physics has come to depend largely on experiments performed with accelerators. These machines produce high-intensity beams of electrons or positive ions which are closely controlled in energy and direction. In the realm of "low-energy" nuclear physics (below about 100 MeV) more and more accurate measurements have become feasible as a result of repeated technical improvements in the design of particle accelerators and detectors.

(a) Electrostatic generators

The simplest type of machine for accelerating particles such as protons (hydrogen nuclei) and deuterons (deuterium nuclei) to high speeds is an electrostatic generator in which a terminal is maintained at a constant high potential relative to ground. The positively charged particles are produced by a suitable ion source, located inside the terminal, and are directed along an evacuated tube toward a target at ground potential, where the resulting nuclear reactions are conveniently studied. The early experiments of Cockcroft and Walton (1932) were performed with a bank of capacitors and rectifiers which converted ac input at low voltage into a dc voltage of 0.7 MV at the terminal. This type of machine suffers from a residual ac ripple voltage superimposed on the accelerating potential difference, but it pioneered the investigation of many nuclear reactions in the energy region up to 1 MeV.

The most common electrostatic generator is the Van de Graaff machine (Figure 9.1) in which positive charge is carried from a spray supply to the terminal by means of a motor-driven endless belt. The charge is removed from the belt by a set of needles inside the terminal housing and travels to the surface of the terminal. The belt also serves to drive electrical supplies for the positive-ion source situated at the top of the accelerating tube. Various types of source have been used, but most of them depend on the extraction of positive ions from a plasma maintained in low-pressure gas by radio-frequency excitation or other means. The extracting electrodes are kept at negative potential relative to the top terminal and they serve to focus the ion beam along the accelerating tube. This tube is fitted with numerous electrodes maintained at potentials intermediate between the terminal and ground by current flowing through a chain of resistors, which act as a multiple potential divider. The beam emerging from the tube is usually deflected magnetically on to the target; this magnetic control ensures that only ions of the correct specific charge produce reactions.

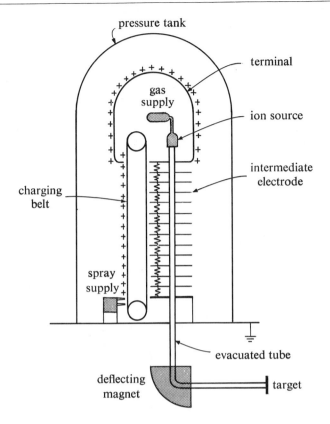

FIGURE 9.1 *Outline diagram of a Van de Graaff generator designed to accelerate positive ions from the source down the evacuated tube and to direct them, after magnetic deflection, to the target.*

The great merit of the Van de Graaff generator lies in its extremely steady potential when it is suitably stabilized. The whole high-potential assembly is enclosed in a tank filled with high-pressure gas (for example, nitrogen and freon) to prevent leakage of charge from the terminal. It is possible to maintain potential differences of the order of 5 or 6 MV between terminal and ground. Recently designs have been produced for generators reaching 10 MV or more.

Development work by the High Voltage Engineering Corporation and others has led to the production of the "tandem" machine which is effectively two accelerators in series (Figure 9.2). The main high-potential terminal is placed at the center of a long high-pressure tank and is maintained at about 5 MV relative to ground. The ion source is designed to emit negative ions, for example H^-, which consists of a proton with two electrons in the $1s$ shell. After magnetic analysis the negative ions are directed into a tube passing through the main terminal. First the ions are accelerated from ground to the high positive potential. Inside the terminal they are stripped of their electrons by passage through a metal foil or a canal containing a little water vapor or oxygen. The ions, now positively charged, are then accelerated a second time to ground potential at the far end of the tube. In this way the energy gained by a singly charged particle is twice that produced by a single acceleration in the same machine, for example, a 5 MV generator produces protons or deuterons of 10 MeV energy. The same principle can be used to accelerate heavy ions, for example those

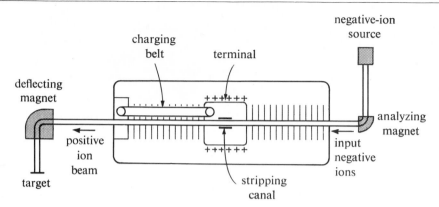

FIGURE 9.2 *The "tandem" Van de Graaff accelerator, in which negative ions are first accelerated to the high-voltage terminal, then stripped of their electrons and accelerated a second time to the target.*

of carbon or oxygen, the energy attained depending on the charge states of the ions before and after the stripping process.

(b) Linear accelerators*

In order to reach the highest possible energies by artificial means, it is necessary to accelerate particles repeatedly through a comparatively small potential difference, the phase of each small acceleration being automatically adjusted to give successful operation of the machine. Some early work on heavy-ion acceleration was done by Wideröe, Lawrence, and Sloan, who used linear accelerators of the drift-tube type (Figure 9.3). Groups of positive ions are accelerated into the first drift tube by negative pulses applied between this tube and the source. As each "burst" of ions emerges from the first tube, the alternation of potential difference causes a second acceleration across the gap into the next tube. This process is repeated successively by the application of alternating voltage to alternate tubes. As the speed of the particles increases, the drift tubes must have greater length to maintain the correct conditions for repeated acceleration. However, in the relativistic region the particle speed approaches c (the speed of light *in vacuo*) and the drift-tube length approaches a limit depending on the frequency of the alternating supply. In the early stages, beam focusing depends on the electric-field configuration in the gaps (Figure 3.5) but this action becomes less and less efficient as the energy rises. Accordingly the drift tubes are made with decreasing diameters in the high-energy end of the accelerator. However, the original type of machine was very wasteful of the radio-frequency power supplied to the drift tubes and the first successful proton "linac," the 32 MeV accelerator at Berkeley, California, had the tubes set within a tuned cavity fed by several rf oscillators. This type of machine has been developed chiefly for use as the injector in a proton synchrotron (Section 9.1.e).

A second type of linear accelerator employs an electromagnetic wave traveling down a corrugated waveguide, a system which is suitable for accelerating high-speed electrons. The waveguide is loaded in such a way that the wave velocity increases along the tube and the electrons "ride" on the wave in bunches, their kinetic energy being steadily increased. This kind of machine was developed into an important instrument of research at Stanford University, California, where electron energies up to 1 GeV per particle have been attained. The latest electron accelerator at Stanford is the most expensive research

---

* W. Panofsky, "The Linear Accelerator," *Scientific American*, **191**, No. 4, 40 (1954).

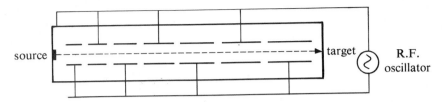

FIGURE 9.3 *The principle of the drift-tube type of linear accelerator. Certain groups of positive ions are repeatedly accelerated as they pass across the gaps between successive drift tubes.*

project yet undertaken in the United States and consists of a linear waveguide 10,000 ft long, made in 960 sections. In the initial stages, the machine will be powered by 240 klystron oscillators and the average beam power will reach 0.6 MW, corresponding to an average beam current of 30 μA at a maximum electron energy of 20 GeV. It is intended that the accelerator will eventually be powered by 960 klystrons and the maximum electron energy will be as high as 40 GeV.

The main drawbacks of linear accelerators as nuclear research installations are the extreme length of tube required when high energies are to be reached and the need for high accuracy in fabrication and alignment of the tube sections. On the other hand there are many advantages, especially in the provision of accurate beam focusing and of accessible target arrangements. Electron accelerators have proved to be versatile instruments in the study of nuclear structure by electron scattering and in producing intense beams of bremsstrahlung and neutrons.

(c) The cyclotron and synchrocyclotron

The principle of the cyclotron, proposed by Lawrence in 1930, depends on the fact that the period of revolution (t) of nonrelativistic particles in a uniform magnetic field (B) is independent of the speed. We have, from Equation (3.3.6),

$$t = \frac{2\pi m}{Be}$$

so that t depends only on the specific charge (e/m) of the particles and the field B. If the particles are accelerated by some means, the radius of their orbit increases and they describe a spiral path in a plane perpendicular to the field B, but they still pass a fixed point at equal intervals of time. In the cyclotron, acceleration is provided by a high-frequency alternating potential difference applied to two hollow semicircular "dees" (Figure 9.4). Positive ions from a central source are attracted into the dee which is negatively charged during one half-cycle of the electric field and they describe a semicircular path within this dee. If the frequency is correctly adjusted, the ions emerge from the dee after exactly one half-cycle and are attracted into the opposite dee, which is now negatively charged. This process is repeated and the particles gain energy at a rate determined by the magnitude of the rf voltage applied to the dees. The acceleration effects are confined to the gap region between the dees, where there is an electrostatic focusing action (Figure 3.5). When the particles approach the designed maximum energy of the machine, they are extracted from one of the dees by means of a negatively charged deflector plate which directs the beam on to an external target. Alternatively, *negative* ions (for example H⁻ ions) are accelerated from the source until they strike a "stripping" foil near the periphery; the stripped ions, now positively charged, are deflected outwards by the magnetic field on to a target.

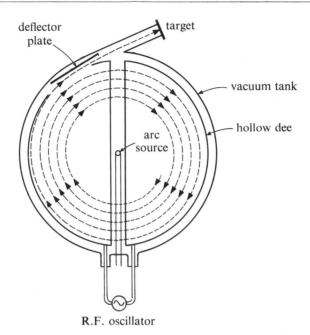

deflector
plate

target

vacuum tank

hollow dee

arc
source

R.F. oscillator

FIGURE 9.4 *The principle of operation of a cyclotron. Positive ions from the central source are repeatedly accelerated by the alternating electric field applied across the gap between the "dees" and they describe spiral paths in the perpendicular magnetic field. Finally the ions are directed by the deflector plate on to the target.*

The frequency of the rf supply is given by Equation (3.3.7):

$$\nu = \frac{eB}{2\pi m}$$

thus for protons with $e/m = 9.65 \times 10^7$ C/kg in a magnetic field $B = 1$ weber/m², the frequency is about 16 Mc/sec. The maximum kinetic energy produced (K_{max}) is fixed by the field strength and the radius (r) of the outermost orbit of particles within the dees. For nonrelativistic particles we have the relation

$$mv_{max} = Ber \qquad \text{[Equation 3.3.5]}$$

and

$$K_{max} = \tfrac{1}{2}mv_{max}^2 = \frac{B^2e^2r^2}{2m}. \qquad [9.1.1]$$

Thus for $B = 1$ weber/m² over a maximum radius of 0.5 m the maximum proton energy is about 12 MeV. If deuterons are used at the same radio frequency, the field strength must be doubled and, if the design allows this, the maximum energy is also doubled.

As the energy of the beam increases inside the cyclotron, the electrostatic focusing in the gap between the dees becomes less effective and it is conventional to provide extra magnetic focusing in the outer region. If the magnetic field strength B decreases near the maximum orbit radius (r) there is focusing action on particles which are away from the central plane. This action may be understood from Figure 9.5, where the outward curvature of the magnetic field lines indicates a region of field decreasing outward. Here there is always a component of magnetic force directing the particles back to the central plane.

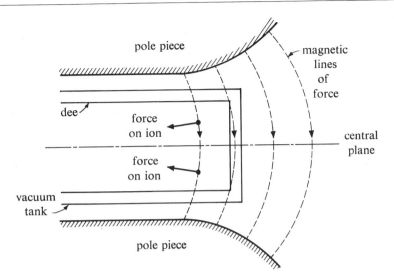

FIGURE 9.5 *The magnetic focusing action of the fringing field in a cyclotron. The curvature of the lines of force has the effect of directing any beam ions off the axis back towards the central plane.*

This valuable focusing action is, however, unsuitable for a cyclotron designed to reach high energies. The mass term (m) in Equation (3.3.7) is increased in the relativistic region, so that, for a fixed frequency v, the field B should be increased in the high-energy part of the acceleration cycle, that is, toward the outer edge of the vacuum chamber. This requirement is incompatible with the magnetic focusing action, a conflict which made a new departure essential for cyclotrons designed to exceed about 20 MeV in proton energy. In 1938 Thomas suggested that the magnetic field should be varied in azimuth, that is, around the perimeter of the orbit, as well as in the radial direction. This "AVF" (azimuthally varying field) concept has been realized in the "spiral-ridge cyclotron," where specially strong magnetic-field regions are produced by spiral sectors built into the pole faces (Figure 9.6). The magnetic field strength increases radially everywhere inside the vacuum chamber and is designed to satisfy the fixed-frequency condition into the relativistic region. At the same time the strong azimuthal field variations provide extra focusing action to overcome the defocusing effects of the radial field variation.

Historically the first breakthrough into the high-energy region was achieved in 1947 at Berkeley, where the existing 184 in. cyclotron was modified to allow the rf supply to be modulated in frequency. In a fixed magnetic field B, it should be possible to retain the conditions for acceleration of a given group of particles passing through the machine by decreasing the frequency as the effective mass is increased relativistically. The main problem lies in ensuring *phase stability*, which means the property of particles being successfully guided through the acceleration cycle in intense "bursts." Thus if one particle falls behind a given bunch of particles the field must act in such a way that the particle picks up extra energy, while the opposite occurs if the particle gets too far ahead. The theory of phase stability was worked out by McMillan and Veksler independently in 1945 and it has guided the designers of all accelerators in the high-energy region.

The frequency-modulated cyclotron, or "synchrocyclotron," has been successful in reaching proton energies close to 800 MeV with comparatively simple mechanism. For example, the Berkeley machine operates with a single dee and has been rebuilt to give

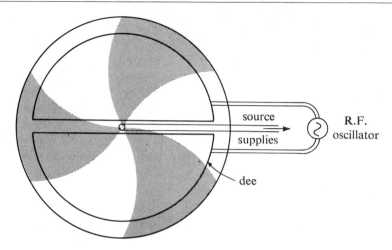

FIGURE 9.6 *Schematic diagram of an AVF cyclotron layout. The shaded areas represent the spiral shims on the magnetic pole pieces which provide azimuthal focusing action to overcome the defocusing action of the radial increase in magnetic field strength.*

protons of 720 MeV energy. This is ample for the production of intense beams of charged mesons, which are given off at the target and can be directed along exit channels to experimental equipment. A large investment in magnet iron is necessary because the whole of the acceleration process takes place in the same fixed magnetic field. The relation between maximum kinetic energy achieved (K) and the maximum orbit radius (r) is given by the relation (Problem 5.17a)

$$B^2 e^2 r^2 c^2 = K(K + 2E_0), \qquad\qquad [9.1.2]$$

where E_0 is the rest-mass energy per particle. Thus for protons of maximum kinetic energy 800 MeV in a fixed field $B = 1.5$ weber/m^2, with $E_0 = 938$ MeV, we find

$$r = 3 \text{ m approximately.}$$

It is evident that a synchrocyclotron designed to reach particle energies of several GeV would be prohibitively expensive and that considerable economies could be effected by using magnetic guidance only in the latter stages of acceleration. If the orbital radius could be kept nearly constant over a large part of the acceleration cycle, a ring-shaped magnet could be used and this would represent the most efficient deployment of a given amount of magnet material. These considerations led to the design of the first proton synchrotron, the 1 GeV machine at Birmingham, England, initiated by Oliphant and his collaborators in 1947.

(d) The betatron and beta-synchrotron

The betatron employs the principle of electromagnetic induction to accelerate electrons from low energies into the relativistic region. The particles are injected from an electron "gun" into an orbit of fixed radius within a ring-shaped vacuum chamber known as the "donut" (Figure 9.7). A magnetic field applied at right angles to the plane of the orbit alternates at fairly low frequency (for example, 60 c/sec) and over a certain range of each cycle the electrons are accelerated by the emf induced as a result of the changing magnetic flux through the orbit. The main condition for successful operation is the confinement of the orbital radius within strict limits despite the large difference between the initial and

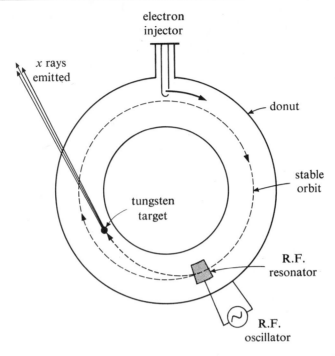

FIGURE 9.7 *Plan view of a beta-synchrotron, in which electrons are first accelerated by the betatron action of the alternating magnetic field, then supplied with energy by the high-frequency electric field applied to the resonator. The target is internal and a powerful beam of x rays emerges tangentially to the electron beam striking the target.*

final electron energies. This condition can be met by arranging for the magnetic field strength to vary radially in a suitable manner, as was demonstrated by Kerst in 1939.

The work done in one particle revolution by the induced emf acting on an electron (of charge $-e$) is

$$-e \frac{d\Phi}{dt},$$

where Φ is the net magnetic flux through the particle orbit. Over the same path the work done is the product of force and distance traveled, that is,

$$-e \frac{d\Phi}{dt} = 2\pi r \frac{d(mv)}{dt},$$

where r is the orbital radius and mv is the particle momentum. Also, if B is the magnetic field strength at the orbit, we have the relation

$$mv = Ber. \qquad \text{[from Equation (5.6.6)]}$$

If, therefore, we impose the condition that the radius be constant we obtain

$$-d\Phi = 2\pi r^2 \, dB. \qquad [9.1.3]$$

This "betatron condition" can be satisfied by making the field strength B vary *inversely* as the radius r, that is, we may write

$$B = \frac{B_0 r_0}{r}, \qquad [9.1.4]$$

where B_0 is the field strength at some particular radius r_0. Then the total flux through any orbit of radius r is

$$\Phi = \int_0^r B \, 2\pi r \, dr$$

$$= \int_0^r \frac{B_0 r_0}{r} 2\pi r \, dr$$

or

$$d\Phi = 2\pi B_0 r_0 \, dr.$$

Also, from Equation (9.1.4),

$$-dB = \frac{B_0 r_0}{r^2} \, dr$$

so that

$$-d\Phi = 2\pi r^2 \, dB.$$

A more general treatment of the problem shows that, with radial field variations of the form

$$B \propto r^{-n} \qquad \text{(where } n \text{ lies between 0 and 1),}$$

the electron beam executes oscillations in both the radial direction and the direction perpendicular to the orbit. These oscillations about the mean orbital radius are important in synchrotrons as well as betatrons because their amplitude determines the minimum size of the vacuum chamber. The machines have to be designed in such a way that oscillations are of small amplitude throughout the acceleration cycle and this involves a proper choice of the index n.

The betatron principle applies to particles of any speed and it enables electrons to be brought rapidly from the injection energy to energies of several MeV. When the designed maximum energy is reached the orbit is artificially collapsed, usually by arranging for part of the magnetic pole assembly to reach saturation. The electrons then spiral inwards to strike a target, which commonly consists of a tungsten rod. At the end of each acceleration cycle the target emits an intense burst of x rays, produced by the bremsstrahlung process (Section 4.8).

Since the electrons in a betatron reach speeds close to c (the speed of light *in vacuo*) early in the acceleration cycle, they circulate at nearly constant intervals of time during the major part of the cycle. It is then a comparatively simple matter to supply extra energy to the beam by applying an electric field of fixed frequency, as is done in the "beta-synchrotron." The beam passes repeatedly through a tuned cavity forming part of the donut (see Figure 9.7) and rf power is switched on in this cavity at a suitable moment in the duty cycle. Many electrons enter the cavity when it is at positive potential relative to the grounded internal surface of the donut and these receive extra energy, although their increase in *speed* is negligible. The process is repeated for all electron groups possessing phase stability and the final energy greatly exceeds the betatron limit, as was first shown by Goward and Fry in 1947. The beta-synchrotron is an economical arrangement for reaching high electron energies but it is limited both in the maximum beam current attainable and in energy stability.

One notable feature of electron accelerators of the cyclic type is the emission of electromagnetic radiation from the beam itself. Since the particles are continually accelerated toward the center of the orbit, they radiate according to classical laws [Equation (4.1.11)] and an intense *synchrotron radiation* is seen. The energy losses from this effect are not serious until the electron energy approaches the GeV region, but they represent a considerable fraction of the power supplied to the beam in the 6 GeV electron synchrotron at

Cambridge, Massachusetts. For this reason the linear accelerator is favored for the production of electrons with energies exceeding 10 GeV. Synchrotron radiation is negligible in all proton accelerators yet built or contemplated.

(e) *The proton synchrotron*

The synchrotron principle was first applied to an electron accelerator of the betatron type in 1947, but already designs had been produced for proton synchrotrons exceeding 1 GeV in particle energy. The difficulties confronting the designers of such a machine are formidable. The protons are injected at comparatively low energy into an orbit of fixed radius, where they must be confined throughout the duty cycle. The frequency of the electrical oscillators which accelerate the particles has to be linked at every step to the magnetic field guiding the beam in its fixed orbit and the proton synchrotron (unlike the beta-synchrotron) requires a very wide range of radio frequencies. During the duty cycle each particle travels a distance exceeding 10^8 m, so a very low pressure has to be maintained in the ring-shaped vacuum chamber. In the first proton synchrotrons, those at Birmingham (1 GeV), Brookhaven (3 GeV), and Berkeley (6 GeV), the magnet design allowed considerable oscillations of the beam about its mean radius, so the vacuum chamber had to be of large cross section, and this made a large magnet assembly necessary. In the largest machine of this type, the 10 GeV "Synchro-Phasotron" at Dubna near Moscow, the magnet weighs about 36,000 tons.

Some details of the "Bevatron" at Berkeley may suffice to indicate the magnitude of the design and construction problems encountered:

Orbit radius:	15.2 m	
Injection energy:	9.8 MeV (proton linac)	
Final energy:	6.2 GeV	
Initial magnetic field:	0.03 weber/m²	Radio frequency: 0.36 Mc/sec
Final magnetic field:	1.6 weber/m²	Radio frequency: 2.5 Mc/sec
Vacuum chamber cross section:	0.3 m (vertical) × 1.2 m (radial)	
Magnet weight:	approx. 10,000 tons	
Gain in energy per rev:	1500 eV	
Total acceleration time:	2.0 sec	
Repetition rate:	10 cycles/min.	

An outline of a typical synchrotron is shown in Figure 9.8.

The main problem in designing a high-energy accelerator is the confinement of the beam within a narrow compass. In the original synchrotrons the magnet was intended to focus the beam in both radial and vertical directions simultaneously. However, if the field is modified in such a way that alternate magnet sections focus the beam in the radial and vertical directions *separately*, the net result is a much stronger focusing action than is possible with one type of magnet section. This "strong-focusing principle," discovered by Christofilos and independently by Courant, Livingston, and Snyder in 1952, was employed in the construction of two 30 GeV machines, one at Geneva and the other at Brookhaven (Plate I). These machines have very large orbital radii (about 100 m) but the vacuum chamber is very narrow in each—about 8 × 15 cm in the Geneva synchrotron. This feature results in a large saving in magnetic material, which amounts to about 4000 tons as against nine times this figure in the Dubna machine, but it also necessitates extreme accuracy in the fabrication and alignment of the magnet sections. The "alternating-gradient" fields needed for strong focusing are shown schematically in Figure 9.9. Each

PLATE I. *The Alternating-Gradient Synchrotron (AGS) at Brookhaven National Laboratory, New York. Top: an aerial view of the buildings, with the 840 ft diameter circular tunnel showing as a mound where earth-fill has been added. The tunnel houses the ring-shaped vacuum chamber in which protons are accelerated to a kinetic energy of 33 GeV per particle. Below: some of the magnet sections inside the tunnel, with human figures to show the scale. Strong focusing of the proton beam is achieved by making the transverse magnetic field gradient change direction in successive sections (see Fig. 9.9).*
(From Ford, The World of Elementary Particles. New York: Blaisdell, 1963, p. 14.)

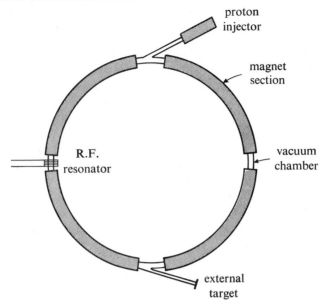

proton
injector

magnet
section

R.F.
resonator

vacuum
chamber

external
target

FIGURE 9.8 *Outline diagram of the layout of a proton synchrotron. Protons are injected into a stable orbit in the ring-shaped vacuum chamber and energy is supplied by varying both the magnetic field strength and the frequency of the rf field applied to the resonator.*

magnet section has the effect of focusing the beam in one plane and defocusing it in the transverse plane, but the net effect is still similar to that of a converging lens system (consisting of separated positive and negative lenses) in optics. This principle has been applied with great success to three high-energy accelerators, namely, the Geneva and Brookhaven proton synchrotrons and the Cambridge electron synchrotron.

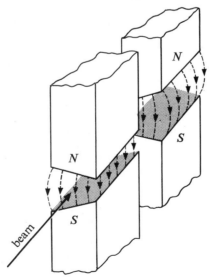

beam

FIGURE 9.9 *The principle of the "strong-focusing" or alternating-gradient magnetic field employed in high-energy accelerators. Alternate magnet sections are arranged to focus the beam separately in the horizontal and vertical directions.*

(f) The energy available for reactions

At very high energies the collision of protons with other nucleons becomes comparatively inefficient for producing new types of reaction because the energy available is much less than the bombarding energy as measured in the laboratory frame of reference. In any nuclear reaction the product particles, observed in the laboratory frame, recoil with considerable kinetic energy, as is required by the conservation of linear momentum. Thus the energy available for reaction is always less than the bombarding energy and if the incident particle is much more massive than the target particle very little "free energy" is present. In high-energy nucleon-nucleon collisions the incident particle has a very high effective mass compared with the target particle, which is at rest in the laboratory frame, so a large fraction of the bombarding energy is not available for reactions. The "free energy" is best calculated as the kinetic energy of both particles in the center-of-mass system of coordinates, in which the total momentum is always zero.

Let a particle A of total energy E (including its rest-mass energy m_0c^2) collide with a second particle B, of identical rest-mass energy m_0c^2, which is stationary in the laboratory frame. The momentum of particle A in the laboratory frame can be calculated from the relativistic Equation (5.6.5)

$$p^2 = \frac{E^2}{c^2} - m_0^2c^2.$$

That is, if E and p are the total energy and momentum of A in the laboratory frame, there exists a constant quantity

$$m_0^2c^2 = \frac{E^2}{c^2} - p^2.$$

If we make a Lorentz transformation from the laboratory frame to the center-of-mass frame, the quantity m_0c^2 is invariant, so we can write for the same particle A

$$m_0^2c^2 = \frac{E'^2}{c^2} - p'^2,$$

where E' and p' are the energy and momentum in the center-of-mass frame. The same transformation may be applied to the total energy and momentum of $A + B$ as a whole. In the laboratory frame we have

Total energy: $E + m_0c^2$

Total momentum: p.

In the center-of-mass frame, the total momentum is always zero and the total energy is the sum of the kinetic energy or "free energy" (K_{cm}) and *twice* the rest-mass energy, that is,

$$K_{cm} + 2m_0c^2.$$

According to the invariance principle quoted above, we have the relation

$$\frac{(K_{cm} + 2m_0c^2)^2}{c^2} = \frac{(E + m_0c^2)^2}{c^2} - p^2$$

or

$$(K_{cm} + 2m_0c^2)^2 = (E + m_0c^2)^2 - (E^2 - m_0^2c^4)$$
$$= 2m_0c^2(m_0c^2 + E).$$

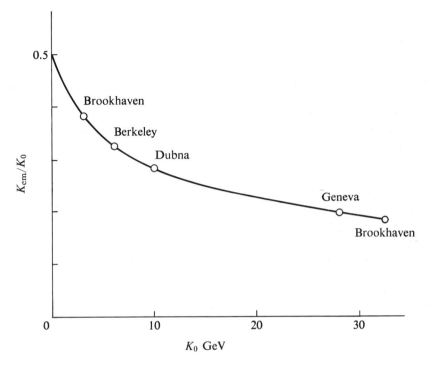

FIGURE 9.10   *The ratio of the "free-energy" (K_{cm}) to the bombarding energy (K_0) for nucleon-nucleon collisions, plotted against the bombarding energy in GeV. The points indicate the maximum bombarding energies of five proton synchrotrons now in operation.*

Finally, if we write the total energy of A in the laboratory frame as the sum of the kinetic energy (K_0) and the rest-mass energy

$$E = K_0 + m_0 c^2$$

the equation for K_{cm} becomes

$$K_{cm}^2 + 4K_{cm}m_0 c^2 - 2K_0 m_0 c^2 = 0. \qquad [9.1.5]$$

The solution of physical significance is

$$K_{cm} = 2m_0 c^2 \left[\sqrt{1 + \frac{K_0}{2m_0 c^2}} - 1 \right]. \qquad [9.1.6]$$

For nucleon-nucleon collisions we can substitute $m_0 c^2 = 0.938$ GeV and find the free energy K_{cm} at different bombarding energies K_0. A graph of K_{cm}/K_0 against K_0 (Figure 9.10) shows that the fraction of energy available decreases steadily from a value of 0.5 at low bombarding energies to less than 0.2 at the maximum energies presently reached by proton synchrotrons. It therefore appears that there would be immense advantage in avoiding this large wastage of the energy which has been concentrated in the proton beam. Proposals have been made for machines in which two high-energy beams meet in head-on collision, when all the energy acquired by both beams in the laboratory frame would be available for reactions. This would require beams of extraordinary intensity to produce an appreciable number of events for analysis.

9.2 The Detection of Charged Particles

When an accelerator delivers a charged-particle beam on to a suitable target, a great variety of nuclear reactions may take place and many of these involve the emission of further charged particles of different types. In such a situation the main task of the experimental nuclear physicist is to sort out the different groups of particles emerging from the target and to identify the reactions responsible. In this way he hopes to discover characteristic properties of the reactions and of the nuclei taking part in them. An indispensable part of any experimental arrangement is some form of detector responding to charged particles and yielding information about their number, direction and energy or momentum.

(a) Energy measurements

Many methods of detection have been employed, but they all depend on the ionization produced by a charged particle as it traverses the material of the detector. Often the particle expends all its energy inside the detector and the total ionization produced is simply proportional to the original energy, according to the relation

$$\text{Number of ion pairs produced} = \frac{E_0}{W},\qquad\qquad [9.2.1]$$

where E_0 is the kinetic energy expended by the particle in ionization, W is the mean energy required to produce an ion pair. Values of W for gases range from about 25 to 40 eV, that is, W is somewhat greater than the first ionization potential of the atoms (depicted in Figure 4.7). For a given gas, W varies slightly according to the type of particle detected.

If all the ions produced can be collected successfully, as in an ion chamber working in the saturation region (Figure 3.16), the ionization charge (the current integrated over the time of collection) is proportional to the particle energy E_0. Even when the particle energy is known, its identity may remain uncertain. In such a case, it may be possible to deflect the particles by a magnetic field before they reach the detector. The amount of deflection depends on the particle momentum [Equation (5.6.6)], which can be found if the charge per particle is known. Finally the energy and momentum may be combined to yield the rest mass of the particle [by Equation (5.6.5)].

An alternative method is often used to find the energy of particles such as protons or alpha particles, which are massive compared with the electrons of the atoms through which they travel in the detector. Massive particles pass almost undeviated through matter and their total *range* in a given medium depends on the medium and on their initial energy E_0. It is possible to construct, by experimental or theoretical means, calibration curves relating range to energy for different types of particle in different media. So long as the identity of a particle group is clear, simple range measurements suffice to give an estimate of the energy per particle. This method is extremely convenient but it is not so accurate as the ionization-charge or magnetic-deflection methods and it cannot be applied easily to electrons, because their tracks show frequent deflections from collisions with the atoms of the medium. Nevertheless, the maximum range of fast electrons in metal absorbers is often used to yield a rough estimate of their initial energy.

In addition to detectors recording the total ionization produced by a particle of energy E_0, devices measuring partial energy losses are frequently employed. If a small portion

(Δx) of the total range is spent in the detector, the corresponding energy loss (ΔE) can be found by ionization measurements, based on Equation (9.2.1), or, in suitable circumstances, it may be calculated from a "stopping-power" formula. For particles more massive than electrons, the energy loss per unit distance traversed in a material can be expressed as follows:

$$- \frac{dE}{dx} = \frac{4\pi nZ^2 e^4}{(4\pi\varepsilon_0)^2 mv^2} \left\{ \ln \left[\frac{2mv^2}{\overline{W}(1 - v^2/c^2)} \right] - \frac{v^2}{c^2} \right\}, \qquad [9.2.2]$$

where n is the number of electrons per unit volume of material;

    Ze is the charge on the ionizing particle;

    m is the rest mass of the electron;

    v is the speed of the particle relative to the material;

and $\overline{W}$ is a mean effective ionization potential for electrons in the material.

Thus $(-dE/dx)$ decreases rapidly with increasing speed v up to a high-energy region where the speed ratio v/c approaches unity, and the logarithmic term becomes important. In the extreme relativistic region, where $v \to c$, the energy loss rises slowly from a minimum value which occurs in the energy region near the rest-mass energy of the ionizing particle.

The energy loss of fast electrons in matter is given by an expression rather more complicated than Equation (9.2.2), plus an additional term expressing energy losses by radiation through the bremsstrahlung process (Section 4.8). Radiative energy losses become more important than those due to ionization when the electron's kinetic energy exceeds a limit depending on the material—for example, this limit is about 7 MeV in lead. At energies above this limit, fast electrons are accompanied in matter by large numbers of photons, produced as bremsstrahlung, also secondary electrons (both positive and negative) produced by the Compton and pair-creation effects (Section 4.9).

It is evident that photons cannot be detected directly but only by their interaction with atoms or other particles. High-energy radiation in the form of x rays and gamma rays loses energy in matter by three processes, described in Section 4.9. The energy per photon may be found by several methods, including the measurement of absorption coefficients (which may, however, be ambiguous, as seen in Figure 4.24), the analysis of Compton-electron recoils [see Equation (4.9.7)], or of electron pairs (see Problem 4.21 and Figure 4.25). Figure 4.24 shows how the different processes vary in importance with energy, when the absorbing material is lead. In general, the pair-creation process is dominant at high energies, while the photoelectric effect is responsible for most of the photon absorption in the low-energy region.

The total ionization current produced by high-energy photons in a suitably designed chamber serves to measure the photon *flux*, which is the number of photons crossing unit area at right angles to the beam per second. Flux measurements of this type are closely related to the problem of measuring radiation dosage due to photons and electrons. In practice the unit of dosage, the *roentgen*, is defined in terms of the ionization produced in "standard air" (dry air at $273°K$ and 1 atm pressure). One roentgen creates 1 statcoulomb of ions of either sign in 1 cm^3 of this medium, which has a W value of 35 eV per ion pair. It follows that a dosage of one roentgen is equivalent to 1.17×10^{-8} J of energy being absorbed from the radiation by each cubic centimeter of air.

(b) Visible-track methods of detection

A great deal of information can be obtained about particles if their tracks are rendered visible. For example, their collisions with other particles can be studied, their momenta determined from the track curvature in a magnetic field and in some cases their initial

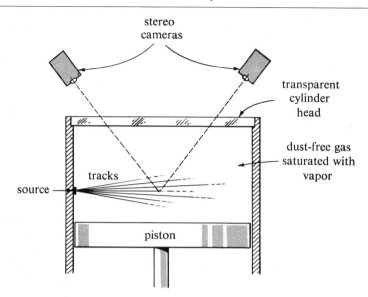

FIGURE 9.11 *The principle of operation of the Wilson expansion chamber illustrated. The gas is suddenly expanded by means of the piston and the region becomes supersaturated with vapor, which condenses preferentially on ions along the tracks of charged particles.*

energies can be found from their ranges in the detecting medium. For these reasons many fundamental discoveries have been made with the aid of cloud chambers, photographic emulsions, and bubble chambers.

The expansion type of cloud chamber was invented by C. T. R. Wilson, who did a great amount of research on the formation of liquid droplets in a supersaturated vapor. He showed that in dust-free air the formation of drops is inhibited by surface-tension effects and that these effects are counteracted by ionization in such a way that drops will form preferentially along the ionized path of a charged particle. The Wilson chamber (Figure 9.11) consists of a cylinder, containing air plus water or alcohol vapor, closed by a tight-fitting piston. The air is suddenly expanded by moving the piston and the vapor becomes supersaturated, owing to the sudden fall in temperature. The chamber is sensitive to the passage of charged particles for a short period of time, during which stereoscopic photographs are taken of the particle tracks. The cloud chamber is often placed in a uniform magnetic field so that the sign of the charge on each particle may be found (if the direction is known) and the momentum determined (if the magnitude of the charge is known).

In some experiments, especially investigations of cosmic rays, it is advantageous to expand the air in the cloud chamber only when a particle is passing through, an event which may be rare. If high-energy particles are being studied, Geiger counters may be placed on either side of the chamber, with a coincident circuit to register the passage of a particle through both counters. This circuit is used to trigger the expansion of the air in the chamber and the cameras which record the event. Operation of a counter-controlled chamber is possible because the ionized column of air in the chamber does not disperse very rapidly. On the other hand the chamber is limited in many applications because its sensitive time is too short (of the order of 10^{-1} sec). A continuously recording chamber can be devised on the "diffusion" principle. Here the base of the chamber is kept cold (usually at the temperature of solid carbon dioxide) and the top is at room temperature, so that a temperature gradient exists inside the space filled with vapor. At a certain level in the chamber the air is supersaturated and this layer acts as the recording agent for charged particles, the tracks of which may be photographed with cine cameras.

The cloud chamber is a cumbersome piece of apparatus to transport and maintain; in its place it is often possible to use photographic plates, the emulsions of which are sensitive to the passage of charged particles. The silver bromide grains traversed by a particle contain a "latent image," similar to that produced by exposure to light, and during development of the plate these grains are reduced to silver. After fixation of the plate, the tracks are revealed, under microscope examination, as rows of black silver grains in the transparent gelatin. The ranges of nuclear particles possessing a few MeV energy are quite short (from a few microns upwards) but they are readily measured with a microscope. The emulsion may be sensitive for a few months before being processed, or it may be used for a few minutes to record the particles emitted from the target of an accelerator. In either case the plate acts as a permanent record of events occurring during the exposure period. Moreover the plates are highly portable and are often used in cosmic-ray research, being carried to great altitudes by balloons or rockets. The chief drawbacks of the emulsion method are the fixed chemical composition of the recording medium and the fact that many long tracks reach the top or bottom surface of the emulsion, so that full information is not available about these tracks. The escape of particles from the boundary layers of the emulsion can be reduced by using thick coatings, up to a millimeter thick, but these emulsions are difficult to process properly. An elaborate technique has been developed whereby stacks of emulsion layers, forming a rectangular block, are exposed to cosmic rays; afterwards each layer is mounted on a plate, processed in the usual way and examined. Long tracks are then traced from one layer to the next through considerable thicknesses of emulsion and complex events may be reconstructed from data accumulated from the various layers.

High-energy particles produced by accelerators in the GeV region possess extremely long ranges in gases, so their properties are not readily discovered by cloud chambers, and they tend to produce complex nuclear reactions in nuclear emulsions. Moreover, the emulsion method is not easily adapted to experiments where magnetic deflection of the particles is required in the recording medium. For these and other reasons, the most powerful method for studying high-energy reactions employs a "bubble chamber,"* which uses a superheated liquid as the recording medium. When a charged particle traverses the liquid, which may be a hydrocarbon like pentane or, in the most elaborate equipment, liquid hydrogen, the track is formed as a row of minute bubbles and is photographed in the usual way. The perfection of the liquid-hydrogen bubble chamber has led to many discoveries in the high-energy region—largely due to the purity of the recording medium, which is effectively made of protons and electrons only, and to the success of magnetic-deflection methods applied in conjunction with the bubble chamber.

Another powerful method for recording the tracks of high-energy particles is by use of a "spark chamber,"† which consists of a gas chamber containing many parallel metal plates (Plate II). A high electrostatic potential difference can be applied between each pair of plates on passage of a charged particle through the chamber and the ionization produced along the path causes small sparks to pass between the plates. Cameras record the positions and directions of the sparks produced, so that a complete trajectory can be reconstructed. The main disadvantage of this apparatus is its inability to reveal the details of events occurring inside the metal plates, which provide most of the stopping material inside the chamber.

* D. A. Glaser, "The Bubble Chamber," Scientific American, **192**, No. 2, 46 (1955).
† G. K. O'Neill, "The Spark Chamber," Scientific American, **207**, No. 2, 36 (1962).

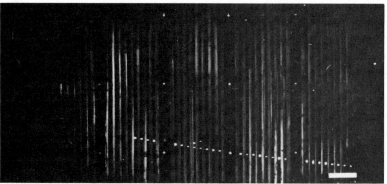

PLATE II. *A spark chamber used in neutrino experiments at the Brookhaven National Laboratory. Top: a view of the 10-ton spark chamber containing 90 parallel aluminum plates, each about 4 ft square. A high voltage supply is connected to alternate plates on passage of a charged particle through the chamber and the sparks caused by the residual ionization are registered photographically. Below: a photograph of spark tracks caused by the passage of a muon through the chamber. In this experiment the muons were created by absorption of neutrinos and about 10^{14} neutrinos passed through the chamber to produce 29 muon events. (From Ford, The World of Elementary Particles. New York: Blaisdell, 1963, pp. 142–143.)*

(c) Light-detection techniques

Many of the earliest experiments in nuclear physics were carried out with scintillation screens used to detect the arrival of alpha particles (see Section 6.3 for the experiments of Geiger and Marsden). It was found that a zinc sulfide screen emits a single flash of light when an alpha particle strikes it, a property akin to the fluorescence produced by cathode rays bombarding the screen of a cathode-ray tube. In due course the scintillation method was superseded by electrical counting methods because of the errors and strain attendant upon visual examination of the screen. However, the development of sensitive photoelectric detectors, notably the photomultiplier tube, led to the revival of the scintillation counter, partly because the light flashes can be recorded electrically at much higher rates than ionization pulses from a counter. The modern scintillation apparatus (Figure 9.12) consists of a suitable scintillator inside a light-tight cell and a photomultiplier tube in contact with one face of the scintillator. The evacuated multiplier tube contains a photosensitive cathode which emits electrons on the arrival of a light flash from the scintillator. The electrons are accelerated from the cathode to the first of a series of "dynodes" which form the multiplication device. The energy gained by an electron passing from one dynode to the next is sufficient for it to eject further electrons from the metal surface of the next dynode, with the result that an exponential multiplication of electrons takes place down the chain. The pulse-amplification factor is of the order of 10^6 to 10^7 when the tube is operated at a total potential difference of 1 or 2 kV and the time of transit to the final anode is very short. The resolving time of the apparatus is of the order of 10^{-9} sec (1 nsec), so fast counting rates can be tolerated and the accurate timing of fast particles is feasible. The modern counter employs special materials to produce the fast light pulses; for example, sodium iodide crystals are suitable for detecting fast electrons and are therefore used to record the Compton electrons and pair electrons produced by gamma rays.

Another process by which light is emitted when charged particles travel through matter is the Čerenkov effect. If the speed of a particle exceeds the local speed of light, a "bow

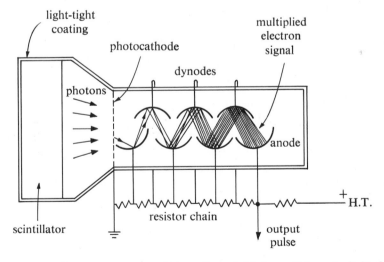

FIGURE 9.12 *A scintillation counter, consisting of a scintillator, which emits light flashes under the action of incident rays, and a photomultiplier tube which amplifies the electron signal received from the photo-cathode by the secondary emission of electrons from a number of "dynodes" between the cathode and the final anode.*

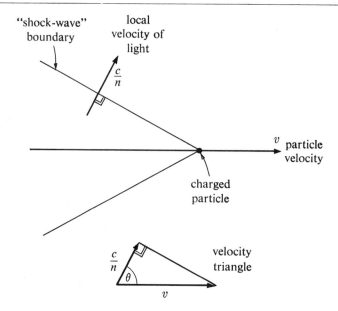

FIGURE 9.13   *The Čerenkov effect produced by a charged particle in a dense medium. If the particle velocity (v) is greater than the local velocity of light (c/n) a "shock-wave" is set up and light is emitted at angle θ to the path of the particle.*

wave" is set up, similar to the shock waves generated in air by missiles which exceed the speed of sound. The light is emitted in the forward direction at an angle to the particle path which depends on the particle speed and the refractive index of the material (n). It is seen from Figure 9.13 that the angle (θ) between the direction of the shock wave and the particle path is given by the relation

$$\cos \theta = \frac{c}{nv},$$ [9.2.3]

where c is the speed of light *in vacuo* and v is the speed of the particle. By putting $\theta = 0°$, we find the lowest speed, v_{min}, at which Čerenkov emission is possible,

$$v_{min} = c/n.$$

Thus in lucite ($n = 1.5$) the lowest electron energy for Čerenkov emission is 0.17 MeV and the lowest proton energy is 320 MeV. The thresholds are much higher in the case of a gas (where n is just greater than 1). This threshold feature is valuable in high-energy work because the inevitable background of low-energy particles is not recorded by a Čerenkov counter. The counter usually consist of a lucite block shaped in such a way that the light generated is sent forward and converged on to the cathode of a photomultiplier tube. In some designs the light emitted in a small range of angles, from particles in a narrow speed range, is detected.

(d) *Ion-collecting chambers and counters*

The basic properties of gas-filled ion chambers have been outlined briefly in Section 3.7. Practical detectors of this type may be divided into two classes—current-measuring chambers and pulse counters. A simple gold-leaf electroscope is discharged in the presence of an ionizing radiation at a rate which depends on the total ionization current passing between the charged leaf and the grounded case. Pierre and Marie Curie used this method to measure the radioactivity in the samples they obtained during the extraction of the elements polonium and radium from pitchblende, an ore of uranium. Simple radiation dosimeters consist of quartz-fiber electrometers which retain a charge indefinitely unless acted upon by ionizing radiation, which causes a measurable amount of discharge. More elaborate current-measuring instruments include a parallel-plate type of ion chamber (Figure 3.15) connected to an electrometer circuit and operated in the saturation part of the characteristic curve (Figure 3.16).

Gas-filled pulse counters are classified into three groups, according to which part of the characteristic current-voltage curve is employed. In the saturation region, the total charge (Q) collected by one electrode following the passage of a particle is equal to the product of the number of singly charged ion pairs produced and the elementary charge (e). The corresponding change in the potential of this electrode is given by the basic relation

$$\Delta V = \frac{Q}{C},$$

where C is the total capacitance of the collector system. Under normal counting conditions, the size of the pulse fed through the amplifying circuits is proportional to ΔV and therefore, by Equation (9.2.1), to the energy expended by the particle in the chamber. For example, if a 5 MeV alpha particle is stopped in a gas with a W value of 25 eV, the number of ion-pairs produced is, by Equation (9.2.1),

$$\frac{5 \times 10^6}{25} = 200,000 \text{ approximately.}$$

If all the ions of one sign are collected by an electrode system of capacitance 10^{-10} farad, the change in potential is

$$\Delta V = \frac{2 \times 10^5 \times 1.6 \times 10^{-19}}{10^{-10}} = 3.2 \times 10^{-4} \text{ V.}$$

In practice, pure argon or nitrogen is employed as the counter gas because electrons travel rapidly through these gases with no appreciable attachment to atoms or molecules; the negative pulses produced at the anode are therefore of short duration (a few microseconds). Fairly high counting rates can then be maintained and ion counters of this type are able to resolve particle groups differing in energy by about 2%.

The second type of gas-filled counter is the "proportional" counter, which is usually cylindrical in shape and is operated in the region where ion multiplication is appreciable. Provided that this multiplication of ions does not reach the pitch of avalanche discharge, the size of the output pulse is still proportional to the ionization produced by the particle and therefore to the energy expended in the counter. This may be seen in Figure 9.14, where the logarithm of the pulse size is plotted schematically against the operating voltage for two particle groups of different energy. In the saturation region the two lines are separated by an amount which represents the *ratio* of ionizations produced. As the voltage rises into the "proportional" region the pulse size increases but the two lines remain equidistant for some way before the steep rise indicates the onset of discharge conditions. Proportional counters are used for detecting low-energy particles because a certain degree of pulse amplification is obtained in the gas before the signal reaches the external amplifier, which inevitably introduces considerable electronic noise into the signal pattern. These counters are, however, inferior in energy resolution to the saturation type of counter and

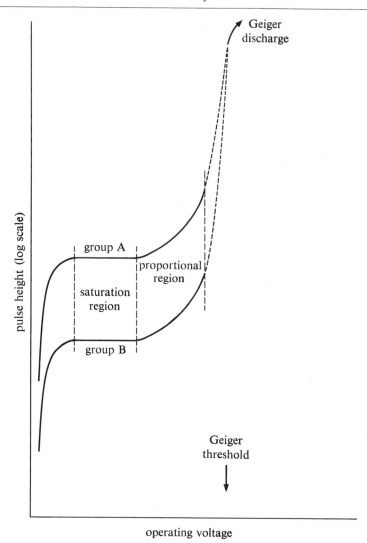

FIGURE 9.14   *Schematic diagram of the pulse height in a cylindrical ion counter plotted on a logarithmic scale against the applied voltage to show the saturation, proportional, and Geiger regions.*

they require highly stabilized voltage supplies if constant gas amplification is to be maintained.

If a cylindrical counter is set up with a fine wire as the central anode and the operating voltage is raised beyond the proportional region, the tube acts as a "Geiger-Müller" counter over a limited range of the applied voltage. Within this range a single ion triggers an avalanche discharge which is, however, rapidly quenched either by external means or by the presence of organic vapor in the tube. The output pulse is large and bears no relation to the input ionization, as is indicated by Figure 9.14. The counter is extremely sensitive to all forms of ionizing radiation and it always registers a considerable background of counts due to cosmic rays and stray traces of radioactivity. The pulse typically lasts at least 10^{-4} sec and when one pulse is initiated the counter is "dead" to other events during this period; but the rise of the pulse is rapid and it is possible to identify the onset of

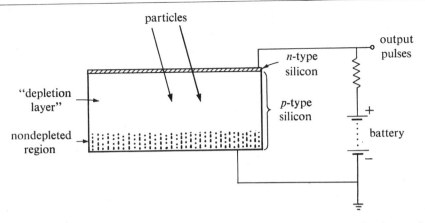

FIGURE 9.15 *A solid-state counter in which charged particles penetrate a thin layer of "n-type" silicon and reach a "depletion layer" in "p-type" silicon, giving rise to pulses in the output circuit.*

ionization within about 10^{-6} sec. Thus if two Geiger tubes are employed in coincidence, they may be used to measure the time interval between two pulses provided that this interval exceeds a fraction of a microsecond.

Recently gas-filled counters have been largely replaced in research by compact solid-state counters* which depend for their operation on the properties of impurity-controlled semiconductors (Section 8.4). For example, a counter may be constructed of a thin layer of a metal or of n-type silicon superimposed on a thicker layer of p-type silicon, with a "reverse bias" applied to the layers by means of a battery (Figure 9.15). The action of the battery depletes a considerable thickness of the p-type semiconductor of its "holes" and this "depletion layer" is the sensitive region of the counter. When a charged particle penetrates the depletion layer via the thin n-type layer, it produces a burst of ionization and a brief flow of current, which is converted into a pulse of considerable size, because of the low capacitance of the collector system. The duration of the pulse may be extremely short (of the order of 10^{-8} sec). The compact construction of solid-state counters allows experimental arrangements to be made with counters in accurate geometrical relation to the target or source of particles. The energy resolution of these counters is good (about 1%) and very high counting rates can be maintained.

(e) Auxiliary equipment

Pulse counters of different kinds produce signals lasting from 10^{-8} sec upwards and ranging in size from a fraction of a millivolt to several volts. The output from a counter is often fed into a fast-pulse linear amplifier and thence into various analyzing circuits. The amplifier must be of uniform amplification over a wide range of high frequencies if fast pulses are to be transmitted without distortion. At the same time it is conventional to limit the low-frequency response of the amplifier at one stage so that only the rapidly varying components of a pulse are transmitted. By this means the pulse is effectively "differentiated" with respect to time and the differentiated pulses are less subject to mutual interference at high counting rates.

The pulses from an ion counter, solid-state counter, or photomultiplier often have to be sorted into groups according to their size, so that a group of certain energy may be identified and its behavior investigated. The pulses are automatically grouped by a pulse-height

* O-M. Bilaniuk, "Semiconductor Particle Detectors," Scientific American, **207**, No. 4, 78 (1962).

analyzer or "kick-sorter," which divides the pulses into 100 or more equally spaced channels or "bins." The analyzer has facilities for display and storage of the information received and the pulse-height distribution or "spectrum" is finally printed out or recorded graphically. Such instruments include *scaling* circuits which divide the number of pulses received by a known factor, usually a power of 2 or 10, so that large numbers of pulses may be handled and represented digitally. *Coincidence* circuits record pairs or groups of pulses from different counters when they coincide in time within a very short interval (down to 10^{-9} sec). In addition, deliberate delays may be introduced into certain signals. In these ways the maximum information is extracted from the counting devices in use, in order to yield data concerning particle energies or their temporal relations with each other.

An important piece of equipment in many fields of research is the magnetic analyzer, which sorts out particles on the basis of their momentum per unit charge [Equation (5.6.6)]. This is the most accurate method of finding the energy of a particle whose charge and mass are known. Alternatively the magnetic field may be used to make a preliminary sorting of particles emitted from a target, especially when many different types are present. The most extensive applications of magnetic analyzers are in the fields of mass spectroscopy (Section 3.4) and beta-ray spectroscopy. Much of the early work on beta rays was done with 180° deflection systems similar to the mass spectrographs of Dempster and Bainbridge (Figure 3.10). This method of measuring particle momentum possesses accuracy but it is not suitable for weak beta sources because of the small solid angle for collection of particles into the instrument. A larger solid angle can be achieved in beta-ray spectrometers of the *magnetic-lens* type, where a ring-shaped coil focuses particles from the source on to a counter and the spectrum is explored by varying the magnetic field strength.

9.3 The Neutron and Nuclear Stability

(a) *The discovery of the neutron*

Following the first artificial disintegration of nuclei by Rutherford in 1919, experimenters used similar techniques to investigate other effects of fast alpha particles on light nuclei. In 1930 Bothe and Becker reported that several nuclides bombarded by alpha particles emit gamma rays, which were detected by means of Geiger counters. The elements beryllium and boron produced a very penetrating radiation and this radiation was particularly strong from beryllium. The absorption coefficient in lead for these rays was found to be 0.22 cm^{-1}, which is now known to be lower than the minimum value for photons (Figure 4.24). At the time, however, it was believed that very high-energy gamma rays must be responsible for the result.

The situation became rather confused when Irène Curie and Frédéric Joliot discovered in 1932 that the penetrating rays from beryllium bombarded with alpha particles are capable of ejecting protons from hydrogenous substances like paraffin wax. This effect was detected by placing an ionization chamber in the path of the rays. Shortly afterwards Chadwick showed that the rays eject charged particles from all substances containing light nuclei and that the ejected particles were probably recoiling nuclei. Chadwick proceeded to adduce several reasons why the "beryllium radiation" cannot be composed of gamma rays but must be a beam of neutral particles.

Chadwick's experimental arrangement is shown in outline in Figure 9.16. Beryllium metal was bombarded with alpha particles from a polonium source, which emits almost no

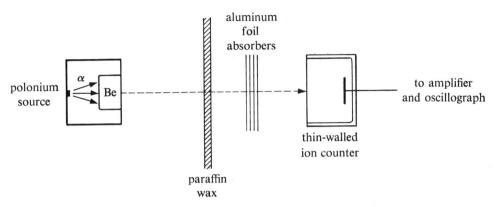

FIGURE 9.16 *Chadwick's apparatus used in the identification of neutrons produced by disintegration of beryllium nuclei with alpha particles from polonium.*

gamma rays. A few centimeters away from the beryllium was placed a thin-walled ion counter, the collecting electrode of which was connected via a linear amplifier to an oscillograph. The output pulses from the counter appeared as "kicks" on the oscillograph trace and were recorded photographically.

With nitrogen in the ion counter, a considerable number of pulses was recorded and these were reduced slightly in number when lead absorbers were placed between the beryllium and the counter. When a thin layer of paraffin wax was substituted for the lead, however, the counting rate increased markedly, as observed by Curie and Joliot. Aluminum absorbers were then placed between the wax and the chamber to find the effective range of the particles ejected from the wax. This range turned out to be equivalent to 40 cm of air, corresponding to a proton energy of 5.7 MeV.

When the paraffin wax was replaced by thin layers of materials such as lithium, boron, and carbon, the ion counter produced pulses due to recoiling atoms of these elements. Similar results were obtained when the counter itself was filled with gases such as helium, nitrogen, oxygen, and argon. Recoiling nitrogen atoms in a cloud chamber were studied by Chadwick and Feather, who found that the maximum kinetic energy of these particles was about 1.5 MeV. This figure agreed with the maximum pulse height observed when the ion counter was filled with nitrogen.

Chadwick then proceeded to show that the recoil results could not easily be explained by the gamma-ray hypothesis. Extremely high gamma-ray energies would be required, from 50 to 90 MeV, and even these figures were not consistent. On the other hand, the hypothesis that the radiation consists of neutral corpuscles accounts readily for the observations, if one assumes that the corpuscles make simple elastic collisions with the atomic nuclei they encounter. A nonrelativistic treatment of the elastic collision process in the laboratory frame of reference is adequate for analysis of the results.

Suppose that a particle of initial momentum $M\mathbf{U}$ strikes a particle of mass m which is stationary in the laboratory frame. After collision the incident and recoiling particles are supposed to have velocities $\mathbf{V}$ and $\mathbf{v}$ which make angles of ψ and φ, respectively, with the direction of the incident particle (Figure 9.17). We obtain directly from the momentum triangle the relation $M^2V^2 = M^2U^2 + m^2v^2 - 2MmUv \cos \varphi$.

Also kinetic energy is conserved in elastic collisions, so

$$\tfrac{1}{2}MU^2 = \tfrac{1}{2}MV^2 + \tfrac{1}{2}mv^2$$

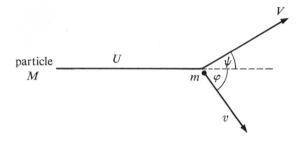

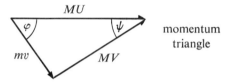

FIGURE 9.17 *Elastic collision of a particle M, traveling at speed U in the laboratory frame, with a stationary particle m, the velocities after collision being* **V** *and* **v**, *respectively, at angles ψ and φ to the original* **U**.

and by elimination of the M^2V^2 term we find

$$v = \frac{2MU}{(M + m)} \cos \varphi. \qquad [9.3.1]$$

The kinetic energy (K_r) of the recoiling particle is therefore

$$K_r = \tfrac{1}{2}mv^2 = \frac{2mM^2U^2}{(M + m)^2} \cos^2 \varphi$$

$$= \frac{4Mm}{(M + m)^2} K_0 \cos^2 \varphi, \qquad [9.3.2]$$

where $K_0 = \tfrac{1}{2}MU^2$ (the original kinetic energy). It should be noted that the maximum energy lost to the recoil particle is fixed by the condition $\varphi = 0$ and amounts to

$$\frac{4Mm}{(M + m)^2} K_0$$

which reduces to K_0 if $M = m$ and to $\dfrac{4M}{m} K_0$ if $M \ll m$.

If Chadwick's data for maximum recoil energies are substituted in the above formula, with all masses expressed in proton units, two equations are obtained for the two unknowns K_0 and M

$$\text{Protons:} \quad K_r^{\max} = 5.7 = \frac{4M}{(M + 1)^2} K_0 \text{ MeV,}$$

$$\text{Nitrogen:} \quad K_r^{\max} = 1.5 = \frac{56M}{(M + 14)^2} K_0 \text{ MeV.}$$

From these relations we obtain $M = 1.07$ proton units, $K_0 = 5.7$ MeV.

This method of measuring the mass of the neutron is subject to considerable errors because of the uncertainty in the energy of the recoiling nitrogen atoms. However, Chadwick was able to show from energy arguments that the rest mass of a neutron must be close to that of the proton but slightly greater.

Assuming that the baryon number of a neutron is 1, like that of the proton, the beryllium-alpha reaction may be written

$$_4Be^9 + {_2}He^4 \rightarrow {_0}n^1 + {_6}C^{12}. \qquad [9.3.3]$$

Chadwick also studied the neutrons produced by alpha-particle bombardment of boron and attributed to the reaction $_5B^{11} + {_2}He^4 \rightarrow {_0}n^1 + {_7}N^{14}.$ $\qquad [9.3.4]$

In further experiments Feather discovered that neutrons are capable of causing the disintegration of nitrogen nuclei, with the emission of alpha particles, according to the scheme

$$_7N^{14} + {_0}n^1 \rightarrow {_2}He^4 + {_5}B^{11}. \qquad [9.3.5]$$

This is clearly the inverse process to that of Equation (9.3.4) and the fact that both reactions can be produced with a modest energy input shows that the energy release in this particular nuclear reaction is very small.

A more accurate determination of the neutron mass emerged from the study of a nuclear *photodisintegration* process, represented by the equation

$$_1D^2 + \hbar\omega \rightarrow {_1}H^1 + {_0}n^1. \qquad [9.3.6]$$

Chadwick and Goldhaber passed gamma rays of energy 2.62 MeV, emitted by a thorium C'' source, into deuterium gas filling an ion counter. Pulses obtained from the counter were identified as proton pulses and later work showed that neutrons are also emitted from the deuterium. The mean proton energy observed was 0.185 MeV and the mean neutron energy should be the same, because the masses of neutron and proton are very similar to each other and there is little momentum imparted by the incident photon. If, now, we make up an energy balance for the reaction, we have

Input	Output
$_1D^2 + 2.62$ MeV	$_1H^1 + {_0}n^1 + 0.37$ MeV.

Energy conservation then leads to the equation

$$_1H^1 + {_0}n^1 - {_1}D^2 = 2.25 \text{ MeV},$$

where each symbol refers to the rest-mass energy of the neutral atom or particle. Mass-spectrograph experiments by Aston showed that the deuterium atom is less massive than two hydrogen atoms and that the difference in energy is

$$2\,_1H^1 - {_1}D^2 = 1.41 \text{ MeV}$$

so that
$$_0n^1 - {_1}H^1 = 0.84 \text{ MeV}.$$

More accurate measurements have led to the present figure for the difference in mass between a neutron and a neutral hydrogen atom

$$_0n^1 - {_1}H^1 = 0.7826 \pm 0.0005 \text{ MeV}.$$

It follows from this result that a neutron does not consist of a proton plus an electron in close combination, as had been envisaged by Rutherford. On the contrary, a neutron may presumably break up into a proton plus an electron if various conservation rules can be satisfied in such a process. The neutron-proton conversion is in fact possible via the weak *Fermi* interaction and is responsible for beta decay in radioactive nuclei (see Section 9.11). Here we are concerned only with the empirical fact that a neutron in free flight is unstable with respect to breakup into a proton and an electron. Also the emission of negatively charged beta particles is a process characteristic of nuclides which are rich in neutrons. The converse process, whereby a proton is converted into a neutron plus a positron, takes place also, if sufficient energy is available, and this form of beta decay is observed in nuclides which are rich in protons.

(b) Neutron cross sections

Shortly after Chadwick's identification of the neutron, Dee carried out a cloud-chamber experiment to see if neutron-electron collisions occur on any appreciable scale. He found no examples of neutron-electron interaction and later work has shown that such an interaction is very weak indeed, in agreement with the hypothesis that the charge on a neutron is exactly zero. It follows that a neutron loses energy in matter chiefly by nuclear collisions of the type studied by Chadwick. In addition to elastic scattering processes there may be various inelastic processes, in which kinetic energy is not conserved, and many kinds of nuclear reaction induced by neutrons, which are able to enter nuclei much more easily than charged particles. Data relating to these phenomena are usually expressed in the form of *cross sections*, similar to those defined in Sections 4.1 and 4.9.

For example, if a neutron beam is incident upon a layer of matter of thickness x, which acts as a simple absorber of neutrons, the relation between the incident flux of particles (F_0) and the emergent flux (F) is

$$F = F_0 \exp\left(-n\sigma_{ab}x\right), \qquad [9.3.7]$$

where each F is defined as the number of particles crossing unit area perpendicular to the beam per second; n is the number of absorbing nuclei per unit volume; and σ_{ab} is the absorption cross section.

In nuclear physics cross sections are expressed in terms of a unit called the "barn," which is 10^{-28} m^2, or in millibarns. Distances on the nuclear scale are often expressed in terms of the "fermi," which is 10^{-15} m.

In cases of scattering, the cross section σ_{sc} is best defined by the equation

$$-\Delta F = Fn\sigma_{sc}\,\Delta x, \qquad [9.3.8]$$

where the left-hand side represents the number of particles scattered out of the incident beam by nuclei in a layer of thickness Δx, which is supposed to be small. Provided that the scattered particles are not allowed to affect measurements, that is, no multiple scattering occurs, the attenuation of a beam by scattering processes obeys Equation (9.3.7) with the scattering cross section substituted for the absorption cross section. More generally, if both scattering and absorption take place, we may write

$$-\Delta F = Fn\sigma_T\,\Delta x, \qquad [9.3.9]$$

where σ_T is the total cross section for all processes. The effective absorption coefficient under these conditions is

$$\mu_T = n\sigma_T. \qquad [9.3.10]$$

Thus for the neutrons emitted by bombardment of beryllium with alpha particles, the measured absorption coefficient was 0.22 cm^{-1} in lead, which contains 3.3×10^{28} nuclei per m^3. The estimated total cross section is therefore 6.7×10^{-28} m^2 or 6.7 barns. It may be enquired if this figure bears any relation to the actual cross-sectional area of the nucleus of lead. Further investigation shows that both scattering and absorption cross sections behave in an irregular way when different neutron energies and different nuclides are employed. Graphs of cross section against neutron energy exhibit sharp peaks known as "resonances" which are characteristic of the nuclide employed. Even if the resonances are smoothed out the cross-section plot does not have the same shape in all parts of the periodic table of the elements.

Despite these difficulties, it is possible to make certain theoretical predictions concerning the behavior of neutron cross sections at fairly high energies, from 10 MeV upwards. If the target nucleus is a strong absorber of neutrons, it acts essentially like a black disk of radius r, which both absorbs and scatters the neutrons. The absorption cross section, which is the sum of all possible reaction cross sections, then takes the form

$$\sigma_{ab} = \pi\left(r + \frac{\lambda}{2\pi}\right)^2, \qquad [9.3.11]$$

where λ is the de Broglie wavelength of the incident neutrons. In agreement with this prediction, the absorption cross section for 25 MeV neutrons increases monotonically as the baryon number (A) increases. It is therefore possible to relate the effective nuclear radius (r) to the atomic mass, for example, by plotting r against A. More significantly, the data may be represented on a graph of $\sqrt{\sigma/\pi}$ against $\sqrt[3]{A}$, as is done in Figure 9.18.

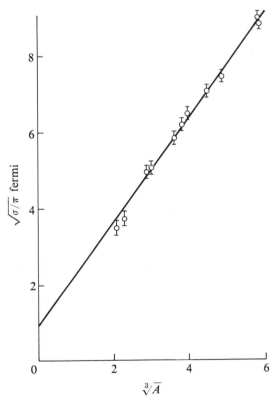

FIGURE 9.18 *Plot of* $\sqrt{\dfrac{\sigma}{\pi}}$, *where σ is the cross section per nucleus for absorption of 25 MeV neutrons, against $\sqrt[3]{A}$ for different nuclides with mass number A.*

Allowing for a certain amount of experimental error, the points lie on a straight line which intersects the ordinate axis near 0.9 fermi, which is the value of $\lambda/2\pi$ for 25 MeV neutrons. The straight line shows that we may express the effective nuclear radius in the form

$$r = r_0 \sqrt[3]{A}, \qquad\qquad [9.3.12]$$

where r_0 is constant for all nuclei, with the value 1.4 fermi (as indicated by these data).

The same type of relation between radius and A is found in many branches of nuclear physics. For example, when alpha particles are scattered by nuclei there is, in addition to the Rutherford or Coulomb scattering (Section 6.3), a "nuclear size" effect which can be used to estimate r. The same applies to the scattering of high-energy electrons, although in this case the value of r_0 turns out to be rather smaller, in the neighborhood of 1.2 fermi. The experimental data reveal that the nucleus does *not* act as though it has a sharp boundary and so the value of r depends to some extent on the precise definition adopted. Nevertheless Equation (9.3.12) retains its general validity and it leads to the conclusion that the nuclear volume $\left(\dfrac{4\pi}{3} r^3\right)$ is essentially proportional to the atomic mass number A, that is, the number of baryons present.

(c) Neutrons in the nucleus

The practical importance of the neutron in nuclear physics cannot be overrated, but it also plays a highly significant role in nuclear theory. Before the identification of the neutron in 1932, the only elementary particles known to exist were protons and electrons. It was assumed that a nucleus must consist of these particles in some form of combination, although elementary calculations suffice to prove that no known interaction is capable of binding electrons within a nucleus (see Problem 7.8). Electron-scattering experiments have now demonstrated that the proton-electron interaction is of the Coulomb type even when very small distances separate the particles.

If neutrons are regarded as essential constituents of any complex nucleus, it is necessary to invoke new forces, the "nuclear forces" between neutron and proton, to account for nuclear stability. Evidence for the importance of such forces is obtainable from experiments on the absorption of neutrons by nuclei; scattering experiments also show that a nucleus exerts a strong force of attraction on incident neutrons. In many applications it is conventional to treat the potential energy of a neutron close to a nucleus as a double-step function of distance, similar to the rectangular potential well considered in Section 7.4.

In present-day theory, therefore, a nucleus is regarded as an assembly of A particles, each with baryon number $+1$ and similar mass; of these Z are protons and $(A - Z)$ are neutrons. For many purposes it is convenient to treat the neutron and the proton as two states of the same particle, the *nucleon*, which always interacts strongly with other nucleons, whatever their charges may be. This model avoids many of the difficulties encountered by the proton-electron model. For instance, it is possible to measure the total angular momentum, often called the "nuclear spin," of nuclei in their ground states. It is found that all nuclides with even A have zero or integral spin (measured in terms of the fundamental unit $\hbar$). An important example is the deuteron, $_1D^2$, which has a measured spin of one unit ($\hbar$). In the modern view the neutron and proton each contribute spin momentum $\frac{1}{2}\hbar$ and the spins are parallel to account for the deuteron spin. On the older hypothesis, however, a deuteron had to consist of two protons (each of spin $\frac{1}{2}\hbar$) and one electron (also of spin $\frac{1}{2}\hbar$). Any orbital angular momentum present can contribute only integral multiples of $\hbar$ to the total, so the proton-electron combination cannot explain the observed deuteron spin.

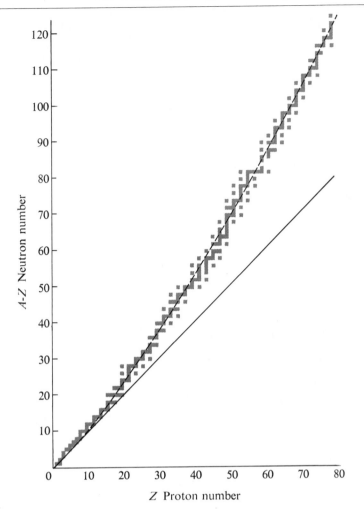

FIGURE 9.19   *Chart of the stable nuclides up to Z = 80, each being plotted as a small square against the proton number (Z) and neutron number (A − Z). The full line is at 45° to each axis while the dotted line follows the general trend for stability, showing that heavy nuclei require more neutrons than protons for this condition.*

Another reason for supposing that electrons do not exist freely inside the nucleus is the small magnitude of nuclear magnetic moments, which are about 1000 times smaller than the Bohr magneton, the value appropriate to a single electron spin.

Some information about the forces binding nuclei together can be obtained by direct study of the systematics of stable nuclides. If, for example, we plot the neutron number $(A − Z)$ against the proton number (Z) for stable isotopes from $Z = 1$ to $Z = 82$, we find the pattern shown in Figure 9.19. Certain details of this pattern require considerable attention later on, but it is clear that the general trend is for the points to be grouped about a line which starts off at 45° to each axis. Thus in light nuclides stability is achieved when the neutron and proton numbers are roughly equal. However, the line curves upwards, indicating that the stable heavy nuclides always contain many more neutrons than protons. This result may be explained on the supposition that extra Coulomb repulsion between

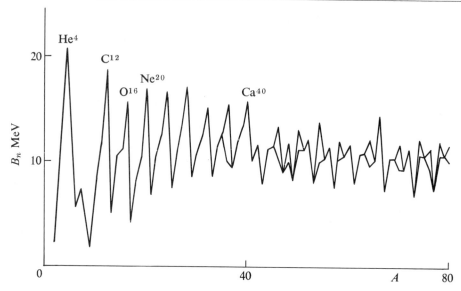

FIGURE 9.20   *The binding energy of the last neutron in a nucleus (B_n in MeV) plotted against the atomic mass number A for light and medium nuclides which are stable.*

the protons at high Z values must be overcome by extra binding, which is provided by an increase in the ratio of neutrons to protons.

A property of considerable interest in nuclear theory is the *binding energy* of a neutron in a complex nucleus, that is, the minimum energy required to remove a neutron from the nucleus. This quantity (B_n) may be calculated if the masses of initial and final nuclei are known. Thus if the process is represented by

$$_{Z}\mathrm{X}^{A} \rightarrow {}_{0}\mathrm{n}^{1} + {}_{Z}\mathrm{X}^{A-1}$$

and the masses are M_A, M_n, and M_{A-1}, respectively, the binding energy is, by Einstein's relation [Equation (5.6.4)],

$$B_n = c^2(M_n + M_{A-1} - M_A).$$

The conversion from carbon-12 mass units (u) to MeV is usually expressed by the equation

$$1\ \mathrm{u} = 931.48\ \mathrm{MeV}.$$

A graph of B_n values against the atomic mass number A for stable nuclides (Figure 9.20) shows a considerable scatter of points between a minimum value of 1.67 MeV (for $_4\mathrm{Be}^9$) and a maximum of 20.6 MeV (for $_2\mathrm{He}^4$). The general trend of average values is fairly steady around 10 MeV, which may be taken as a mean binding energy for the *last* neutron in a nucleus. It also represents the mean internal excitation energy of a nucleus which has captured a slow neutron, before the energy is dissipated by gamma-ray emission or some other process.

A much smoother binding-energy curve can be obtained by calculating the *mean* binding energy per nucleon ($\bar{B}$) and plotting this against the atomic mass number (Figure 9.21). $\bar{B}$ is found by subtracting the mass of the nucleus from the total mass of all the component nucleons, converting this difference to energy units and dividing the result by A. The curve for stable nuclides rises to a very broad maximum of about 8.8 MeV near $A = 50$ and then

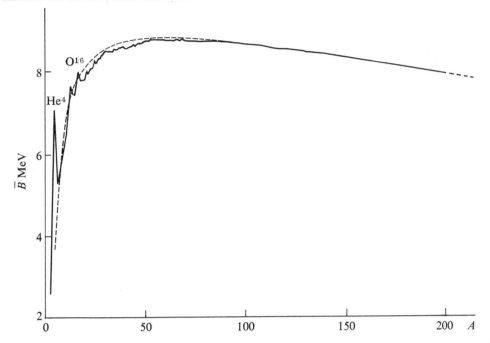

FIGURE 9.21   *Graph of the mean binding energy per nucleon ($\bar{B}$ in MeV) plotted against A for stable nuclides in the region below $A = 200$. The dotted line is a theoretical curve based on Equation 9.3.16.*

falls slowly. Over a very wide range of nuclear masses, therefore, the mean binding energy per nucleon is about 8 MeV. Certain exceptional nuclides, such as $_2He^4$ and $_6C^{12}$, are represented by points lying well above the curve, but the great majority of points are close to a line which is derived theoretically in the next section.

(d) The semiempirical mass formula of Weizsäcker

The principal properties of nuclear radii and binding energies can be correlated by a semiempirical argument due to Weizsäcker. The fact that the effective volume of a nucleus is nearly proportional to the number of particles (A) suggests that nuclear forces exhibit the phenomenon of "saturation"—that is, when a large number of nucleons interact, the total potential energy does not increase as the square of the number, as one might expect, but linearly with the number. Thus if "nuclear matter" of infinite extent existed it would possess a constant mean density and a constant mean binding energy per nucleon ($\bar{B}$). The saturation hypothesis derives from Equation (9.3.12) for nuclear radii and receives general support from the data of Figure 9.21, although it is clear that there are modifying effects which produce the curve in the binding-energy plot.

Saturation effects are found in other many-body systems besides nuclei, notably in the liquid state, where closely packed molecules interact in such a way that the liquid density is effectively constant. This analogy leads to the "liquid-drop" model of nuclei, which provides a general description of certain nuclear properties, such as the mean binding energy, but does not attempt to account for the behavior of particular nuclides. This model is valuable in dealing with the fission of heavy nuclei such as those of uranium, which split into roughly equal halves when suitably excited. In this section the liquid-drop analogy is used to establish an approximate mass relation for stable nuclides.

The nuclide $_Z X^A$ is supposed to consist of atoms, each containing Z extranuclear electrons (mass M_e) and a nucleus composed of Z protons (mass M_p) and $(A - Z)$ neutrons (mass M_n). Neglecting the small mass differences due to electronic binding energy and chemical binding effects, the mass of the neutral atom should be

$$M_A = Z M_e + Z M_p + (A - Z) M_n - A\bar{B}$$
$$= Z M_H + (A - Z) M_n - A\bar{B}, \qquad [9.3.13]$$

where M_H is the mass of the neutral hydrogen atom. The total binding energy is expressed as $-(A\bar{B})$ and is calculated as a sum of terms in the following way:

(i) according to the hypothesis of nuclear saturation, there should be a negative potential energy, due to attractive nuclear forces, which is proportional simply to the number of nucleons (A);

(ii) on the liquid-drop analogy, there should be a surface-energy term, proportional to the spherical surface area, that is, to $A^{2/3}$ according to Equation (9.3.12), and opposite in sign to term (i);

(iii) the evidence of Figure 9.19 indicates that the Coulomb force of repulsion between protons is not negligible in heavy nuclei, so we should include a positive potential energy term of electrostatic origin;

(iv) Figure 9.19 also suggests that nuclear stability is achieved when $A = 2Z$ approximately, if Coulomb effects are ignored, so there should presumably be a positive energy term which increases with the magnitude of $(A - 2Z)$.

This list is not exhaustive but it is sufficient to give a formula in agreement with the curve of Figure 9.21. The exact form of term (iii) is suggested by the total electrostatic energy of a uniformly charged sphere of radius r, namely,

$$U_{el} = \frac{3q^2}{5r(4\pi\varepsilon_0)}, \text{ where } q \text{ is the net charge.}$$

Thus with $q = Ze$ for the nucleus and $r \propto \sqrt[3]{A}$, we obtain

$$U_{el} \propto \frac{Z^2}{A^{1/3}}.$$

The simplest form for term (iv) is derived by considering the nucleus as an assembly of fermions, like the electrons in a metal, and is

$$U \propto \frac{(A - 2Z)^2}{A}.$$

Combining the four terms specified for the total binding energy of the nucleus, we obtain the relation

$$-A\bar{B} = -a_1 A + a_2 A^{2/3} + a_3 \frac{Z^2}{A^{1/3}} + a_4 \frac{(A - 2Z)^2}{A}$$

and the mean binding energy per nucleon becomes

$$\bar{B} = a_1 - a_2 A^{-1/3} - a_3 Z^2 A^{-4/3} - a_4 (A - 2Z)^2 A^{-2}, \qquad [9.3.14]$$

where a_1, a_2, and a_4 are arbitrary constants,

and $a_3 = \dfrac{3e^2}{5r_0(4\pi\varepsilon_0)}$ for uniformly charged spheres. The latter constant can be evaluated by substituting $r_0 = 1.3$ fermi (a mean value from several determinations) and this yields

$$a_3 = 0.667 \text{ MeV}.$$

The mean binding energy given by Equation (9.3.14) is a function of Z as well as of A and we first examine the relation to see if it accounts for the stable-nuclide curve of Figure 9.19. For a stable nucleus the mean binding energy (and likewise the total binding energy) must reach a maximum as a function of Z, that is, we can write

$$\frac{\partial \bar{B}}{\partial Z} = 0$$

whence we derive

$$Z = \frac{A}{2 + \dfrac{a_3 A^{2/3}}{2a_4}}. \qquad [9.3.15]$$

This relation is not in exactly the form given by Figure 9.19 but it fits the trend of the stable-nuclide curve very closely if we put

$$\frac{a_3}{2a_4} = 0.015,$$

that is, if $\qquad a_3 = 0.667 \text{ MeV}, \qquad$ then $\qquad a_4 = 22.2 \text{ MeV}.$

The remaining two constants can be obtained from the shape of the $\bar{B} - A$ curve shown in Figure 9.21. The maximum value of $\bar{B}$ is found from the condition

$$\frac{\partial \bar{B}}{\partial A} = 0$$

and the A number at which the maximum occurs is A_m, where

$$\frac{a_2 A_m^{-1/3}}{3} - a_3 \left. \frac{\partial}{\partial A}\left(\frac{Z^2}{A^{1/3}}\right)\right|_{A_m} - a_4 \left. \frac{\partial}{\partial A}\frac{(A - 2Z)^2}{A^2}\right|_{A_m} = 0.$$

Near the maximum, which occurs close to $A_m = 60$, the term in a_3 can be replaced by the approximate value $\dfrac{Z^2}{A^{1/3}} = \dfrac{A^{2/3}}{5}$, which is based on Equation (9.3.15).

Also the term in a_4 is negligible in this part of the curve, so we may reduce the equation for A_m to the simple form

$$\frac{a_2 A_m^{-1/3}}{3} = \frac{2a_3 A_m^{-1/3}}{15},$$

that is, $A_m = 2.5\, a_2/a_3 = 60$ approximately.
Thus if $a_3 = 0.667$ MeV, $a_2 = 16.0$ MeV approximately. The remaining constant is found by substituting the maximum binding energy (8.8 MeV) in Equation 9.3.14, at $A = 60$, with $Z = 28$, whence we obtain

$$a_1 = 15.2 \text{ MeV}.$$

The combined expression for the mean binding energy per nucleon ($\bar{B}$ in MeV) becomes

$$\bar{B} = 15.2 - 16.0 A^{-1/3} - 0.667 Z^2 A^{-4/3} - 22.2(A - 2Z)^2 A^{-2} \qquad [9.3.16]$$

and this is plotted as a dotted line in Figure 9.21. The choice of parameters is by no means unique and improved methods can be used to get a better fit; nevertheless the agreement is satisfactory in view of the simple model adopted. Extra terms are added to Equation (9.3.14) for estimating the masses of unstable nuclides.

One immediate consequence of Equation (9.3.16) is that we can extrapolate its results to the hypothetical extreme of "infinite nuclear matter," that is, a very large assembly of neutrons and protons in equal numbers, where surface effects may be ignored. The purely nuclear binding energy per nucleon is then given by the first term in Equation (9.3.16) and amounts to about 15 MeV. This figure provides a criterion for testing theories of nuclear forces when applied to large assemblies of nucleons.

(e) *Fast neutrons: production and detection*

Fast neutrons in the medium-energy range (up to about 20 MeV) are readily produced in the laboratory. Portable neutron sources usually consist of intimate mixtures of beryllium with either radium or polonium, the alpha particles from which eject neutrons from the beryllium according to the reaction of Equation (9.3.3). Such sources are inconvenient for some purposes because they emit neutrons of several different energies. The radium–beryllium source has the extra disadvantage of being a powerful emitter of gamma rays as well as neutrons. "Photoneutron" sources have also been employed; in these the gamma rays emitted by a radioactive body such as ThC'' disintegrate deuterium according to the reaction of Equation (9.3.6). The neutrons produced are nearly *monoergic*, that is, they are confined to a narrow range of energies, and their energies are usually less than 1 MeV.

Powerful sources of neutrons with well-defined energies are provided by accelerators in which deuterons bombard thin targets of suitable elements. Among the reactions of highest utility are the following:

$$_1D^2 + _1D^2 \rightarrow _0n^1 + _2He^3 \tag{9.3.17}$$

$$_1T^3 + _1D^2 \rightarrow _0n^1 + _2He^4 \tag{9.3.18}$$

$$_6C^{12} + _1D^2 \rightarrow _0n^1 + _7N^{13}. \tag{9.3.19}$$

Of these the first two are *exoergic*, with positive total energy release, while the last one is *endoergic* and requires a certain minimum bombarding energy for neutrons to be produced at all. The D + D reaction yields neutrons in the energy region from 2 MeV upwards, the precise value depending on the bombarding energy and the angle between the incident beam and the neutrons emitted. The T + D reaction, which may be studied by allowing deuterons to strike a metal foil containing occluded tritium (the beta-unstable isotope of hydrogen), generates neutrons with energies from 14 MeV upwards. The C^{12} + D reaction, being endoergic, produces neutrons from zero energy upwards.

Fast neutrons may be detected by means of elastic collisions with light nuclei, as employed by Chadwick, or by the nuclear reactions they produce, for example the fission of the uranium isotope U^{238}. Elastic collisions with protons occur readily in hydrogen, paraffin wax, or in the gelatin of a photographic emulsion. Thus if a hydrogen-filled cloud chamber or a photographic plate is exposed to fast neutrons, the tracks of recoiling protons are recorded. For each track the recoil energy K_r may be found and, if the recoil angle φ is also known, the neutron energy K_0 can be calculated with the aid of Equation (9.3.2). It is usually sufficiently accurate to put the neutron and proton masses equal, so that the formula reduces to

$$K_r = K_0 \cos^2 \varphi \text{ approximately.} \tag{9.3.20}$$

In this way data can be accumulated for the composition of a neutron "energy spectrum," in which the abscissae represent the neutron energy and the ordinates are proportional to the numbers of neutrons per unit energy interval. A complex neutron spectrum obtained by

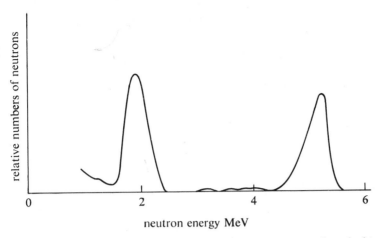

FIGURE 9.22   *Fast neutron energy spectrum determined by the proton-recoil method in photographic emulsion. The neutrons were emitted at 150° to a 0.9 MeV deuteron beam bombarding a target containing nitrogen and deuterium.*

the photographic-plate method is shown in Figure 9.22. The neutron group near 5 MeV is due to the reaction

$$_7N^{14} + _1D^2 \rightarrow _0n^1 + _8O^{15} \qquad [9.3.21]$$

while the prominent group at 2 MeV is due to the D + D reaction, since deuterons from the beam are necessarily present in the target employed. Such contamination groups must be allowed for when new reactions are being investigated.

The analysis of proton recoil tracks is a slow operation and many advantages are found in the use of counting methods. For example, a hydrogen-filled ion counter may be bombarded with fast neutrons, the recoil-proton pulses being amplified and analyzed. If a single neutron energy K_0 is involved, the proton energies (K_r) range from zero up to a maximum which is close to K_0, according to Equation (9.3.20). The actual shape of the proton pulse distribution depends on the angular distribution of neutron-proton collisions in the laboratory system of coordinates. Over a wide range of energies below about 10 MeV, it is found experimentally that the number of protons scattered between angles φ and $(\varphi + d\varphi)$ is given by the expression

$$f(\varphi)\,d\varphi = \text{const } \cos \varphi \sin \varphi \, d\varphi. \qquad [9.3.22]$$

This result may also be expressed in terms of the differential scattering cross section (the element of cross section per unit solid angle), which is written $\dfrac{d\sigma}{d\Omega}$ [see Equation (6.3.5)]. Since the element of solid angle between two cones of semiangle φ and $(\varphi + d\varphi)$ is

$$d\Omega(\varphi) = 2\pi \sin \varphi \, d\varphi$$

we find

$$\frac{d\sigma}{d\Omega} = \text{const } \cos \varphi$$

for neutron-proton scattering in the laboratory frame.

If, now, we transform the angular distribution $f(\varphi)$ into a distribution of recoil energies K_r, we have

$$f(\varphi)\,d\varphi = F(K_r)\,dK_r$$

and since

$$K_r = K_0 \cos^2 \varphi \qquad \text{from Equation (9.3.20)}$$

then
$$-dK_r = 2K_0 \cos \varphi \sin \varphi \, d\varphi.$$

It follows that the pulse distribution is given by the relation

$$F(K_r) \, dK_r = \text{const} \frac{dK_r}{K_0} \tag{9.3.23}$$

for K_r values between 0 and K_0.

Thus for this particular angular distribution the recoil-energy distribution is constant up to the maximum value K_0 (see Figure 9.23). In practice various effects cause the distribution to fall gradually to zero through K_0, as shown; this means that the derived neutron energy spectrum has an effective width due partly to the apparatus. The shape of the neutron spectrum is found by inverting the proton recoil energy distribution and differentiating it.

The analysis of proton pulse distributions to obtain the neutron energy spectrum is feasible only if a large proportion of the protons spend all their energy in the sensitive volume of the counter. In fact a number of erroneous pulses are always recorded because the protons strike the walls of the counter and this "wall effect" becomes extremely serious as the neutron energy rises above a few MeV. The wall effect may be reduced by substituting helium for hydrogen in the counter, because the recoils derive less energy from the neutrons in the case of helium, but the angular distribution of neutron-helium scattering is more complex than that of Equation (9.3.22) and analysis is correspondingly more involved. At high energies, therefore, it is often necessary to record the proton recoils ejected within a narrowly defined solid angle, by means of several counters working in coincidence. Both proportional counters and scintillation detectors have been used in this way, chiefly for measuring the number of protons ejected per unit time, which is proportional to the flux of fast neutrons.

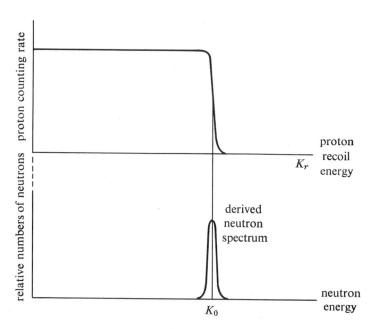

FIGURE 9.23   *The ideal shape of a proton-recoil energy spectrum produced in a hydrogen-filled ion counter by fast neutrons of a single energy K_0 (below about 10 MeV). The pulse distribution is of constant height, except near K_0, and the neutron spectrum may be derived by differentiation.*

With the advent of high-speed scintillation counters, it has become feasible for neutron speeds to be measured directly by the time-of-flight method, provided that the particles are generated in a sharply defined burst at the target. A 1 MeV neutron covers a distance of 1 m in about 70 nsec so that circuits with a resolving time of a few nanoseconds can sort out neutrons into different energy groups according to their times of arrival at the detector. The method can be used to measure the spectrum of neutrons liberated from a target bombarded with the electron beam in a linear accelerator. Another application is in deuteron reactions of the type $(d, n\gamma)$ where the gamma ray is emitted almost simultaneously with the neutron and a gamma counter close to the target can be used to signal the departure of a neutron which is finally recorded in a distant scintillation counter.

Finally, fast neutrons are frequently detected by the reactions they induce. A number of materials become radioactive under neutron bombardment as the result of reactions which are endoergic and which are therefore not induced by slow neutrons. An example is

$$_{15}P^{31} + {}_0n^1 \rightarrow {}_1H^1 + {}_{14}Si^{31},$$

where the nuclide Si^{31} has a half-life of 2.6 hr for beta decay and can therefore be detected easily. A more direct way of counting fast neutrons is in a "fission chamber" containing the isotope U^{238}, which undergoes fission only with neutrons of energy exceeding 1 MeV. Each fission event causes a very large pulse to be recorded in the chamber and the fission pulses are readily identified and counted. If the fission cross section is known accurately, the flux of fast neutrons can be found by Equation (9.3.9) with the fission cross section σ_F substituted for the total cross section.

(f) Slow neutrons

The discovery of the neutron's characteristic property of losing energy by elastic collisions with nuclei led to experiments with slow neutrons. Fermi and his collaborators showed that these particles are extremely effective in producing nuclear reactions, both simple capture reactions and those involving disintegration of the target nucleus. This phenomenon is readily understood because the presence of attractive nuclear forces and the lack of electric charge enable neutrons to enter the heaviest nuclei. Moreover, very slow neutrons spend a comparatively long time in the field of any nucleus they encounter and it is found that, in general, cross sections for nuclear reactions increase as the neutron speed is reduced. In fact for certain neutron-induced reactions involving charged-particle emission, the cross section at low energy varies inversely as the neutron speed

$$\sigma \propto \frac{1}{v} \propto K_n^{-1/2}, \qquad [9.3.24]$$

where v and K_n are the neutron speed and kinetic energy, respectively.

Slow neutrons are nearly always produced by "moderation" of a beam of fast neutrons, in a medium which causes the neutrons to lose energy rapidly by elastic collision. The most efficient moderator is a dense hydrogenous material like water or paraffin wax. It is readily shown, with the aid of Equation (9.3.20), that the mean neutron energy after one neutron-proton collision is just $\frac{1}{2}K_0$ and the mean energy after n collisions is $(\frac{1}{2})^n K_0$. Thus, provided that the moderator is sufficiently extensive to cause repeated collisions of each incident neutron, the mean neutron energy must decrease rapidly. The process of energy loss continues until the neutrons reach "thermal" energies, when the particles approach thermal equilibrium with the molecules of the moderator. The speeds of thermal neutrons have been measured by the time-of-flight method and their distribution is essentially Maxwellian

(Figure 2.5) although there is often an excess number of neutrons in the high-speed region of the Maxwellian curve.

The choice of a moderator in a slow-neutron "pile" or reactor is very important because efficient moderation is essential if the reacting core (consisting of fissionable material plus the moderator) is to be kept within reasonable limits of size and expense. The internal flux of neutrons is required to be a maximum for a given size of core and so the moderator must not capture appreciable numbers of slow neutrons. Ordinary water is not ideal, despite its efficient moderating action, because of the capture reaction

$$_1H^1 + {}_0n^1 \rightarrow {}_1D^2 + \hbar\omega \qquad\qquad [9.3.25]$$

which has a considerable cross section at low energies. "Heavy water," D_2O, is often used instead, since there is very little chance of slow neutrons being captured by deuterons. Another moderator in wide use is graphite, composed largely of the nuclide C^{12}, which has a low capture cross section for slow neutrons.

Radiative capture of slow neutrons, as exemplified by Equation (9.3.25), is by far the most probable process of neutron absorption in medium and heavy elements. The target nucleus absorbs a neutron and the resultant *compound nucleus* is highly excited, to about 8–10 MeV according to the data of Figure 9.20. The excitation energy is subsequently lost in the form of gamma rays, the spectrum of which is complex because of the many excited states accessible in such nuclei. A typical example is the absorption of neutrons by the element rhodium, which possesses one stable isotope, Rh^{103}, transformed into an excited state of the isotope Rh^{104}

$$_{45}Rh^{103} + {}_0n^1 \rightarrow {}_{45}Rh^{104*}, \qquad\qquad [9.3.26]$$

where the asterisk (*) indicates excitation of the product nucleus. Following the emission of gamma rays the nuclide Rh^{104} is formed in the ground state, but it remains unstable and proceeds to emit beta rays with a half-life of 44 sec

$$_{45}Rh^{104} \rightarrow {}_{-1}e^0 + {}_{46}Pd^{104} \qquad\qquad [9.3.27]$$

giving a stable isotope of palladium. It should be noted that the upper numbers in such an equation refer to baryon numbers, so that the electron counts as zero on this scale. Measurements of the radioactivity induced in a rhodium sample by slow neutrons may be used to estimate the slow-neutron flux, since the cross section is known in detail.

Detection of slow neutrons by the beta activity produced on absorption is a common technique, but it involves the removal of the activated specimen from the slow neutron flux in order that the activity be assessed. An alternative method employs direct counting techniques in which the slow neutrons eject charged particles from the nuclei of the counter gas. Suitable reactions are found in the light elements, for example,

$$_2He^3 + {}_0n^1 \rightarrow {}_1H^1 + {}_1H^3 \qquad\qquad [9.3.28]$$

$$_5B^{10} + {}_0n^1 \rightarrow {}_2He^4 + {}_3Li^7. \qquad\qquad [9.3.29]$$

Thus a proportional counter filled with helium–3 gas or boron trifluoride (preferably enriched in the boron-10 isotope) acts as a slow-neutron detector. The cross section of each of these two reactions obeys the "$1/v$" law [Equation (9.3.24)] in the low-energy region. (See Figure 9.36.)

A third method for detecting slow neutrons employs the fission properties of such nuclides as $_{92}U^{235}$ and $_{94}Pu^{239}$. These heavy nuclei undergo fission with slow neutrons as well as fast neutrons; indeed they form the fuel in a slow-neutron reactor. The fission rate in an ion

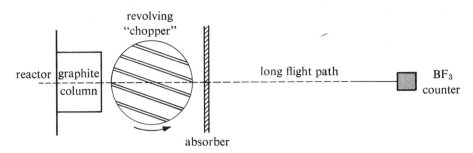

FIGURE 9.24 *Layout of a slow-neutron "chopper" experiment, in which the neutron beam is modulated by the revolving chopper and the particles are sorted out into groups of differing velocity. The total cross section of an absorber for different neutron energies is found by measuring the attenuation of the beam for different velocity groups.*

chamber containing a sample of U^{235} is an indicator of the slow-neutron flux, provided that the fast-neutron background has been eliminated or allowed for.

Slow-neutron energies are best measured by timing the particles over a known distance. Frequently the source of the neutrons is "modulated," that is, interrupted at a known rate, which may be several thousand times per second. If the modulated neutron beam is allowed to travel several meters before being detected (for example, in a boron trifluoride counter) the times of arrival of individual neutrons can be sorted out and their speeds estimated. This method requires an intense source, since a long flight path is desirable. Nuclear reactors are often used for these experiments and the modulator consists of a "chopper," for example, a drum fitted with slots and rotated at high speed about its axis. The general layout is then as shown in Figure 9.24, where the graphite column is inserted to act as an efficient moderator of the neutrons as they emerge from the reactor core. Various materials may be inserted between the chopper and the detector and their absorption properties studied as a function of neutron speed; thus the absorption cross section at different energies may be derived.

(g) Fission

Experiments carried out by Fermi and others on the absorption of slow neutrons by uranium showed that a number of radioactive products can be obtained. At the time it was supposed that these must be "transuranic elements" formed by beta decay of nuclides such as U^{239}, which should be produced by neutron capture

$$_{92}U^{238} + {}_0n^1 \rightarrow {}_{92}U^{239} \qquad [9.3.30]$$

followed by

$$_{92}U^{239} \rightarrow {}_{-1}e^0 + {}_{93}Np^{239}.$$

This process, leading first to neptunium ($Z = 93$) and then to plutonium ($Z = 94$) by a second beta decay, does in fact occur, but it cannot account for many of the beta activities which are found. In 1938 Hahn and Strassmann showed that some of the material with intense beta activity is associated with the element barium, being chemically identical with that element. This result was hard to understand until, in 1939, Frisch and Meitner introduced the concept of *fission* as a process whereby the nuclei of heavy elements split into much smaller fragments. These workers showed that large amounts of energy are released in fission and that the fragments exhibit a wide variety of radioactive half-lives.

The new results may be explained in terms of the stable-nuclide graph (Figure 9.19) and the mean binding-energy curve (Figure 9.21). If the nucleus of a heavy element, such as uranium or thorium, is split into two halves, each half must contain a higher proportion of neutrons than stability requires. Accordingly the products of the fission process must get rid of excess energy either by emitting neutrons, which requires a large energy excess, or by negative beta emission, which is equivalent to converting neutrons into protons. Moreover, since the mean binding energy per nucleon is higher for medium-weight nuclei than for the heaviest ones, the normal masses of the two fission fragments must add up to much less than the original mass present. Therefore a large release of kinetic energy is possible and this is readily detected in a fission chamber.

A theoretical treatment of the fission process was given by Niels Bohr and Wheeler in 1939. If the massive nucleus of uranium is thought of as a liquid drop, the absorption of a neutron should cause it to oscillate as a result of the excitation energy provided. If the nucleus is spherical to begin with, it has a certain surface energy, which *increases* as the deformation of the surface proceeds. However, if the deformation is appreciable, there is also a *decrease* in electrostatic energy because the proton charges get further apart and this effect counteracts the increase in surface energy. It is possible for the drop to become unstable during oscillations if the nuclear charge is high enough—more precisely, if the ratio Z^2/A exceeds a value close to 35. The excited heavy nucleus then splits into two highly excited fragment nuclei, which fly apart with considerable kinetic energy. It is evident that any means of excitation, such as particle bombardment or gamma-ray absorption, may lead to fission; certain nuclides, for example U^{238}, undergo spontaneous fission at a very slow rate.

An estimate of the energy released per fission process can be made either from the empirical data concerning $\bar{B}$ (Figure 9.21) or from the semiempirical formula of Equation (9.3.16). Using the latter, we estimate the mean binding energy per nucleon for a nuclide such as $_{92}U^{238}$,

$$\bar{B} = 15.2 - 2.58 - 3.83 - 1.14 = 7.65 \text{ MeV}.$$

This figure is necessarily somewhat approximate because the formula is being extrapolated into the heavy-nucleus region where all the nuclides are unstable. Nevertheless we may estimate the total binding energy as about $238 \times 7.65 = 1820$ MeV. Now for a hypothetical nuclide of half the atomic mass and charge of $_{92}U^{238}$, we should have a mean binding energy per nucleon

$$\bar{B} = 15.2 - 3.26 - 2.42 - 1.14 = 8.38 \text{ MeV}$$

so that the total binding energy for both fragments is

$$238 \times 8.38 = 1990 \text{ MeV}.$$

The total energy release is therefore about 170 MeV, considerably greater than the energy release in simple nuclear reactions involving light nuclei.

In fact the energy release is nearer 200 MeV per fission and the division of nuclear mass between the two fragments is by no means symmetrical. Experiments have shown that asymmetrical fission is most common, the distribution in mass number having the form of Figure 9.25, which refers to the fission of $_{92}U^{235}$ by slow neutrons. It is noteworthy that the odd-numbered nuclides U^{233}, U^{235}, Pu^{239}, and so forth are fissionable by slow neutrons whereas the even-numbered nuclides Th^{232}, U^{238}, and so forth are split only by fast neutrons.

The kinetic energy acquired by the fission fragments is appreciably less than the total energy release because a certain number of "prompt" neutrons are given off during the fission process. The mean number of neutrons emitted per fission is greater than 2, in most cases, so the possibility arises of setting off a chain reaction with an enormous total energy output. The mean energy of the prompt fission neutrons is about 2 MeV, which is enough to

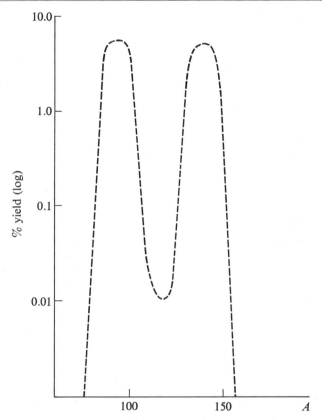

FIGURE 9.25 *Approximate distribution of fission fragment nuclides from the slow-neutron fission of U^{235} plotted against A. The two peaks show the predominance of asymmetric fission processes.*

cause fission in most isotopes of uranium, thorium, and plutonium; but the energy losses of fast neutrons in these materials are such that a chain reaction is self-sustaining only in the odd-numbered nuclides such as U^{235}. This isotope occurs with an abundance of one part in 140 in natural uranium and it has to be extracted laboriously from the natural element to provide material for nuclear bombs, which depend primarily on fast neutrons for their action.

A fission chain reaction can also be self-sustaining with slow neutrons incident on natural uranium as fuel, if a suitable moderator is present to slow down the fission neutrons to the region where they break up the U^{235} nuclei most efficiently. The fuel consists of uranium rods, suitably sheathed, in the form of a lattice embedded in the moderator, which consists usually of heavy water or graphite. If the reactor core, made up in this way, is big enough, the chain reaction commences and builds up a high flux of neutrons in the center. The level of activity has to be controlled so that the cooling system is not overloaded and for this purpose materials such as boron and cadmium, which absorb slow neutrons readily, are employed. Control is facilitated by the fact that a small fraction of the fission neutrons are "delayed," that is, they are emitted from the excited fragments some time after the fission process. This happens only when the nuclides produced by fission are so unstable that neutron decay is more likely than beta decay. Examples of such nuclides, with their half-lives, are

$$_{35}Br^{89} \text{ (4.5 sec)} \quad \text{and} \quad _{53}I^{137} \text{ (22 sec)}.$$

It will be noted that these bodies contain many more neutrons per nucleus than their stable isotopes. After emitting a neutron, each nucleus of this type loses further energy by beta-particle emission.

9.4 Elastic Scattering Processes

Much information about nuclei has been obtained from scattering experiments, notably those carried out by Rutherford's group with alpha particles (Section 6.3). We are still dependent on this type of experiment for our knowledge of particle-particle interactions, the data being usually in the form of scattering cross sections and angular distributions of the particles after collision. In such experiments it is necessary to transform the laboratory data into the center-of-mass coordinate system of the two particles in order that the full significance of the results may be appreciated. For example, a certain process may have an isotropic angular distribution in the center-of-mass system but this simple form is not observed in the laboratory frame unless the target particle happens to be massive compared with the incident particle. In the latter event the center of mass coincides effectively with the target particle, which remains stationary in the laboratory frame, as was assumed in the treatment of Rutherford scattering (Section 6.3).

(a) Transformation into the center-of-mass frame (nonrelativistic)

Suppose that we have a target particle of mass m which is initially stationary in the laboratory frame and which is struck by a particle of mass M moving at velocity $\mathbf{U}$, where U is much smaller than the speed of light. In the center-of-mass system of coordinates the total momentum is always zero, so we have an initial situation in which the particle M moves at speed $U(m/M + m)$ one way and particle m moves at speed $U(M/M + m)$ in the opposite direction. We may note at this stage that the total kinetic energy as measured in the center-of-mass system is

$$K_{cm} = \tfrac{1}{2}MU^2\left(\frac{m}{M + m}\right)^2 + \tfrac{1}{2}mU^2\left(\frac{M}{M + m}\right)^2$$
$$= \tfrac{1}{2}\mu U^2, \tag{9.4.1}$$

where μ is the reduced mass [see Equation (7.7.2)].

At collision the total momentum remains zero in the center-of-mass system, so we suppose that the two particles receive equal and opposite additions of momentum, of magnitude p. The vector $\mathbf{p}$ makes an angle θ with the initial direction of particle M and is to be added to this particle's momentum in the end; while another vector of equal magnitude makes an angle of $(\pi - \theta)$ with the initial direction of M and is to be added finally to particle m (Figure 9.26). The angular distribution of scattering in the center-of-mass frame is denoted by

$$g(\theta)\,d\theta.$$

We now have to find the way in which this distribution transforms into distributions of the recoil angle φ and the scattered-particle angle ψ in the laboratory frame, all angles being measured relative to the incident-particle direction.

In order to pass from the center-of-mass frame to the laboratory frame we have to add, to each velocity, a component of velocity equal in magnitude to that of m in the center-of-mass frame but opposite in direction, that is, $U(M/M + m)$ to the right in Figure 9.26. This is

momenta in center-of-mass frame

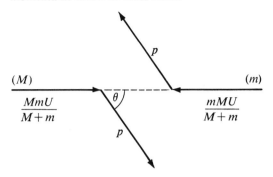

momenta in laboratory frame

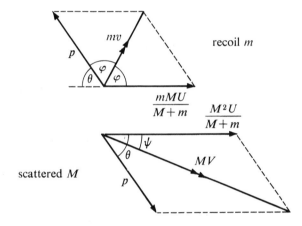

FIGURE 9.26 *Above: elastic collision between particles M and m in their center-of-mass frame, where the angle of scattering is θ and the momentum of each collision is* **p**. *Below: the same collision transformed into the laboratory frame where the final momenta are* **MV** *and* **mv**, *at angles ψ and φ to the original direction of M.*

equivalent to adding a parallel momentum component of magnitude $mU(M/M + m)$ to the momentum of m and a component $MU(M/M + m)$ to the momentum of M. Dealing first with the recoil particle m we find that the final momentum as measured in the laboratory frame, $m\mathbf{v}$, is the vector sum of the momentum $\mathbf{p}$ and the component $m\mathbf{U}(M/M + m)$. Since the recoil angle as observed in the laboratory is φ, we have

$$p^2 = m^2v^2 + \left(\frac{MmU}{M+m}\right)^2 - \frac{2Mm^2vU}{M+m} \cos \varphi.$$

Also from Equation (9.3.1) the recoil velocity is related to φ by the equation

$$v = \frac{2MU}{M+m} \cos \varphi$$

so that

$$p^2 = \left(\frac{MmU}{M+m}\right)^2 \qquad\qquad [9.4.2]$$

and all the sides of the momentum parallelogram (Figure 9.26) are equal. The relation between φ and the center-of-mass angle θ follows

$$2\varphi = \pi - \theta. \tag{9.4.3}$$

Thus while θ ranges from zero to π rad, the recoil angle is necessarily limited to the range from $\frac{\pi}{2}$ rad to zero.

In the special case of scattering which is *isotropic* in the center-of-mass system, the fundamental angular distribution in θ is given by the relation

$$g(\theta) \, d\theta = \text{const} \sin \theta \, d\theta, \tag{9.4.4}$$

since the number of events yielding angles between θ and $(\theta + d\theta)$ is simply proportional to the element of solid angle between those angles. This distribution transforms into an angular distribution of recoils in the laboratory frame which is given by the expression

$$f(\varphi) \, d\varphi = \text{const} \sin (\pi - 2\varphi) \, d(\pi - 2\varphi)$$
$$= \text{const} \sin \varphi \cos \varphi \, d\varphi. \tag{9.4.5}$$

Such a distribution is in fact observed in neutron-proton collisions at low and medium energies (below 10 MeV in the laboratory frame) and it gives rise to the uniform distribution of proton pulse sizes recorded in an ion counter (Figure 9.23).

The relation between the center-of-mass angle θ and the angle of deflection, ψ, of the incident particle is rather complex. However, certain results emerge from direct application of the energy and momentum conservation principles in the laboratory system (see Figure 9.17). The final momentum is MV, where

$$m^2v^2 = M^2U^2 + M^2V^2 - 2M^2UV \cos \psi,$$

also

$$\tfrac{1}{2}mv^2 = \tfrac{1}{2}MU^2 - \tfrac{1}{2}MV^2,$$

whence

$$V^2(M + m) - 2MUV \cos \psi + U^2(M - m) = 0$$

and

$$V = \frac{U}{M + m} [M \cos \psi - \sqrt{m^2 - M^2 \sin^2 \psi}]. \tag{9.4.6}$$

If, therefore, the incident particle is more massive than the target particle, that is, $M > m$, there is a maximum angle of deflection fixed by the condition that the expression

$$(m^2 - M^2 \sin^2 \psi) \quad \text{must be positive.}$$

Thus the maximum deflection, ψ_m, is given by the relation

$$\sin \psi_m = \left| \frac{m}{M} \right|. \tag{9.4.7}$$

For example, if an alpha particle collides with an electron the maximum angle is approximately

$$\psi_m = \frac{1}{4 \times 1840} \text{ rad}$$
$$= 28 \text{ sec of arc.}$$

Although alpha particles lose nearly all their energy by electron collisions in traversing matter, their tracks remain almost straight. Occasional nuclear collisions of the Rutherford type do, however, cause sharp bending of alpha-particle and proton tracks.

(b) Charged-particle scattering

The Rutherford theory of alpha-particle scattering was outlined in Section 6.3 for the special case where the target nucleus (m) is massive and stationary in the laboratory frame. When alpha particles strike electrons or light nuclei, the motion of the target particle has to be taken into account. In the center-of-mass system of coordinates, the angle θ replaces the angle of scattering used in Figure 6.3 and the path of the scattered particle remains hyperbolic, with the impact parameter (b) related to the closest distance of approach ($2a$) in head-on collision by the expression

$$b = a \cot \tfrac{1}{2}\theta.$$

The value of $2a$ is found by equating the *reduced* kinetic energy [Equation (9.4.1)] to the electrostatic potential energy of the two particles (of charges $Z_1 e$ and $Z_2 e$) at the distance $2a$, that is,

$$\tfrac{1}{2}\mu U^2 = \frac{Z_1 Z_2 e^2}{(4\pi\varepsilon_0)2a},$$

or

$$a = \frac{Z_1 Z_2 e^2 (M + m)}{(4\pi\varepsilon_0)Mm U^2}, \qquad [9.4.8]$$

where $\tfrac{1}{2}MU^2$ is the incident kinetic energy (K) in the laboratory frame.

Substituting for θ from Equation (9.4.3), we find the impact parameter in terms of the recoil angle φ (in the laboratory)

$$b = \frac{Z_1 Z_2 e^2 (M + m)}{(4\pi\varepsilon_0)Mm U^2} \tan \varphi. \qquad [9.4.9]$$

Thus the scattering process is treated conveniently in terms of φ. The differential cross section for recoil particles to be ejected into unit solid angle at the angle φ is found to be

$$\frac{d\sigma}{d\Omega} = \frac{2\pi b \, db}{2\pi \sin \varphi \, d\varphi}$$

$$= \left[\frac{Z_1 Z_2 e^2 (M + m)}{(4\pi\varepsilon_0)Mm U^2}\right]^2 \sec^3 \varphi. \qquad [9.4.10]$$

When a particle flux F is incident upon a foil of thickness t, containing n target nuclei per unit volume, the number of recoils observed in a small solid angle, $\Delta\Omega$, at the angle φ is

$$\Delta F = Fnt \, \Delta\sigma$$

$$= Fnt \left[\frac{Z_1 Z_2 e^2 (M + m)}{(4\pi\varepsilon_0)Mm U^2}\right]^2 \sec^3 \varphi \, \Delta\Omega \qquad [9.4.11]$$

which replaces Rutherford's result in this more general treatment.

A very important class of collisions is that in which the incident particle is much more massive than the target particle, as in the case of alpha particles hitting electrons. The basic impact-parameter relation [Equation (9.4.9)] then takes the form

$$b = \frac{MZe^2}{2m(4\pi\varepsilon_0)K} \tan \varphi,$$

where K is the kinetic energy of the incident particle and Z is the charge number of the incident particle.

The kinetic energy lost by the incident particle in a single collision is equal to the energy of the recoiling electron, that is,

$$\Delta K = \frac{4Mm}{(M+m)^2} K \cos^2 \varphi$$

$$= \frac{4mK}{M} \left[1 + \left(\frac{2mbK(4\pi\varepsilon_0)}{MZe^2} \right)^2 \right]^{-1}$$

in the limit when $M \gg m$.

In actual electron collisions the chief energy losses occur when φ is close to $\pi/2$ rad, where the term $\dfrac{2mbK(4\pi\varepsilon_0)}{MZe^2}$ is large compared with unity. Thus, in terms of b, the energy loss per collision is approximately

$$\Delta K = \frac{MZ^2e^4}{(4\pi\varepsilon_0)^2 mb^2 K} . \qquad [9.4.12]$$

This result may be used to formulate a simple classical theory of energy loss by a charged particle as it traverses matter. The particle is supposed to travel in a straight line through a medium containing n electrons per unit volume. A cylinder of radius b may be described with the path as axis and the number of electrons enclosed between two such cylinders, of radii b and $(b + db)$, is $2\pi nb\, db$ per unit length of path. The energy loss to electrons in this cylindrical shell of unit length is therefore

$$2\pi nb\, db\, \frac{MZ^2e^4}{(4\pi\varepsilon_0)^2 mb^2 K}$$

and the total loss must be found by integrating over suitable limits of the parameter b, denoted as $b_{\max}$ and $b_{\min}$. Thus the energy loss per unit distance traveled by the particle at energy K is

$$-\frac{dK}{dx} = \frac{2\pi nZ^2e^4 M}{(4\pi\varepsilon_0)^2 mK} \int_{b_{\min}}^{b_{\max}} \frac{db}{b}$$

$$= \frac{2\pi nZ^2e^4 M}{(4\pi\varepsilon_0)^2 mK} \ln \left(\frac{b_{\max}}{b_{\min}} \right). \qquad [9.4.13]$$

Different theories of the collision process between a fast particle and an atom containing electrons yield different forms for the ratio of $b_{\max}$ to $b_{\min}$. The nonrelativistic formula of Bethe is frequently employed in practical calculations

$$\frac{b_{\max}}{b_{\min}} = \frac{4mK}{M\overline{W}}, \qquad [9.4.14]$$

where $\overline{W}$ is a mean ionization potential of all electrons in an atom of the medium traversed.

Here we shall confine ourselves to a rough estimate of the total range (R) of a particle of original energy K_0. This energy is the total lost over the entire distance from $x = 0$ to $x = R$, that is, we obtain the relation

$$R = \int_0^R dx$$

$$= \int_{K_0}^{0} \frac{dx}{dK}\, dK$$

$$= \frac{(4\pi\varepsilon_0)^2 m}{2\pi nZ^2e^4 M} \int_0^{K_0} \frac{K\, dK}{\ln (b_{\max}/b_{\min})} .$$

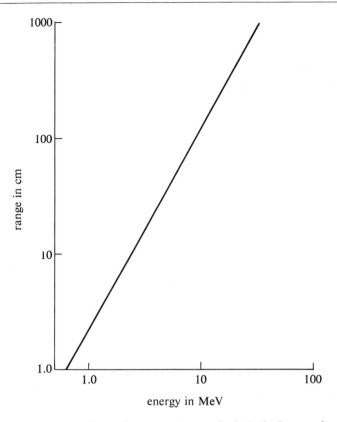

FIGURE 9.27 *The range-energy relation for protons in standard air, both range (in cm) and energy (in MeV) being plotted logarithmically to give a line of mean gradient 1.8.*

If the logarithm term varies only little over the range of energy covered, we may replace it with a mean value, taken outside the integral, and obtain

$$R \propto \int_0^{K_0} K \, dK = \tfrac{1}{2} K_0^2.$$

In fact the logarithm term has the effect of reducing the power of K_0 and in many applications the "Geiger relation" is used instead

$$R \propto K_0^{\frac{3}{2}}.$$

Neither relation is sufficiently accurate for detailed work, as may be seen from a logarithmic plot of the observed range-energy relation for protons in air (Figure 9.27). Over a wide range of energies the range (R) varies nearly as $K_0^{1.8}$. Such experimental data are usually interpreted by detailed calculations based on Bethe's formula [Equations (9.4.13) and (14)], or on the more complete expression of Equation (9.2.2).

Much information has been gathered concerning the rates of energy loss by different particles in different media.* The data show that the charge number Z is not constant but decreases near the end of the particle's range, due to a process whereby the particle picks up one or more electrons to form finally a neutral atom. Thus the rate of energy loss of an

* S. K. Allison and S. D. Warshaw, Rev. Mod. Phys., **25**, 779 (1953).

alpha particle in the region below 1 MeV is reduced considerably from the value given by Equation (9.4.13) with $Z = 2$. Calculations of range are difficult in the "electron-pickup" region because of uncertainties in the value of Z and because the track is likely to be bent appreciably by nuclear collisions, which are more probable at low kinetic energies.

(c) Neutron-proton scattering

This particular type of scattering process is extremely important because it is dominated by the fundamental nuclear forces which bind nuclei together. We have found that the mean binding energy per nucleon in a nucleus is consistent with the hypothesis of "saturation" of nuclear forces, that is, the total potential energy is approximately proportional to the total number (A) of nucleons present. This suggests that the forces are of short range, like the intermolecular forces in a liquid. The suggestion is reinforced by studies of neutron-proton scattering at low and medium energies.

In the energy region below 10 MeV the angular distribution of neutron-proton scattering is essentially isotropic in the center-of-mass system [see Equation (9.4.5)]. In other words, if the angular distribution is expanded in spherical harmonics [Equation (7.6.8)] the only considerable term is of lowest order, $P_0(\cos \theta)$, and the higher values of the orbital angular momentum number l contribute little to the scattering. This result receives a semiclassical description in terms of the impact parameter b. If the neutron is incident with momentum MU at impact parameter b, its angular momentum about the center of mass is very approximately $MU\frac{1}{2}b$. We assume that this orbital angular momentum can be quantized according to the relation

$$\tfrac{1}{2}MUb \approx l\hbar. \qquad [9.4.15]$$

If, now, the interaction is of very short range, say b_0, the maximum value of l which contributes appreciably to the scattering is

$$l_{\max} = \frac{MUb_0}{2\hbar}. \qquad [9.4.16]$$

If this $l_{\max}$ is less than unity, it means that only the $l = 0$ harmonic appears in the center-of-mass distribution, that is, we have "s wave" or isotropic scattering.

The observation that neutron-proton scattering is isotropic up to about 10 MeV (as measured in the laboratory frame) therefore enables us to estimate the maximum effective range of nuclear forces responsible for scattering. We put

$$\frac{MUb_0}{2\hbar} < 1,$$

where

$$MU = (2MK)^{\frac{1}{2}} = 7.3 \times 10^{-20} \text{ kg m/sec}$$

that is,

$$b_0 < \frac{2.1 \times 10^{-34}}{7.3 \times 10^{-20}} = 3 \times 10^{-15} \text{ m, approximately.}$$

If either the kinetic energy increases or a larger range of interaction is effective, values of l higher than zero become important and the scattered wave amplitude involves a number of spherical harmonics of the Legendre type, $P_l(\cos \theta)$, as is shown by a wave-mechanical treatment of the problem. We suppose that the incident neutron is represented in the center-of-mass coordinates by a plane wave traveling in the z direction, that is, we have a wave function of the form

$$\Psi_n = A \exp [i(\kappa z - \omega t)] \qquad \text{see Equation (7.3.13).}$$

The spatially dependent part of Ψ_n is the expression

$$\exp(i\kappa z) = \exp i(\varkappa r), \qquad\qquad [9.4.17]$$

where $\varkappa$ is the wave-number vector of magnitude

$$\kappa = \frac{2\pi}{\lambda} = \frac{p}{\hbar},$$

p is the linear momentum, and $\mathbf{r}$ is the radius vector from the center of mass to any point.

If, now, the angle between the radius vector $\mathbf{r}$ and the wave-number vector $\varkappa$ is α, the scalar product becomes

$$(\varkappa r) = \kappa r \cos \alpha.$$

The imaginary exponential function can then be expanded in terms of Legendre polynomials, $P_l(\cos \alpha)$, on the assumption that the wave has cylindrical symmetry about the z axis, as follows*:

$$\exp(i\kappa r \cos \alpha) = \sum_{l=0}^{\infty} i^l (2l+1)\, P_l(\cos \alpha)\, j_l(\kappa r), \qquad\qquad [9.4.18]$$

where $j_l(\kappa r)$ is a "spherical Bessel function" of order l and takes the approximate form

$$j_l(\kappa r) \propto (\kappa r)^l$$

if (κr) is small compared with unity.

Similar expressions obtain for the scattered wave and for the waves representing the incident and scattered proton. Provided that the quantity (κr) is small, the zeroth-order Bessel function is much larger than any other orders and we have to consider only the $l = 0$ waves in the scattering process. This is the case if either the momentum is small or the effective range of interaction is small.

In low-energy problems, therefore, it is necessary only to represent the nuclear forces as of short range and the results do not depend sensitively on the exact shape of the radial function $U(r)$ assumed for the potential energy. For example, a rectangular-well potential is often employed and the width or depth is adjusted to fit one or more constants of the neutron-proton system. It is known from experiments on the photodisintegration of the deuteron [Equation (9.3.6)] that the two particles are bound with a net energy of -2.225 MeV in the ground state of the deuteron. This figure may be used to fix the depth of a rectangular well representing the potential energy $U(r)$ by the methods of Section 7.4 (see Problem 7.18). For example, if the radius of the rectangular well is taken to be 2.8 fermi, the well depth is $U_0 \approx 20$ MeV; also this depth has to be increased if the radius is reduced.

These parameters may be used to calculate the total neutron-proton scattering cross section at low energies. The result comes out as about five times too *small* compared with the observed thermal-neutron cross section of 20 barns. The discrepancy is much too large to be explained by variations in the well shape or depth. The solution to this difficulty was pointed out by Wigner, who observed that only one $l = 0$ state had been taken into account in the calculation, namely, the deuteron *ground* state with total spin $\hbar$ ($S = 1$). This state is presumably formed with neutron and proton spins parallel, but there is another $l = 0$ state with the spins antiparallel, giving zero total angular momentum. Wigner was able to account for the scattering data by supposing that the second deuteron state is "virtual," that is, its net energy is slightly positive with respect to the situation in which the neutron

---

* G. N. Watson, *Theory of Bessel functions* (Macmillan Co., New York, 1945) 2nd ed., p. 128.

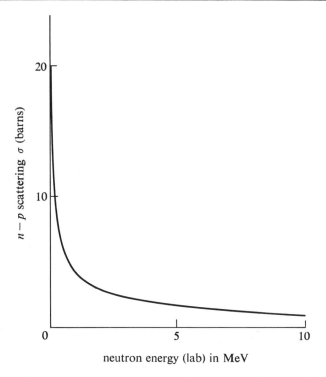

FIGURE 9.28   *The total neutron-proton scattering cross section as a function of neutron energy (in the laboratory frame). The curve represents both experimental points and theoretical calculations.*

and proton are separate. This deduction is supported by experiments on slow-neutron scattering in molecular hydrogen.

The low-energy scattering data are therefore useful in locating the extra state of the deuteron and, with the aid of parameters fixed by *both* the deuteron states, it is possible to account very satisfactorily for the total neutron-proton scattering cross section for energies between zero and about 10 MeV (Figure 9.28). Above this region it is necessary to bring in spherical harmonics with *l* values greater than zero, and the details depend specifically on the properties of the nuclear forces between neutron and proton. So far we have discovered that the forces are of very short range and that they must be spin dependent to some extent, since the two states of the deuteron correspond to different well depths in the rectangular-well treatment.

(*d*) Proton-proton scattering

Proton-proton scattering is more difficult to analyze than neutron-proton scattering for several reasons:

(i) at long ranges the Coulomb repulsion is dominant over the purely nuclear forces and there is a large amount of Rutherford-type scattering at low angles and low energies;

(ii) the fact that two identical particles are involved introduces a wave-mechanical effect akin to interference of the waves representing the protons, due to the fact that there is no distinction between the scattered and scattering particle.

Since Pauli's Exclusion principle applies to protons it is not possible for two protons to interact in certain states which are allowed in the neutron-proton system. For example, in

"*S*" states ($l = 0$), the only possible proton-proton interaction has spins *opposed*, equivalent to ${}^1S_0$ in atomic physics, whereas a neutron and proton can interact in both ${}^1S_0$ and ${}^3S_1$ states, as exemplified by the two deuteron states.

Analysis of the proton-proton scattering data reveals that at low energies there is in fact an appreciable nuclear contribution due to the ${}^1S_0$ state and that the effective well depth is very nearly the same as that for neutron-proton scattering in the same state. This result provides useful support for the *charge-independence* hypothesis, according to which the forces between any two nucleons (whether neutron-neutron, neutron-proton, or proton-proton) are the same in the same kind of state, when Coulomb effects are ignored. The hypothesis has been extremely valuable as a guide in the theory of nuclear forces and it serves to emphasize the idea that neutron and proton are two aspects of the same particle, the nucleon.

(e) *Electron scattering*

The use of electrons in studies of nuclear structure has chiefly developed since intense beams of high-energy electrons became available from linear accelerators, notably the machines at Stanford.* At energies below about 100 MeV the de Broglie wavelength of electrons is too long for them to reveal fine detail in the target, that is, the scattering nuclei, but at higher energies it is possible to pick out the nuclear contribution to scattering.

Scattering experiments with hydrogen gas as the target have shown clearly that the proton does not act as a point scatterer but as an extended target, with the Coulomb law operating down to a small but measurable distance. The root-mean-square radius of the charge distribution which represents a proton in scattering is 0.76 fermi, which is by no means negligible in nuclear measurements. The theoretical significance of this result has not been fully worked out, but it is clear that the Dirac theory of fermions, which applies strictly to point particles, cannot be used in its original form to describe the proton. Not only does the proton have a finite size, in effect, but it possesses structural features which are now being explored with the aid of electron beams in the GeV region. Unfortunately the neutron cannot be used as a target in electron experiments, but some evidence has been obtained from electron-deuteron interactions which indicates that the neutron has some electromagnetic structure, although its net charge is zero.

With heavier target nuclei it is found that the effective radius of the nucleus for electron scattering behaves rather like the neutron-absorption radius at high energies (Section 9.3.b). The results are in general agreement with the expression

$$r = r_0 \sqrt[3]{A} \qquad \text{[Equation (9.3.12)]}$$

but here it is found that the parameter r_0 is about 1.2 fermi, significantly lower than the value obtained from Figure 9.18. Some work has been done to investigate the possibility that the neutrons and protons in a heavy nucleus do not have quite the same spatial distribution. However, the discrepancy between the different r_0 values may be more apparent than real and Green† has indicated that the semiempirical mass formula [Equations (9.3.13) and (14)] fits the data best with a value of r_0 close to 1.2 fermi in the a_3 term. It should be emphasized that the nucleus does not have a sharp boundary so that any radius measurement depends on the definitions adopted.

* R. Hofstadter, Rev. Mod. Phys., **28**, 214 (1956).
† A. E. S. Green, Rev. Mod. Phys., **30**, 569 (1958).

9.5   Nuclear Reaction Characteristics

(a) General considerations

In any nuclear reaction or disintegration process, an unstable nuclear system exists at some stage and the nucleons in this system may be redistributed in several ways. Thus when one kind of particle penetrates nuclei of a single nuclide, many different final products may be detected if there is sufficient energy for their liberation. Occasionally the final particles are of the same character as the combining particles but one of the products is in an excited state—this process is described as *inelastic scattering*. Some of the simplest reactions are capture reactions in which two particles combine to form a *compound nucleus*, which then emits surplus energy in the form of gamma rays. There are also many types of reaction in which two particles combine and two different particles emerge, examples including the (α, p) and (α, n) reactions studied by Rutherford and Chadwick. In all such processes where a definite amount of energy is available the two product particles must divide the energy in a definite ratio so that they emerge with well-defined kinetic energies. This is not the case when *multiple* breakdown occurs, that is, three or more particles emerge at the same time. In these reactions the kinetic energies form continuous distributions because the conditions of energy and momentum conservation do not impose unique values on the particle energies. In this section we shall be concerned with simple processes only.

When two particles react to form new particles, for example,

$$A + a \rightarrow B + b$$

the rest masses of the final products add up, in general, to a sum which is different from the sum of the original rest masses. The energy of reaction appears as the difference between these two sums and is usually denoted as Q, expressed in MeV. If all the particles are in their ground states, we may write the energy difference as Q_0. If one or more of the products is in an excited state, its internal energy causes it to possess a higher rest mass (see Section 5.6) and the Q value is different from Q_0. Thus different excited states lead to different Q values, as determined directly from experimental data. Conservation of energy requires that the difference between any Q and Q_0 is equal to the excitation energy, as may be seen from Figure 9.29. Here we represent the total mass of $A + a$ by one horizontal line and the

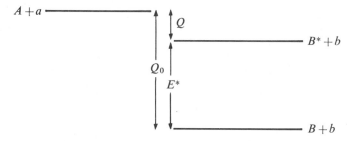

FIGURE 9.29   *The representation of a nuclear reaction on an energy-level diagram. Here $A + a$ represents the mass of the reacting particles and $B + b$ the mass of the products in their ground states, the energy release being Q_0. If one of the products (B) is formed in an excited state with excitation energy E^*, this amount has to be subtracted from Q_0 to yield the effective energy release Q.*

sum $B + b$ by another, which is a vertical distance Q_0 below the first (for an exoergic reaction). If, however, B is also formed in an excited state, denoted by B^*, then the level of $(B^* + b)$ is at a distance Q below the $(A + a)$ line. It follows that the energy of excitation (E^*) of B is

$$E^* = Q_0 - Q. \qquad [9.5.1]$$

If there is no possibility of final excited states being involved, a unique Q_0 is found from the known masses of the reacting particles. For example, if we require the energy of reaction for the process

$$_1D^2 + {_1}D^2 \rightarrow {_0}n^1 + {_2}He^3 \qquad \text{from Equation (9.3.17)}$$

and we are given the atomic masses (in C^{12} units) as

$$_1D^2 = 2.014102 \qquad _0n^1 = 1.008665 \qquad _2He^3 = 3.016030$$

then the mass excess of the combining particles is

$$\Delta m = 0.003509 \text{ u}.$$

The conversion ratio 1 u = 931.44 MeV then yields $Q_0 = 3.27$ MeV.

Tables now frequently quote nuclide mass excesses or defects (the differences between atomic masses and the nearest integers) in energy units, so that the conversion step is avoided. The masses of extranuclear electrons balance out on both sides of simple reactions.

When the Q value for any nuclear reaction is known, it may be necessary to calculate the kinetic energies of the product particles at different angles relative to the incident-particle direction. When only two particles are emitted, a simple classical treatment is usually adequate for solution of the problem. Suppose, for example, that we have an incident particle of mass m_0 and velocity $\mathbf{u}_0$ in the laboratory frame, where u_0 is very much smaller than the speed of light, and this particle strikes a mass M_0 which is initially stationary in the laboratory frame. The product particles are m, traveling with velocity $\mathbf{v}$ at angle ψ, and M, traveling with velocity $\mathbf{V}$ at angle φ, both angles being relative to the incident beam (Figure 9.30). The momentum triangle shows that, if we require the energy of particle m as a function of angle ψ, we must use the relation

$$M^2 V^2 = m_0^2 u_0^2 + m^2 v^2 - 2m_0 m u_0 v \cos \psi.$$

In an exoergic reaction the energy-balance equation is

$$\tfrac{1}{2} m_0 u_0^2 + Q = \tfrac{1}{2} m v^2 + \tfrac{1}{2} M V^2,$$

whence we find a quadratic equation

$$(M + m)mv^2 - 2m_0 m u_0 v \cos \psi - 2MQ - (M - m_0)m_0 u_0^2 = 0. \qquad [9.5.2]$$

Solutions for v and hence for the energy of the particle m can be found for different values of the angle ψ.

A simple solution exists in the special case: $\psi = \dfrac{\pi}{2}$ rad, when we find

$$(M + m)mv^2 = 2MQ + (M - m_0)m_0 u_0^2$$

or, writing $\tfrac{1}{2} m_0 u^2 = K_0$ (the bombarding energy), the result is

$$K = \tfrac{1}{2} m v^2 = \frac{MQ + (M - m_0)K_0}{(M + m)}. \qquad [9.5.3]$$

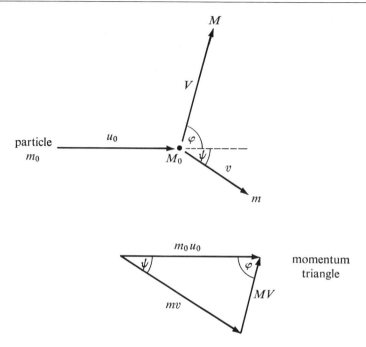

FIGURE 9.30 *A nuclear reaction between particles m_0 (with original speed u_0) and M_0, which is stationary in the laboratory frame. After the reaction, particles m and M emerge with velocities **v** and **V** respectively, at angles ψ and φ to the original direction of m_0.*

For example, the energy of neutrons produced at 90° to an incident deuteron beam of energy 1 MeV by the D + D reaction is

$$K = \frac{3.016030 \times 3.27 + 1.001928 \times 1.0}{4.024695}$$

$$= 2.70 \text{ MeV.}$$

It will be appreciated that, unless extremely accurate results are required, the whole-number masses may often be used in calculations of this type. The full solution shows that the neutron energy varies from about 4.1 MeV at the forward angle $\psi = 0°$ to about 1.7 MeV at the backward angle $\psi = 180°$.

In all exoergic reactions there is a finite yield even at very low bombarding energies, although this yield may be strongly inhibited by Coulomb repulsion if the reacting particles are charged. In every endoergic reaction there exists a *threshold* bombarding energy below which no yield is possible. This threshold is greater than the magnitude of the Q value, because the conservation of momentum requires that the product particles recoil with a certain kinetic energy which is additional to the reaction energy. As in the calculations of Section 9.4.a, we can work in the center-of-mass coordinate system, where the net momentum is always zero. The reduced kinetic energy in this frame is

$$K_{cm} = \tfrac{1}{2}\mu u_0^2 = \frac{M_0 m_0 u_0^2}{2(M_0 + m_0)}$$

and this is the "free energy" available for reaction. Thus the threshold bombarding energy (K_t) is found by putting the free energy equal to the magnitude of the Q value

$$\frac{M_0 m_0 u_0^2}{2(M_0 + m_0)} = |Q|,$$

whence

$$K_t = \frac{M_0 + m_0}{M_0} |Q|. \qquad [9.5.4]$$

For example, the neutron-producing reaction $C^{12}(d, n)N^{14}$ of Equation (9.3.19) has $Q_0 = -0.28$ MeV, so the threshold bombarding energy for deuterons is $K_t^d = \frac{14}{12} \times 0.28 = 0.33$ MeV approximately. On the other hand, if we used C^{12} ions to bombard a deuterium target, the threshold bombarding energy would be $K_t^C = \frac{14}{2} \times 0.28 = 1.96$ MeV approximately.

(b) Inelastic scattering

This type of nuclear reaction is denoted by the equation

$$A + a \rightarrow A^* + a,$$

where A^* stands for a target nucleus left in an excited state after bombardment with particle a. In inelastic scattering the general theory of nuclear reactions applies, with different Q values for different degrees of excitation of A^*. One type of inelastic scattering

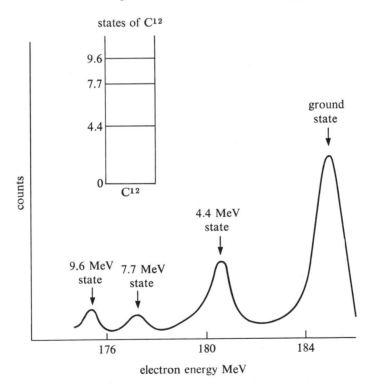

FIGURE 9.31 *The energy spectrum of high-energy electrons scattered from a carbon target showing the presence of groups due to inelastic scattering, with the excitation of C^{12} nuclei to various states. The energy levels of C^{12} at low excitation are also shown.*

is called *Coulomb excitation* because the bombarding particle causes excitation of the target nucleus through its long-range Coulomb interaction, without actually penetrating the target.

In all cases of scattering the fundamental Q value (Q_0) is zero, but, when inelastic scattering occurs, different groups of scattered particles may be sorted out by analyzing the scattered beam and each energy group yields a different Q value. For example, Figure 9.31 depicts the energy distribution of 185 MeV electrons after they have been scattered by carbon. In addition to an elastically scattered group close to 185 MeV (which indicates that the carbon recoil energy is very small), there are groups at 181, 177, 175 MeV, and lower energies. The differences in Q value are consistent with known excited states of the C^{12} nucleus at 4.4, 7.7, and 9.6 MeV above the ground state. These states have also been detected by the inelastic scattering of fast neutrons in carbon.

(c) Nonresonant capture processes

We have mentioned that slow neutrons often undergo radiative capture whereby the neutron is absorbed by a nucleus and the excess energy appears in the form of gamma rays. The same kind of process occurs with protons but with a lower probability because of the Coulomb repulsion between the charged particles. Nevertheless many proton-capture reactions have been reported among the lighter nuclides and some of these are of considerable interest.

In all cases of capture, the excitation energy of the compound nucleus formed is equal to the total energy input minus the kinetic energy of the recoiling nucleus. Thus if the mass relations are

$$c^2(M_0 + m_0) = Mc^2 + Q_0$$

and the bombarding energy is

$$K_0 = \tfrac{1}{2}m_0 u_0^2$$

the recoiling nucleus has kinetic energy

$$K_r = \tfrac{1}{2}MV^2,$$

where, by conservation of linear momentum, we find that

$$K_r = \frac{m_0}{M} K_0.$$

Thus the excitation energy of the compound nucleus is

$$E^* = K_0 + Q_0 - K_r$$
$$= Q_0 + \frac{M - m_0}{M} K_0 \qquad\qquad [9.5.5]$$

and this energy is normally expended in gamma-ray emission.

Several cases of simple capture are known among the lightest nuclides, including the neutron-proton capture process [Equation (9.3.25)]. Proton capture and alpha-particle capture have been studied in experiments where the bombarding energy is low and the reaction is detected by the gamma rays emitted. Examples include

$$_1H^1 + {}_1D^2 \rightarrow {}_2He^3 + \hbar\omega \qquad Q_0 = 5.5 \text{ MeV} \qquad [9.5.6]$$
$$_1H^1 + {}_1T^3 \rightarrow {}_2He^4 + \hbar\omega \qquad Q_0 = 19.8 \text{ MeV} \qquad [9.5.7]$$
$$_2He^4 + {}_1T^3 \rightarrow {}_3Li^7 + \hbar\omega \qquad Q_0 = 2.47 \text{ MeV.} \qquad [9.5.8]$$

It is evident from Equation (9.5.5) that the gamma-ray energy depends on the bombarding energy (K_0) and this feature makes these reactions useful occasionally as gamma-ray sources, the chief drawback being the low yields obtained.

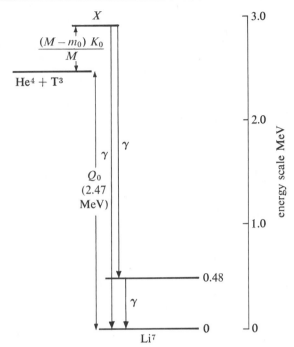

FIGURE 9.32 *Energy-level diagram depicting the nonresonant capture process:* $He^4 + H^3 \rightarrow Li^7$ *which involves the emission of gamma rays leading to either the ground state or the first excited state of the nuclide* Li^7.

One important feature of the $He^4 + T^3$ capture reaction [Equation (9.5.8)] is the fact that, at low bombarding energies, *two* groups of gamma rays are emitted, one corresponding to Li^7 being formed in the ground state and the other with about 0.5 MeV less energy. It is therefore supposed that the Li^7 nucleus has an excited state, 0.5 MeV above the ground state, which can be reached in the capture reaction. The two different capture processes may be represented on an energy-level diagram, as in Figure 9.32. The lowest state, that of Li^7 in its ground state, is denoted by zero on the energy scale and the Q_0 value (2.47 MeV) separates this from the line marked $He^4 + T^3$, which corresponds to these particles combining with zero kinetic energy. Any bombarding energy which is supplied then contributes an amount $\dfrac{(M - m_0)}{M} K_0$ to the free energy available and this is indicated by an appropriate point X. From this point two transitions can be made, either to the Li^7 ground state or to its excited state, and the vertical arrows show the gamma-ray energies produced in these transitions. It follows from the diagram that a third gamma-ray group must be emitted when the excited Li^7 nuclei pass to the ground state. This gamma radiation is, in fact, detected in a number of reactions, including the inelastic scattering of alpha particles by lithium, and the energy is found to be 0.48 MeV.

(d) Resonant capture processes

In many nuclides in the region above helium and lithium, the capture of a proton occurs preferentially at certain bombarding energies, because the compound nucleus is formed in well-defined excited states. Under these conditions the chief gamma rays detected are sharp

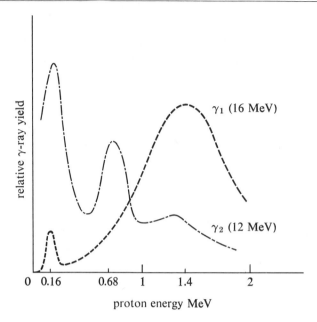

FIGURE 9.33 *Approximate gamma-ray yield curves for two energy groups—at about 16 MeV and at about 12 MeV—produced in the $B^{11} + H^1$ capture reaction. The yield is plotted against proton bombarding energy to locate resonances due to excited states of the compound nucleus C^{12}.*

"lines" characteristic of the compound nucleus and forming a recognizable spectrum. For example, if a target containing B^{11} nuclei is bombarded with protons and the gamma-ray yield is plotted against the bombarding energy, the graph obtained is as shown in Figure 9.33. At 0.16 MeV proton energy there is a sharp peak or "resonance" for gamma-ray emission. This peak is ascribed to the compound nucleus, C^{12}, being formed in an excited state and the excitation energy is given by Equation (9.5.5). With $Q_0 = 15.96$ MeV

$$E^* = Q_0 + \frac{M - m_0}{M} K_0$$

$$= 15.96 + \frac{11 \times 0.16}{12} = 16.11 \text{ MeV.}$$

This state has somewhat higher energy than those C^{12} states detected by inelastic scattering (Figure 9.31) but its existence has been confirmed by experiments on other nuclear reactions.

At proton energies above 0.16 MeV two broad peaks are seen in Figure 9.33 and these are ascribed to states of C^{12} at 16.58 and 17.22 MeV above the ground state. When the gamma rays are analyzed it is found that they consist of three chief components—a high-energy component (γ_1) at about 16 MeV, a second component (γ_2) near 12 MeV, and a third component (γ_3) at 4.4 MeV. At the first resonance, all three components are present and it appears that in the 16.11 MeV state the C^{12} nuclei lose energy either by direct transition to the ground state (by γ_1) or by emitting γ_2 and γ_3 in cascade, the intermediate level being the well-known state at 4.4 MeV (Figure 9.31). These changes can be drawn on an energy-level diagram, as in Figure 9.34. It is conventional to draw a small graph similar to that of Figure 9.33 on its side above the $B^{11} + H^1$ level at 15.96 MeV, so that the resonance peaks correspond in position to the compound-nucleus states (apart from the correction due to recoil energy). Two such small graphs are depicted, one for the γ_1 component and the other for the γ_2 component.

It is found that the resonance at 0.68 MeV bombarding energy (16.58 MeV in the compound nucleus) yields only the γ_2 and γ_3 components and this observation indicates that the cascade process is dominant, with a slightly higher energy (γ_2') for the γ_2 component here compared with γ_2 at the 0.16 MeV resonance. At the higher resonance of 1.4 MeV bombarding energy (17.22 MeV in the compound nucleus) all three components are detected; these may be due either to direct deexcitation of this level to the ground and 4.4 MeV excited states or to deexcitation via the 16.11 MeV level. It will be appreciated that a considerable amount of experimental work is required to elucidate the details of transitions even in such a light nuclide as C^{12}.

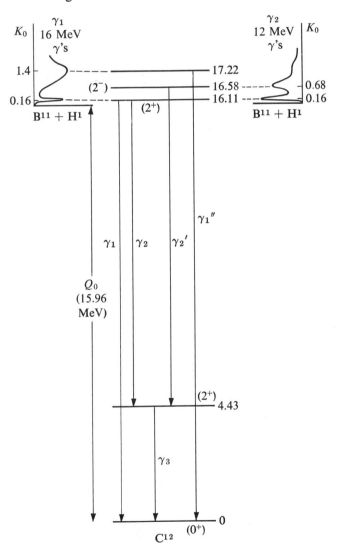

FIGURE 9.34 *Energy-level diagram to show proton-capture processes in* B^{11} *forming high-energy states in* $C^{12}*$, *which lead by various gamma-ray transitions to the ground state and first excited state of the same nuclide.*

Another well-known case of resonant proton capture is the reaction

$$_3\text{Li}^7 + {}_1\text{H}^1 \rightarrow {}_4\text{Be}^8 + \hbar\omega \qquad Q_0 = 17.23 \text{ MeV}. \qquad [9.5.9]$$

At a bombarding energy of 0.44 MeV a sharp resonance is observed for the emission of gamma rays with energy 17.6 MeV and these are clearly due to deexcitation of the compound nucleus Be^8* from a state 17.6 MeV above its ground state. It is interesting to observe that Be^8 is itself a highly unstable nuclide, even in the ground state, which breaks up very rapidly into two He^4 nuclei with a small release of energy (0.094 MeV). Furthermore the 17.6 MeV gamma rays from $\text{Li}^7 + \text{H}^1$ are accompanied by a weaker 14.5 MeV

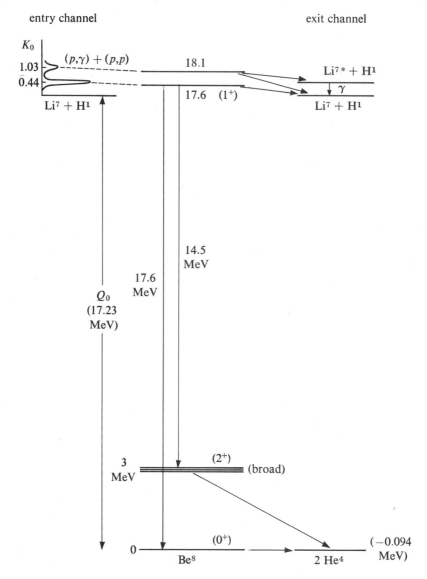

FIGURE 9.35 *Energy-level diagram to show various* $\text{Li}^7 + \text{H}^1$ *processes. Capture of the protons may lead to gamma-emission from the 17.6 MeV and 18.1 MeV states of* Be^8*, *which lead eventually to two* He^4 *nuclei, and elastic or inelastic scattering of the protons is also possible from the same states.*

component which is due to transitions between the 17.6 MeV state and a broad state in Be^8* at 3 MeV above the ground state. The 3 MeV state breaks up directly into two He^4 nuclei, so no low-energy gamma rays are detected in conjunction with the 14.5 MeV line. The various changes are depicted on the energy-level diagram of Figure 9.35, which has its zero located at the ground state of Be^8 and has the "entry channel" ($Li^7 + H^1$) on the left with various "exit channels" on the right.

The same diagram serves to illustrate a fundamental feature of nuclear reactions in which a compound nucleus is involved. Since the 17.6 MeV state of Be^8* can be formed by the particles Li^7 and H^1 in the entry channel, it is presumably possible for this state to lose its energy by producing the same particles in the exit channel. Such a process is interpreted as *elastic* scattering but it has the special feature of a resonance in the scattering cross section at 0.44 MeV proton bombarding energy. Such "compound-elastic" scattering does occur, in addition to the usual Rutherford-type scattering between charged particles, and the transition is included in Figure 9.35. Moreover, we have found that the nuclide Li^7 itself has an excited state 0.48 MeV above its ground state. This is not accessible from the 0.44 MeV proton resonance, but if we employ a bombarding energy of 1.03 MeV we find a resonance for both elastic and inelastic scattering, the latter process being represented by the equation

$$Li^7 + H^1 \rightarrow Li^{7*} + H^1. \quad [9.5.10]$$

At this 1.03 MeV resonance, therefore, there are gamma-ray components from the de-excitation of Li^{7*} nuclei as well as gamma rays from Be^8*. It should be emphasized that Figures 9.34 and 9.35 represent only a small number of the possible reactions and transitions in these nuclides.

In heavy elements proton capture is extremely unlikely because of enhanced Coulomb repulsion and a much more probable process is the capture of slow neutrons, which always produce isotopes of the element bombarded. We have mentioned that the element rhodium, for instance, readily captures slow neutrons to produce $Rh^{104}*$, which in turn emits gamma rays and beta rays to end up as Pd^{104} (Section 9.3.f). The value of Q_0 for the capture reaction [Equation (9.3.26)] is 6.8 MeV and this is essentially the excitation energy of the compound nucleus, since the kinetic energy of the incident neutron is negligible. If the total cross section of rhodium for slow neutrons is measured, for example by the chopper technique (Figure 9.24), the results exhibit a marked resonance in the low-energy region. Figure 9.36 is a logarithmic plot of the total cross section against neutron energy and it shows a maximum value of 4800 barns at 1.3 eV. By way of contrast, the same diagram shows the absorption cross section of the nuclide B^{10} for slow neutrons, the absorption being due to the (n, α) reaction [Equation (9.3.29)], which obeys the "$1/v$" law in this energy range.

The very large cross section of rhodium for slow neutrons at 1.3 eV is due almost entirely to the (n, γ) absorption process [Equation (9.3.26)] and it shows that there must be an excited state of the compound nucleus Rh^{104} which happens to lie just 1.3 eV above the Q_0 value (which is approximately 6.8 MeV). Slow-neutron resonances of this kind are comparatively common in heavy nuclides because their nuclei possess numerous excited states in the energy region above a few MeV.

The most remarkable feature of the slow-neutron resonances in heavy nuclei is their extreme narrowness when compared with the excitation energy — in rhodium, for instance, the estimated width (Γ) is 0.16 eV while the excitation energy is about 6.8 MeV. According to the Uncertainty principle (Section 7.2) a small value of Γ indicates a large value of the mean lifetime (τ) of the state. In the example quoted, the estimated lifetime is 3×10^{-15} sec,

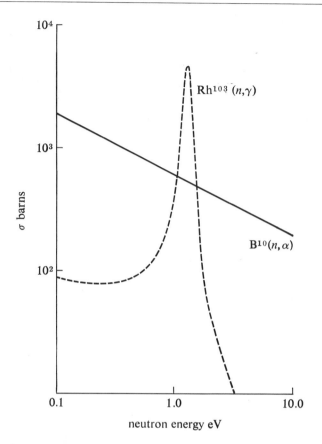

FIGURE 9.36   *The absorption cross sections of the nuclides* B^{10} *and* Rh^{103} *for slow neutrons plotted logarithmically. The* (n, α) *reaction in* B^{10} *obeys the "$1/v$" law while the* (n, γ) *reaction in rhodium exhibits a sharp resonance.*

which is long compared with the time for a nucleon to cross the nuclear diameter (about 10^{-22} sec). Thus the compound nucleus is a well-defined entity, even in highly-excited states, and the energy of excitation should be thoroughly redistributed before deexcitation finally takes place. This process is characteristic of many nuclear reactions, though not of all, and it means that there is almost complete independence between the entry and exit channels, shown in Figure 9.35. In this kind of reaction the final products depend on the specific properties of the compound-nucleus state and not on the manner in which the compound nucleus was formed.

(e) Compound-nucleus reactions

   The existence of sharp resonances at certain bombarding energies in several types of nuclear reaction, and notably in capture reactions, indicates the important role played by the compound nucleus in these processes. All compound-nucleus reactions start off as simple capture reactions, the excitation energy of the compound nucleus being given by Equation (9.5.5). Resonances observed in the yield curve, as in Figure 9.33, are characteristic of the compound nucleus and enable us to locate some of its energy levels, if Q_0 is known. Data may be accumulated to show how the various states of light nuclides are linked by different nuclear reactions. Thus one particular state may figure in one reaction with the nuclide acting as the compound nucleus and at another time may appear as a feature of the residual nucleus in a reaction (compare Figures 9.32 and 9.35). It follows that numerous experiments with different techniques are needed before all the excited states of one nuclide are explored, even in a limited energy region.

In order to illustrate the complexity of compound-nucleus relations we return to the $B^{11} + H^1$ reactions, displayed partly in Figure 9.34. At the 0.16 MeV resonance, two groups of long-range alpha particles are detected in addition to the three groups of gamma rays. One group (α_0) is formed by the reaction

$$_5B^{11} + {}_1H^1 \rightarrow {}_2He^4 + {}_4Be^8 \qquad Q_0 = 8.59 \text{ MeV} \qquad [9.5.11]$$

with the ground state of Be^8 breaking up further into two low-energy alpha particles (see Figure 9.35). The second alpha-particle group of appreciable energy (α_1) is obtained from

$$_5B^{11} + {}_1H^1 \rightarrow {}_2He^4 + {}_4Be^{8*} \qquad Q = 5.6 \text{ MeV}.$$

with the excited Be^8 nuclei in the broad 3 MeV state, which again breaks up finally into two alpha particles. Both of the alpha groups (α_0 and α_1) are emitted from the 16.11 MeV excited state of $_6C^{12}$ and are depicted in the exit channel of Figure 9.37.

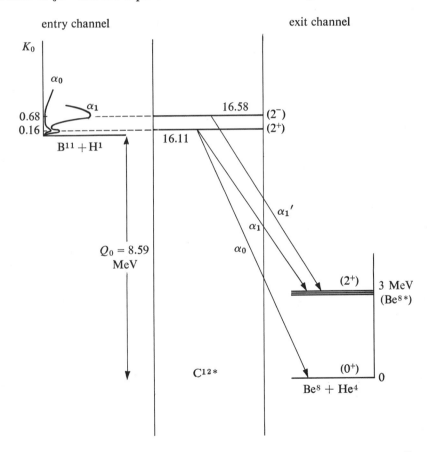

FIGURE 9.37 *The $B^{11}(p, \alpha)$ reaction proceeds predominantly via the compound nucleus C^{12}, two states of which give rise to long-range alpha groups leading to the ground state and first excited state of Be^8.*

Further experiments show that the 16.58 MeV level in C^{12*} gives rise to the lower-energy alpha group (α_1) but not the highest energy group (α_0). This type of preferential transition is not unexpected because the gamma-decay relations of the 16.11 and 16.58 MeV states are also different. The task of the nuclear physicist is often to explain preferential behavior in terms of selection rules, based on angular momentum changes and other characteristics of the states involved.

Further study of the Be^8 states can be made with the $Li^7 + H^1$ combination, already shown in Figure 9.35. Up to the resonance in proton bombarding energy at 1.03 MeV, the only products detected are gamma rays and protons, scattered elastically and inelastically. At bombarding energies near 2 MeV, neutrons are produced, according to the scheme

$$_3Li^7 + {}_1H^1 \rightarrow {}_0n^1 + {}_4Be^7 \qquad Q_0 = -1.65 \text{ MeV}. \qquad [9.5.12]$$

This is an endoergic reaction with a threshold for proton bombardment given by Equation (9.5.4), that is,

$$K_t^p = \tfrac{8}{7} \times 1.65 = 1.88 \text{ MeV}.$$

At 2.25 MeV bombarding energy there is a resonance for neutron emission and this appears to be the dominant mode for deexcitation of the corresponding Be^{8*} state at 19.2 MeV. At still higher bombarding energies there are no clear resonances but the neutrons produced have a spectrum which consists of two groups separated by about 0.5 MeV. This result

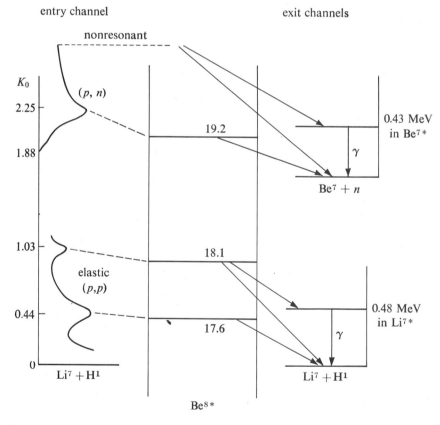

FIGURE 9.38   *The (p, p) and (p, n) reaction in Li^7 lead via certain states of Be^{8*} to either the ground or first excited states of the residual nuclei Li^7 and Be^7.*

indicates the occurrence of *nonresonant* reactions in which the residual nuclide Be^7 is formed either in its ground state or in an excited state at 0.43 MeV above ground, as shown in Figure 9.38.

Several publications are available in which the complex interrelations of the various light nuclides are displayed in the form of energy-level diagrams. We may summarize the methods employed to establish the details of these diagrams, as follows:

(i) first the occurrence of a given reaction is established by identification of the particles emitted and, if possible, by measurement of the quantity Q_0 for checking with the atomic mass values;

(ii) the yield of the reaction, or preferably the total cross section for the reaction, is plotted against bombarding energy to locate resonances which may indicate the part played by a compound nucleus in the process;

(iii) at different bombarding energies the energy spectrum of emitted particles or gamma rays must be examined to see if different groups, with different Q values, occur, indicating the existence of excited states in the residual nuclei;

(iv) finally more information can be obtained about the levels involved in both the compound and residual nuclei by measuring the angular distributions of emitted particles and, in some cases, by polarization measurements. Such angular properties are determined by the angular momentum conditions of particles in the entry and exit channels. In favorable circumstances a unique specification of angular momenta can be made from the angular distribution data.

(f) Other types of reaction

In the compound-nucleus theory of nuclear reactions, strong interactions between the target nucleus and the incident particle are supposed to lead to the formation of a definite compound nucleus which lasts for an appreciable interval before breaking up or being deexcited. This theory accounts for many processes, including slow-neutron absorption, but other evidence indicates that nucleon-nucleus interactions are not always sufficiently strong for compound-nucleus formation. For example, fast-neutron scattering experiments (Section 9.3.b) are not entirely consistent with the simple "black-nucleus" model, although the latter receives some support from the data of Figure 9.18. When all the fast-neutron data are examined it appears that, over a wide range of energies, the interaction between the target nucleus and the incident neutron is comparatively weak. Estimates of the mean free path of a neutron in nuclear matter come out as several times bigger than the largest nuclear diameters. This has led to the formulation of the "optical model" of nucleon scattering, which treats the target nucleus as a semitransparent body in the path of the neutron wave.

The development of the optical model has important implications for the theories of nuclear structure and nuclear reactions. In the first place, it appears that a nucleon can travel through the interior of a nucleus without interacting too frequently with the other nucleons. This is the basis of the *individual-particle model* of nuclear structure, described in Section 9.9. Secondly, it is likely that many reactions proceed by short-period interactions which do not involve compound-nucleus states. For example, it is possible by particle bombardment to eject protons from nuclei in the forward direction and these "direct" processes have quite different characteristics from compound-nucleus reactions.

One important group of direct-interaction processes includes "deuteron-stripping" reactions of the types (d, n) and (d, p). The deuteron consists of a neutron and a proton which are loosely bound to each other and in a short-period interaction it is possible for a target nucleus to capture a proton or neutron from a passing deuteron, leaving the other particle free to travel onwards. Thus many (d, p) and (d, n) reactions show characteristic angular distributions of the product particles, with pronounced peaks in the forward direction. Butler and others have shown that these angular distributions may be analyzed to find the net change in orbital angular momentum (Δl in $\hbar$ units) transferred from the deuteron to the target nucleus.

In addition to "direct-interaction" processes there are nuclear reactions in which individual excited states of the compound nucleus are grouped together to form broad maxima in the cross-section curves. This happens in fast-neutron scattering experiments, the broad maxima being explained by the optical model. However, the most striking maxima are the resonances observed in the photodisintegration of medium and heavy

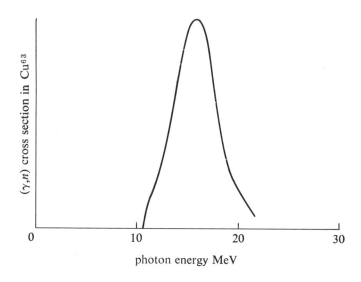

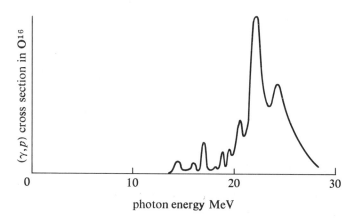

FIGURE 9.39 *Photodisintegration cross sections plotted against incident photon energy in MeV. The Cu^{63}(γ, n) curve exhibits a pronounced "dipole resonance" but in the light-nuclide reaction O^{16}(γ, p) the resonance is split into subsidiary maxima, some of which are identified with individual levels of the O^{16*} nucleus.*

nuclei. For example, it is possible to measure the cross section for the reaction

$$_{29}Cu^{63} + \hbar\omega \rightarrow {}_{0}n^{1} + {}_{29}Cu^{62} \qquad [9.5.13]$$

by bombarding copper with bremsstrahlung from a betatron and recording the Cu^{62} activity produced as the maximum electron energy is varied over the energy region from the threshold (10.8 MeV) upwards. The results (Figure 9.39) show a broad peak centered at about 16 MeV photon energy. Similar peaks are observed for (γ, n) and (γ, p) reactions in all medium and heavy elements, the peak energies ranging from about 22 MeV (in light nuclides) to about 14 MeV (in the heaviest nuclides). Detailed study shows that these "giant resonances" are due to electric-dipole interaction between the nucleus and the incident photons.

Some explanation of the dipole-resonance effect can be obtained from a "collective" model in which the nucleus as a whole is supposed to execute oscillations; the model is similar in many ways to the liquid-drop theory of fission (Section 9.3.g) but the oscillation modes are different. However, this type of theory describes only the broad features of the process and the question arises whether individual excited states of the nucleus are involved. The question cannot easily be answered by experiments on heavy nuclides such as copper, because they possess too many states in the high-excitation region. In order to detect possible contributions from individual states, it is necessary to work with light nuclides. One set of results, from the reaction

$$_{8}O^{16} + \hbar\omega \rightarrow {}_{1}H^{1} + {}_{7}N^{15}, \qquad [9.5.14]$$

is shown in Figure 9.39. Here the "giant resonance" is split into at least two peaks and on the low-energy side there are many subsidiary peaks which have been attributed to known excited states of the nuclide $_{8}O^{16}$. Although the results are not conclusive they suggest that the dipole resonance is made up of many sharp peaks clustered together in the resonance region. Similar conclusions have been drawn in other types of nuclear reaction.

It appears, therefore, that nuclear interactions are strong enough to induce a certain amount of collective behavior and to allow the existence of sharp compound-nucleus states; on the other hand, the success of optical-model calculations in scattering problems indicates that, to a first approximation, one can treat the interaction between a single nucleon and the nucleus as a whole as being comparatively weak. The mathematical difficulties inherent in the expression of these ideas have led to the coexistence of several nuclear models, each of which has a restricted domain of validity.

9.6 Properties of Nuclear States

It has been shown that many features of nuclear reactions, and particularly of compound-nucleus reactions, are to be interpreted in terms of definite excited states of the nuclei taking part. Reactions are often used to determine properties of these states—for example, the measurement of Q values enables the energy levels to be fixed and in some cases the effective width of a state can be found. For the purposes of nuclear theory it is also important to fix properties such as the total angular momentum and the parity associated with each state. These properties are involved in the selection rules which govern transition probabilities between states and in the angular distributions of particles emitted during such transitions.

(a) *Total angular momentum or "spin" (I)*

Studies of the excited states of *atomic* systems (Section 7.11) show that it is possible to ascribe to each state a definite electron configuration. In cases of small spin-orbit interaction we have Russell-Saunders coupling of the orbital and spin momenta and each state is assigned a definite total spin number (S), an orbital momentum number (L), and a total angular momentum number (J). This is possible essentially because the atom is a comparatively open structure and the Coulomb interactions between electrons are not excessive. In a nucleus, on the other hand, the nucleons interact more strongly and the nuclear forces are complex, involving considerable spin-orbit interaction. As a result it is not possible, in general, to separate spin and orbital angular momentum; thus the situation approaches j–j coupling as described in Section 7.11. However, the total angular momentum must be conserved always and each state possesses a total angular momentum number (I) which has the same properties as the number J in atomic physics. The number I is often called the nuclear "spin" although in fact orbital momentum may contribute to it.

Since the neutron and proton each have spin $\frac{1}{2}\hbar$ and the orbital momentum numbers (l) are always integral, it follows that the I numbers are integers for all nuclides in which the baryon number (A) is even and are half odd integers for all nuclides with A odd. This rule is strictly obeyed and it illustrates the validity of angular momentum conservation in all nuclear processes.

Measurements of I for nuclear states can be divided into two classes, namely, those in which the state is long-lived (as in the ground states of stable nuclides) and those where the state is short-lived (as in most compound-nucleus states). In the latter event, it is necessary to deduce I from the properties of nuclear reactions in which the state occurs or from decay characteristics such as the mean lifetime. Here we are concerned with the establishment of I numbers for long-lived states.

Many determinations of I for nuclear ground states have been based on the hyperfine structure of atomic spectral lines. In Section 7.10 we found that the lowest state of the hydrogen atom, denoted in spectroscopy by $1^2S_{1/2}$, is split into two close levels (Figure 7.19). This effect is due to the $\frac{1}{2}\hbar$ spin of the proton, which can be combined in two ways with the $\frac{1}{2}\hbar$ spin of the single electron, to yield a total angular momentum number of either 0 or 1. The energy difference between the two levels is due to a magnetic interaction, the magnitude of which may be estimated by semiclassical methods (see Problem 7.26). The detailed theory shows that such splittings are always very small except in the lowest S state of an atom.

If we consider a more general case, where the extranuclear electrons combine to form a total angular momentum number J and the nucleus has a total angular momentum number I, we may use the rules of quantum mechanics to specify the net angular momentum (F) of the entire system. In vector notation we have

$$\mathbf{F} = \mathbf{I} + \mathbf{J} \qquad\qquad [9.6.1]$$

and the rules of Section 7.11 (Figure 7.23) yield the following results:
  (i) if $I > J$, F takes the values

$$I+J, I+J-1, \ldots, I-J;$$

(ii) if $J > I$, F takes the values

$$J+I, J+I-1, \ldots, J-I.$$

In the former case, the atomic ground state is split into $(2J + 1)$ components and in the latter case it is split into $(2I + 1)$ components. If, therefore, the value of J is known, for example, from Hund's rules (Section 7.11 and Section 8.5), it may be possible to find I by investigation of the ground-state splitting. Measurements are performed by radio-frequency absorption techniques or, in suitable cases, by high-resolution spectroscopy of optical lines leading to the ground state.

An alternative method is available when an element forms diatomic molecules, because the molecular spectra exhibit lines of alternating intensity, the ratio of intensities depending on the I numbers for the identical nuclei present. This method has been used with molecular hydrogen (H_2) and deuterium (D_2) to confirm the assignment of $I = \frac{1}{2}$ and $I = 1$ to the proton and deuteron, respectively.

The most common way of determining I is through magnetic-moment measurements, which are dealt with in the next section. Here, however, we may note that an experiment of the Stern-Gerlach type (Section 6.5) demonstrates clearly the principle of spatial quantization of angular momentum. In the original experiments on silver atoms in the $^2S_{1/2}$ state, the splitting of the silver beam into two components by an inhomogeneous magnetic field showed that $J = \frac{1}{2}$ for the atomic state. In principle, each component can be split further into $(2I + 1)$ components if a field of sufficient transverse gradient ($\partial B / \partial z$) is used, the latter condition being necessary because of the small magnetic moments associated with nuclear spin. This method has been employed in a few favorable cases only but the principle is of general validity in all methods based on magnetic interactions.

(b) Parity

A detailed study of the quantum mechanics of nuclear systems shows that the orbital angular momentum ($\mathbf{G}_l$) is not, in general, conserved because its operator does not commute with the nuclear Hamiltonian. This result may be explained in classical terms by supposing that there are noncentral forces between nucleons, since forces of this type continually redistribute the available angular momentum between spin and orbital components. However, the total angular momentum is constant and experiments have shown that the parity of any nuclear state is also conserved, to an accuracy of about 1 part in 10^5. This means that the nuclear Hamiltonian is effectively invariant under reversal of spatial coordinates. In spectroscopic terms, we may say that any nuclear state is a mixture of even-parity states (S, D, G, and so forth) or of odd-parity states (P, F, H, and so forth), but all the contributing states must have the same I number. For example, the ground state of the deuteron has $I = 1$ and is dominantly $L = 0$ in character, that is, the parity is even. In atomic physics the state would be specified as $^3S_1$, but in nuclei the interactions are such that an admixture of states like $^3D_1$ or $^3G_1$ is possible.

For this reason the spectroscopic notation is of limited utility in nuclear physics and nuclear states are described simply in terms of the I number and the parity, thus $I^\pm$, where the "+" superscript stands for even parity and the "−" for odd parity. The deuteron ground state is therefore written 1^+. An examination of the states possible in atomic physics shows that all combinations of even and odd parity with all possible J numbers exist. This applies also to the I numbers in nuclear physics.

(c) Isospin (T)

Isospin, also called "isotopic" or "isobaric" spin, is a purely formal quantity which was introduced to describe the "state" of a nucleon, that is, to specify whether it is in the neutron or the proton state. It is possible to assign a generalized isospin number (T) to nuclear states, but this quantity does not commute with the nuclear Hamiltonian because of the Coulomb interaction between protons and therefore, unlike the spin I, it is not strictly conserved. Nevertheless the concept of isospin is extremely useful in classifying nuclear states and it is of great significance in the theory of elementary particles.

The basic hypothesis of the isospin formalism is that the neutron and proton are equivalent particles in nuclear interactions despite their different charges and masses. This charge-independence hypothesis receives some support from experimental data on neutron-proton and proton-proton scattering (Section 9.4). If the neutron and proton are regarded as two states of the same particle, and no other states exist, we may write down a two-valued variable t which is analogous to the spin of a fermion in that it takes only the values $\pm\frac{1}{2}$; that is, the observable values of t are

$$t = +\tfrac{1}{2} \text{ for the proton state}$$

$$t = -\tfrac{1}{2} \text{ for the neutron state.}$$

These correspond to the "spin up" and "spin down" states of an electron in an atomic configuration.

In an atomic state, the electron spins are normally combined to produce a total spin number S, which is determined by sorting out all the possible combinations of the individual spins. Likewise it is possible to work out the isospin configurations of nucleons in a complex nucleus and to assign a total isospin number T to certain states. The action of Pauli's Exclusion principle in restricting the number of possible combinations is very important, since neutrons and protons obey the principle separately. For example, in the ground state of the deuteron we have, to a first approximation, $L = 0$ and $S = 1$, that is, the neutron and proton spins are parallel. Such a state could not arise with two neutrons or two protons because the set of quantum numbers (l, m_l, m_s) is the same for the two particles. This state is only possible, therefore, for nucleons of opposed *isospin*, that is, the sum of t numbers is zero

$$\Sigma t = \tfrac{1}{2} - \tfrac{1}{2} = 0$$

and so this state is denoted by $T = 0$.

The other known state of the deuteron is the virtual state detected in low-energy neutron-proton scattering (Section 9.4.c) and this must be of the type $L = 0$, $S = 0$, with the neutron and proton spins opposed. Such a state is possible for any two nucleons, and is, in fact, detected in proton-proton scattering, so that we have three states which are nearly equivalent

Proton-proton $\Sigma t = +1$ (the "di-proton" state),

Proton-neutron $\Sigma t = 0$ (the virtual deuteron),

Neutron-neutron $\Sigma t = -1$ (the "di-neutron" state).

These three states are regarded as components of an isospin *multiplet* $T = 1$, analogous to the three spatially quantized substates of the spin state $S = 1$.

The energy relations of the $T = 0$ and $T = 1$ states for the two-nucleon system ($A = 2$) are shown in Figure 9.40, where the zero of energy corresponds to a neutron-proton pair separated by a large distance. The $T = 0$ state is at -2.225 MeV (the binding energy of the deuteron in its ground state) and the central $T = 1$ state is at $+0.07$ MeV, as determined by scattering experiments. According to present evidence, the $T = 1$ di-neutron state is also virtual and the di-proton state should be somewhat higher than the di-neutron state because of the Coulomb repulsion.

Similar arguments may be used to identify T in some of the states of more complex nuclides. For example, in $_3\text{Li}^6$ there are three neutrons and three protons, while the *isobaric* nuclide $_2\text{He}^6$ (with the same A) possesses four neutrons and two protons. It is known that

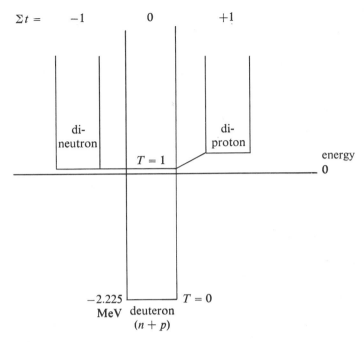

FIGURE 9.40 *States of the two-nucleon system classified according to their isospin number* (T); *the bound state of the deuteron is described as $T = 0$ and the three $T = 1$ states are all virtual.*

the latter configuration, in its lowest state, has higher energy than the lowest state of Li⁶, because He⁶ decays by beta emission to Li⁶. Now the lowest value of T which can be obtained for He⁶ is 1, since, even if two pairs of nucleons have opposed isospins, the two remaining neutrons yield $\Sigma t = -1$. In Li⁶, on the other hand, it is possible to have $T = 0$ states as well as $T = 1$ states and the ground state of Li⁶ is believed to be of the type $T = 0$. The situation is, therefore, somewhat as in the two-nucleon configuration of Figure 9.40, with the lowest Li⁶ state corresponding to the deuteron ground state and the He⁶ ground state analogous to the di-neutron ($T = 1$) state. It should be noted, however, that other states, with $T > 1$, are produced by the more complex $A = 6$ configuration.

In several pairs of light nuclides, it is possible to interchange the neutron and proton numbers; these pairs are often called "mirror" nuclides. Examples include ₃Li⁷ and ₄Be⁷, ₅B¹¹ and ₆C¹¹. If the charge-independence hypothesis is valid, the various states of a mirror pair should correspond to each other in character (spin and parity) and to some extent in energy, although there should be appreciable energy corrections due to the different Coulomb interactions in the two nuclides. We see from Figure 9.38 that the lowest two states of ₃Li⁷ and ₄Be⁷ have similar energy separations (0.48 MeV and 0.43 MeV, respectively) and other evidence indicates that they are of similar character. The correspondence extends to higher states of the $A = 7$ pair; but more detailed evidence is provided by the pair ₅B¹¹ and ₆C¹¹ (Figure 9.41). Here the lowest four states have very similar groupings in energy; it is not possible to be certain of the detailed correspondence because the spins and parities of some states are unknown, but the data lend considerable support for the charge-independence idea. In all such mirror pairs with A odd, the lowest states are of the $T = \frac{1}{2}$ type, with $\Sigma t = -\frac{1}{2}$ or $+\frac{1}{2}$ according to whether the neutron or proton number is the greater.

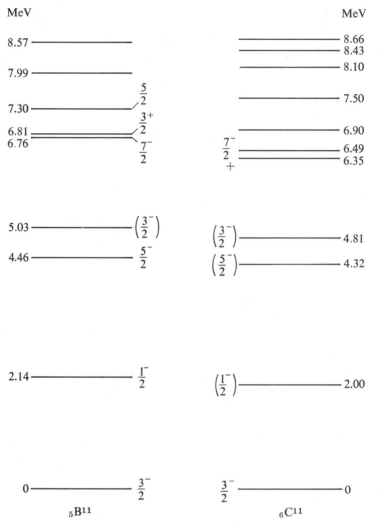

FIGURE 9.41 *The lowest states of the "mirror" nuclides B^{11} and C^{11}, showing the similar sequence of level energies, spins and parities.*

(*d*) *Mean lifetime and width*

In both classical and quantum physics there is an intimate connection between the mean lifetime of an excited state and the energy distribution of the emitted photons or particles. In Section 7.2 we found that the classical theory of radiation damping agrees with Heisenberg's Uncertainty principle in predicting a relation of the type

$$\tau \Gamma = \hbar, \qquad \text{from Equation (7.2.12),}$$

where τ is the mean lifetime of the state and Γ is the full width at half-maximum of the peaked energy distribution (expressed in energy units).

In any quantum system we have to allow for the fact that a state may be deexcited in several different ways. The probability of transition per unit time by a certain channel is obviously inversely proportional to the mean lifetime for that isolated channel; so in practice we can replace the transition probabilities by partial widths (Γ_i) and sum them all to find the total width

$$\Gamma = \sum_i \Gamma_i, \qquad\qquad [9.6.2]$$

where the sum is taken over all accessible channels.

In experimental nuclear physics the total width is often found from the resonance curve (for example, Figure 9.33) which serves to locate the position of a state formed in the compound nucleus, or from the energy distribution of emitted particles which leave the residual nucleus in a certain state. Widths ranging from a fraction of an electron volt (as in Figure 9.36) to over 1 MeV can be measured in this way, the corresponding lifetimes ranging from about 10^{-14} sec to about 10^{-21} sec. If the widths are too small for direct measurement, it may be possible to find the lifetime by observing the exponential decay of the excited state and this method is feasible for lifetimes down to about 10^{-10} sec. There remains a region of lifetimes between 10^{-10} and 10^{-14} sec which has to be explored by special methods (see Section 9.6.g).

It is found that, in general, the total widths of nuclear states increase with increasing excitation energy and this variation is to be expected from the quantum theory of transitions. At the same time, there are many exceptions to this rule. For example, the 3 MeV state in Be^8* is broad, indicating a high probability for the state to decay by emission of two alpha particles (Figure 9.35). On the other hand, the 17.6 MeV state in the same nuclide is narrow and this state does not decay by alpha-particle emission. The reason for this behavior is to be found in the operation of selection rules governing the emission of gamma rays and particles from excited states. These rules are dealt with later, but in the particular example quoted we have the possibility of Be^8* breaking up into two identical particles (He^4) of zero spin. This is forbidden unless the initial state is of even spin and parity, a condition which is satisfied by the Be^8 ground state (0^+) and the 3 MeV state (2^+) but not by the 17.6 MeV state, which is believed to be 1^+ in character. The high-energy state must decay, therefore, either by gamma ray or proton emission, as shown in Figure 9.35. It follows that widths are dependent on the types of exit channel available and on the spins and parities of the states involved.

(e) Baryon emission

Nuclei which are excited to energies above 10 MeV are usually capable of emitting one or more particles, the threshold for neutron emission being given by the data of Figure 9.20. Many nuclides are unstable with respect to alpha-particle emission even in their ground states, as is shown notably by heavy nuclides above lead ($Z = 82$) in the periodic table (Section 6.1). In these examples the particle emitted is massive, consisting of one or more baryons, and is either neutral or positively charged. An important feature of baryon emission is the inhibition of charged-particle decay by the *Coulomb barrier* effect.

If a charged particle, for example an alpha particle, approaches a nucleus, its potential energy varies according to the Coulomb law over a wide range of distances. The particle may be imagined as climbing an incline, the height of which at any point varies inversely as the distance (r) from the center of force (Figure 9.42). If the original kinetic energy of the particle was low, it reaches a minimum distance (r_{min}) in head-on collision which is fixed by equating the original kinetic energy and the final potential energy [see Equation (6.3.8)]. Rutherford's analysis of alpha-particle scattering experiments showed that the $1/r$ law is obeyed down to very small distances from the center of a nucleus. However, it is clear that

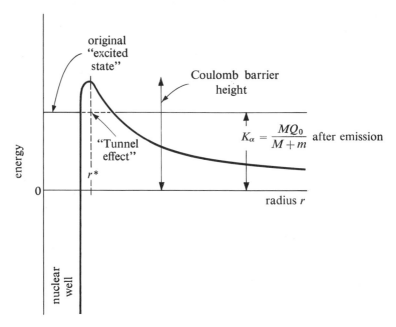

FIGURE 9.42 *The solid curve represents the potential energy of an alpha particle as a function of its distance from the center of a nucleus and shows the "Coulomb barrier" which inhibits entry and exit of the particle. When alpha emission from a heavy nucleus occurs, the particle emerges with final kinetic energy K_α after penetrating the Coulomb barrier.*

the nucleons of an alpha particle can be bound into the nucleus and at some distance, r^*, the force of repulsion must be overcome by the attractive nuclear forces. Inside this distance the potential energy has to be represented by some kind of potential well, similar to the model used in theories of neutron scattering. However, there must be a high positive potential energy at the point $r = r^*$ and this represents a Coulomb barrier, of height depending on the interacting charges and on the effective nuclear radius. If the alpha particle can surmount or penetrate this barrier, it may enter the nucleus proper and provoke reactions.

Numerous experiments have shown that incident charged particles frequently penetrate the Coulomb barrier to stimulate nuclear reactions and this penetration is to be explained by quantum mechanics (see Section 7.4). The "tunneling" effect is particularly important in the emission of an alpha particle by a heavy nucleus, which may be written

$$_ZX^A \rightarrow {}_2He^4 + {}_{Z-2}X^{A-4} \qquad [9.6.3]$$

with an overall energy release denoted by Q_0.

The initial state may be represented on the potential-energy diagram (Figure 9.42) as an excited state of the nuclide X^{A-4} with an alpha particle inside its appropriate potential barrier. The final state is a combination of this nuclide in its ground state and an external alpha particle possessing kinetic energy (K_α) which is a little less than Q_0, owing to the kinetic energy of the recoiling X^{A-4} nucleus. The transition probability between these two states is governed by the same factors as those which determine the reaction cross section of nuclide X^{A-4} with alpha particles of energy K_α.

The relation between alpha-particle energy K_α and the total energy release Q_0 is found directly from the conditions of energy and momentum conservation. In obvious notation, we have

Momentum balance:

$$MV = mv.$$

Energy balance:

$$Q_0 = \tfrac{1}{2}mv^2 + \tfrac{1}{2}MV^2$$

$$= \tfrac{1}{2}mv^2\left(1 + \frac{m}{M}\right),$$

that is,

$$K_\alpha = \frac{MQ_0}{M + m}. \qquad [9.6.4]$$

This relation gives the alpha-particle energy for ground-state transitions but there may also be other energy groups due to transitions leaving X^{A-4} in one or more excited states. For example, the nuclide $_{88}\text{Ra}^{226}$ emits two principal alpha-particle groups, of energy 4.777 and 4.590 MeV, the former group leaving the residual $_{86}\text{Em}^{222}$ (radon) in its ground state. The Q values calculated for these two transitions are 4.863 and 4.673 MeV, so we deduce that Em^{222} possesses an excited state 0.19 MeV above its ground state. The transitions are depicted in Figure 9.43; it should be noted that the more powerful ground-state transition is from one 0^+ state to a similar state, whereas the weaker transition ends at a 2^+ state.

The quantum mechanics of barrier penetration by particles shows that the probability of transition from the initial state to the final state in alpha emission depends sensitively upon the alpha-particle energy (K_α), since this fixes the effective thickness of barrier to be penetrated. Calculations made by Gamow and by Gurney and Condon showed that the theory fits the experimental data and provides an explanation of the empirical *Geiger-Nuttall*

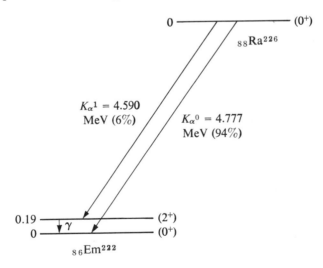

FIGURE 9.43 *Energy-level diagram depicting the two principal transitions in the alpha decay of Ra²²⁶. One group leads to the ground state and the other to the first excited state of the residual nuclide Em²²².*

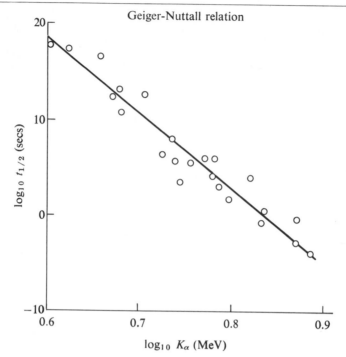

FIGURE 9.44 *Half-lives of the natural alpha emitters plotted logarithmically against the alpha-particle kinetic energies, showing an approximately linear relation:* $\log_{10} t_{1/2} + n \log_{10} K_\alpha = constant.$

rule connecting the alpha-particle decay constant (λ) and the alpha-particle energy (K_α):

$$\ln \lambda = n \ln K_\alpha + \text{const,}$$

or

$$\left.\ln \tau + n \ln K_\alpha = \text{const,}\right\} \qquad [9.6.5]$$

where τ (the mean lifetime) is the reciprocal of λ [Equation (6.2.7)]. Here the factor n is a constant number of the order of 80 for the alpha emitters of the natural radioactive series (Appendix III), as may be seen from Figure 9.44, where the *half-lives* are plotted logarithmically against the logarithms of the alpha-particle energies (for ground-state transitions). The relation is necessarily approximate because of the extremely wide range in values of the half-lives.

The Geiger-Nuttall relation serves to emphasize the profound effect of the Coulomb barrier on rates of transition for charged-particle emission when the energy release is small compared with the maximum barrier height. If, however, the initial excitation energy is large compared with the barrier height there is little inhibition of charged-particle decay. This is the situation in highly excited light nuclei, such as those of Be^{8*} which are able to split into two alpha particles. In these examples, and in all cases of neutron emission, the factors governing transitions are selection rules which may be strict, such as the even-parity and even-spin rule for $Be^{8*} \rightarrow 2He^4$, or merely indicative of relative probabilities. In the latter category are the angular momentum rules for particle emission, which may best be illustrated by considering a spinless particle such as an alpha particle.

The emitted alpha particle may be represented by a plane wave when it is some distance away from the emitting nucleus and this plane wave may be expanded in Legendre polynomials of the type $P_l(\cos \alpha)$, as in Equation (9.4.18). The relative importance of the different Legendre terms with different *l* values depends on the magnitude of the parameter κr and we have seen that at low energies the low *l* values are favored. Different *l* values correspond to different "waves" or components of the plane wave, with different effects on the angular momentum of the system. For example, *s*-wave emission has $l = 0$ and there is no effect of this component on either the spin or parity of the state. Thus for emission of a spinless particle in the *s* wave, the initial and final states (of the initial and final nuclides, respectively) must have the same spin and parity. Rather less probable than *s*-wave emission is *p*-wave emission with $l = 1$ and components of angular momentum change given by

$$\Delta m_l = 1, 0, -1.$$

This type of emission involves a change in parity, so the selection rules may be written

$$\Delta I = 1, 0, -1: \text{"Yes"} \quad \text{(with } I = 0 \text{ to } I' = 0 \text{ forbidden).} \quad [9.6.6]$$

Likewise the selection rules for *d*-wave emission are

$$\Delta I = 2, 1, 0, -1, -2: \text{"No"} \quad \text{(with } 0 \leftrightarrow 0 \text{ and } 0 \leftrightarrow 1 \text{ forbidden)} \quad [9.6.7]$$

and this, in turn, is less probable than *p*-wave emission.

These rules may be illustrated by reference to the 16.58 MeV level of C^{12*} (Figure 9.37) which decays by alpha-particle emission to the 3 MeV state (2^+) of Be^{8*} but not to the ground state (0^+) of the same nuclide. Studies of the angular distributions indicate that the 16.58 MeV state is of character 2^-, and this is allowed to pass to the 2^+ state of Be^{8*} by *p*-wave emission. On the other hand, a transition to the ground state would require a change of parity and of two units of angular momentum, which cannot be achieved by spinless particles in any approximation.

If a neutron or a proton is emitted from a certain state, the selection rules have to be modified to allow for the intrinsic spin of the emitted particle. This amounts to an angular momentum component of $\pm\frac{1}{2}\hbar$ in addition to any changes introduced by the *l* components, but the parity rules are not affected. The parity changes are particularly significant in "deuteron-stripping" reactions (Section 9.5.f) where angular distributions can be used to find the amount of angular momentum imparted to the target nucleus in addition to the spin momentum of the captured nucleon. For example, the reaction $C^{12}(d, p)C^{13}$ has been observed with C^{13} formed in its ground state, the data indicating that the change in orbital momentum corresponds to $\Delta l = 1$. Now the ground state of C^{12} is known to be of the type 0^+, so the rules for *p*-wave changes indicate that the ground state of C^{13} must be of odd parity and of spin $\frac{1}{2}$ or $\frac{3}{2}$. Other evidence assigns the character $\frac{1}{2}^-$ to this state. Again, deuteron stripping occurs in the reaction $O^{16}(d, p)O^{17}$ and the angular distribution indicates $\Delta l = 2$, so the ground state of O^{17} should be $\frac{3}{2}^+$ or $\frac{5}{2}^+$, since the ground state of O^{16} is known to be 0^+. Experiments of this kind are therefore valuable in suggesting spin and parity assignments for final states, when the initial states are known.

(f) Gamma-ray emission

The deexcitation of a nucleus by gamma-ray emission follows the same general selection rules as those derived for electromagnetic transitions in atoms (Section 7.13). Since, however, in nuclei the spin and orbital momenta are not strictly distinguishable, the rules refer only to changes in total angular momentum (*I*) and parity. Thus for electric-dipole emission or absorption we have the rules

$$\Delta I = 0, \pm 1: \text{"Yes"} \quad (0 \leftrightarrow 0 \text{ forbidden)}; \quad [9.6.8]$$

for magnetic-dipole emission or absorption

$$\Delta I = 0, \pm 1: \text{``No''} \qquad (0 \leftrightarrow 0 \text{ forbidden}); \qquad\qquad [9.6.9]$$

and for electric-quadrupole emission or absorption

$$\Delta I = 0, \pm 1, \pm 2: \text{``No''} \qquad (0 \leftrightarrow 0 \quad \text{and} \quad 0 \leftrightarrow 1 \text{ forbidden}). \qquad [9.6.10]$$

Two further points may be noted with respect to radiative transitions in nuclei. Firstly, the isospin has some effect on transition probabilities, so that, for example, electric-dipole changes with $\Delta T = \pm 1$ are more probable than those with $\Delta T = 0$. Secondly, nuclei are of such a size, relative to the wavelengths of the radiations emitted, that radiations of high multipole order (quadrupole, octupole, and so forth) are frequently significant, whereas in atomic systems the electric-dipole transitions are dominant.

The rules may be used to correlate various data referring to gamma-ray emission from nuclear states. For example, the 17.6 MeV line from Be^8* (Figure 9.35) is emitted when the nuclide changes from a 1^+ state to the ground state (0^+) and this change requires a magnetic-dipole transition, in agreement with the estimated gamma-ray width of the excited state.

The various gamma rays produced from the $C^{12}*$ states formed in the $B^{11} + H^1$ reaction (Figure 9.34) have been assigned multipole characters in detail. For example, the 16.11 MeV excited state is deexcited by alpha emission or by gamma-ray emission (γ_1) to the ground state or by gamma-ray emission (γ_2) to the 4.43-MeV state. Of the gamma-rays, γ_1 is supposed to be of electric-quadrupole character, linking the 2^+ upper state with the 0^+ ground state, while the γ_2 transition is a magnetic-dipole change from 2^+ to 2^+. It follows that the 4.43 MeV gamma rays (γ_3) emitted from the lower state are of electric-quadrupole type. It is noteworthy that nuclei in the 16.58 MeV state, which has already been identified as 2^-, cannot decay by gamma-ray emission directly to the ground state but pass by electric-dipole transition to the 4.43 MeV level. It will be appreciated that the pattern of transitions can be extremely complex, especially in regions where levels overlap and interference effects occur between the transition amplitudes for different kinds of change.

It has been seen that the states of light nuclides are frequently deexcited either by gamma-ray or by particle emission, the two processes being competitive. The same competition occurs in heavy nuclides during radioactive changes if the transition rates for alpha-particle decay and gamma-ray emission are comparable. It was found that the highly unstable nuclides ThC' and RaC', which are formed by beta decay from ThC and RaC, respectively, occasionally emit alpha particles of phenomenally long range. Whereas the great majority of alpha particles from ThC' have a mean energy of 8.780 MeV, there are also weak long-range groups at 9.492, 10.422 and 10.543 MeV. The corresponding Q values for the alpha-decay process are 8.949 MeV for the strong transition, which leaves the final nuclide ThD (Pb^{208}) in its ground state, and 9.675, 10.623, and 10.746 MeV for the other transitions. It should be noted that here the Q_0 value is *lower* than the other Q values, showing that the weak groups are not due to excitation of the residual nuclide ThD. We assume instead that the ThC' nuclei are formed from the parent ThC nuclei in several excited states, some of which are at 0.726, 1.674, and 1.797 MeV above the ground state. These states normally proceed to the ground state of ThC' by gamma-ray emission, but the probability of alpha decay is not negligible and a few of the excited nuclei decay directly to ThD, as shown in Figure 9.45. A valuable feature of this observation is the demonstration that energy is conserved in these nuclear changes, since the total energy released in transitions between ThC and ThD is found to be the same for all possible routes via the states of ThC'.

Most excited states of nuclei are of short lifetime, whether they decay by particle or gamma-ray emission. In a few cases, however, all electromagnetic transitions are forbidden between

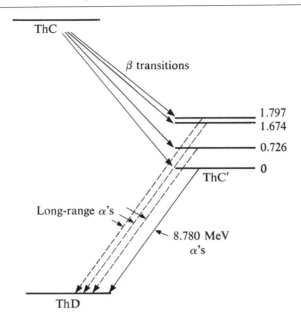

FIGURE 9.45 *The occurrence of high-energy groups in the alpha-particle spectrum of* ThC′ *is due to direct decay from excited states of* ThC′ *to the ground state of* ThD, *these states being formed in the beta decay of* ThC.

two states and baryon emission is not energetically possible. An example is the first excited state of the nuclide O^{16}, which is at 6.06 MeV above the ground state and is of the type 0^{+}, the same as the ground state. This excited state decays to the ground state by emission of a pair of electrons, negative and positive, which are detected by coincidence measurements. In other examples, there is such a large spin change involved between a pair of states that the electromagnetic transition has to be of very high multipole order and the decay rate is very slow. In such a case, the "metastable" state is described as being *isomeric* with the ground state and the nuclide is supposed to consist of two *isomers* with different effective half-lives.

An example of isomerism is provided by the element rhodium, which absorbs slow neutrons to produce the nuclide Rh^{104} [Equation (9.3.26)] in a variety of states. Some of these pass rapidly to the ground state, which then decays by beta emission to Pd^{104} [Equation (9.3.28)] with a half-life of 44 sec. There is, however, a metastable state of Rh^{104}, at 0.128 MeV (written Rh^{104m}), which has a half-life of 4.4 min for gamma-ray emission via an intermediate state to the ground state. The metastable state also decays in about 0.1 % of events by beta emission to Pd^{104}, the various possibilities being represented in Figure 9.46.

In the example of isomerism quoted above, the spin change required for decay of the metastable state is of the order of three units and the half-life is comparatively long. This circumstance facilitates the detection of the isomer because subsequent beta decay appears to have two half-lives. However, no rigid distinction can be drawn between isomer states of long half-life and the numerous short-lived states, since a wide range of gamma-ray half-lives is observed, from many days down to the present lower limits of time measurements (about 10^{-10} sec). This range can be extended towards lower figures by methods based on resonant nuclear absorption and the Doppler effect.

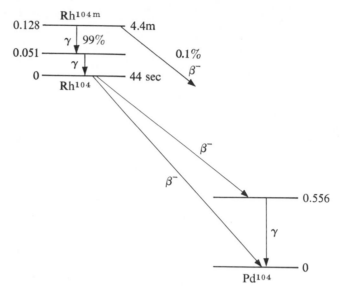

FIGURE 9.46 *The decay scheme of the isomeric state Rh^{104m} of half-life 4.4 min. About 99% of transitions go via the ground state of Rh^{104} which decays by beta-emission to states of Pd^{104} and about 0.1% of transitions involve beta decay to Pd^{104} direct.*

(g) Resonant nuclear absorption and the Mössbauer effect

Measurements of excited-state lifetimes in the region below 10^{-9} sec have been carried out in several ways based on estimating the natural width (Γ) of the state for gamma-ray emission. From Equation (7.2.12) we have the relation

$$\tau\Gamma = \hbar, \qquad \text{where } \Gamma \text{ is in energy units.}$$

For $\tau = 10^{-12}$ sec, for instance, Γ is about 7×10^{-4} eV, which is extremely small compared with the energy of typical gamma rays. Moreover Γ is so small that it may be masked in practice by other effects which broaden the gamma-ray line. For example, if the excited nuclei form part of the molecules of a gas, the molecular motion introduces a Doppler broadening which is much greater than the natural width. The amount of Doppler broadening may be estimated by supposing that the effective width (Γ_D) is due to the mean molecular speed

$$\bar{v} = \left(\frac{8kT}{\pi M}\right)^{1/2}, \qquad \text{(Problem 2.8)}$$

where T is the temperature on the absolute scale (°K) and M is the molecular mass.
To a first approximation, the Doppler frequency shift is given by the relation

$$\frac{\Delta\omega}{\omega} = \frac{\bar{v}}{c}$$

so that

$$\frac{\Gamma_D}{E} = \frac{\bar{v}}{c} = \left(\frac{8kT}{\pi Mc^2}\right)^{1/2} \text{ approximately,} \qquad [9.6.11]$$

where E is the mean energy of the gamma rays.
Thus for $E = 10^5$ eV, $T = 300°$K, $M = 100$ u, we have

$$\Gamma_D = 0.085 \text{ eV approximately.}$$

If the emitting nuclei are part of a liquid or solid material the theory is more complex, but in general the Doppler effects observed are of the magnitude indicated by Equation (9.6.11).

We may note in passing that Doppler effects of much greater magnitude are present in gamma rays emitted during nuclear reactions at high bombarding energy. For example, if a light nuclide captures a proton of kinetic energy 1 MeV, the compound nucleus recoils with a speed of about 10^6 m/sec in the laboratory frame. If the gamma rays emitted while the nucleus retains its full recoil velocity are studied, there is an appreciable energy difference in the forward and backward directions, amounting to

$$\Delta E = \frac{2v}{c} E \approx \frac{E}{150} \text{ approximately.}$$

Such energy differences are observable with modern gamma-ray detectors. It is possible to make rough estimates of lifetimes by stopping the compound nucleus in a suitable medium and finding the Doppler shift as a function of the stopping time.

Since the natural linewidth (Γ) for states in the 10^{-12} sec region is so small compared with the gamma-ray energy, it might be considered impossible of measurement. However, the method of *resonant absorption* offers a possible solution to the problem. By "resonant" absorption is meant the absorption of a gamma-ray line emitted from some nuclide by nuclei of the same nuclide, which are excited thereby to the same state as that responsible for the emission. This kind of process is common in atomic systems but is not easily realized in nuclei. If, however, the resonant absorption cross section can be measured for a single transition, the width of the excited state may be found, as follows.

For example, suppose that the absorption cross section (σ) is given as a function of the incident gamma-ray energy (E) by a typical resonance relation [similar to that of Equation (7.2.11)]

$$\sigma(E) = \frac{\frac{1}{4}\Gamma^2 \sigma_{max}}{(E - E_0)^2 + \frac{1}{4}\Gamma^2}, \qquad [9.6.12]$$

where E_0 is the gamma-ray energy for maximum absorption;

Γ is the full width at half-maximum;

σ_{max} is the maximum cross section, at $E = E_0$.

Then the total cross section integrated over all energies is

$$\Sigma = \int_0^\infty \sigma(E)\, dE.$$

This integral is effectively the same as that over the range $-\infty$ to $+\infty$, in all cases of interest, and can be evaluated by contour integration. In the positive half-plane there is a pole at $E = \left(E_0 + i\frac{\Gamma}{2}\right)$ with a residue $\frac{\frac{1}{4}\Gamma^2 \sigma_{max}}{i\Gamma}$, so by Cauchy's theorem

$$\Sigma = \int_{-\infty}^\infty \sigma(E)\, dE = 2\pi i \frac{\frac{1}{4}\Gamma^2 \sigma_{max}}{i\Gamma}$$

$$= \frac{\pi \Gamma \sigma_{max}}{2}. \qquad [9.6.13]$$

This result is independent of the Doppler broadening effect, so if the quantities Σ and σ_{max} can be measured, Γ can be found.

At this stage a further experimental difficulty appears, due to a shift in energy between gamma rays emitted and those absorbed by the same material—a shift caused by the nuclear recoil effect. When a gamma ray of energy E_0 (the mean energy of the observed resonance) is given off by a nucleus of mass M, the recoiling nucleus normally takes kinetic energy (K_r) corresponding to the photon momentum E_0/c,

$$K_r = \frac{E_0^2}{2Mc^2} \text{ for nonrelativistic particles.}$$

Thus the total energy release for this process is

$$Q = E_0 + K_r = E_0\left(1 + \frac{E_0}{2Mc^2}\right). \qquad [9.6.14]$$

If an absorber of the same material as the source is placed in the path of the gamma rays, its nuclei can be excited fully only if they receive the correct energy Q (for excitation) plus an extra instalment of kinetic energy for recoil. To a sufficient degree of accuracy, the total energy discrepancy is

$$2K_r = \frac{E_0^2}{Mc^2} \qquad [9.6.15]$$

which, for $E_0 = 10^5$ eV, $M = 100$ u, is approximately 0.1 eV, or rather greater than the Doppler broadening at ordinary temperatures.

If resonant absorption is to be observed in nuclei, therefore, extra energy of the order of $\frac{E_0^2}{Mc^2}$ must be supplied to the gamma rays employed. The same applies to resonant "fluorescence" or scattering whereby the incident gamma rays are reemitted by the nuclei of a scatterer. Both these effects have, in fact, been observed in favorable cases, for example, the 0.41 MeV state in Hg^{198} investigated by Davey and Moon.[*] The Hg^{198} source was mounted on the rim of an ultracentrifuge rotor, which could be revolved at such a rate that the rim approached linear speeds of about 800 m/sec. A scatterer containing mercury was placed behind shields, in such a way that it received gamma rays only when the source was approaching, so that the Doppler effect would provide the extra energy for resonance. The scattered gamma rays were counted by a detector and the counting rate was plotted against the speed of the source relative to the scatterer. This graph yielded the outline of a resonance curve with the peak at about 700 m/s, the corresponding Doppler shift being

$$\frac{v}{c}E_0 = \frac{700 \times 410,000}{3 \times 10^8} = 0.96 \text{ eV approximately.}$$

This figure may be compared with the calculated recoil shift

$$\frac{E_0^2}{Mc^2} = \frac{0.41 \times 410,000}{198 \times 931} = 0.89 \text{ eV.}$$

The measured cross sections yielded a mean lifetime of 3×10^{-11} sec for the excited state.

Although various methods have been developed for detecting resonant absorption in nuclei, the most remarkable phenomenon in this field was discovered experimentally in 1958 by Mössbauer.[†] Working with a Ir^{191} source of 129 keV gamma rays, he showed that at low temperatures resonant absorption occurs with *no* appreciable recoil shift or Doppler

[*] W. G. Davey and P. B. Moon, Proc. Phys. Soc. (London), **A66**, 956 (1953).
[†] R. L. Mössbauer, Z. Physik, **151**, 124 (1958).

broadening. It had been shown theoretically by Lamb that in the solid state there is the possibility of "recoilless" emission, in which the recoil motion is imparted to the crystal lattice as a whole instead of to the nucleus emitting the photon. Since the mass of the lattice is very large compared with that of a nucleus, the recoil shift [Equation (9.6.15)] is negligible. The probability of the *Mössbauer effect* being observed depends on the temperature, as compared with the Debye temperature (T_D of Section 8.1), and is greatly enhanced at low temperatures. The effect is exhibited very strongly by the nuclide Fe^{57}, formed by beta decay from Co^{57}, in a state which decays by emission of a 14.4 keV gamma-ray line with a mean lifetime of 6.9×10^{-8} sec.

In a typical experiment on the Mössbauer effect, the resonance curve for absorption of the gamma rays is traced out by employment of the Doppler effect to introduce small energy changes which are accurately known. The source may be mounted on a lathe carriage, or some similar slow-motion device, and an absorber made of the same material, in a suitable crystalline form, is placed between the moving source and a gamma-ray counter. The counting rate is plotted against the relative velocity of source and absorber, measured in both positive and negative senses, and the graph forms a distinct resonance curve, as shown in Figure 9.47 for the 129 keV line of Ir^{191}. The small relative velocities, of the order of a few cm/sec or less, are translated into energy differences and the width is *twice* the value for the emission or the absorption process taken singly, since both processes are represented in

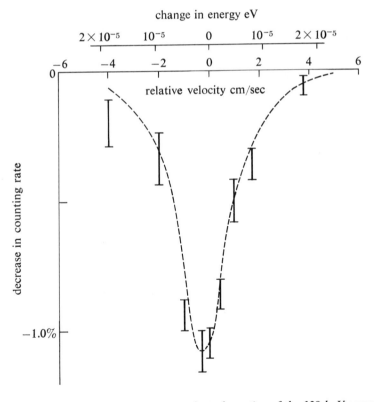

FIGURE 9.47 *Mössbauer's results on resonant nuclear absorption of the 129 keV gamma rays from Ir^{191}, the counting rate being plotted against the relative velocity of source and absorber. The dotted line shows the theoretical curve based on the natural line width: $2\Gamma = 9.2 \times 10^{-6}$ eV and this is followed closely by the experimental points.*

the curve. Mössbauer found for this particular state

$$2\Gamma = 9.2 \times 10^{-6}\,\text{eV}$$

which yields, from the basic width-lifetime relation, the mean lifetime $\tau = 1.4 \times 10^{-10}$ sec approximately. The result agrees with the observed decay rate and supports the supposition that the "natural" linewidth is measured in this kind of Mössbauer experiment. Other experimenters have confirmed this result and the method has been extended by Wu and others to show that the effective width depends on the time of observation, in agreement with the Uncertainty principle (Section 7.2).

The Mössbauer effect therefore enables experimenters to use gamma-ray lines of natural width, many of these lines being extremely sharp. For example, the 14.4 keV line from Fe^{57} has a mean lifetime of 6.9×10^{-8} sec and a width (Γ) of 10^{-7} eV, which is less than 10^{-11} of the energy change. This nuclide was used by Pound and Rebka in their classic experiment on the gravitational frequency shift (Section 5.2), which amounts to 1 part in 10^{15} for a vertical height change of 10 m. The source and absorber were separated by the height of a tall tower and repeated Doppler experiments were carried out to establish the existence of a lineshift due to gravity alone. These refined experiments form only a small fraction of the research undertaken with the new technique introduced by Mössbauer.

9.7   Nuclear Moments

In addition to the spin, parity, and isospin, each nuclide has certain electromagnetic properties which vary from one state to another. In practice, measurements of nuclear moments are confined almost entirely to nuclei in their ground states, but even this limited amount of information is invaluable in formulating theories of nuclear structure. We have already noted that the proton has an appreciable magnetic moment, which gives rise to the hyperfine splitting of the hydrogen ground state. More surprisingly, the neutron is found to possess a magnetic moment and it appears that the moments of both the proton and the neutron are "anomalous," in the sense that they cannot be explained by treating these particles as simple point entities of charge $+ e$ and zero, respectively.

(a) Expansion of the Wiechert potential

The definition and classification of electromagnetic moments can be based on an expansion of electromagnetic potentials due to charges and currents distributed over a small region. For example, the Wiechert potential at a point P at radius vector **R** from the origin, due to a static *charge* distribution described by the density function

$$\rho(\mathbf{r}),$$

is

$$\varphi = \frac{1}{4\pi\varepsilon_0} \int \frac{\rho(\mathbf{r})\,dV}{|\mathbf{R} - \mathbf{r}|}, \qquad\qquad [9.7.1]$$

where the integral is taken over all the charged region. If the charge distribution is small in extent compared with R, the term $\dfrac{1}{|\mathbf{R} - \mathbf{r}|}$ may be expanded in terms of the radius r and the angle (θ) between **r** and **R** according to the equation*

$$\frac{1}{|\mathbf{R} - \mathbf{r}|} = \frac{1}{(R^2 + r^2 - 2Rr \cos \theta)^{\frac{1}{2}}}$$

$$= \frac{1}{R} \sum_{l=0}^{\infty} P_l(\cos \theta) \left(\frac{r}{R}\right)^l. \qquad [9.7.2]$$

The potential φ can then be expressed in terms of a series of electric moments, the first term ($l = 0$) being due to the total charge, the second due to the electric dipole moment, the third due to the quadrupole moment, and so on,

$$4\pi\varepsilon_0\varphi = \frac{1}{R} \int \rho(\mathbf{r}) \, dV + \frac{1}{R^2} \int \rho(\mathbf{r}) \, r \cos \theta \, dV + \frac{1}{R^3} \int \rho(\mathbf{r}) r^2 (3 \cos^2 \theta - 1) \, dV + \cdots \quad [9.7.3]$$

These terms define the moments as follows:

Dipole moment:
$$DM = \int \rho(\mathbf{r}) r \cos \theta \, dV.$$

Quadrupole moment:
$$QM = \int \rho(\mathbf{r}) r^2 (3 \cos^2 \theta - 1) \, dV.$$

In quantum-mechanical form, the charge distribution for a particle can be written as

$$\rho(\mathbf{r}) = q\psi^*\psi = q |\psi|^2,$$

where ψ represents the normalized state function for the particle and q denotes the net charge.

In a simple system, with the origin located at the center of the charge distribution, the function ψ is either symmetrical or antisymmetrical about the origin, according as the parity is even or odd, but the product $|\psi|^2$ is necessarily of *even* parity. Under these conditions, where the particle has a definite parity, the electric dipole moment

$$DM \equiv q \int r |\psi|^2 \, dV$$

must *vanish* because of the odd parity of the r term. This appears to be the case with all known elementary particles and nuclei.

However, the same argument does *not* lead to vanishing of the even-numbered electric moments (quadrupole, and so forth). Further analysis shows that the electric quadrupole moment is a measure of the departure from spherical symmetry of the charge distribution and that QM is positive for "egg-shaped" distributions, negative for "pancake-shaped" distributions. These distributions are usually represented by prolate and oblate spheroids, for which the QM can be worked out analytically. All states with $I = 0$ or $\frac{1}{2}$ have zero quadrupole moment; the same applies to states with spherical symmetry, such as pure "S" states with $L = 0$.

Measurements of the electric quadrupole moment can be performed by investigating the hyperfine structure of spectral lines or by atomic beam methods. This moment has the dimensions (charge × area) and the QM per elementary charge (e) is conveniently expressed in barns (10^{-28} m²) or in millibarns. It is noteworthy that some nuclides, for example, the

* H. Margenau and G. M. Murphy, *The Mathematics of Physics and Chemistry* (Van Nostrand Co. Princeton, 1956) 2nd ed., Chap. 2.

isotopes of lutecium, have quadrupole moments of several barns, but these still correspond to moderate ellipsoidal deformations, the maximum difference between major and minor axes being about 20%. More significant is the discovery that the deuteron has a small positive quadrupole moment in its ground state. This result proves that the state is not a pure $^3S_1$ state, as is often assumed in simple calculations. The effect can be accounted for by assuming that a few percentage of the $^3D_1$ state is mixed in with the $^3S_1$ state (see Section 9.6.b).

(b) Magnetic moments

Magnetic dipole moments in nuclei are defined in a manner analogous to electric moments, with the *current* density distribution $\mathbf{j}(\mathbf{r})$ replacing the charge distribution. Since the current is a polar vector, of odd parity, the odd-numbered magnetic moments are nonzero and the even-numbered moments are zero. The net magnetic moment is represented by an axial vector $\boldsymbol{\mu}$ which is parallel or antiparallel to the total angular momentum vector, $\mathbf{G}$, of magnitude $\hbar\sqrt{I(I+1)}$. If $I = 0$, the magnetic moment vanishes. In all other cases, the moment can take up $(2I + 1)$ different orientations relative to an applied magnetic field $\mathbf{B}$ and the potential-energy differences cause splittings of magnitude

$$\Delta E = -m_I g_I \mu_n B \qquad\qquad [9.7.4]$$

which is similar to Equation (7.14.3). In the nuclear case

m_I takes the values $I, (I - 1), \ldots (-I)$;

g_I is a nuclear gyromagnetic factor;

μ_n is the *nuclear* magneton, defined as the intrinsic moment of a Dirac particle possessing the mass of a proton,

$$\mu_n = \frac{e\hbar}{2M_p} = 5.05 \times 10^{-27} \text{ Am}^2.$$

Since nuclear moments are small, the energy splittings ΔE are small unless a very strong field B is employed.

If a beam of nuclei is sent through an inhomogeneous magnetic field of gradient $\partial B/\partial z$, it is split into $(2I + 1)$ components in a way analogous to the beam of silver atoms in Stern and Gerlach's experiment (Section 6.5). Early attempts to measure nuclear moments with atomic and molecular beams were based on this technique, but great difficulty was encountered because of the masking effects of large electronic contributions to the total moment. Moreover, the type of Stern-Gerlach splitting observed depends a great deal on the magnitude of the magnetic field employed. Suppose, for instance, we have a beam of atoms in which the electrons have a total angular momentum number $J = \frac{1}{2}$ and the nuclear spin number is I. The total angular momentum of each atom is described by the number F, where

$$F = I + \tfrac{1}{2} \qquad \text{or} \qquad I - \tfrac{1}{2}$$

and these two states have different magnetic moments. In a weak field, therefore, the energy levels consist of two groups containing $(2I + 2)$ and $(2I)$ substates, respectively, as shown in Figure 9.48 for the special case of $I = \frac{3}{2}$. In a strong field, on the other hand, the $\mathbf{I}$ and $\mathbf{J}$ vectors become uncoupled in a manner similar to the $\mathbf{L}$ and $\mathbf{S}$ vectors in the Paschen-Back effect (Section 7.14). The net result is a splitting of the two groups of levels by $\mu_B B$ (for the electron spin alone) and each group now contains $(2I + 1)$ substates, due to the nuclear spin alone. It is seen from Figure 9.48 that the total number of substates remains the same throughout but the groupings differ according to the field strength.

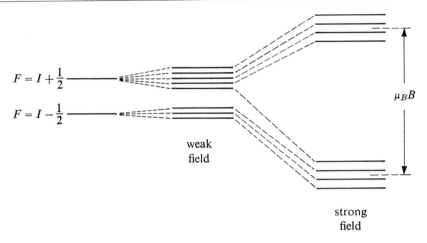

$$F = I + \frac{1}{2}$$

$$F = I - \frac{1}{2}$$

weak
field

$\mu_B B$

strong
field

FIGURE 9.48   *Schematic diagram of energy levels of an atom-plus-nucleus system in weak and strong magnetic fields, illustrated for $J = \frac{1}{2}$, $I = \frac{3}{2}$. In a weak field the total angular momentum number F determines the splittings, but in strong fields the electron and nuclear momentum vectors become uncoupled and the large-scale splitting is fixed by the Bohr magneton moment of the electron spin ($J = \frac{1}{2}$).*

In an early experiment on nuclear moments, Cohen and Rabi used a beam of sodium atoms in their ground state ($3\,^2S_{1/2}$) and split the beam into two major components with a strong inhomogeneous field. One of these components was selected and sent through a weaker field of great length and extreme inhomogeneity, which divided the beam further into four components. This observation showed that the Na²³ nuclei in their ground state have $I = \frac{3}{2}$ and the magnetic moment was estimated as $+2.2$ nuclear magnetons, the positive sign indicating that the μ and G vectors point in the same direction. In another experiment, hydrogen molecules with zero total electronic moment and $I = 1$ (parallel proton spins) were used and the beam was split into three components by a suitable inhomogeneous field, indicating that $I = \frac{1}{2}$ for each proton and that the magnetic moment is $+2.8$ nuclear magnetons. Thus in Equation (9.7.4) we have to substitute $g_I = 5.6$ for the proton and the moment is clearly anomalous from the point of view of the Dirac theory, which would require $g_I = 2$.

(c) Nuclear magnetic resonance

A great advance in magnetic-moment measurements was the introduction of radio-frequency resonance techniques by Rabi and his collaborators. In their original experiments on nuclear moments, the beam was first deflected in an inhomogeneous field $\mathbf{B}_A$ and a particular component was selected by passing the beam through a slit. This component then traversed a homogeneous field $\mathbf{B}_B$, which introduced no deflection, and was finally deflected back to the axis of the apparatus by a third field $\mathbf{B}_C$ which was inhomogeneous with the gradient opposed to that of $\mathbf{B}_A$. A beam detector was placed to record the arrival of atoms which traversed the three fields (Figure 9.49) with their spin and moment orientation fixed throughout. A small magnetic field oscillating at high frequency was then imposed on the beam in the homogeneous field region (B_B) and the frequency was varied until the beam signal showed a sharp "resonance" dip. This dip was due to defocusing of the beam and indicated that the spin orientation was materially affected in the B_B region. For a simple

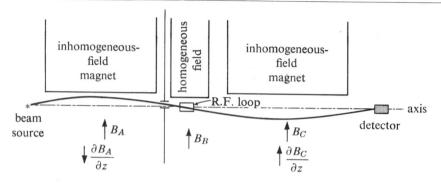

FIGURE 9.49   *The principle of a molecular-beam apparatus designed to measure magnetic moments by the resonance method. The beam is deflected by the inhomogeneous field B_A, passes through a slit into a homogeneous field B_B and then through an inhomogeneous field B_C which brings the beam back to the axis. "Spin-flip" changes can be induced by a resonant rf field applied to the beam by the loop in B_B.*

"spin-flip" change the appropriate frequency is given by

$$\hbar\omega = g_I\mu_n B_B \qquad \text{(see Problem 7.35).}$$

Further work by Purcell, Bloch, and others has shown that the nuclear magnetic resonance technique can be applied to matter in bulk. For example, the protons in liquid water respond to a radio-frequency field and absorb energy from an rf oscillator at the correct resonance frequency, which depends on the uniform magnetic field applied to the specimen. Extremely accurate frequency measurements lead to a value of $\mu_P = +2.79270\ \mu_n$ for the proton and this figure is now widely used in standardization of magnetic field strengths by the proton-resonance method.

The magnetic moment of the neutron was first measured in a classic experiment by Alvarez and Bloch,[*] who employed the resonance principle in an apparatus similar in essentials to that of Figure 9.49. A beam of slow neutrons was first "polarized" by passage through a ferromagnetic slab which was magnetized close to its saturation point. The interaction between the neutron moment and the aligned electron spins of the ferromagnetic (Section 8.6) resulted in the neutron beam being partially polarized, with a preponderance of spins in one direction. A second ferromagnetic slab was used to "analyze" the beam, that is, with the same orientation as the first slab it transmitted the neutrons to a slow-neutron counter. In between the two slabs the beam passed through a homogeneous field B and the small radio-frequency field produced by a single loop of wire. The correct frequency for depolarizing the neutron beam was located and, since the main field B was known, the value of g_I could be found. The present value for μ_N is $-1.91316\ \mu_n$, the negative sign showing that the vectors μ and G are *opposed* in the neutron.

The magnetic moment of the deuteron in its ground state has been measured and the result is

$$\mu_D = +0.857393\ \mu_n.$$

By way of comparison the proton and neutron moments are

$$\mu_P = +2.79270\ \mu_n$$
$$\mu_N = -1.91316\ \mu_n$$

so that $$\mu_P + \mu_N = +0.87954\ \mu_n.$$

* L. W. Alvarez and F. Bloch, Phys. Rev., **57**, 111 (1940).

Now if the spins of neutron and proton were parallel in the deuteron and there were no orbital motion at all (a pure S state), the sum of moments should agree with μ_D exactly. The small discrepancy is explained by assuming that there is a small admixture of the $^3D_1$ state with $^3S_1$ in the deuteron, as described in connection with the deuteron's quadrupole moment.

(d) The Schmidt moments

A survey of nuclear moments carried out over the wide range of nuclides investigated reveals certain systematic features which are of the utmost value in theories of nuclear structure. In the first place, all "even-even" nuclides (those with even numbers of neutrons and of protons) have zero magnetic moment and zero electric quadrupole moment. It is believed that all these nuclides have ground states of type 0^+, suggesting that there is some form of nuclear interaction which pairs off nucleons in such a way that their net angular momentum is zero.

Secondly, the observed magnetic moments of odd-A nuclides can be correlated with those of the neutron and proton on the assumption that the "odd" nucleon is chiefly responsible for the moment. These nuclides are divided into two groups according to whether the odd nucleon is a neutron or a proton. We first define effective gyromagnetic factors (g_s) for these two particles due to their intrinsic spin momentum and also g_l factors due to orbital angular momentum. In the proton, the spin momentum produces a magnetic moment of $2.79270\ \mu_n$, so, by Equation (9.7.4), the effective "spin g" is

$$g_s^p = 5.5854.$$

Also, the proton may have angular momentum due to orbital motion with the quantum number l, and, if the proton behaves like the electron in atomic states, we can assume that

$$g_l^p = 1 \text{ (exactly)}.$$

Also, the neutron, being uncharged, has

$$g_l^n = 0.$$

The neutron spin, on the other hand, produces a magnetic moment of $-1.91316\ \mu_n$ so its effective gyromagnetic ratio for spin is

$$g_s^n = -3.8263.$$

Having defined the g factors, we can calculate the magnetic moment of a nuclear state of total spin number I by the methods of Section 7.14, where the Landé gyromagnetic factor was found for Russell-Saunders coupling of the **L** and **S** vectors to make total **J**. Here the situation is simplified by the condition that the total spin is due to the odd nucleon with orbital number l, so we have the values

$$I = (l + \tfrac{1}{2}) \quad \text{and} \quad (l - \tfrac{1}{2}) \quad \text{only.}$$

Retaining the L^* and S^* vectors of Figure 7.26, with I^* replacing the electronic J^*, we see that the total magnetic moment along the I^* direction is given by the expression

$$\mu = \mu_n(g_l L^* \cos\theta_1 + g_s S^* \cos\theta_2)$$

$$= \mu_n \left\{ \frac{g_l}{2I^*} [I(I+1) + L(L+1) - S(S+1)] + \frac{g_s}{2I^*} [I(I+1) + S(S+1) - L(L+1)] \right\}.$$

Hence the nuclear gyromagnetic factor as defined by Equation (7.14.2) can be found from the above expression, with $S = \frac{1}{2}$ and $L = l$,

$$g_I = \frac{\mu}{\mu_n I^*} = g_l\left[\frac{I(I+1) + l(l+1) - \frac{3}{4}}{2I(I+1)}\right] + g_s\left[\frac{I(I+1) + \frac{3}{4} - l(l+1)}{2I(I+1)}\right]. \qquad [9.7.5]$$

The *maximum* value of the magnetic moment, as derived by resonance-frequency and beam-deflection methods, is given by putting $m_I = I$ and $\Delta E = -\mu_I B$ in Equation (9.7.4), that is,

$$\mu_I = Ig_I\mu_n$$

or

$$\frac{\mu_I}{\mu_n} = g_l\left[\frac{I(I+1) + l(l+1) - \frac{3}{4}}{2(I+1)}\right] + g_s\left[\frac{I(I+1) + \frac{3}{4} - l(l+1)}{2(I+1)}\right]. \qquad [9.7.6]$$

The results for odd-A nuclides may be summarized as follows:
Odd Proton

$$\text{with} \qquad I = l + \tfrac{1}{2} \qquad \frac{\mu_I}{\mu_n} = I + 2.29 \text{ approximately}$$

$$\text{with} \qquad I = l - \tfrac{1}{2} \qquad \frac{\mu_I}{\mu_n} = \frac{I^2 - 1.29I}{I + 1}.$$

Odd Neutron

$$\text{with} \qquad I = l + \tfrac{1}{2} \qquad \frac{\mu_I}{\mu_n} = -1.91$$

$$\text{with} \qquad I = l - \tfrac{1}{2} \qquad \frac{\mu_I}{\mu_n} = \frac{1.91I}{I + 1}.$$

This theory was first proposed by Schmidt in 1937 and it may be tested by plotting values of μ_I/μ_n against I for known nuclides in their ground states. There is no reason why we

TABLE 9.1
Parity Assignments of Nuclidic Ground States Based on the Schmidt Theory.

Nuclide	H³	He³	Li⁷	Be⁹	B¹¹	C¹³	N¹⁵	O¹⁷	F¹⁹	Ne²¹	Na²³	Mg²⁵	Al²⁷
Spin I	$\frac{1}{2}$	$\frac{1}{2}$	$\frac{3}{2}$	$\frac{3}{2}$	$\frac{3}{2}$	$\frac{1}{2}$	$\frac{1}{2}$	$\frac{5}{2}$	$\frac{1}{2}$	$\frac{3}{2}$	$\frac{3}{2}$	$\frac{5}{2}$	$\frac{5}{2}$
Orbital l	0	0	1	1	1	1	1	2	0	?	?	?	2
Parity	+	+	−	−	−	−	−	+	+	?	?	?	+

should immediately choose either $I = l + \frac{1}{2}$ or $I = l - \frac{1}{2}$ for a particular nuclide, so we plot both theoretical expressions on the graph (Figure 9.50) and compare the theoretical lines with experimental points for a group of light and medium nuclides. Clearly the theory is not adequate to account completely for the data, but, with a few exceptions, the nuclides show a distinct tendency to lie close to one or other of the Schmidt lines. If the theory were entirely misleading no such correlation would be expected. As it is, many of the points lie within the area bounded by the lines, an effect which can be attributed to mixing of the nucleon configurations in the ground state.* The main point is that for a number of nuclides the data serve to fix an effective l value, which in turn fixes the parity of the ground state. Some results obtained from the diagram are shown in Table 9.1.

Several of the results in the region around $A = 23$ are inconclusive but the rest of the data show an impressive consistency with the idea that groups of nuclides with the same

* R. J. Blin-Stoyle, *Rev. Mod. Phys.*, **28**, 75 (1956).

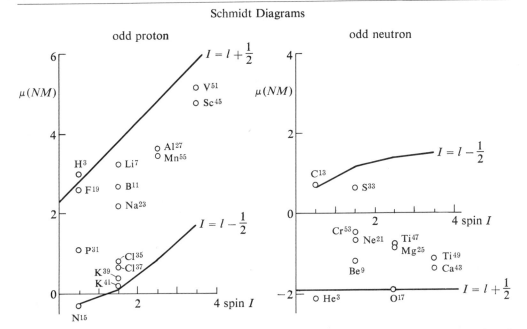

FIGURE 9.50 *The Schmidt diagrams of nuclear magnetic moment (in nuclear magnetons) plotted against the spin number I for odd-A nuclides (i) with an odd proton (ii) with an odd neutron.*

parity occur together. This idea is fundamental in the development of the *shell model* of nuclear structure, which seeks to explain nuclear ground-state properties by describing the motion of individual nucleons in definite "shells." The Schmidt theory plays an important role in this model, but it should be emphasized that the odd-nucleon approach is of limited value in other fields. For example, the observed electric-quadrupole moments are not consistent with a single odd-nucleon contribution, since they are often much too large to be explained in this way.

9.8 Nuclear Forces

(a) General properties

In the foregoing sections a certain amount of experimental material relating to nucleon-nucleon interactions has been discussed and some deductions have been made concerning the fundamental nuclear forces between nucleons. A brief summary may take the form:

(i) the neutron-proton and proton-proton scattering data at low energies indicate that the specifically nuclear forces are of short range, that is, they are negligible outside a separation distance of the order of 3×10^{-15} m;

(ii) the low-energy data are consistent with the charge-independence hypothesis, which requires the *nuclear* interaction between any pair of nucleons to be the same in the same state;

(iii) the two-nucleon system has energy levels which depend on spin and isospin as indicated by Figure 9.40 and which may be correlated with the scattering data on the assumption that the interaction potential is in the form of a rectangular well;

(iv) the existence of a small positive electric quadrupole moment in the deuteron, and the magnitude of its magnetic moment, show that there are noncentral forces between neutron and proton;

(v) the approximately constant density of nuclear matter in medium and heavy nuclei suggests that nuclear forces "saturate" in large nucleon assemblies, this idea being the basis of the Weizsäcker formula for nuclear binding energies.

An additional fact, which is not related to nuclear forces proper, but is important in the theory of nucleons, is the existence of "anomalous" magnetic moments in both the neutron and the proton. The partial success of the Schmidt theory of nuclear magnetic moments suggests that these anomalous values are retained when the nucleons enter a complex nucleus, so the magnetic moments are presumably closely connected with the nucleons. We should also remember the electron-scattering data which show that the proton has a finite size in its electromagnetic interactions; recent experiments have revealed some structure in the proton, used as a target for electron scattering.

So far no complete theory has been given to account for all the properties of nucleons and nuclei. It is possible to devise a system of phenomenological interactions (with suitable parameters), which are consistent with the experimental data, notably the great amount of material relating to nucleon-nucleon scattering at different energies. These interactions are frequently employed in theoretical work but they possess many features demanding further explanation. For example, in order to account for saturation and other effects, it is conventional to introduce a "hard core," that is, a strongly repulsive force at very short distances, but this feature has no fundamental justification at the present time.

It would be more satisfactory if nuclear forces could be explained by some kind of field theory, analogous to the theory of electromagnetic interactions. For example, the static Coulomb interaction between electric charges can be accounted for by supposing that the charges exchange photons, since each charge acts as a source for the photon "field." It is tempting, therefore, to ascribe nucleon-nucleon interactions to some kind of exchange mechanism via a new field possessing both field and particle properties, like the electromagnetic field. Indeed data obtained from high-energy experiments strongly support the idea of an exchange mechanism operating between pairs of nucleons.

(b) Neutron-proton scattering at high energies

If neutron-proton scattering experiments are extended up to 40 MeV bombarding energy and beyond, the angular distributions in the center-of-mass system of coordinates become markedly anisotropic. For example, with neutrons at 90 MeV laboratory energy, the results of many experiments combine to give the curve of Figure 9.51, where the differential scattering cross section is plotted against the angle θ in the center-of-mass system. The curve is almost symmetrical about the center line at $\theta = \frac{1}{2}\pi$ rad and there is a pronounced minimum near this angle. In terms of "partial-wave analysis," that is, the expansion in Legendre polynomials of Equation (9.4.18), both s-wave and d-wave components are present in the distribution, but the p-wave effects are very weak.

A theoretical analysis of the results shows that they cannot be explained in terms of "ordinary" forces between the neutron and proton. A complete treatment of the scattering theory is beyond the scope of this book, but a simple calculation of the angular distribution produced by ordinary short-range forces can be made by the perturbation method (Section 7.12), with the incident and scattered particles represented by plane-wave functions. This method is called Born's first approximation. It is not generally valid, but it serves to indicate qualitatively the kind of results which would be found by exact analysis.

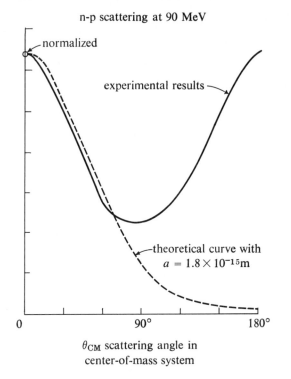

n-p scattering at 90 MeV

normalized

experimental results

theoretical curve with
$a = 1.8 \times 10^{-15}$m

0   90°   180°

θ_{CM} scattering angle in
center-of-mass system

FIGURE 9.51   *The differential cross section of elastic neutron-proton scattering in the center-of-mass system for 90 MeV neutrons. The experimental data (full line) may be compared with the theoretical predictions of the Born approximation, based on a rectangular-well interaction.*

In the Born approximation, the incident particle is represented by a plane wave function of the form

$$\psi_a = \exp i(\mathbf{x}_0 \mathbf{r})$$

and the final state of this particle by

$$\psi_b = \exp i(\mathbf{x} \mathbf{r})$$

where $\mathbf{x}_0$, $\mathbf{x}$ are wave-number vectors related to the linear momenta by $\mathbf{x}_0 = \dfrac{\mathbf{p}_0}{h}$ and $\mathbf{x} = \dfrac{\mathbf{p}}{h}$.

We consider first the scattering of the particle by a center of force which is effectively stationary in the laboratory frame and which causes the particle to have potential energy $U(r)$, corresponding to a spherically symmetrical field. This term is identified with the perturbation part, H', of the total Hamiltonian and is supposed to induce transitions from state a to state b. We therefore write down a matrix element of the form [see Equation (7.12.2)]

$$U_{ab} = \int \psi_b^* U(r) \psi_a \, dV$$

$$= \int \exp \left[-i(\mathbf{x} \mathbf{r})\right] U(r) \exp \left[i(\mathbf{x}_0 r)\right] dV$$

$$= \int U(r) \exp \left[i(\mathbf{x}_0 - \mathbf{x})\mathbf{r}\right] dV, \qquad\qquad [9.8.1]$$

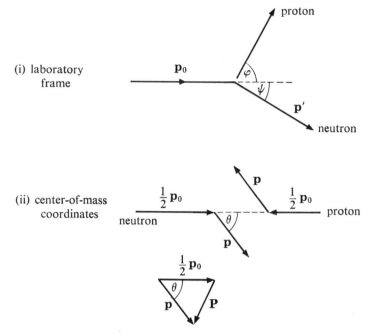

FIGURE 9.52 *Momentum relations in neutron-proton scattering (i) in the laboratory frame, where the neutron momentum changes from $\mathbf{p}_0$ to $\mathbf{p}$, (ii) in the center-of-mass system of coordinates, where each particle changes from momentum $\frac{1}{2}\mathbf{p}_0$ to momentum $\mathbf{p}$ at angle θ and the vector change is denoted by $\mathbf{P}$.*

where the integral is taken over the entire volume where the interaction is effective. Conservation of momentum yields the relation (see Figure 9.52)

$$\mathbf{x}_0 - \mathbf{x} = \mathbf{K} = \frac{\mathbf{P}}{\hbar}, \qquad [9.8.2]$$

where $\mathbf{P}$ is recoil momentum imparted to the target by the particle. For purposes of integration we denote the angle between the $\mathbf{r}$ and $\mathbf{P}$ vectors by α, and the element of volume becomes

$$dV = 2\pi r^2 \sin \alpha \, dr \, d\alpha$$

in spherical polar coordinates, since the scattering distribution possesses cylindrical symmetry about the line of approach.

With these substitutions the integral becomes separable as follows:

$$U_{ab} = 2\pi \int U(r) r^2 \, dr \int_0^\pi \exp{(iKr \cos \alpha)} \sin \alpha \, d\alpha$$

$$= 4\pi \int U(r) r^2 \, dr \frac{\sin Kr}{Kr}. \qquad [9.8.3]$$

If this integral can be evaluated, the differential scattering cross section is readily found, since by perturbation theory it is proportional to the transition rate,

$$\frac{d\sigma}{d\Omega} \propto |U_{ab}|^2. \qquad [9.8.4]$$

In the neutron-proton problem, we have to transform into the center-of-mass system of coordinates, with r now standing for the particle separation distance. In the special case of particles with equal mass colliding, the incident momentum ($\frac{1}{2}M$U in Figure 9.26) and the imparted momentum (**p**) are equal in magnitude and the angle between these two vectors is θ (the center-of-mass scattering angle) so the magnitude of the momentum difference P is

$$P = 2p \sin \tfrac{1}{2}\theta = Mu \sin \tfrac{1}{2}\theta, \qquad [9.8.5]$$

where M is the proper mass of each nucleon and u is the relative velocity before collision. In this problem it is convenient to represent the short-range nuclear interaction by a rectangular well of radius $r = a$ and depth $U = -U_0$, in which case the matrix element for scattering [Equation (9.8.3)] becomes

$$U_{ab} = -4\pi \int_0^a U_0 r^2 \, dr \, \frac{\sin \mathrm{K}r}{\mathrm{K}r}$$

$$= -\frac{4\pi U_0}{\mathrm{K}^3} (\sin \mathrm{K}a - \mathrm{K}a \cos \mathrm{K}a). \qquad [9.8.6]$$

The differential scattering cross section in center-of-mass terms is

$$\frac{d\sigma}{d\Omega} \propto \frac{U_0^2}{\mathrm{K}^6} (\sin \mathrm{K}a - \mathrm{K}a \cos \mathrm{K}a)^2 \qquad [9.8.7]$$

with

$$\mathrm{K}\hbar = Mu \sin \tfrac{1}{2}\theta.$$

When applied to high-energy neutron-proton scattering, this expression is subject to considerable uncertainties concerning the correct values of U_0 and a. If the value of a is known, it is possible to derive U_0 for the ground state of the deuteron, since the binding energy is also available, but this yields a value of the well depth for the $^3S_1$ state only, whereas the high-energy scattering clearly brings in states of higher angular momentum. However, the shape of the *angular distribution* given by Equation (9.8.7) does not depend on the magnitude of U_0 but only on the momentum Mu and the well radius a. With $a = 1.8 \times 10^{-15}$ m and a neutron energy of 90 MeV (in the laboratory frame), the theoretical result is shown by the dotted line in Figure 9.51, where the experimental and theoretical curves have been fitted together at $\theta = 0$. Unfortunately the shape of the theoretical line is sensitively dependent on the value of a, which is not certainly known, but all theoretical lines with reasonable values of a agree in giving a strong maximum in the forward direction and very little scattering backwards. In other words, this type of theory, with ordinary forces of attraction, cannot explain the minimum near $\frac{1}{2}\pi$ rad; the same conclusion is reached whatever the choice of potential function $U(r)$.

However, a simple solution to the problem is suggested by Figure 9.51. If we assume that about half of the neutron-proton interactions leave the particles unchanged in identity while the other half cause an *exchange* of identity, the angular distribution of one kind of particle in the center-of-mass system is the sum of two distributions—one in the angle θ and the other in the supplementary angle $(\pi - \theta)$. If, now, we add together two theoretical curves, one of them plotted versus θ and the other versus $(\pi - \theta)$, the result is very similar to the experimental curve. It should be emphasized that this mixture of 50% "ordinary" and 50% "exchange" terms, known as the *Serber potential*, is not generally successful in describing nuclear forces—for instance, it is not consistent with the charge-independence hypothesis—but its partial success is sufficient to establish the existence of exchange forces between neutron and proton. This deduction is confirmed by the observation that, when protons of energy 400 MeV strike a target, a beam of high-energy neutrons is ejected in the forward direction, due presumably to a direct exchange effect.

(c) The Yukawa theory

If we now try to set up a detailed theory of exchange forces between nucleons, we have to postulate the existence of some entity which is suitably exchanged. The idea was developed by Yukawa in 1935 and is the basis of all subsequent "meson" theories of nuclear forces. Yukawa pointed out that a quantized boson field obeying the Klein-Gordon equation [Equation (7.9.2)] includes static solutions of the form

$$\psi = \text{const} \, \frac{\exp{(-\mu r)}}{r} \qquad \text{(see Problem 7.24)}$$

where

$$\mu = \frac{m_0 c}{\hbar}$$

and m_0 is the rest mass of the particles composing the boson field.

If such a field interacts with each of two particles placed a distance r apart, the potential energy of the particles is

$$U(r) = \frac{g^2 \exp{(-\mu r)}}{r}, \qquad [9.8.8]$$

where g is a coupling constant analogous to electric charge in the electromagnetic field. The form of the radial function $U(r)$ is a short-range interaction due to the presence of the exponential term and the effective range of the interaction is given approximately by the reciprocal of the constant μ, that is, we can write

$$a \approx \frac{1}{\mu} = \frac{\hbar}{m_0 c}. \qquad [9.8.9]$$

Yukawa proposed the following mechanism for the process of interaction between a neutron and a proton placed a short distance apart. One of the particles, say the neutron, is supposed to emit a "meson" of rest mass m_0 and at the same time to change itself into a proton. The meson is absorbed by the proton to form a neutron and so the two nucleons have exchanged identity

$$n \rightarrow p^+ + \pi^- \qquad \pi^- + p^+ \rightarrow n, \qquad [9.8.10]$$

where π^- stands for a negatively charged meson.*

Alternatively the same kind of interaction might involve the emission of a positively charged meson by the proton. If neutral mesons also exist and have the same kind of interaction with nucleons, they might account for the occurrence of neutron-neutron and proton-proton forces. All these forms of exchange yield essentially the same interaction potential energy $U(r)$ of Equation (9.8.8), but there may be different g factors in different cases.

It should be emphasized that the meson-exchange process is supposed to happen only when the nucleons are very close together. This condition is necessary because the meson-emission process of Equation (9.8.10) literally violates the conservation of energy if the

---

* In high-energy physics, the proton is represented usually by symbol p, and π^- stands for a negative *pion*.

meson has a finite rest-mass m_0, as is required by the short-range parameter (μ) of Equation (9.8.9). Thus the mesons exchanged are "virtual," in the sense that their temporary existence is allowed only by the conditions of the Uncertainty principle. The rest-mass energy of the meson is m_0c^2 and this can be created only for a short period of time (Δt), given by expression

$$\Delta E \, \Delta t \approx \hbar,$$

where

$$\Delta E = m_0c^2.$$

In the time Δt, the meson can cover a maximum distance (a) fixed by the velocity of light (c)

$$a = c \, \Delta t$$

so the effective range of interaction by meson exchange is

$$a \approx \frac{c\hbar}{m_0c^2} = \frac{\hbar}{m_0c} \qquad \text{as in Equation (9.8.9).}$$

Thus a meson-exchange interaction is essentially a quantum-mechanical effect and detailed calculations of the interaction potential have to be carried out by the theory of transitions (Section 7.12). The form taken by the interaction in its most general form includes "ordinary" forces in addition to exchange forces, also spin-dependent terms, but the effective range is still fixed by Equation (9.8.9). Assuming that the theory is basically correct, we can estimate the meson rest mass from the effective range of nuclear forces, or, more strictly, impose a lower limit to m_0 by putting

$$a \leqslant 3 \times 10^{-15} \text{ m}$$

that is $m_0 \geqslant \dfrac{\hbar}{ca} = 1.2 \times 10^{-28}$ kg approximately.

This figure is about 130 electron masses and various considerations suggest that it is probably one-half of the proper meson mass. The word "meson" was coined to indicate that m_0 is intermediate in value between the electron and nucleon masses.

Yukawa's theoretical speculations therefore led to the prediction that bosons of mass about 200 times that of the electron must exist and should be found in strong nuclear interactions at high energy. It was also considered that the mesons must be unstable because of their high rest-mass, decaying probably into electrons and photons. These predictions were apparently fulfilled when Anderson and Neddermeyer discovered "mu-mesons" (now called *muons*) in 1937. Both positively charged and negatively charged muons are present in cosmic rays at sea level; they have a rest mass 207 times that of the electron and they are unstable, breaking up to yield electrons and other particles. However it soon became evident that the nuclear interactions of muons are very weak and it is now known that their spin is $\frac{1}{2}\hbar$; that is, they are fermions, *not* bosons. In 1947 Lattes, Occhialini, and Powell discovered positive and negative "pi-mesons" (now called *pions*) in cosmic rays at high altitudes. This was followed by the artificial production of neutral pions at Berkeley. Studies of these three types of particle showed that they are unstable, with strong nuclear interactions, and that they are indeed of the correct form for Yukawa's theory. The charged pions have a rest mass 273 times that of the electron, corresponding to an effective-range parameter (a) of 1.4×10^{-15} m.

Since suitable mesons undoubtedly exist, it may be asked if the meson theory accounts satisfactorily for the nucleon properties listed at the beginning of this section. In the low-energy region there is little to choose between the Yukawa results and those of the simple rectangular-well treatment, so far as the scattering data are concerned. The most successful meson theory is based on the hypothesis that the meson is a *pseudoscalar* particle, of zero spin and odd intrinsic parity, in agreement with the known properties of the pions.* This theory divides the nucleon-nucleon interactions into two types:

(i) a "spin-spin" interaction proportional to the scalar product

$$(\mathbf{G}_s \mathbf{G}_s'),$$

where the $\mathbf{G}_s$ terms each represent spin angular momentum;

(ii) a noncentral "tensor" interaction similar to that between two magnetic dipoles (see Problem 7.28).

Of these two terms, the first accounts for the difference in energy between the two spin states of the two-nucleon system (Figure 9.40) and the second explains the existence of the deuteron's electric quadrupole moment.

Although some form of meson theory can be adopted to explain the deuteron states and low-energy scattering data, severe difficulties are encountered in the high-energy field. The simple perturbation theory employed in working out the interaction potential [Equation (9.8.8)] is of limited validity for strong interactions at any distance and is probably quite fallacious at very short distances, where multiple meson exchange can occur. The mathematical difficulties are of such a high order that no reliance can be placed on theoretical results by themselves, although the meson theory is undoubtedly useful as a guide in interpretation of phenomenological potentials. The high-energy data on nucleon-nucleon scattering suggest that there are two features of the interaction which are not accounted for by the simple meson theory:

(i) at very short distances, there appears to be a strong repulsion effect—this may be of significance in producing saturation of nuclear forces;

(ii) the interaction appears to be velocity-dependent, that is, a purely static potential is inadequate to explain the data, and the velocity dependent term is probably proportional to the product

$$(\mathbf{G}_l \, \mathbf{G}_s). \qquad\qquad \text{[see Equation (7.10.3)]}$$

The latter effect is clearly a spin-orbit interaction, but its magnitude is much greater than the Dirac theory would suggest for nucleons, and its sign is opposite to that in atomic systems, that is, it tends to make the states of *maximum* total angular momentum lowest in the sequence of energy levels.

A further difficulty of the meson theory lies in the calculation of the anomalous magnetic moments of the neutron and proton. At first sight the meson theory offers an explanation of the anomalies, since, according to the exchange process of Equation (9.8.10), each neutron carries with it a cloud of virtual negative mesons, which would give rise to a negative magnetic moment. Likewise the proton should have an extra positive moment in addition to its intrinsic moment of one nuclear magneton, the extra contribution coming from virtual positive mesons. However, the theory has not been successful in predicting the correct moments and further developments must await an explanation of the observed electromagnetic structure of the proton.

An important development of the theory of nuclear forces is its extension to an assembly of many nucleons and the treatment of the saturation effect. Brueckner and his collaborators

* R. E. Marshak, "Pions," *Scientific American*, **196,** No. 1, 84 (1957).

have used phenomenological nucleon-nucleon potentials to find the mean density and binding energy per nucleon ($\bar{B}$ of Section 9.3.d) in nuclear matter, and their theoretical results are in general agreement with the data. A significant feature of the Brueckner theory is the effect of the velocity-dependent forces, such as large spin-orbit interactions, on the *effective mass* per nucleon. It is found that the ratio m^*/m (see Section 8.4) has to be of the order of 0.5 to explain various nuclear properties. On the other hand, the proper nucleon mass (m) is apparently appropriate in the Schmidt theory of magnetic moments (Section 9.7). This difficulty is typical of many-body problems where multiple interactions occur and in this respect nuclear theory shows several similarities to the theory of metals (Section 8.4). Nevertheless the Brueckner treatment has been valuable in indicating that, to a first approximation, the nucleons in a complex nucleus may be regarded as moving independently, except insofar as the nucleus as a whole affects their motion. Thus the *individual-particle model* has at least a limited range of validity, like the Bloch single-electron theory of metals, and we shall employ this oversimplified model as the basis of nuclear shell theory.

9.9 The Nuclear Shell Model

Since we do not yet possess a complete theory of the forces between a pair of nucleons, it is not possible to set up a fundamental theory of nuclear structure. However, certain simplified models can be used to correlate nuclear data and to throw light on the basic two-body forces.* For example, in Section 9.3.d we employed the "liquid-drop" model with some success in deriving an expression for the mean binding energy per nucleon, although this model made great use of empirical data. Such a model is based on the idea that nucleons interact strongly with each other, like the molecules in a liquid. The same idea was used by Niels Bohr to interpret the results on slow-neutron resonances (Section 9.5.d) and to elaborate the compound-nucleus theory of nuclear reactions (Section 9.5.e).

Bohr's strong-interaction hypothesis was generally accepted until about 1948, when the individual-particle model was revived by Mayer and by Haxel, Jensen, and Suess. A few years later the details of fast-neutron scattering were analyzed to show that, in general, strong nucleon absorption does not occur and this led to the optical model of nucleon interactions with complex nuclei. It appears that nucleon-nucleon interactions in complex nuclei are restricted by the operation of Pauli's principle in limiting the number of states accessible to an incident nucleon. The present picture is therefore one of "intermediate" interaction which is best expressed by the optical model. However, in working out the details of nuclear states, it is necessary to adopt an extreme view as a first approximation and we shall assume that single nucleons interact only with the nucleus as a whole. With the aid of a single extra hypothesis—the existence of strong spin-orbit interaction—the individual-particle model can account for the existence of "magic" nucleon numbers and for most of the available data concerning nuclear ground states.

(a) Magic numbers

The existence of certain nucleon numbers with special properties, the so-called *magic numbers*, can be deduced from several pieces of evidence:

(i) the data of Figure 9.19 show that the number of stable isotopes possessed by an element varies considerably, being greatest in regions around $Z = 20, 50$; also, in terms of the

---

* R. E. Peierls, "Models of the Nucleus," Scientific American, **200**, No. 1, 75 (1959).

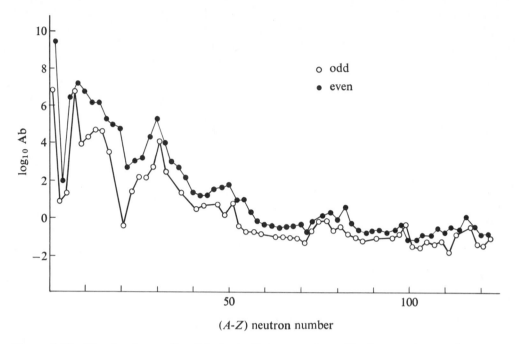

FIGURE 9.53 *The abundances of nuclides in the Universe, estimated by Suess and Urey, plotted on a logarithmic scale against the neutron number (A–Z). The occurrence of certain peaks in the curve is taken as evidence for magic numbers nearby.*

neutron number $(A - Z)$ the maximum numbers of stable nuclides occur around $(A - Z) = 20, 28, 82$;

(ii) the binding energy of the last neutron in a nucleus (B_n of Figure 9.20) has regular maxima at intervals of four units in A in the light-nuclide region and this periodicity is evidently related to the extremely high stability of the alpha particle (He^4). It is also noteworthy that the peak at Ca^{40} (which contains 20 neutrons and 20 protons) is higher than subsequent peaks;

(iii) the mean binding energy per nucleon ($\bar{B}$ of Figure 9.21) has pronounced maxima in the low-mass region at the nuclides He^4, C^{12}, O^{16};

(iv) neutron capture cross sections have been measured for a number of elements in the energy region near 1 MeV, where the effects of resonances are less important than in the slow-neutron region, and the results show marked minima at neutron numbers $(A - Z) = 50, 82, 126*$;

(v) nuclidic abundances for elements in the accessible regions of the Universe have been estimated, notably by Suess and Urey.† The logarithm of the abundance (measured relative to silicon) is plotted against neutron number in Figure 9.53, with odd-numbered nuclides distinguished from even-numbered nuclides. The data show a general trend downward as the mass increases, but there are peaks above the general level at $(A - Z) = 8, 30, 50, 82$;

(vi) the natural radioactive series all end with a stable isotope of lead ($Z = 82$) and, of the three isotopes, Pb^{208} with 126 neutrons is the most abundant. Theoretically, elements

* R. A. Alpher and R. C. Herman, Rev. Mod. Phys., **22**, 153 (1950).
† H. E. Suess and H. C. Urey, Rev. Mod. Phys., **28**, 53 (1956).

below lead are unstable with respect to alpha-particle emission but emission is inhibited by the Coulomb barrier (Section 9.6.e); these observations serve to emphasize that there must be a significant change in nuclear properties through $Z = 82$, allowing alpha-particle decay in higher elements;

(vii) the occurrence of long-lived nuclear states or isomers (Section 9.6.f) shows that these states have a large spin difference from the neighboring states. Goldhaber and Hill* have shown that isomers are particularly abundant when the odd-nucleon number is close to 50, 82, and 126;

(viii) if the Schmidt theory of magnetic moments for odd-A nuclides is correct (Section 9.7) the ground states of these nuclides change from even parity to odd parity or vice versa at the numbers $A = 4, 16, 40$, when the nucleon numbers are 2, 8, and 20, respectively;

(ix) the electric quadrupole moments of many odd-A nuclides in the ground state are known and the figures indicate the degree of departure from spherical symmetry. In Figure 9.54 we plot the ratio QM/A per unit charge against the odd-nucleon number. Although the data are far from completely adequate there is a strong indication that the moments vary in a systematic way, changing from positive to negative when the odd-nucleon number is close to 8, 15, 28, 50, 82, 120 and from negative to positive when the number is 10, 18, 30, 55, 90. These data require theoretical interpretation if their full significance is to be realized,

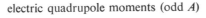

electric quadrupole moments (odd A)

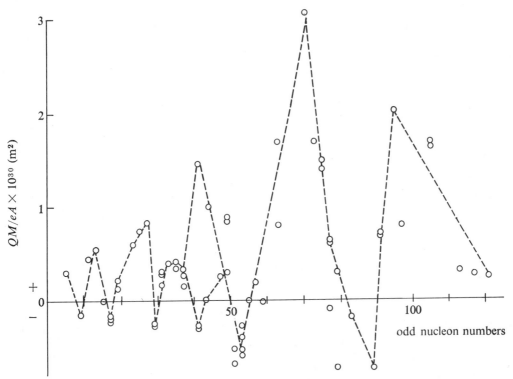

FIGURE 9.54 *The electric quadrupole moment per unit charge, divided by A, plotted against the odd nucleon number for a wide range of nuclides with A odd. The nuclear shape is supposed to be spherical at magic numbers and shows appreciable deviations from sphericity in between these numbers.*

* M. Goldhaber and R. D. Hill, Rev. Mod. Phys., **24**, 179 (1952).

but they show directly that spherical symmetry occurs only at certain values of the nucleon number.

These and other data have been studied intensively, with the result that the magic numbers have been identified as 2, 8, 20, 28, 50, 82, 126. Nuclides with these nucleon numbers tend to show extra stability and to be spherically symmetrical. The "doubly magic" nuclides

$$_2\text{He}^4, \quad _8\text{O}^{16}, \quad _{20}\text{Ca}^{40}, \quad \text{and} \quad _{82}\text{Pb}^{208}$$

are particularly notable for high stability. The task of nuclear theory is to explain the occurrence of these magic numbers and, if possible, to draw further conclusions about the details of nuclear configurations and the states they produce.

(b) Single-particle levels in a deep well

In the individual-particle model of nuclear structure, each nucleon is supposed to move in the field produced by the remaining $(A - 1)$ nucleons situated in the nucleus. Since full details of the interactions are not known, the simplest possible assumptions are made concerning the type of force acting on a single nucleon. For example, we might suppose that the force is similar to that governing simple harmonic oscillations in three dimensions, for which the potential energy is

$$U(r) = \tfrac{1}{2}m\omega^2 r^2.$$

If this expression is substituted into Schrödinger's equation (Problem 7.20) the resulting energy eigenvalues are given by the equation

$$E = (n + 1\tfrac{1}{2})\hbar\omega, \tag{9.9.1}$$

where n takes the values 0, 1, 2, ...

The number n includes the orbital momentum number l in such a way that the equally spaced energy levels alternate in parity and are degenerate except for the first two levels, that is, we have

		levels
$n = 0$	$l = 0$	$1\,s$
$n = 1$	$l = 1$	$1\,p$
$n = 2$	$l = 0, 2$	$2\,s, 1\,d$
$n = 3$	$l = 1, 3$	$2\,p, 1\,f$ and so forth.

It should be noted that the numbers in front of the letters s, p, d, . . . are purely *ordinal*. This usage is different from the spectroscopic notation in atoms, where Bohr's principal quantum number is employed.

The parabolic-well potential is useful for indicating the general pattern of single-particle levels in a deep well, and it is sometimes adopted because its state functions are convenient for calculations, but it does not reproduce very closely the short-range character of nucleon-nucleus forces. A rather more realistic potential, used greatly in the theory of scattering, is in the form of a rectangular well of radius (a) given by Equation (9.3.12) as a function of A. Neutron-scattering results indicate that the effective depth of such a well is of the order of 40 MeV in medium and heavy nuclei. This figure is considerably larger than the mean binding energy per nucleon so it may not be too erroneous a procedure if we assume that the well is *infinitely* deep in a first calculation. This simplifies the theory because we can impose the boundary condition

$$\psi(r) = 0 \quad \text{when} \quad r = a$$

on the state function $\psi(r)$ for the individual nucleon.

Schrödinger's equation for a nucleon of mass m in a field of potential energy $U(r)$ may be written in spherical polar coordinates and the radial part of the function ψ isolated (Section 7.6) to yield the equation

$$\frac{d^2R}{dr^2} + \frac{2}{r}\frac{dR}{dr} + \kappa^2 R - \frac{l(l+1)}{r^2}R - \frac{2m}{\hbar^2}UR = 0,$$

where

$$\kappa^2 = \frac{2mE}{\hbar^2}$$

and E is the energy eigenvalue.

We assume that U is zero inside the well of radius $r = a$ and is so large outside the well that the function $R(r)$ vanishes at the boundary. Inside the well we have to solve the equation

$$\frac{d^2R}{dr^2} + \frac{2}{r}\frac{dR}{dr} + \kappa^2 R - \frac{l(l+1)}{r^2}R = 0 \qquad [9.9.2]$$

for which the solutions are the "spherical Bessel functions" $j_l(\kappa r)$ of Equation (9.4.18). These functions may be found by direct solution or expressed in terms of the proper Bessel functions $J_n(\kappa r)$. The latter may be reached by the substitution

$$R(r) = \frac{u(r)}{r^{1/2}}$$

in Equation (9.9.2), when we find that the equation for $u(r)$ is

$$\frac{d^2u}{dr^2} + \frac{1}{r}\frac{du}{dr} + \left[\kappa^2 - \frac{(l+\frac{1}{2})^2}{r^2}\right]u = 0 \qquad [9.9.3]$$

with the solution

$$u(r) = J_{l+1/2}(\kappa r).$$

The solutions are conveniently expressed in sinusoidal functions and the non-normalized radial functions then become

$$l = 0 \quad R_0(r) = b_0\frac{\sin \kappa_0 r}{\kappa_0 r},$$

$$l = 1 \quad R_1(r) = b_1\frac{\sin \kappa_1 r - \kappa_1 r \cos \kappa_1 r}{(\kappa_1 r)^2},$$

$$l = 2 \quad R_2(r) = b_2\frac{(\sin \kappa_2 r)(1 - \kappa_2^2 r^2/3) - \kappa_2 r \cos \kappa_2 r}{(\kappa_2 r)^3},$$

$$l = 3 \quad R_3(r) = b_3\frac{(\sin \kappa_3 r)(1 - \frac{2}{5}\kappa_3^2 r^2) - \kappa_3 r(\cos \kappa_3 r)\left(1 - \frac{\kappa_3^2 r^2}{15}\right)}{(\kappa_3 r)^4}, \qquad [9.9.4]$$

where the different κ parameters refer to different eigenvalues.

The sequence of energy levels of different types $s, p, d, \ldots$, and so forth is then found by putting $R(r) = 0$ at $r = a$, which yields

States

$s \quad l = 0, \quad \dfrac{\kappa_0 a}{\pi} = n \quad$ and $\quad E = \dfrac{n^2 h^2}{8ma^2} \quad$ with $n = 1, 2, 3, \ldots$,

$p \quad l = 1, \quad \dfrac{\kappa_1 a}{\pi} = 1.43, 2.46, 3.47,$ and so forth,

$$\text{and} \quad E = \frac{h^2}{8ma^2}(1.43^2, 2.46^2, 3.47^2, \ldots)$$

$d \quad l = 2, \quad \dfrac{\kappa_2 a}{\pi} = 1.835, 2.89, 3.90,$ and so forth,

$$\text{and} \quad E = \frac{h^2}{8ma^2}(1.835^2, 2.89^2, 3.90^2, \ldots),$$

$f \quad l = 3, \quad \dfrac{\kappa_3 a}{\pi} = 2.25, 3.30,$ and so forth, $\quad E = \dfrac{h^2}{8ma^2}(2.25^2, 3.30^2, \ldots)$

$g \quad l = 4, \quad \dfrac{\kappa_4 a}{\pi} = 2.6, 3.7,$ and so forth, $\quad E = \dfrac{h^2}{8ma^2}(2.6^2, 3.7^2, \ldots).$

The full sequence of energy levels in the infinitely deep well consists of the series $1s, 1p, 1d, 2s, 1f, 2p, 1g, 2d, 3s$, and so forth with a nearly constant spacing, as is seen in Figure 9.55. The mean spacing between single-particle levels is approximately

$$\Delta E = \frac{h^2}{8ma^2} = 120A^{-\frac{2}{3}} \text{ MeV if we choose } r_0 = 1.3 \text{ fermi.}$$

Thus in light nuclei ΔE may approach 30 MeV, while in the heaviest nuclei it is about 3 MeV. These figures have to be reduced when the effects of a finite well depth are taken into account, but the general sequence is not greatly modified. It is clear that the single-particle level spacings are of the same order of magnitude as the mean binding energy per nucleon (around 8 MeV) so, on this basis, the level structure should have significant influence on nuclear behavior. Direct measurements of the level spacing are not easily carried out because the lower levels are normally filled and, by virtue of Pauli's Exclusion principle, can accommodate no more nucleons, while the nucleons in the upper levels have many excited states available. Nevertheless certain results obtained from $(p, 2p)$ and (d, p) reactions in medium nuclides have been interpreted as evidence for single-particle spacings of the order of 4 MeV.

However, the most important test of the individual-particle model is its application to the problem of magic numbers. We suppose that each type of nucleon obeys Pauli's Exclusion principle separately, so that each level with an orbital number l can accommodate $2(2l + 1)$ neutrons and the same number of protons, the factor 2 allowing for the two spin states of the particles. On this basis the numbers at which the levels are filled up, for each type of nucleon, are

$$\left. \begin{array}{c} Z \text{ or} \\ A - Z \end{array} \right\} = 2 \quad 8 \quad 18 \quad 20 \quad 34 \quad 40 \quad 58 \quad 68 \quad 70 \quad \text{and so forth.}$$

It is satisfactory to note that the first two of these numbers are magic numbers, but beyond these there are obviously far too many values to agree with experimental data.

Some measure of improvement is achieved by "rounding off" the edges of the rectangular

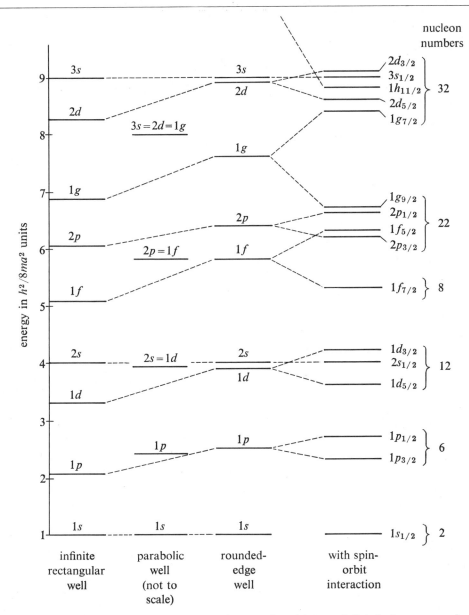

FIGURE 9.55 *The sequence of energy levels for a nucleon (a) in an infinitely deep rectangular well, (b) in a parabolic well, (c) in a rectangular well with rounded edges, (d) with levels split by strong spin-orbit interaction yielding shell groupings in agreement with experiment.*

potential well, that is, by letting the function $U(r)$ rise less steeply than a step function to its value outside the well. This modification has the effect of raising the energy levels and the high l values are raised more than the low l values, so that there is a grouping of the levels. The general effect is rather like a compromise between the rectangular and parabolic wells, as may be seen in Figure 9.55, where the parabolic-well levels are inserted, though not exactly to scale, between the rectangular-well pattern on the left and the rounded-edge well results on the right. The regrouping of levels then yields predictions about the magic numbers as follows:

Levels:	1s	1p	1d-2s	1f-2p	1g-2d-3s	1h-2f-3p
$2(2l + 1)$	2	6	12	20	30	42
Total number	2	8	20	40	70	112

This scheme gives the first three magic numbers correctly but the rest are wrong.

The modification necessary to make the theory fit the observed magic numbers was introduced by Mayer and by Haxel, Jensen, and Suess, who pointed out that the single-particle levels may be split considerably by spin-orbit interactions. In particular, if the interaction is of the type which couples the spin and orbital momenta *parallel* to each other, every level, except the *s* levels, divides into two substates with total angular momentum

$$i = l + \tfrac{1}{2} \quad \text{and} \quad i = l - \tfrac{1}{2}*$$

and the higher *i* value indicates the lower substate. For example, each *p* level splits into a $p_{3/2}$ and a $p_{1/2}$ substate, each *d* level into a $d_{5/2}$ and a $d_{3/2}$ substate, and so on. Moreover, the magnitude of the splitting increases with the value of *l*, so that the 1*f* level, for instance, is widely separated into its substates. The final scheme is shown on the right in Figure 9.55† and the substates each contain $(2i + 1)$ nucleons of each type, so that the assembly of nucleons is as follows:

Substate:	$1s_{1/2}$	$1p_{3/2}$-$1p_{1/2}$	$1d_{5/2}$-$2s_{1/2}$-$1d_{3/2}$	$1f_{7/2}$	$2p_{3/2}$-$1f_{5/2}$-$2p_{1/2}$-$1g_{9/2}$
$2i + 1$	2	4 + 2	6 + 2 + 4	8	4 + 6 + 2 + 10
Total number	2	8	20	28	50

Substate:	$1g_{7/2}$-$2d$-$3s$-$1h_{11/2}$	$1h_{9/2}$-$2f$-$3p$-$1i_{13/2}$
$2i + 1$	8 + 10 + 2 + 12	10 + 14 + 6 + 14
Total number	82	126.

This scheme is the basis of present shell-model calculations and it goes far toward explaining the systematics of nuclear ground states. The agreement with the observed magic numbers shows that there is a definite shell structure of nucleons within the nucleus, but this structure cannot be correlated with spatial properties as is done in the theory of atomic structure. Indeed the study of nuclear states leads to the conclusion that nucleon configurations are usually mixed and it is rarely possible for a single-nucleon state to be identified unambiguously. However, nuclear *ground* states can often be specified with the aid of a few empirical rules.

(c) *The properties of nuclear ground states*

The shell model of the nucleus has to be supplemented with certain rules which emerge from a study of the stable-nuclide pattern (Figure 9.19). It is found that even-even nuclides are more common and more stable than other types and that they always have zero spin and even parity. This observation, combined with the evidence of the magnetic moments of odd-*A* nuclides (Section 9.7) indicates that pairs of similar nucleons frequently combine to yield zero total angular momentum and therefore zero magnetic moment. We may ascribe this effect to a "pairing" interaction which lowers the total energy when a pair of similar nucleons has opposed spins and raises the total energy when the spins are parallel. This interaction does not apply to dissimilar particles, evidently, because stable odd-odd nuclides are extremely rare and, where they exist, they tend to have large spin numbers in the ground state, for example $_5B^{10}$ has $I = 3$.

---

* The symbol *i* denotes the total angular-momentum quantum number for a single nucleon.
† For details, see P. F. A. Klinkenberg, Rev. Mod. Phys., **24**, 63 (1952).

TABLE 9.2

Comparison of Shell-Model Predictions of Nuclidic Ground States with
Experimental Results

Odd-Nucleon Number	Nuclides	Odd-Nucleon Shell	Predicted State	Observed State[a]
1	H^3, He^3	$1s_{1/2}$	$\frac{1}{2}+$	$\frac{1}{2}+$
3	He^5, Li^5, Li^7, Be^7	$1p_{3/2}$	$\frac{3}{2}-$	$\frac{3}{2}-$
5	Be^9, B^{11}	$1p_{3/2}$	$\frac{3}{2}-$	$\frac{3}{2}-$
7	C^{13}, N^{13}, N^{15}, O^{15}	$1p_{1/2}$	$\frac{1}{2}-$	$\frac{1}{2}-$
9	$\left(\dfrac{O^{17},\ F^{17}}{F^{19},\ Ne^{19}}\right)$	$1d_{5/2}$ or $2s_{1/2}$	$\frac{5}{2}+$ or $\frac{1}{2}+$	$\left(\dfrac{\frac{5}{2}+}{\frac{1}{2}+}\right)$
11	Ne^{21}, Na^{21}, Na^{23}	$1d_{5/2}$ or $2s_{1/2}$	$\frac{5}{2}+$ or $\frac{1}{2}+$	$\frac{3}{2}$
13	Mg^{25}, Al^{25}, Al^{27}, Si^{27}	$1d_{5/2}$ or $2s_{1/2}$	$\frac{5}{2}+$ or $\frac{1}{2}+$	$\frac{5}{2}+$
15	Mg^{27}, Si^{29}, P^{29}, P^{31}, S^{31}	$2s_{1/2}$	$\frac{1}{2}+$	$\frac{1}{2}+$
17	S^{33}, Cl^{33}, Cl^{35}, Cl^{37}	$1d_{3/2}$	$\frac{3}{2}+$	$\frac{3}{2}+$
19	S^{35}, K^{39}, K^{41}, K^{43}	$1d_{3/2}$	$\frac{3}{2}+$	$\frac{3}{2}+$
21	A^{39}, Ca^{41}, Sc^{45}	$1f_{7/2}$	$\frac{7}{2}-$	$\frac{7}{2}-$
23	A^{41}, Ca^{43}, V^{49}, V^{51}	$1f_{7/2}$	$\frac{7}{2}-$	$\frac{7}{2}-$
25	$\left(\dfrac{Ca^{45},\ Mn^{53}}{Ti^{47},\ Cr^{49},\ Mn^{55}}\right)$	$1f_{7/2}$	$\frac{7}{2}-$	$\left(\dfrac{\frac{7}{2}-}{\frac{5}{2}-}\right)$
27	Ti^{49}, Cr^{51}, Co^{55}, Co^{57}, Co^{59}, Co^{61}	$1f_{7/2}$	$\frac{7}{2}-$	$\frac{7}{2}-$
29	Ca^{49}, Cr^{53}, Fe^{55}, Ni^{57}, Cu^{61}, Cu^{63}, Cu^{65}	$2p_{3/2}$	$\frac{3}{2}-$	$\frac{3}{2}-$
31	$\left(\dfrac{Cr^{55},\ Ni^{59},\ Ga^{67},\ Ga^{69},\ Ga^{71},\ Ga^{73}}{Fe^{57}}\right)$	$1f_{5/2}$ or $2p_{3/2}$	$\frac{5}{2}-$ or $\frac{3}{2}-$	$\left(\dfrac{\frac{3}{2}-}{\frac{1}{2}-}\right)$

[a] It should be noted that not all of these spin and parity assignments are final.

Adopting the pairing hypothesis, we may suppose that the odd-A nuclides have properties due chiefly to the odd nucleon, especially in low energy states. At higher energies the pairings presumably break up and multiple nucleon excitation is the rule. Also when a particular shell is about half-full it may happen that certain nucleon configurations arise with lower total energy than the single-nucleon state. Ignoring these possibilities, we proceed to work out the spins and parities of nuclidic ground states, for A odd, on the basis of the odd-nucleon properties. For example, if the odd nucleon is in the $1p_{3/2}$ shell, we expect the ground state to be $\frac{3}{2}-$ in character. If the same shell is full except for one nucleon, the "hole" has the same properties as the missing nucleon. In Table 9.2 the shell-model predictions are compared with experimental results for all the odd-A nuclides with nucleon numbers from 1 to 31. This serves to illustrate the kind of agreement obtained. Evidently the predictions are wrong in some cases, notably the nuclides with 11 and 25 nucleons, and here the Schmidt theory (Section 9.7) fails also. In general, however, the model is extremely successful and provides clear evidence of the importance of spin-orbit effects in nuclear interactions.

(d) Excited states of light nuclei

The nuclear shell model has been employed, notably by Inglis* and Kurath, in efforts to explain the observed structure of energy levels in light nuclides, especially those nuclides in which the $1p$ shell is incomplete. These structures are frequently complex (see Figure 9.41)

* D. R. Inglis, Rev. Mod. Phys., **25**, 396 (1953).

but often certain single-particle characteristics can be identified. This is not the case, however, in heavier nuclides or in nuclei where there are several nucleons outside closed shells. The simplest applications are to nuclides where one or two nucleons occur outside a "core" of closed shells.

The first pair of nuclides beyond the very stable He^4 configuration, namely He^5 and Li^5, each have one nucleon in the $1p_{3/2}$ shell and these nuclides are very short-lived, breaking up into a nucleon plus He^4. Nevertheless, the broad (virtual) ground states of these nuclides have been located in scattering experiments and the data are consistent with the assignment $\frac{3}{2}^-$ which would be required by the shell model. There is some evidence that each of these nuclides has a very broad $\frac{1}{2}^-$ level above the ground state and this may be regarded as the single-particle $1p_{1/2}$ level predicted by the theory.

In the nuclides with $A = 6$ we have to distinguish clearly between states with the isospin number $T = 0$, in which the two nucleons outside the He^4 core do not necessarily obey the Pauli principle, and those in which $T = 1$, where the two nucleons must be identical or must be in the same configuration as identical nucleons. The $T = 1$ states are characteristic of He^6 and Be^6 (assuming that no core excitation occurs) but similar states are found in Li^6 also. These states can be enumerated for two $1p$ nucleons in the same way as the states of the $(2p)^2$ electron configuration (Section 7.11). Either in Russell-Saunders coupling or in $j-j$ coupling the states are found to be

$$0^+ \quad 2^+ \qquad 0^- \quad 1^- \quad 2^-$$

equivalent to

$$^1S_0 \quad ^1D_2 \qquad \quad ^3P_{0,1,2}$$

in the atomic situation. The actual energy-level sequence is *inverted* relative to that shown in Figure 7.24, so that we predict from the shell model that the lowest $T = 1$ state should be 0^+, the rest being, in order, 2^+, 2^-, 1^-, 0^-. This sequence agrees with the general shell-model assumption that the $(\frac{3}{2}, \frac{3}{2})$ states must be lowest and the $(\frac{1}{2}, \frac{1}{2})$ state highest in this group.

In addition to the $T = 1$ states, we have to enumerate the $T = 0$ states which occur in the nuclide Li^6. These states are found by adding together the orbital and spin momenta of the two nucleons in all possible ways, without reference to Pauli's Exclusion principle. In $j-j$ coupling we have the total angular-momentum numbers (denoted by I in nuclei) as follows:

$$\text{Configuration:} \quad (\tfrac{3}{2}, \tfrac{3}{2}) \qquad I = 3, 1*$$
$$(\tfrac{3}{2}, \tfrac{1}{2}) \qquad I = 2, 1$$
$$(\tfrac{1}{2}, \tfrac{1}{2}) \qquad I = 1.*$$

In Russell-Saunders coupling, the same set of states is denoted by

$$^3D_{1,2,3} \quad ^1P_1 \quad ^3S_1$$

which, in conjunction with the rules for spin-orbit interaction in *nuclei*, yields the energy-level sequence

$$\text{(lowest)} \quad 1^+ \quad 3^+ \quad 2^+ \quad 1^+ \quad 1^- \quad \text{(highest)}.$$

If the two sets of states are combined in one sequence, as has been done by Inglis, the predicted order, for a modest amount of spin-orbit interaction, is (starting with the lowest level)

$$(1^+, T = 0) \quad (3^+, T = 0) \quad (0^+, T = 1) \quad (2^+, T = 0) \quad \begin{matrix} (2^+, T = 1) \\ (1^+, T = 0) \end{matrix} \quad (2^-, T = 1) \quad (1^-, T = 1).$$

---

* These I values are obtained after elimination of the $T = 0$ configurations.

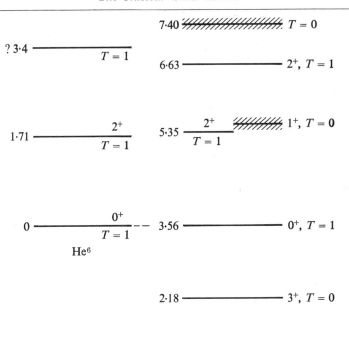

FIGURE 9.56 *Observed energy levels in the nuclides* He⁶ *and* Li⁶ *with the determined energies, spins, isospin numbers, and parities. The ground state of* He⁶ *has been adjusted to coincide with the lowest T = 1 state of* Li⁶.

This scheme may be compared with the experimental data of Figure 9.56 which refer to the known levels of the nuclides Li⁶ and He⁶. The ground state of He⁶ has been adjusted to coincide in level with the first $T = 1$ state of Li⁶: above this level the $T = 0$ states of Li⁶ are noticeably broader than the $T = 1$ states because they can decay more readily by particle emission than the $T = 1$ states. In this way the two overlapping levels near 5.5 MeV can be distinguished. It is clear from the diagram that the theory gives a reasonable account of the Li⁶ states but further data on the He⁶ states would be desirable.

The next pair of nuclides, Li⁷ and Be⁷, form a mirror pair with predominantly $T = \frac{1}{2}$ states, which should, according to the charge-independence hypothesis, be similar in the two systems. Both nuclides have a $\frac{3}{2}^-$ ground state and a first excited state about 0.5 MeV above the ground state (see Figure 9.38). It may be guessed that in each case the first excited state is the upper member of the $1p$ pair of single-nucleon states, that is, it should be $\frac{1}{2}^-$, and this is confirmed by experimental evidence. However, the separation of these two states is certainly very small and other features of the Li⁷, Be⁷ states show that the simple shell-model predictions are not fulfilled in detail. The situation becomes more complicated as extra nucleons are added to the $1p$ shell, until this shell is filled at O¹⁶. The nuclides N¹⁵, O¹⁵, and O¹⁶ all display a considerable separation between the ground and first excited states, as is expected in the shell model.

In the next series of nuclides, from $A = 17$ to $A = 40$, both $1d$ and $2s$ shells are being filled and there is a great deal of overlapping between these, as is shown by the fact that O^{17} and F^{17} have $\frac{5}{2}^+$ ground states while F^{19} and Ne^{19} have $\frac{1}{2}^+$ ground states. Very detailed calculations have been carried out to account for the low-lying levels of these nuclides and others in the same region. In general, it is found that some agreement can be reached with the experimental data, but only at the expense of treating the core of filled shells as a body interacting with the other nucleons. Already it becomes evident that the nucleus has collective modes of oscillation and rotation which impose an overall pattern on the excited-state sequence. The need for making some scheme of interpretation of levels in heavy nuclei is met by the *collective model* of nuclear excitations, developed originally by Aage Bohr and Mottelson.

9.10   The Collective Model

(a)   Evidence for collective effects in nuclei

Although the nuclear shell model, supplemented with suitable semiempirical rules, is successful in giving the magic numbers correctly and in explaining many nuclear ground states, it is not easily applied to find the excited states of complex nuclides (above about $A = 20$). The many different nucleon configurations which can arise (and the consequent "mixing" of states defined by the methods of spectroscopy) render detailed calculations almost impossible. It might be expected that no systematic behavior would emerge in heavy nuclei, but this is not the case, as was pointed out by A. Bohr and Mottelson in a series of papers from 1953 onward. For example, it is found by experiment that many even-even nuclides have their lowest states forming the sequence $0^+, 2^+, 4^+, \ldots$, suggesting a series of even-parity rotational levels. Other even-even nuclides exhibit the sequence $0^+, 2^+, 2^+, \ldots$, indicative of vibrational states.

One line of approach to the problem was explored in 1950 by Rainwater, who showed theoretically that, if a single nucleon exists outside a core of closed shells, its interaction with the core tends to deform the nucleus from a spherical shape. In the simplest form of the theory, the shape is an oblate spheroid (QM negative) in nuclides which are a little heavier than closed-shell nuclides and is prolate when shells are not quite complete, in fair agreement with the experimental data (Figure 9.54). However there are complications due to spin-orbit interaction and the net result is a preponderance of positive quadrupole moments over negative moments. An immediate consequence of the theory is the existence of large quadrupole moments among nuclides which are far from the closed-shell configuration and this feature helps to explain why the simple shell-model calculations are not valid for these nuclides.

The importance of collective nucleon interactions in the production of appreciable nuclear deformation can be illustrated by the following results:

(i) the magnitude of the quadrupole moments is frequently much larger than the maximum value allowed by single-nucleon motion;

(ii) the odd-neutron nuclides have quadrupole moments which are, in general, as great as the odd-proton nuclides, showing that the single-particle charge does not determine the moment;

(iii) gamma-ray widths for transitions between the ground and first excited states have been measured and they are frequently greater than the maximum single-particle values.

It appears, therefore, that collective nucleon motions are very important, despite the partial success of the single-particle model, and the collective model of nuclear structure, though based primarily on the shell-model data, represents a compromise between the extreme individual-particle theory and the earlier liquid-drop model.

(b) Vibrational and rotational levels

According to present views of nuclear structure, the closed-shell nuclides possess spherical symmetry and therefore cannot display rotational properties in any quantum-mechanical scheme. These nuclei can, however, exhibit various modes of vibration even at low energies of excitation. A common mode is a type of quadrupole deformation [involving terms like $P_2(\cos \theta)$], which is strongly excited by electric-quadrupole photon absorption from the 0^+ ground state of an even-even nuclide. Ideally all *vibrational* levels should fit in with the simple equally-spaced pattern of a harmonic oscillator (see Problem 7.20), the separation between any two adjacent levels being $\hbar\omega$, where ω is the fundamental angular frequency. Detailed calculations show that the expected state sequence for quadrupole vibrations is

$$0^+ \qquad 2^+ \qquad (0^+, 2^+, 4^+) \qquad (0^+, 2^+, 3^+, 4^+, 6^+),$$

where the parentheses enclose states which are degenerate in the simple theory of the harmonic oscillator. These predictions may be compared with selected experimental data shown in Figure 9.57, where the ratio E_n/E_1 is plotted for observed states of nuclides with nearly spherical shape (E_n is the energy of the nth state). The evidence suggests that the vibrational scheme may explain the positions of the first two excited states in special cases but it breaks down at higher excitations.

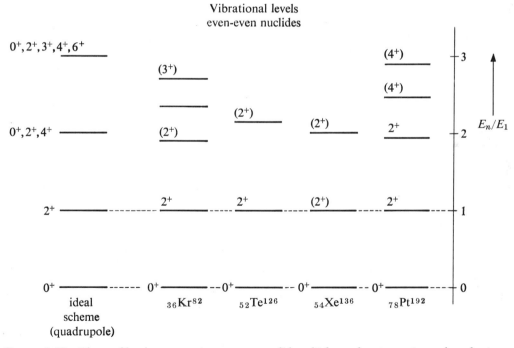

FIGURE 9.57 *Observed level sequences in even-even nuclides which are close to magic numbers, having approximately spherical nuclei and approaching the vibrational pattern of levels. The ratio E_n/E_1 is unity for the first excited state in each example and ideally all other states should be spaced evenly on this scale.*

Much more numerous are the nuclides with large quadrupole moments, which occur in the regions between closed-shell configurations. In these cases the nucleus may be regarded as an ellipsoid of revolution, with major and minor axes denoted by (2*a*) and (2*b*), respectively. The quantum-mechanical treatment of such a "symmetrical top" is well known in the theory of molecular rotational spectra and, if the ground state is 0⁺, the energy levels are given by the formula

$$E = \frac{\hbar^2}{2\mathscr{I}} I(I + 1) \quad \text{(see Problem 7.14),} \qquad [9.10.1]$$

where $\mathscr{I}$ is the effective moment of inertia about a minor axis. I takes the values 0, 2, 4, 6, ..., and so forth, since only even-parity state functions are allowed by the symmetry of the body. Many nuclides are known in which the first states follow the sequence 0⁺, 2⁺, 4⁺ with spacings agreeing approximately with the formula of Equation (9.10.1). In Figure 9.58 the ideal scheme may be compared with selected examples of nuclides where many levels have been located. The ordinates represent the ratio E_n/E_1 as before, the ideal values of this ratio being, in order,

$$1 \qquad 3\tfrac{1}{3} \qquad 7 \qquad 12 \qquad 18\tfrac{1}{3}.$$

The collective model is clearly in close agreement with experiment for the first four located states of certain nuclides. The theory may be extended to include odd-*A* nuclides

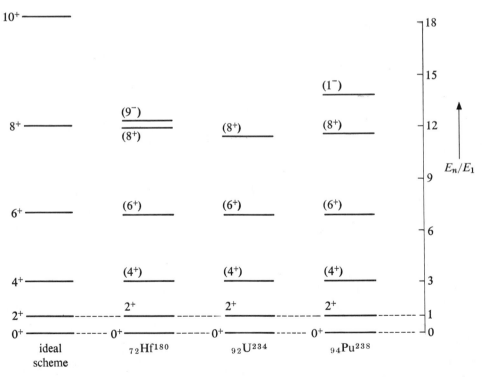

FIGURE 9.58 *Observed level sequences in even-even nuclides which are far from magic numbers, having deformed nuclei and a rotational pattern of levels. Ideally the ratio E_n/E_1 should take the values: 1, $3\tfrac{1}{3}$, 7, 12, $18\tfrac{1}{3}$, and so on.*

in which the ground states are $\frac{3}{2}-$, $\frac{5}{2}-$, and so forth, and some measure of agreement is reached with observation. It is found that interaction between rotational and vibrational motion takes place, with the production of characteristic state sequences in vibration-rotation bands. These bands have the property that all the states embraced by one band have the same parity and have much stronger electromagnetic transitions within the band than outside it. Such bands have been identified in nuclides as different in mass as $_{10}Ne^{20}$ and $_{94}Pu^{238}$ and it is probable that many observed sequences of energy levels can be interpreted in this way.

Where pure rotational levels are observed to agree with the theoretical expression [Equation (9.10.1)], it is possible to derive values for the effective moment of inertia, $\mathscr{I}$. The question then arises whether this bears any significant relation to the known mean radius of the nuclide, as given by Equation (9.3.12),

$$r = r_0 \sqrt[3]{A}.$$

If the nucleus were a rigid body of mass (Am) in the form of a prolate ellipsoid of mean density ρ, the moment of inertia about a minor axis $0x$ would be

$$\mathscr{I}_{rig} = \int \rho(z^2 + y^2)\, dx\, dy\, dz,$$

where x, y are Cartesian coordinates in planes parallel to the plane containing the minor axes, each of length $2b$, and z is the coordinate along the major axis, of length $2a$. This integral yields

$$\mathscr{I}_{rig} = \frac{Am}{5}(a^2 + b^2) \qquad [9.10.2]$$

for a rigid prolate spheroid.

If the deformation from sphericity is small we may introduce a deformation parameter δ defined by the expression

$$\delta = \frac{a - b}{r}, \qquad [9.10.3]$$

where r is a mean radius fixed by the condition that the spherical volume $\frac{4\pi}{3}r^3$ is actually equal to the ellipsoid volume $\frac{4\pi}{3}ab^2$. This condition is met, for small deformations, by writing

$$a = r\left(1 + \frac{2\delta}{3}\right) \quad \text{and} \quad b = r\left(1 - \frac{\delta}{3}\right)$$

so that, to first order in δ, the moment of inertia becomes

$$\mathscr{I}_{rig} = \frac{2Amr^2}{5}\left(1 + \frac{\delta}{3}\right). \qquad [9.10.4]$$

Now the deformation parameter δ may be estimated, for those nuclides which possess a quadrupole moment in the ground state, by treating the nucleus as a uniformly-charged ellipsoid, the total charge being Ze. The definition of QM [Equation (9.7.3)] can be expressed in terms of a *charge* density ρ_c as follows:

$$QM = \int (3z^2 - r^2)\rho_c\, dV,$$

where

$$\int \rho_c\, dV = Ze$$

and both integrals are taken over the volume of the ellipsoid. Since the z axis is the axis of symmetry, we can take a section of the ellipsoid in the xz plane and this has an elliptical outline described by the equation

$$\frac{z^2}{a^2} + \frac{x^2}{b^2} = 1$$

so the volume integral becomes

$$\rho_c \int_{-a}^{a} \pi x^2 \, dz = Ze,$$

whence

$$\frac{4\pi}{3} a b^2 \rho_c = Ze.$$

Also

$$QM = \rho_c \int (2z^2 - x^2) 2\pi x \, dx \, dz,$$

which is evaluated to yield the electric quadrupole moment per elementary charge as

$$\frac{QM}{e} = \frac{2Z(a^2 - b^2)}{5}. \qquad\qquad [9.10.5]$$

Expressed in terms of the deformation parameter δ, this becomes

$$\frac{QM}{e} = \frac{4Zr^2 \delta}{5}. \qquad\qquad [9.10.6]$$

If this expression is employed to find the values of δ, they turn out to be fairly small, of the order of 0.15, for even the most strongly deformed nuclei. Thus the rigid-body formula for the moment of inertia [Equation (9.10.4)] approximates to that of a sphere of radius r. However, the observed values of $\mathscr{I}$ taken from the rotational spectra are always much less than the rigid-body values, the ratio $\mathscr{I}/\mathscr{I}_{\text{rig}}$ depending on the degree of deformation. This ratio approaches a value of approximately 0.5 in the nuclides of largest deformation. However this result may be interpreted, it is clear that the nucleus does not behave like a rigid ellipsoid, and is presumably more like a liquid drop in which the surface energy is not sufficiently great to impose a spherical shape.

Most applications of the collective model have been to the structure of low energy levels and the transitions between these levels. It may be asked if the "core" of filled shells in a typical nucleus can be excited and in what ways. Here the collective model has been used in attempts to account for the "giant dipole" resonances observed in photodisintegration reactions (Section 9.5.f and Figure 9.39). Although the single-particle model is required to explain many features of these reactions, some simplification is achieved by regarding the resonance as a collective effect due to dipole-type oscillations of the core. According to the collective-model treatment the peak energy is related to the effective mean radius of the nucleus (r) but in a highly deformed nuclide there should be a double peak due to the two principal semiaxes of the ellipsoid (a and b). This phenomenon has in fact been observed in nuclides like Ta^{181} and the experimental data yield estimates for the quadrupole moment which are in fair agreement with those obtained by other methods.

9.11   Beta Decay

Frequent mention has already been made of the decay mode of unstable nuclei which involves the emission of fast electrons, that is, beta activity. For many years the only beta emitters known were members of the natural radioactive series (Appendix III). However, all elements possess radioactive isotopes which can be produced in suitable nuclear reactions and the great majority of these isotopes are beta active. Artificially induced radioactivity was discovered in 1933 by Irène Curie and Frédéric Joliot, who bombarded aluminum with alpha particles and found that the sample emitted positrons, with a characteristic exponential decay of activity, after the alpha irradiation ceased. This effect was due to the formation of an unstable isotope of phosphorus, according to the reaction

$$_{13}Al^{27} + {}_2He^4 \rightarrow {}_{15}P^{30} + {}_0n^1. \qquad [9.11.1]$$

The proton-rich phosphorus nuclide then reverts to the stable nuclide $_{14}Si^{30}$ by positron emission. After further experiments it became clear that neutron-rich nuclides (above the stability line in Figure 9.19) tend to emit negative electrons while proton-rich nuclides (below the stability line) may emit positrons. Both phenomena obey essentially the same rules and are described as beta decay.

In this section various aspects of beta decay, including the serious difficulties raised by the energy-spectrum of beta particles, are described, with particular reference to their significance in nuclear physics. Consideration of more fundamental aspects, involving the nonconservation of parity in weak interactions, is deferred until the final chapter.

(a) The decay of the neutron

It was pointed out in Section 9.3.a that the rest-mass energy of a neutron exceeds that of a proton plus an electron by about 0.78 MeV. It therefore appears possible that a free neutron should decay into a fast electron and a proton (of low energy, due to the conservation of momentum), provided that a suitable interaction exists between these particles and that various conservation rules are satisfied. It is clear, however, from elementary studies of the behavior of slow neutrons that the decay process must be very slow compared with other nuclear processes. Estimates of the free neutron's half-life, based on beta-decay parameters, are in the region of a few minutes, which is time for a fast neutron to travel several million miles. It is therefore necessary to employ a very high flux of *slow* neutrons if the decay is to be observed and the genuine proton-electron pairs produced must be distinguished from a heavy background of events associated with the high neutron flux.

Decay of the neutron was first reported by Snell and Miller in 1948. A series of detailed experiments on the process was carried out subsequently by Robson,* using slow neutrons generated by the NRX and NRU reactors at Chalk River, Ontario. In one of these experiments, illustrated by Figure 9.59, Robson passed a slow-neutron flux of about 10^9 particles per cm^2 per second through an evacuated "decay region" into a "catcher," which was designed to absorb the excess flux of neutrons without sending too many particles back into the decay region. In this region a high positive potential applied to an electrode was effective in separating electrons from slow protons, the latter being accelerated away from the electrode and through a magnetic analyzer to a counter of the multiplier type. Any electrons associated with counted protons passed through a ring-shaped magnetic spectrometer of the lens type into a scintillation counter, which worked in coincidence with the proton counter. The arrangements were such that, for each genuine proton-electron pair recorded, the electron momentum (P) was determined by means of the magnetic spectrometer.

Robson's results led to an energy spectrum of electrons emitted in neutron decay as shown in Figure 9.60, where the coincidence counting rate is plotted against the electron's kinetic energy. This spectrum is a continuous distribution, electrons of all energies up to a

* J. M. Robson, Phys. Rev., **78**, 311 (1950); **83**, 349 (1951); **100**, 933 (1955).

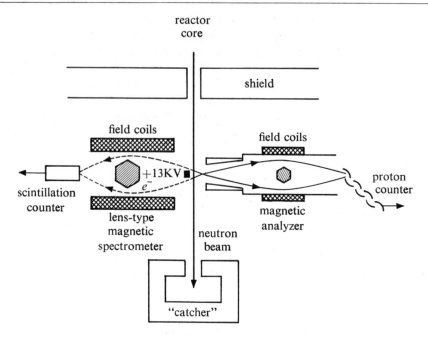

FIGURE 9.59   *Layout of Robson's apparatus for detecting the decay of free neutrons. An intense beam of slow neutrons passes a high-voltage electrode in the "decay region," protons and electrons from decay being detected in coincidence after suitable magnetic analysis.*

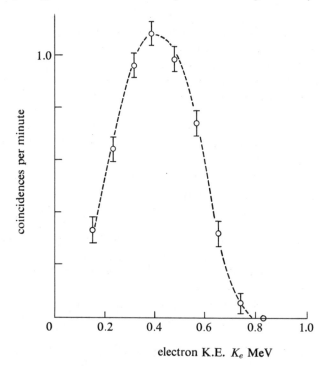

FIGURE 9.60   *The energy spectrum of electrons emitted in decay of slow neutrons, as determined by Robson: the distribution is continuous up to a maximum energy close to 0.78 MeV.*

maximum close to 0.78 MeV being detected. This kind of distribution is observed in all forms of beta decay, although the spectrum is much more complex when several beta groups are present. Now the energy release for the neutron decay process ($Q_0 = 0.78$ MeV) is known from the particle masses (and the slow-neutron kinetic energy is negligible), so one would expect to find a *well-defined* electron energy *if* the only products of decay were a proton and an electron. It follows that either the principle of conservation of energy does not apply in beta-decay processes or there must be a third (undetected) particle emitted in each disintegration. The latter supposition is the basis of the *neutrino* theory of beta decay, according to which the neutron breaks up into a proton (p), a negative electron (e^-) and a very light particle of zero charge, the undetected "neutrino" ($\bar{\nu}$),* which accounts for the missing energy.

Before proceeding to discuss the neutrino theory and positron decay, we should note that Robson's data can be used to estimate the total number of electrons of all energies emitted per second by neutrons decaying in the sensitive region of his apparatus. The result yields an estimated half-life of the neutron of 12 min, and this has been confirmed by later work. This interval is about 10^{25} times greater than the estimated time for a neutron-proton exchange process (Section 9.8) to take place, which serves to emphasize the extreme slowness of the beta decay. Much shorter half-lives are observed in certain unstable nuclides where the energy release is larger, for example, the nuclide $_5B^{12}$ with $Q_0 = 13.4$ MeV has a half-life of 0.02 sec, but in general beta-decay processes are much slower than other nuclear processes.

(b) Positron emission and electron capture

It is known from a study of unstable nuclides that those which contain too many protons usually decay by emitting positrons, a form of beta decay which has similar properties to negative-electron emission. The two types of beta decay may be written as equations

$$(\text{Neutron rich}): \quad _zX^A \rightarrow _{z+1}Y^A + _{-1}e^0 + \bar{\nu} \qquad [9.11.2]$$

$$(\text{Proton rich}); \quad _zX^A \rightarrow _{z-1}Y'^A + _{+1}e^0 + \nu \qquad [9.11.3]$$

where two different kinds of neutrino are specified, in accordance with the hypothesis of *lepton conservation*. Following this hypothesis, we assume that the total number of "leptons," that is, light particles obeying Fermi-Dirac statistics, is the same on both sides of any particle equation. Thus in Equation (9.11.2), where an electron appears on the right-hand side, this counts as $+1$ on the lepton scale and, since there are no leptons on the left-hand side, the electron has to be accompanied by an antiparticle, counting -1 on the lepton scale, which is the "antineutrino" $\bar{\nu}$. On the other hand, in Equation (9.11.3), the emission of a positron (counting -1 on the lepton scale) is accompanied by a "neutrino" proper (ν), counting $+1$ on the lepton scale.

The evidence in support of the lepton-conservation idea will be reviewed later. At this stage it should be noted that the nuclides X^A and Y^A in Equations (9.11.2) and (9.11.3) are represented in tables by their neutral atomic masses. Thus in Equation (9.11.2) the rest-mass of the emitted (negative) electron is included already in the proper mass of Y^A. Accordingly the total energy release (Q_0) in beta decay is found simply by subtracting the mass of Y^A from that of X^A. This is *not* a valid procedure in Equation (9.11.3), where the proper mass of the nuclide Y'^A is deficient in two electron rest masses, or 1.02 MeV, if a positron is to be created. In this case, therefore, the energy release is less than the mass difference by 1.02 MeV

$$Q_0 = (M_X - M_{Y'})c^2 - 1.02 \text{ MeV}. \qquad [9.11.4]$$

* Strictly, an "antineutrino" when a negative electron is emitted.

In energy-level diagrams involving positron transitions, therefore, allowance has to be made for the 1.02 MeV term as well as the mass difference.

This feature of positron emission leads to an interesting situation when the mass difference between two isobaric nuclides, possessing the same value of A, is less than 1.02 MeV. Clearly there is insufficient energy for a positron to be created yet the heavier nuclide is undoubtedly unstable. In such a situation an alternative process is observed, that of orbital electron capture (*EC*). The unstable nucleus, instead of emitting a positron, captures a negative electron from the extranuclear "*k*" or "*l*" shell. For example, the nuclide Be^7 goes to Li^7 in this way

$$_4Be^7 + {_{-1}e^0} \rightarrow {_3Li^7} + \nu, \qquad [9.11.5]$$

where the proper neutrino on the right-hand side balances the electron on the left. The full available energy (0.86 MeV according to the masses) is then divided between the neutrino and the Li^7 atom. It is not difficult to detect *EC* processes because they leave "holes" in either the "*k*" or "*l*" shell and x-ray emission necessarily follows. In the case of Be^7, there is also gamma-ray emission because some of the *EC* transitions lead to the well-known 0.48 MeV excited state of the Li^7 nuclide

$$_4Be^7 + {_{-1}e^0} \rightarrow {_3Li^{7*}} + \nu \qquad [9.11.6]$$

and the energy release is correspondingly reduced.

Many nuclides which are rich in protons decay both by positron emission and by orbital electron capture. There are a few examples of odd-odd nuclides in which the same nuclide can decay either by negative or positive electron emission, for example,

$$_{29}Cu^{64} \rightarrow {_{30}Zn^{64}} + {_{-1}e^0} + \bar{\nu} \qquad [9.11.7]$$
$$\searrow {_{28}Ni^{64}} + {_{+1}e^0} + \nu.$$

These cases are particularly useful in considering the details of nuclear stability rules (Section 9.11.f).

(c) *The neutrino theory*

The theoretical difficulties raised by the phenomenon of beta decay may be summarized briefly as follows:

(i) the continuous energy spectrum of electrons emitted shows that, on the average, about half of the available energy is not detected in the charged particles produced;

(ii) delicate calorimeter experiments were carried out with beta emitters to find the energy release per particle and these gave results agreeing with the *mean* energy of the electron spectrum; thus the missing energy was not absorbed in matter immediately surrounding the beta source;

(iii) early attempts made to detect a third particle emitted in beta decay failed, although this is not surprising if it is a neutrino of zero charge and vanishingly small mass.

The neutrino hypothesis was put forward in 1931 by Pauli, who pointed out that emission of a third particle is necessary for conservation of angular momentum. Taking the decay of the free neutron as the simplest possible case, we can write the equation (in modern terms)

$$n^0 \rightarrow p^+ + e^- + \bar{\nu}. \qquad [9.11.8]$$

Here the neutron, proton, and electron are known to be fermions, that is, each possesses intrinsic spin $\frac{1}{2}\hbar$, and any orbital angular momentum component must be an integral multiple of the unit $\hbar$. The angular momentum cannot be balanced, therefore, unless there is a third particle (the antineutrino in this case) with intrinsic spin $\frac{1}{2}\hbar$ (or possibly $\frac{3}{2}\hbar$). It is generally assumed that all four particles involved are fermions and that they have the formal properties of Dirac particles (Section 7.9). The same deductions may be drawn from studies of beta decay in complex nuclei where the nuclear spin numbers (*I*) are known for the initial and final nuclides.

The results of applying the neutrino hypothesis to beta decay were worked out by Fermi in a classic paper, published in 1934. There is supposed to be a weak interaction, now called the *Fermi* interaction, between the massive fermions [neutron and proton in Equation (9.11.8)] and the leptons (electron and neutrino), which gives rise to various transformation processes. For example, we might suppose that there is "stimulated" beta decay of the neutron

$$n^0 + \nu \rightarrow p^+ + e^- \qquad [9.11.9]$$

which is equivalent, in its net effect, to the spontaneous neutron decay. It should be noted that there is a proper neutrino on the left-hand side of the equation to balance the lepton number $+1$ of the electron on the right. We might also postulate the existence of stimulated proton decay as the result of antineutrino capture

$$p^+ + \bar{\nu} \rightarrow n^0 + e^+. \qquad [9.11.10]$$

For the four-fermion process of Equation (9.11.9), Fermi assumed an interaction Hamiltonian of the form

$$H' = g[\bar{\psi}_p \psi_n \bar{\psi}_e \psi_\nu], \qquad [9.11.11]$$

where *g* is a coupling constant, assumed to be small. Here the ψ's are Dirac state functions describing the particles taking part in the stimulated neutron decay.

With the aid of this simple four-fermion interaction it is possible to calculate the transition probability by perturbation theory (Section 7.12). In spontaneous beta decay, for example the neutron decay of Equation (9.11.8), the rate of transition is proportional to the square of the appropriate matrix element of H' and to the volumes of phase space accessible to the electron and antineutrino. Thus if the electron's linear momentum lies between *P* and $(P + dP)$ in a proper volume *V*, the element of phase space available is, by Equation (8.3.6),

$$d\Phi_e = 4\pi P^2 V \, dP$$

and likewise for the antineutrino

$$d\Phi_\nu = 4\pi P_\nu^2 V \, dP_\nu.$$

Here both *P* and P_ν should be treated as relativistic momenta, since the particles' energies are high. It is convenient, though not essential at this stage, to regard the neutrino and antineutrino as particles of zero rest mass, obeying the energy-momentum relation

$$cP_\nu = E_\nu$$

derived from Equation (5.6.5) with the rest mass $m_0 = 0$.

Moreover, if Q_0 is the total energy release in the decay process and we neglect the small recoil energy of the massive particle [the proton in Equation (9.11.8)], the energy-balance equation is

$$Q_0 = E_\nu + K_e \quad \text{approximately,}$$

where K_e is the kinetic energy of the emitted electron.

Thus the product of the elements of phase space accessible to the leptons can be transformed as follows:

$$d\Phi_e \, d\Phi_\nu = 16\pi^2 V^2 P^2 \, dP \, P_\nu^2 \, dP_\nu$$

$$= -16\pi^2 V^2 P^2 \, dP \, \frac{(Q_0 - K_e)^2 \, dK_e}{c^3} \qquad [9.11.12]$$

Here it has been assumed that the leptons are not correlated in direction, so that the phase-space expressions are independent of each other, and possible Coulomb interaction between the massive recoiling particle and the emitted electron has been ignored. Provided that these simplifying assumptions are justified, we can apply the expression above to all cases of beta decay and find the energy or momentum distribution of the electrons. For example, the *momentum* distribution takes the form

$$f(P)\, dP = \text{const}\, |H'_{ab}|^2 \frac{d\Phi_e\, d\Phi_\nu}{dK_e}$$

$$= \text{const}\, |H'_{ab}|^2 P^2\, dP\, (Q_0 - K_e)^2 \qquad [9.11.13]$$

and this is readily put into the form of an energy distribution with the aid of the relativistic expression of Equation (5.6.5).

For the purpose of comparison with experimental results, it is convenient to retain the momentum distribution $f(P)\, dP$ as given by Equation (9.11.13). In allowed transitions the matrix element H'_{ab} is supposed to be independent of the lepton parameters, so a plot of $\sqrt{\dfrac{f(P)}{P^2}}$ against the kinetic energy K_e should yield a straight line of negative gradient, intersecting the energy axis at Q_0. Robson's results for the neutron decay spectrum (Figure 9.59) can be treated in this way and the resulting graph is shown in Figure 9.61. The data are not reliable at low energies because of experimental errors, but there is a linear portion

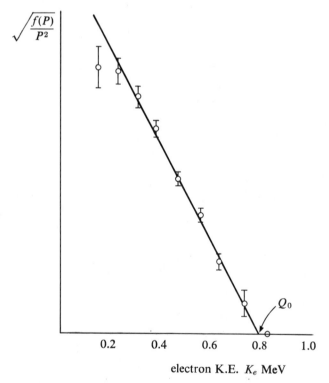

FIGURE 9.61   *Test of the neutrino theory as applied to the decay of the neutron. Robson's data are put in the form of a distribution per unit momentum interval—$f(P)$—and the function $\sqrt{f(P)/P^2}$ is plotted against the electron kinetic energy to obtain a line intersecting the energy axis at Q_0.*

yielding an intercept close to $Q_0 = 0.78$ MeV, as required by the masses of the neutron, proton, and electron. Similar graphical tests can be applied to other beta spectra and there is general agreement with the theory for *allowed* transitions, that is, those with a high transition probability, although it is necessary to make corrections for Coulomb interaction in the decay of high-Z nuclei.

The simple Fermi theory is successful in accounting for the general features of beta-spectra, but much more detailed analysis is required before the *selection rules* for transitions can be worked out. Fermi originally adopted an interaction Hamiltonian H' in the form of a scalar product of two polar vectors, that is, a pure "vector" interaction (V), whereas the simple form of Equation (9.11.11) corresponds to a purely scalar interaction (S). However, in both S and V interactions, the selection rules for allowed transitions are

$$\Delta I = 0, \text{ "No,"} \qquad [9.11.14]$$

that is, no change in spin or parity. This does not exhaust the possibilities of setting up suitable interaction Hamiltonians; Gamow and Teller deduced an alternative set of rules for tensor (T) and axial vector (A) interactions:

$$\Delta I = 0, \pm 1 \quad \text{(but } 0 \leftrightarrow 0 \text{ forbidden), "No."} \qquad [9.11.15]$$

It is necessary to analyze the experimental data to find out which rules actually operate in beta decay. It should be noted that neutron decay, in which both the neutron and proton have spin $\frac{1}{2}\hbar$, satisfies both Fermi and Gamow-Teller rules. However, in complex nuclei there are several examples of special significance, for example, the transition

$$_2\text{He}^6 \rightarrow {}_3\text{Li}^6 + {}_{-1}e^0 + \bar{\nu}, \qquad [9.11.16]$$

where $I = 0$ for the initial nuclide and $I = 1$ for the final nuclide (see Figure 9.56); also

$$_8\text{O}^{14} \rightarrow {}_7\text{N}^{14*} + {}_{+1}e^0 + \nu, \qquad [9.11.17]$$

where $I = 0$ for both initial and final states.

Half-life measurements indicate that both of the quoted transitions are allowed, so that it appears that both Fermi and Gamow-Teller rules are operative, and that no single form of interaction can explain all cases of beta decay.

In addition to the allowed transitions, there are many cases of beta emission which are forbidden by the selection rules but which proceed with appreciable rapidity nevertheless. The neutrino theory has been developed to cover these transitions and it accounts successfully for many peculiar features of the beta spectra observed. Of more fundamental interest is the nature of the Fermi interaction itself and this problem is best studied by a detailed examination of the kinematics of beta decay in allowed transitions, with special reference to possible correlations between the electron and neutrino directions of emission.

(d) The detection of the neutrino

Although the Fermi theory of beta decay accounted for the observed energy spectra, many physicists doubted whether the basic postulate of the theory—the existence of an almost undetectable particle—could be justified. Two main types of experiment have been performed to demonstrate the neutrino's existence; in the first type, the recoil of the massive particle or nucleus is studied in relation to the momentum of the emitted electron, while in the second type search is made for neutrino capture reactions in suitable materials.

The first convincing recoil experiment was performed in 1942 by Allen,* who employed

* J. S. Allen, *Phys. Rev.*, **61**, 692 (1942).

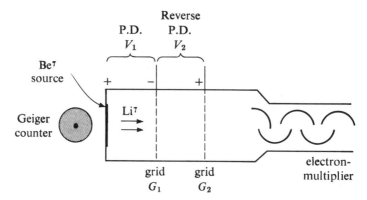

FIGURE 9.62   *Schematic diagram of Allen's apparatus for detecting* Li^7 *recoil atoms from the decay of* Be^7. *The atoms are first accelerated by a voltage* (V_1) *applied between the source and grid* G_1, *then retarded by a greater voltage* (V_2) *between* G_1 *and* G_2 *before being counted in the electron multiplier.*

the nuclide Be^7 which decays to Li^7 by orbital-electron capture [Equation (9.11.5)], so that only two particles emerge. According to the neutrino theory, therefore, the recoiling Li^7 nuclei should travel in a direction opposite to that of the neutrino and form a group with well-defined kinetic energy. This energy is calculated to be 57 eV for a total energy release of 0.86 MeV, derived from the mass data. The experimental problem therefore consists of detecting Li^7 nuclei with this very low energy as products of the decay of Be^7.

Allen's apparatus is shown schematically in Figure 9.62. A Be^7 source was prepared on platinum foil, which has the property that any Li^7 recoils leaving the surface should be singly charged in the positive sense. Particles given off by the Be^7 decay could pass through two grids G_1 and G_2 and into an electron-multiplier counting system. Various potentials were applied to G_1 and G_2 to find the kinetic energies of charged particles passing through to the counter. For example, with a potential difference of +176 V applied between the source and grid G_1, it required a considerably greater reverse voltage between G_1 and G_2 to cut the counting rate down to zero. The estimated cutoff point was about 45 V *greater* than the first accelerating voltage of 176 V, showing that the charged particles leaving the source were of kinetic energy 45 eV or more, if they were singly charged. A Geiger counter was placed near the source on the opposite side to the electron multiplier and in a separate experiment the two counters were run in coincidence to show that the recoil particles detected were *not* due to gamma rays emitted by the source. This precaution was necessary because it is known that a fraction of the Be^7 decays proceed via the 0.48 MeV excited state of Li^{7*} [Equation (9.11.6)] so that photons of 0.48 MeV energy are emitted. However, the maximum recoil energy of Li^7 produced by a 0.48 MeV photon is only 17 eV, so Allen's results are clearly in agreement with the neutrino theory. Later work showed that the Li^7 recoil energy is (56.6 ± 1.0) eV, very close to the theoretical value.

Further experiments have been performed to measure the angular correlations between electrons and neutrinos emitted in beta decay, the usual method being to analyze in detail the energy spectrum of the recoiling nuclei. Robson has measured part of the energy spectrum of protons produced in the beta decay of neutrons in flight and his results indicate an almost isotropic distribution of electrons relative to a given neutrino direction. Such a distribution cannot be explained by either the interactions (S and V) yielding Fermi selection rules or the interactions (T and A) yielding Gamow-Teller selection rules. It is therefore supposed that a mixture of interactions is responsible for beta decay. Many experiments have now shown that the dominant interactions are the vector (V) and axial vector (A) types and an appropriate mixture of these two interactions can account for all the existing data.

The direct detection of neutrinos by capture was finally achieved in 1956 by Reines and Cowan,* who showed that protons may capture antineutrinos to form neutrons [Equation (9.11.10)]. The cross section for such a process is extremely small and it is necessary to start with a very high flux of antineutrinos. Fortunately nuclear reactors contain enormous quantities of beta-active elements produced by the fission process (Section 9.3.g) and these are of the right type to emit antineutrinos. Near a reactor of high power the flux of antineutrinos is of the order of 10^{13} particles per cm^2 per second and this high flux renders a capture experiment just feasible. Reines and Cowan set up a large liquid scintillator system around a water tank placed near the reactor. If a proton present in the water captures an antineutrino, a neutron and a positron should be emitted; of these particles, the latter is rapidly annihilated by a negative electron to produce two photons, each of 0.51 MeV approximately, while the neutron is slowed down by the water. After a delay of a few microseconds the neutron reaches thermal energies and is most probably captured by cadmium nuclei present in the tank, the result being gamma-ray emission from deexcitation of the compound nucleus formed. In the experimental arrangement, the gamma rays produced pulses in the scintillation counters and the sequences observed in these pulses were analyzed rigorously to see if any could be due to the proton-neutron conversion. A genuine counting rate of a few counts per hour was assigned to the antineutrino flux with the reactor operated at full power. This corresponded to a capture cross section of about 10^{-43} cm^2 per proton for fission antineutrinos, in fair agreement with theoretical estimates.

An interesting variant of the experiment was devised by Davis, who attempted to detect the neutrino capture reaction

$$_{17}Cl^{37} + \nu \rightarrow {}_{18}A^{37} + {}_{-1}e^{0}. \qquad [9.11.18]$$

Since this process is inverse to positron emission by A^{37}, we require a proper neutrino on the left-hand side to balance the electron on the right, if lepton conservation holds. Davis used a large tank containing chlorine placed near a powerful reactor and after the irradiation he tried, but failed, to find any A^{37} activity in the tank. This negative result is expected if lepton conservation holds, since the reactor produces predominantly antineutrinos from fission fragments. Other experimental results show clearly that there are two kinds of neutrino, produced in negative-electron and positive-electron decay, respectively. The far-reaching implications of these discoveries, together with the discovery that parity is not conserved in weak-interaction processes, are briefly discussed at the end of the next chapter.

(e) Complex beta spectra

So far we have dealt only with cases of pure beta-ray spectra, in which a single transition is possible between the initial and final nuclides. More complex types of decay occur, in which the final nuclide may be formed in one or more excited states, so that there are several beta groups, each with its own maximum energy release (Q). When the final nucleus is formed in an excited state, it usually loses energy by gamma-ray emission, so that the beta rays are accompanied by photons which are effectively in coincidence with them. One simple example is the nuclide Au^{198} which is made by slow-neutron absorption in gold and which has a half-life of 2.7 days. Coincidence experiments show that about 99% of the

* F. Reines and C. L. Cowan, *Nature*, **178**, 446 (1956).

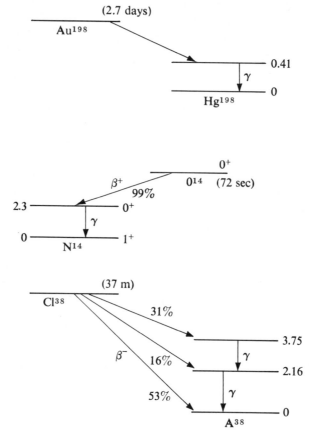

FIGURE 9.63   *Examples of beta-decay schemes involving gamma-ray emission from excited states of the residual nucleus.*

beta decay processes are associated with gamma rays, due to the residual nuclide Hg^{198} being formed in an excited state at 0.41 MeV above its ground state. The decay scheme is therefore of the form shown in Figure 9.63, although there are also weak transitions present. A rather similar situation obtains in the decay of the positron emitter O^{14}, which goes in 99% of cases to the excited state of N^{14} at 2.3 MeV above the ground state. Here the initial state in O^{14} is of the type $0^+(T = 1)$ while the ground state of N^{14} is of the type $1^+(T = 0)$ and it is interesting to note that the preferred transition obeys Fermi selection rules, passing from 0^+ to 0^+ rather than to the ground state of N^{14}. A more complex scheme is exemplified by the nuclide Cl^{38}, which emits three groups of beta rays, two of which are effectively in coincidence with gamma rays which are characteristic of the final nuclide A^{38} (Figure 9.63). In such cases it is common for one or more groups to be "forbidden" to some degree by the selection rules, but the transition rates may be appreciable nevertheless.

When gamma rays are emitted as well as beta rays, the electron energy spectrum contains extra components in the form of sharp lines superimposed on the continuous spectrum of the beta particles proper. These lines consist of extranuclear electrons ejected from the atom by a process which is analogous to photoelectric absorption of the gamma rays. The phenomenon is called *internal conversion* of the gamma rays, although it is not correct to imagine the gamma ray as first emitted and then absorbed. The electron energy (K_{el}) is equal to that of the gamma ray (E_γ) *minus* the work done in extracting the electron from its shell, usually the "k" or "l" shell of the atom

$$K_{el} = E_\gamma - W_k \quad \text{for } k \text{ conversion,}$$

where W_k is the ionization potential of the k shell.

It should be noted that the value of W_k is that appropriate to the atomic number of the *final* nuclide, since gamma-ray emission follows beta emission in these events; also the creation of a "hole" in the extranuclear electron shell leads to x-ray emission which is characteristic of the same element. Internal conversion is of some importance in nuclear experiments because it provides an accurate way of finding the gamma-ray energy (E_γ) and it yields information about the multipolarity of the gamma-ray transition (Section 9.6.f).

(f) Nuclear stability rules

The semiempirical formula of Section 9.3.d for the mean binding energy per nucleon ($\bar{B}$) was derived from simple assumptions about nuclear energy terms and it was adjusted to fit the main trend of the stable-nuclide curve (Figure 9.21). In view of the successes of the nuclear shell model (Section 9.9) we must suppose that certain nuclides depart significantly from the theoretical curve, since possession of a magic number of neutrons or protons confers extra stability on a nuclide. It should also be recalled that a like-nucleon *pairing* effect has to be invoked to explain the observed ground-state characters of even-even nuclides and the rarity of stable odd-odd nuclides. It becomes necessary to modify the semiempirical mass formula in such a way that the odd and even nucleon numbers are taken into account; with this modification many unstable nuclides can be covered and stability against beta decay can be investigated to yield rules concerning the existence of stable nuclides. This treatment is intended to deal only with nuclei below $Z = 82$, where alpha decay is improbable, and it excludes certain cases of extreme instability, for example Be^8, where emission of massive particles occurs.

We first consider nuclides with odd A, that is, those with an odd and an even number of nucleons, where pairing effects may be neglected. The total rest mass of an atom with baryon number A and proton number Z can be written (in carbon-12 units):

$$M = 1.007825Z + 1.008665(A - Z) - A\bar{B} \qquad [9.11.19]$$

[from Equation (9.3.13)]

where the binding-energy terms for extranuclear electrons have been neglected and the mean binding energy per nucleon ($\bar{B}$) is given, in MeV, as

$$\bar{B} = 15.2 - 16.0A^{-1/3} - 0.667Z^2A^{-4/3} - 22.2(A - 2Z)^2A^{-2} \quad \text{from Equation (9.3.16).}$$

If we define a "mass excess" (ΔM) as the difference between the proper atomic mass (M) and the mass of A neutrons, this quantity can be expressed in MeV as follows:

$$\Delta M = (M - 1.008665A)c^2$$

$$= -0.78Z - 15.2A + 16.0A^{2/3} + 0.667Z^2A^{-1/3}$$

$$+ 22.2(A - 2Z)^2A^{-1}. \qquad [9.11.20]$$

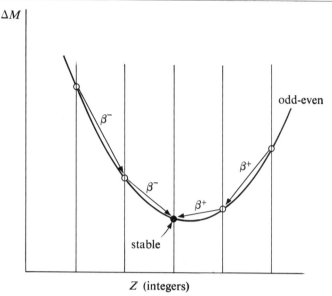

FIGURE 9.64   *Graph of the mass excess (ΔM in MeV) for odd A plotted against Z for a set of isobaric nuclides. In this case only one nuclide can be stable, the remainder being beta active.*

In the problem of beta stability we are concerned only with isobaric nuclides, with the same A, so the most important property of the mass excess ΔM is its variation with Z. This variation can be expressed by the function

$$\Delta M = \text{const} - 89.6Z + Z^2\left(\frac{88.8}{A} + \frac{0.667}{A^{1/3}}\right). \qquad [9.11.21]$$

This is represented graphically by a parabolic curve, as shown in Figure 9.64, the *minimum* occurring at the predicted Z value for stability, that is, at

$$Z = \frac{1.01A}{2 + 0.015A^{2/3}}$$

which is very similar to the expression found in Equation (9.3.15). Since Z can take only integral values, the most stable nuclide for a given A is that with Z closest to the theoretical value. The situation is typically represented by Figure 9.64, where vertical lines intersect the curve at the integral Z values. It is evident that there can be only one stable nuclide for a given odd A, unless by accident two nuclides coincide exactly in their values of ΔM. This is perhaps the case with $A = 123$, where both Sb^{123} and Te^{123} appear to be stable: in all other elements below $Z = 82$, the odd-A rule is obeyed. It can be seen from Figure 9.64 that as one proceeds further from the single stable nuclide on either side the beta-ray energy increases steadily.

   The situation is quite different in nuclides with A even. These are divided into two groups, the odd-odd nuclides (which are rarely stable) and the even-even nuclides (which are very commonly stable). The main difference is supposed to be due to a pairing interaction between like nucleons which favors nucleons bound with spins opposed, resulting in a net 0^+ character in the ground state of any even-even nuclide. This pairing effect can be allowed for in the mass formula by writing

$$\Delta M = \text{const} - 89.6Z + Z^2\left(\frac{88.8}{A} + \frac{0.667}{A^{1/3}}\right) \pm \delta, \qquad [9.11.22]$$

where δ is the "pairing term," the $+$ sign being taken in odd-odd and the $-$ sign in even-even nuclides.

If, now, we plot ΔM against Z for a group of isobaric nuclides with A even, we obtain two parabolic curves separated everywhere by a vertical gap of 2δ. Since the Z values are alternately odd and even, the points corresponding to successive nuclides alternate between the two curves. There may be more than one nuclide stable against beta decay in this situation, depending on the position of the theoretical minimum and the steepness of the parabolic curves. For example, if the minimum occurs near an *odd Z* (Z_0) and the curves are not too steep, the nuclide Z_0 can decay either by negative electron or by positron emission to the stable nuclides $Z_0 \pm 1$, as shown in Figure 9.65. This is the situation in Cu^{64}, already quoted [Equation (9.11.7)], and in such a case a pair of stable nuclides is the rule, because the outlying nuclides $Z_0 \pm 3$ are unlikely to be stable.

On the other hand, it is possible for only one nuclide to be stable, as shown in Figure 9.65 where the parabolic curve is very steep. The conditions for this happening can be worked out theoretically from the mass formula if δ is known. For convenience we shall consider light nuclides in which the minimum of the parabolic curve occurs at $Z_0 = \frac{1}{2}A$. The increase in ΔM for a change of one unit in Z is found from the term

$$\Delta M = \text{const} + 22.2(A - 2Z)^2 A^{-1} \text{ approximately}$$

and with $Z = Z_0 \pm 1$ we find

$$\Delta M = \Delta M_{\min} + \frac{88.8}{A} \text{ MeV.} \qquad [9.11.23]$$

If the increase in ΔM from the minimum value exceeds the value of 2δ, it is possible for $Z_0 = \frac{1}{2}A$ to be the sole stable (odd-odd) nuclide, as indicated by Figure 9.65.

The behavior of δ is not easily predicted by the theory but values of δ can be found empirically from various kinds of nuclear data. For example, Figure 9.65 shows that, in cases where an odd-odd nuclide decays either by negative electron or by positron emission, the *mean* beta-ray energy, after allowance has been made for the extra 1.02 MeV energy in positron emission, is equal to 2δ *minus* the increase of ΔM given theoretically by Equation (9.11.23), that is,

$$\bar{Q}_\beta = 2\delta - \frac{88.8}{A} \text{ MeV.}$$

Values of δ found from the data for nuclides like Cu^{64} show that an appropriate expression for 2δ as a function of A is

$$2\delta = \frac{26}{\sqrt{A}} \text{ MeV,}$$

although it should be pointed out that other functions can be employed. If this value of 2δ is compared with the increase in ΔM given by Equation (9.11.23), it is found that the two expressions are nearly equal at $A = 12$. Below this number the increase in ΔM is greater than 2δ, so that it is possible for one stable odd-odd nuclide to exist; above $A = 12$ the condition is not satisfied. These theoretical predictions are borne out by observation, in general, since the only stable odd-odd nuclides known are D^2, Li^6, B^{10}, and N^{14}. We see that the introduction of the $\pm\delta$ term in Equation (9.11.22) gives a very fair description of the odd-odd stability situation.

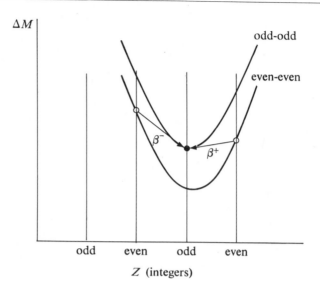

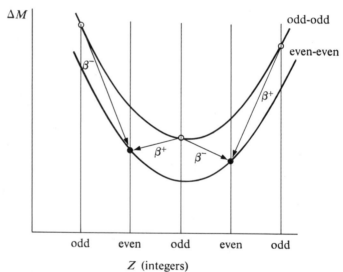

FIGURE 9.65 *Graph of the mass excess* (ΔM *in MeV*) *for even A plotted against Z for a set of isobaric nuclides. Above: if the curves are steep, it is possible for one odd-odd nuclide to be stable. Below: in other cases, it may happen that an odd-odd nuclide is unstable against both positive and negative beta decay.*

Further study of the even-A stability curves of Figure 9.65 shows that, when the minimum occurs close to an even value of Z, either one or three stable isobars can exist, depending on the steepness of the parabolae. Equation (9.11.23) shows that the steepness decreases with increasing A, so that the occurrence of three stable isobars is possible only at high A values. This happens, for instance, at $A = 96$, 124, 130, 136. In some cases the actual behavior depends on the possibility of alpha decay, especially in the rare-earth region, but in general the rules for beta stability are adequate to account for the stable nuclides plotted in Figure 9.19.

FOR FURTHER READING

Accelerators:
M. S. LIVINGSTON, and J. P. BLEWETT, *Particle Accelerators* (McGraw-Hill Book Company, New York, 1962).
Particle detectors:
W. J. Price, *Nuclear Radiation Detection* (McGraw-Hill, Book Co., New York, 1964.) 2nd ed.
Experimental nuclear physics:
Experimental Nuclear Physics, editor E. Segré (J. Wiley & Sons, New York, 1953, 1953, 1959) 3 vols.
Nuclear theory:
H. A. BETHE and P. MORRISON, *Elementary Nuclear Theory* (J. Wiley & Sons, New York, 1956).
L. R. B. ELTON, *Introductory Nuclear Theory* (Pitman Publishing Corp., New York, 1959).
Nuclear moments:
K. F. SMITH, *Molecular Beams* (Methuen Monographs, J. Wiley & Sons, New York, 1955).
Original papers:
Foundations of Nuclear Physics, editor R. T. Beyer (Dover Publications, New York, 1949).
Papers by Cockcroft & Walton, Chadwick, Dee, and Feather, also a discussion on nuclear structure, in Proc. Roy. Soc. (London), **136** 619, 692 ff. (1932).

PROBLEMS FOR CHAPTER 9

DATA REQUIRED:

Specific charge of the proton: 9.6×10^7 C/kg
Specific charge of the electron: 1.76×10^{11} C/kg
Elementary charge: $e = 1.6 \times 10^{-19}$ C
Electron rest mass: $m = 9.1 \times 10^{-31}$ kg (0.51 MeV)
Atomic mass unit: $1u = 1.66 \times 10^{-27}$ kg (931 MeV)
Velocity of light *in vacuo*: $c = 3.0 \times 10^8$ m/sec
Nuclear radius constant: $r_0 = 1.3 \times 10^{-15}$ m
No. of molecules per kilomole: $N^* = 6.0 \times 10^{26}$
Planck's constant: $h = 6.6 \times 10^{-34}$ J sec
$$\hbar = 1.05 \times 10^{-34} \text{ J sec}$$
1 barn (b) $= 10^{-28}$ m².   1 fermi $= 10^{-15}$ m

9.1. A vertical Van de Graaff generator produces a beam of protons with mean energy 2 MeV and these are deflected through a right angle in a magnetic field, striking a target placed 5 m away from the magnet. What is the total spread in beam energy if the beam striking the target spreads over a distance of 5 mm in the vertical direction?

9.2. The 50 MeV linear accelerator at Harwell, England, has protons injected at 0.5 MeV energy and the drift tubes are powered in alternation by a rf supply of 200 Mc/sec. What is the approximate length of (i) the first, (ii) the last drift tube?

9.3. Calculate the magnetic field strength and the size of the pole pieces required in a fixed-frequency cyclotron which is designed to accelerate protons to a maximum energy of 5 MeV with a radio-frequency supply of 8 Mc/sec.

9.4. An electron synchrotron is designed to accelerate electrons to a maximum kinetic energy of 32 MeV in an orbit of radius 0.1 m. Find the magnetic field strength required to keep the particles in orbit at maximum energy, also the frequency of the alternating electric potential applied to the resonator.

9.5. The Birmingham proton synchrotron has a ring-shaped vacuum chamber of mean radius 4.5 m and protons are injected into orbit at energy 0.45 MeV. Calculate the number of revolutions per second and the magnetic field strength required at this stage in the cycle. At the end of the cycle the protons have a kinetic energy of 900 MeV per particle. What are the frequency of revolution and the magnetic field strength at this stage?

9.6. What is the least kinetic energy of a proton, as measured in the laboratory frame of reference, which can produce a pair of "lambda particles," of total rest-mass energy 2220 MeV, in a nucleon-nucleon collision?

9.7.(a) In the Brookhaven alternating-gradient synchrotron, protons describe orbits of mean radius 128 m in the magnetic guiding field. What is the magnetic field strength (i) at the injection kinetic energy of 50 MeV per proton, (ii) at the final energy of 33 GeV per proton?

(b) What fraction of the final kinetic energy (33 GeV) is available for particle reactions when the protons strike protons which are stationary in the laboratory frame?

(c) If an AGS were designed to accelerate protons to kinetic energies of 300 GeV per proton, what fraction of this energy would be available for reactions?

9.8. Calculate the minimum kinetic energy of (i) protons, (ii) electrons, detected by the Čerenkov effect in water (refractive index = 1.33).

9.9. Alpha particles from a sample of uranium, each of energy 4.2 MeV, travel through a parallel-plate ion counter filled with argon, which has $W = 25$ eV/ion pair. What is the magnitude of each pulse as collected by an electrode of net capacitance 10^{-4} microfarad to ground?

9.10.(a) Show that a deuteron has a total range in a given material which is twice the range of a proton possessing half of the deuteron's original energy.

(b) Also show that an alpha particle has a range approximately equal to that of a proton with one-quarter of the energy.

(c) Explain why the result in (a) is precise while that in (b) is necessarily approximate.

9.11. Fast neutrons incident upon nitrogen gas produce recoils of maximum energy 1.2 MeV. What would be the least photon energy needed to cause recoils of this energy by a process analogous to the Compton effect?

9.12. Estimate the absorption cross section of $_{83}Bi^{209}$ nuclei for fast neutrons of energy 14 MeV. If a beam of these neutrons passes through a slab of bismuth metal (density 9.8×10^3 kg/m³) of thickness 0.1 m, what fraction of the neutron beam is absorbed?

9.13.(a) Show that the electrostatic potential energy of a nucleus in which all the protons are concentrated near the surface is given by the expression $\dfrac{(Ze)^2}{2r(4\pi\varepsilon_0)}$, where r is the effective nuclear radius.

(b) Hence set up a Weizsäcker type of expression for the mean binding energy per nucleon ($\bar{B}$) in a nucleus and compare the result with the empirical curve of Figure 9.21.

(c) Calculate the release of energy in symmetrical fission of the nuclide $_{92}U^{238}$ (in its ground state) on this model.

9.14.(a) A fast-neutron flux of 10^5 particles/cm² per second at energy 5 MeV is used to irradiate a photographic emulsion which is 0.1 mm thick and contains 3×10^{28} hydrogen atoms per m³. Use the cross-section data of Figure 9.28 to find the number of proton recoils produced in 1 sq. mm of the plate area if the total irradiation lasts for 10 min.

(b) What fraction of the proton recoils will lie within the angular ranges (i) 0°–10°, (ii) 10°–20°, all angles being measured relative to the direction of the neutrons?

9.15. A deuteron beam of energy 0.5 MeV is used to produce D + D neutrons from a thin target and the neutrons emitted at right angles to the beam are detected by a hydrogen-filled ion counter, of sensitive volume 10^{-4} m³, containing hydrogen gas at 3 atm pressure. Find the neutron flux incident upon the counter if the total number of proton recoils counted is 10^3 per sec. Also draw a sketch graph to show the number of counts per unit energy interval as a function of the pulse height, the latter being expressed in MeV equivalent.

9.16.(a) Estimate the mean kinetic energy of neutrons, originally at 1 MeV, which have undergone 20 collisions with deuterons in a heavy-water moderator.

(b) How many collisions in graphite (chiefly C^{12}) will result in the same final (mean) energy?

9.17. Analyze the elastic scattering process when a particle M is incident with speed U upon a particle m which is initially at rest in the laboratory frame and derive the following relations between the angle θ (the angle of scattering in the CM system) and ψ (the angle of deflection of M in the laboratory frame):

$$\sin \psi = \frac{m \sin \theta}{(M^2 + m^2 + 2Mm \cos \theta)^{1/2}}$$

and

$$\sin \theta = \frac{\sin \psi}{m} [M \cos \psi - (m^2 - M^2 \sin^2 \psi)^{1/2}].$$

9.18. Find the number of protons scattered forward per second in the angular range from $\varphi = 25°$ to 35° by a beam of alpha particles, with energy 5 MeV and flux 10^{12} particles per m² per sec, which is incident upon a thin foil containing 10^{20} hydrogen atoms.

9.19.(a) Set up the Schrödinger equation in relative coordinates for the bound neutron-proton system, taking the masses of the two particles to be equal and assuming that $l = 0$ for the lowest state of the deuteron. Given that the binding energy is 2.225 MeV in the ground state, solve the Schrödinger equation numerically for a rectangular potential well and find the well depth (U_0) if the effective well radius $a = 1.8$ fermi.

(b) Plot the radial function ($r\psi$) against the separation distance r for the range 0 to 5 fermi, to show the behavior of the state function inside and outside the well.

(c) Also plot the probability function ($r^2\psi^2$) on the same graph and show that the net probability of the particles being separated by a distance greater than a is over 50%.

9.20. Calculate the kinetic energy of D + D neutrons emitted at (i) 0° (ii) 180° to a 2 MeV deuteron beam which strikes a thin target containing deuterium.

9.21. Fast neutrons of kinetic energy 14 MeV are scattered by carbon and the energy distribution of the scattered neutrons is measured at 90° to the beam. The resulting spectrum shows groups at 11.8 MeV, 7.8 MeV, and 4.8 MeV. Find the Q values for these groups and identify the states of the nuclide C^{12} responsible for them.

9.22. How many beta-active nuclei are produced per second when a thermal neutron flux of 10^{10} particles per cm² per second is incident upon a thin cadmium foil, of mass 10^{-2} gm? Mean atomic weight of cadmium = 112. Effective cross-section = 2000 b per Cd atom.

9.23. Calculate the proton bombarding energy which is required to produce 22 MeV gamma rays by the $H^1 + H^3$ capture reaction [Equation (9.5.7)]. What H^3 bombarding energy would be needed to give the same energy of gamma rays?

9.24.(a) In an experiment with a Van de Graaff machine, protons are used to bombard a target of C^{12} and a resonance occurs at 0.46 MeV bombarding energy for emission of 2.3 MeV gamma rays. Given the masses (in u): $H^1 = 1.007825$, $N^{13} = 13.005739$, draw an energy-level diagram to illustrate the process.

(b) At a bombarding energy of 5.4 MeV a resonance occurs for inelastic scattering of protons and these protons are coincident with 4.4 MeV gamma rays. Show how this process may be represented on your diagram.

9.25.(a) Thermal neutrons of kinetic energy 0.02 eV are absorbed readily by B^{10} nuclei. Assuming that a compound nucleus is formed, find (i) the speed of the compound nucleus immediately after its formation, (ii) the excitation energy of the compound nucleus, given the masses (in u): $n^1 = 1.008665$, $B^{10} = 10.012939$, $B^{11} = 11.009305$.

(b) It is observed that the reaction

$$B^{10} + n^1 \rightarrow He^4 + Li^7$$

produces two alpha-particle groups, of energies 1.78 and 1.46 MeV, when thermal neutrons are employed. Hence find (i) the Li^7 kinetic energies corresponding to the two alpha groups, (ii) the two Q values of the reaction. What information does this result yield concerning the properties of the nuclide Li^7?

9.26.(a) When a thin target containing N^{14} nuclei is bombarded with protons, a resonance occurs at 1.06 MeV for proton capture with the emission of 3.06, 5.27 and 8.33 MeV gamma-ray groups. Assuming that no higher-energy gammas are possible, find the mass of O^{15}, given that $H^1 = 1.007825$, $N^{14} = 14.003074$ u.

(b) When the same target is bombarded with deuterons, both gammas and neutrons are emitted. With 0.80 MeV deuterons, the neutrons given off at right angles to the deuteron beam consist of two groups, with energies 0.53 and 5.6 MeV; a gamma-ray group of 5.27 MeV energy is coincident with the low-energy neutron group. Draw an energy-level diagram for O^{15} to represent the above reactions.
Masses: $D^2 = 2.014102$, $n^1 = 1.008665$ u.

9.27.(a) Show that the angle of emission (θ) in center-of-mass coordinates of a particle m produced in an exoergic nuclear reaction $M_0 + m_0 \rightarrow M + m$ (release $+Q$) is related to the laboratory angle recorded (ψ) by the equation

$$\theta = \psi + \text{arc sin}\,(\beta \sin \psi)$$

with

$$\beta^2 = \frac{mm_0}{MM_0\left[1 + \dfrac{Q(M + m)}{M_0 K_0}\right]},$$

where K_0 is the bombarding energy ($\frac{1}{2}m_0u_0^2$) in the laboratory frame.

(b) Also show that, in an endoergic reaction with energy release $(-Q)$, the momentum of each product particle in the center-of-mass system vanishes when

$$K_0 = \frac{M_0 + m_0}{M_0}|Q|,$$

that is, at the threshold energy for the reaction.

9.28. The nuclide Li^7 possesses excited states at

(i) 6.54 MeV with estimated total width (Γ) of 1 MeV;

(ii) 7.47 MeV with estimated total width of 0.14 MeV.

Estimate the mean lifetimes of these states and discuss the various factors which might influence these lifetimes, causing the observed difference.

9.29(a). Show that, for a disk of radius r revolving at uniform angular velocity ω, the equivalent gravitational potential difference between the rim and the center is $\Delta\Phi = \frac{1}{2}\omega^2 r^2$. Hence calculate the gravitational frequency shift between the two points for a wheel of radius 0.5 m revolving at 3000 rpm.

(b) If this gravitational shift were to be detected by the Mössbauer effect, what relative velocity between the source and the absorber would just cancel the frequency shift?

9.30. Prove that, when a gamma-ray source emitting photons with a characteristic line-width Γ is placed near a detector and an absorber with the same linewidth for absorption is inserted between source and detector, the total width of the resonant-absorption curve (as found by the Doppler shift or other methods) is 2Γ.

9.31. Use the magnetic moments of the nuclides $_{19}$K^{39}, $_{20}$Ca^{43}, $_{21}$Sc^{45}, and $_{23}$V^{51} as plotted on the Schmidt diagram (Figure 9.50) to derive the shell-model character of the odd nucleon in each case. Do these results agree with the shell-model sequence of Figure 9.55?

9.32.(a) Use the Born-approximation method to find the angular distribution of particles scattered by a massive center of force when the interaction potential is of the Yukawa type

$$U(r) = \frac{g^2 \exp(-\mu r)}{r}.$$

(b) Hence show that when $\mu \rightarrow 0$ and the interaction goes over into the Coulomb form, the Born method yields the Rutherford angular distribution

$$\frac{d\sigma}{d\Omega} \propto \operatorname{cosec}^4 \tfrac{1}{2}\theta.$$

(c) Also apply the Yukawa theory to the neutron-proton scattering problem at high energies and show that, for ordinary forces, the angular distribution in the center-of-mass system is of the same general form as the theoretical (dotted) line in Figure 9.51.

9.33. Use the Born-approximation result for rectangular-well scattering to show that, at very high neutron energies, the angular distributions of neutrons scattered by the well exhibit pronounced "diffraction" maxima and minima in the forward direction.

9.34. Use the nuclear shell model to predict the ground-state characteristics of the following nuclides

$$_{29}\text{Cu}^{63} \qquad _{38}\text{Sr}^{87} \qquad _{51}\text{Sb}^{123} \qquad _{83}\text{Bi}^{209}$$

and in each case make a rough estimate of the magnetic moment in nuclear magnetons.

9.35. (a) Find the effective moment of inertia ($\mathscr{I}$) of the $_{72}$Hf^{180} nucleus from the rotational levels of Figure 9.58, given that the second excited state is 0.31 MeV above the ground state. Compare the value of $\mathscr{I}$ obtained with the moment of inertia for a rigid sphere of the same mass and radius.

(b) The neighboring nuclide Hf^{179} has an electric quadrupole moment per elementary charge of 3 b. From this information find the deformation parameter δ for nuclides in this region.

9.36. (a) Show that the expression of Equation (9.10.5) for the electric quadrupole moment per elementary charge of an ellipsoid applies also to oblate ellipsoids, that is,

$$\frac{QM}{e} = \frac{2Z(b^2 - a^2)}{5}.$$

(b) Hence estimate the deformation parameter δ for $_{89}Ac^{227}$ nuclei, in which

$$\frac{QM}{e} = -1.7\ b.$$

9.37. The nuclide $_{73}Ta^{181}$ is observed to possess an electric-dipole resonance (Figure 9.39) split into two peaks, which are at 12.6 and 15.3 MeV, respectively. Assuming that the resonance energy varies inversely as the effective nuclear radius (as indicated by the collective model) and that the two peaks correspond to the minor and major axes of a prolate ellipsoid, estimate the deformation parameter for this nuclide in the ground state. Is this result consistent with the observed quadrupole moment per elementary charge of between $+3$ and $+6\ b$?

9.38. Calculate the energy of Ne^{22} nuclei produced by neutrino recoil when the unstable Na^{22} decays by electron capture, given that the energy release $Q_{EC} = 2.84$ MeV. Show that this result is more than twice the maximum recoil energy produced when the same Ne^{22} nuclei originate by positron emission from Na^{22}.

9.39. Transform the momentum distribution $f(P)\,dP$ of Equation (9.11.13) into a distribution in kinetic energy of the beta particles (K_e), the latter being in the relativistic region. Hence show that a graph of

$$\frac{F(K_e)}{(K_e^2 + 2K_e mc^2)(K_e + mc^2)^{1/2}}$$

against K_e is a straight line intersecting the K_e axis at Q_0 for allowed beta transitions in which Coulomb corrections may be neglected. (mc^2 = electron rest energy).

9.40. Use the semiempirical mass formula of Equations (9.11.20) and (9.11.22) to estimate the binding energy of the last neutron in the nuclide $_{45}Rh^{104}$ and hence find the total gamma-ray energy released when $_{45}Rh^{103}$ captures a slow neutron, according to the reaction of Equation (9.3.28).

9.41. Draw graphs of the "mass excess" ΔM against Z to illustrate cases in which (i) only one (ii) three isobaric nuclides are stable against beta decay, when A is even.

9.42. Use the odd-even correction term $\delta = \dfrac{13}{A^{1/2}}$ approximately, of Equation (9.11.22), to predict the mean energy release of two kinds of beta-transition (β^+ and β^-) ending on a stable even-even nuclide, for example, C^{12} formed from B^{12} and N^{12}, and S^{32} formed from P^{32} and Cl^{32}.

9.43. The following data refer to the maximum positron and negative-electron energies, also electron-capture energy releases, in the beta decay of odd-odd nuclides which are unstable with respect to both forms of beta decay.

Nuclide:	$_{17}Cl^{36}$	$_{19}K^{40}$	$_{29}Cu^{64}$	$_{33}As^{74}$	$_{45}Rh^{102}$	$_{55}Cs^{130}$	$_{77}Ir^{192}$
Q_{β^-}	0.71	1.32	0.57	1.36	1.15	0.44	1.45
Q_{β^+}			0.66	1.53	1.24	1.97	
Q_{EC}	1.2	1.50					

(1.45)

Plot a log-log graph of estimated δ values to show that these are consistent with the quoted formula

$$\delta = \frac{13}{A^{\frac{1}{2}}} \text{ MeV}$$

and find the mean beta-decay energy release for the nuclide $_{35}\text{Br}^{80}$, which emits both negative electrons and positrons.

9.44. The nuclide $_{55}\text{Cs}^{137}$ is beta active and is known to decay predominantly to an excited state of $_{56}\text{Ba}^{137}$ which in turn reaches the ground state by emission of 0.66 MeV gamma rays. The gammas are internally converted and the electrons emitted include "k" shell and "l" shell conversion electrons. Find the ionization potentials of barium for these shells and hence estimate the kinetic energies of the conversion electrons.

CHAPTER X

ᢣᢣᢣᢣᢣᢣᢣᢣᢣᢣᢣᢣᢣᢣᢣᢣᢣᢣᢣᢣᢣᢣᢣᢣᢣᢣᢣᢣᢣᢣᢣᢣᢣᢣ

PARTICLE PHYSICS

Physical investigation of the fundamental forms of matter has progressed from study of atomic structure and the properties of nuclei into the high-energy field, where many varieties of unstable particle are encountered. Instability can take different forms. The atoms of ordinary matter are stable and their properties are explicable in terms of the properties of three particles, the electron, proton, and neutron. The neutron decays in free flight to yield the stable particles electron, proton, and antineutrino; we already need to introduce one type of "antiparticle" and another type, the positron, is frequently encountered in nuclear physics. In ordinary matter positrons are short-lived because they combine rapidly with negative electrons to yield "annihilation" photons, but in free space positrons are just as stable as negative electrons. We can imagine a world in which positrons are the extra-nuclear electrons bound by pure electrostatic forces to negatively charged "anti-nuclei," composed of antiprotons and antineutrons. Such antiparticles may be described formally by Dirac's theory (Section 7.9), which is applicable to fermions.*

Among the particles which, like the neutron, are intrinsically unstable are the various mesons† found in cosmic rays. In 1935 Yukawa suggested that the strong interactions between nucleons are due to the exchange of mesons and predicted that these particles would prove to be unstable in free flight. In 1938 Anderson and Neddermeyer announced the discovery of mesons, later called "mu mesons," in cosmic rays. However the mu meson did not satisfy the conditions of the Yukawa theory and it was not until 1947 that Powell and his collaborators showed that at least two different kinds of meson, with different masses, occur at high altitudes. Since that time a considerable family of mesons and "hyperons" (unstable particles heavier than nucleons) has been found, both in cosmic rays and among the products of high-energy disintegrations in the laboratory.

The particle picture is therefore one of extreme complexity, with many kinds of particles requiring investigation and classification. Some progress has been made in the theory of particles, chiefly by the formulation of conservation rules obeyed in interparticle transitions and interactions. In addition to the basic rules of energy and momentum conservation, there are apparently fundamental conditions requiring conservation of *electric charge*, of the number of *baryons* (massive fermions), and of the number of *leptons* (light fermions) in any process. However, there are other rules, such as the conservation of parity, which are valid in strong interactions but not valid in weak interactions. It appears that the hierarchy of interactions, ranging from the strong nuclear forces to the extremely feeble gravitational

---

* Special consideration is required for particles with zero rest mass (the neutrinos) and those obeying Bose-Einstein statistics.
† The term "meson" is here applied to any particle of rest mass intermediate between the electron and proton masses.

forces between particles, possesses a structure which is bound up with symmetry requirements, which in turn determine the conservation rules.*

10.1 Cosmic Rays

The earliest experiments on cosmic rays stemmed from the observation that a shielded electroscope is slowly discharged at a rate which depends on altitude, the rate being more rapid at high altitudes. This observation shows that there are ionizing rays entering the Earth's atmosphere from above and these rays must have great penetrating power, since their effects have been detected underground and in deep lakes. It is possible to arrange Geiger counters in coincidence arrays and to show that the detected rays travel predominantly in the vertical direction. Similar techniques reveal the occurrence of cosmic-ray *showers*, that is, groups of particles covering a large horizontal area within a short period of time. It is also found that the numbers of rays reaching ground level depends on the magnetic latitude; hence the Earth's magnetic field must affect the trajectories of the original or "primary" particles entering the upper atmosphere. It is believed that most of the primary particles are protons, but there are also heavier particles in the primary rays, as shown by the heavy-ion tracks produced in photographic emulsions flown to a great height.

It is important to realize that the cosmic rays observed at sea level are produced almost entirely by collisions and disintegrations occurring in the atmosphere following the entry of primary particles, each of which possesses high energy, spread subsequently over a large number of particles. Most of the particles produced by the complex high-energy reactions are either intrinsically unstable, for example mesons and hyperons, or are capable of producing numbers of particles in "cascade" processes. One important component of cosmic rays is called the "soft" component, because it is easily absorbed in lead, and this consists of electrons of both signs, together with photons of high energy. A single fast electron can generate photons in the presence of matter by the bremsstrahlung process (Section 4.8) and high-energy photons readily produce electron-positron pairs (Section 4.9), which in turn may cause further emission of photons. Thus the soft component forms showers of the cascade type and a single shower may spread over a wide area at sea level. The total energy found in some showers is of the order of 10^{17} eV, all of which must have come from a single primary particle entering the atmosphere.

In addition to the soft component, cosmic rays contain a component which can penetrate several feet of lead and which consists of charged particles of both signs. These particles do not lose appreciable amounts of energy by the bremsstrahlung process, but, at the same time, they are much more penetrating than massive particles like the proton. Calculations of the energy losses by fast particles in matter (Section 9.4.b) suggest that the penetrating particles must be intermediate in mass between the electron and the proton. In 1938 Anderson and Neddermeyer published evidence strongly suggesting the existence of mesons with rest mass about 200 times that of the electron.

During the years 1939–1945 theoretical physicists tried to reconcile the cosmic-ray data with the meson theory of nuclear forces (Section 9.8), despite the many difficulties which attend a rigorous theory of strong interactions. Slowly it became clear that the observed

---

* For a survey of the high-energy field, see papers by M. Gell-Mann, L. M. Lederman, and L. J. Laslett, *Physics Today*, **17**, No. 11, 22 (1964).

mesons could not be responsible for nucleon-nucleon forces, since their interaction with nucleons is too weak. This conclusion was emphasized by an experiment performed by Conversi, Pancini, and Piccioni,* who compared the rates of decay of cosmic-ray mesons in lead and in carbon. It was shown that the capture of a negatively charged meson by a lead nucleus gives rise to a reaction in which no charged particles are emitted. This reaction is now written†

$$\mu^- + p^+ \rightarrow n^0 + \nu, \qquad\qquad [10.1.1]$$

where μ^- stands for the muon (originally "μ meson"), which reacts with a proton to yield a neutron and neutrino. However, in carbon a large proportion of stopped negative muons decays instead by electron emission, a process analogous to beta decay. Since beta decay is known to be a slow process due to weak interactions, it follows that the particle reaction of Equation (10.1.1) is also due to a weak interaction.

Shortly after this experiment was reported, Powell and his collaborators were exposing photographic emulsions of a new and improved type at high altitudes in order to study the tracks produced by cosmic rays. Here the advantage of using the photographic method, with its long exposures, was revealed, since many examples of charged-particle decay were found in comparatively small areas of the plates examined. Powell discovered that in several events one meson had stopped in the emulsion and decayed to give a second particle, plus at least one neutral particle which was not recorded. The second particle, in each event of this type, was identified as a muon, similar to those already studied in experiments at sea level. The original meson must, therefore, be more massive than the muon and rough estimates yielded a ratio of the two rest-masses equal to about 1.5. It became clear that the newly discovered meson, called the π meson, interacts strongly with nucleons and therefore corresponds to the meson of Yukawa's theory. π mesons possess a short mean lifetime and are therefore found only at high altitudes, where many of them decay to give the muons which are able to reach sea level‡ (see Section 5.5.f).

There remains the intriguing question of the origin of cosmic rays, which has been the subject of speculation for many years.§ Some physicists have ascribed the rays to outbursts from the Sun; certainly, on rare occasions unusual activity of solar flares has been correlated with sudden increases in cosmic-ray intensity. However, it is equally likely that other stars contribute to the total cosmic-ray flux reaching the Earth's atmosphere and it is doubtful if any purely solar mechanism could produce rays in the extremely high energy range, which certainly extends as far as 10^{17} eV per particle. The discovery that extensive magnetic fields exist in the interplanetary region, causing large-scale deflection of charged particles, implies that the rays arriving near the Earth must be distributed randomly in direction, whatever their source. Further discoveries of measurable magnetic fields in the gaseous nebulae, such as the Crab nebula, have led to electromagnetic theories of particle acceleration in these regions.‖ However, it is at least possible that violent changes in the centers of certain extra-galactic nebulas¶ are responsible for the emission of high-energy particles. Special interest attaches to the question whether there is an upper limit to the energy per primary particle, since such a limit might throw light on the question of the size of the region in

---

* M. Conversi, E. Pancini, and C. Piccioni, Phys. Rev., **71**, 209 (1947).
† In this chapter, p^+ stands for proton, d^+ for deuteron, n^0 for neutron, $e^{\mp}$ for electron and positron, γ for photon, ν for neutrino.
‡ G. P. S. Occhialini and C. F. Powell, Nature, **159**, 186 (1947).
§ B. Rossi, "Where Do Cosmic Rays Come From?" Scientific American, **189**, No. 3, 64 (1953); and "High-Energy Cosmic Rays," *ibid.*, **201**, No. 5, 134 (1959).
‖ P. Morrison, Rev. Mod. Phys., **29**, 235 (1957).
¶ G. R. Burbidge, E. M. Burbidge, and A. R. Sandage, Rev. Mod. Phys., **35**, 947 (1963). Also, A. R. Sandage, "Exploding Galaxies," Scientific American, **211**, No. 5, 38 (1964).

which acceleration occurs. It is difficult to determine an upper energy limit by terrestrial measurements because of the very feeble flux of particles in the extremely high energy range, but some evidence has been obtained of cosmic-ray showers in which the total energy expended was of the order of 10^{20} eV.

10.2 Muons*

The muon was the first type of "meson" to be identified and it carries a unit electric charge which may be either positive or negative, as shown by the deflection of the particle in an applied magnetic field. In matter muons are highly penetrating but their mean lifetime is such that they can be stopped in a block of lead and subsequent changes can be studied experimentally. The negatively charged muons are captured by atoms to form "μ-mesic" atoms with well-defined energy levels (see Problem 6.13) and these temporary atoms can be detected by the x rays they emit during muon transitions from one level to another. In massive elements like lead the muon is eventually captured by the nucleus with the production of a neutron plus neutrino [Equation (10.1.1)]; the recoil neutron usually shares its energy with other nucleons so that more than one low-energy nucleon may be emitted. However, in a light element like carbon most of the muons decay instead of being captured and the decay has affinities with beta decay, in that it is a slow process in which an electron is emitted. Decay is always the result when a positive muon stops in matter.

In early experiments on cosmic rays, the mean lifetime of muons with respect to electronic decay was measured with the type of apparatus shown in Figure 10.1. Here a tray of Geiger

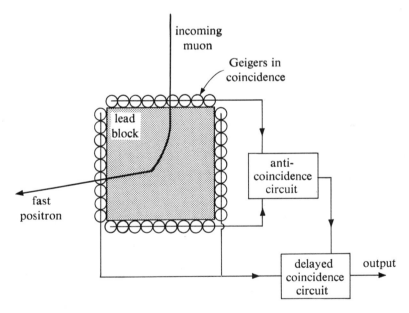

FIGURE 10.1 *Apparatus used in measuring the mean lifetime of positively charged muons which are stopped in a lead block. The emitted fast positrons are recorded in Geiger counters working in delayed coincidence with the counters registering the arrival of muons.*

* S. Penman, "The Muon," Scientific American, **205**, No. 1, 46 (1961).

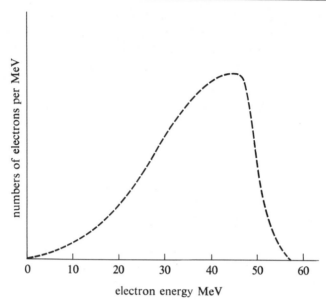

FIGURE 10.2   *The energy spectrum of electrons emitted in the decay of slow muons. The distribution rises to a maximum near the highest electron energy recorded (about 55 MeV).*

counters, working in coincidence, is placed above a lead block and a similar tray of counters beneath the block is run in anticoincidence with the top counters. Thus charged particles which enter the block and stop inside it are recorded as events which include muon decays yielding fast positrons (since only the positive muons decay in lead). Those positrons escaping from the sides of the block are detected by an array of counters working in *delayed* coincidence with events recorded by the top tray of counters. A semilogarithmic plot of counting rate versus the delay time introduced by the electronic circuits shows that the mean lifetime of the stopped muons is 2.2×10^{-6} sec. In flight the effective lifetime of fast muons is, of course, much longer, especially for cosmic-ray muons (see Section 5.5.f).

The decay of a muon involves the emission of an electron (of the same sign as the muon) and one or more neutral particles. Experiments have failed to detect products other than electrons, so it must be assumed that neutrinos are associated with the decay. The energy available for decay is then equal to the difference in rest masses of the muon and electron. If only one neutrino is emitted per decay, the electron and neutrino must divide up the energy in a unique proportion and the kinetic energy of the electron is fixed. Experiments on the energy spectrum of emitted electrons have shown that the number of electrons recorded per unit energy interval varies continuously up to a peak near the maximum energy recorded, close to 55 MeV (Figure 10.2). This form of distribution shows that the decay process must yield at least three particles and the evidence is in agreement with the emission of two neutrinos plus an electron

$$\mu^+ \to e^+ + \nu + \bar{\nu}. \qquad\qquad [10.2.1]$$

Here we have written the two neutrinos as a neutrino plus antineutrino, which preserves the lepton conservation principle if a muon has the same lepton number (L) as its corresponding electron. It should however be emphasized that Equation (10.2.1) is essentially tentative in the absence of evidence concerning the neutrinos themselves.

The spin of the muon is now known to be $\frac{1}{2}\hbar$ from magnetic spin-flip measurements. This result is in agreement with Equation (10.1.1), which has two fermions on each side, and with Equation (10.2.1), where there is an odd number of fermions on each side. The magnetic moment of the muon has been measured with great accuracy and is known to differ from the Dirac value $e\hbar/2M$ by a small amount, due to effects described by quantum electrodynamics (Section 7.10).

A rough estimate of the muon's rest mass can be obtained from the observed upper limit of decay-electron energies (about 55 MeV). The maximum electron momentum is generated when the two neutrinos travel away together in the direction opposite to the electron direction. Regarding the electron as an extremely relativistic particle, it obeys the relation $P = E/c$, which is exact for neutrinos. Therefore the two neutrinos carry away momentum equal to 55 MeV/c and the total energy of the three particles is approximately 110 MeV, or 216 electron rest masses. Thus the rest mass of the muon must be in the region of 215 m_e, where m_e stands for the rest mass of an electron.

A much more accurate determination of the muon mass is achieved by study of the x rays emitted by μ-mesic atoms, particularly those of light elements. In one experiment,* a beam of negative muons was directed at a sample of phosphorus and the x rays emitted at right angles to the beam were detected in a sodium-iodide scintillation counter. Fast coincidence circuits were used to ensure that the counting rate was genuinely due to μ-mesic x rays and thin lead foils were inserted between the phosphorus and the scintillation counter to find the absorption coefficient (μ of Section 4.9.a). This method yields an extremely accurate result for the energy of x rays emitted in the 3^2D–2^2P transitions of the phosphorus μ-mesic atoms because this energy happens to lie close to the k-shell discontinuity in lead (Figure 4.24). Careful work with laboratory-produced x rays has plotted the absorption coefficient as a function of x-ray energy in the region of the discontinuity and the measured absorption coefficient for μ-mesic x rays corresponds to a photon energy of 88,017$^{+15}_{-10}$ eV. This figure is then substituted in the fundamental energy relation for transitions between the nth and mth states of a μ-mesic atom

$$\Delta E = \frac{m_\mu Z^2 e^4}{2\hbar^2 (4\pi\varepsilon_0)^2} (1/n^2 - 1/m^2)F, \qquad [10.2.2]$$

where m_μ stands for the rest mass of the muon; n and m are the principal quantum numbers; and F is a correction factor (close to unity) which allows for the effects of nuclear motion and the finite size of the phosphorus nucleus.

This relation leads to a value for the ratio of the rest masses of the muon and the electron

$$m_\mu = \left(206.78 \begin{array}{c} +0.03 \\ -0.02 \end{array}\right) m_e.$$

An independent value of m_μ can be derived from the measured magnetic moment of the muon by assuming that the muon's gyromagnetic ratio is the same as the electron's, that is,

$$g_\mu = 2\left(1 + \frac{\alpha}{2\pi}\right) \qquad \text{as in Equation (7.10.8)}.$$

This relation yields

$$m_\mu = (206.77 \pm 0.01) m_e$$

showing that the two sets of data are consistent; further work leads to the present figure for the muon mass

$$m_\mu = (206.767 \pm 0.004) m_e.$$

It appears from these discovered properties of the muon that it resembles the electron in nearly all respects, the chief difference being the much greater mass of the muon. The

* S. Devons, G. Gidal, L. M. Lederman, and G. Shapiro, *Phys. Rev. Letters*, **5**, 330 (1960).

existence of a "massive electron" in the list of elementary particles introduces several acute problems of a theoretical nature. The strongest known interaction of the muon is its electromagnetic interaction, which is the same as that of an electron. If the rest mass of the electron be ascribed to its electromagnetic self-energy, it is difficult to account for the much greater rest mass of the muon. A further difficulty is the absence of electromagnetic decay of the muon according to the scheme

$$\mu \to e + \gamma.$$

Such a process does not violate any known conservation rule, but its frequency of occurrence must be extremely small, since experiments have failed to detect any photons emitted in muon decay.

10.3 Mesons Proper

(a) π mesons or pions

The discovery of charged π mesons arose from the observation that in photographic emulsions exposed to high-altitude cosmic rays there are many tracks showing one meson stopping, with a second particle emitted from the point of arrest. Observers have detected complete sequences of decay in which the π meson gives rise to a muon which in turn decays to emit an electron. A distinguishing feature of π-meson decay is the well-defined range of muons produced by π mesons which have come to rest (Plate III). This range is about 610 microns in standard emulsion, corresponding to a kinetic energy of 4.15 MeV. If momentum is conserved at each pion-muon conversion, there must be a neutral particle emitted as well as the muon. Attempts to detect this second particle have failed, so it is generally assumed that it must be a neutrino

$$\pi = \mu + \nu, \tag{10.3.1}$$

where the pion and muon can have either positive or negative charge and the nature of the neutrino is not yet determined,* since the leptonic status of the π meson is unknown. However, if it is assumed that the pion has lepton number *zero*, the negative muon must be associated with an antineutrino and the positive muon with a neutrino proper.

If the principle of conservation of momentum is applied to π-meson decay according to the scheme of Equation (10.3.1), it is found that the energy of the neutrino is approximately 30 MeV and the energy release of the pion decay process is 34 MeV. Assuming that no energy has been lost by any other process, we can find the rest-mass energy of the positively charged pion by adding 34 MeV to the rest-mass energy of the muon, and the result is 139 MeV, or 272 electron masses. This result agrees with independent estimates based on range and magnetic deflection, and more refined experiments have yielded the present value for the pion mass (m_π^+)

$$m_\pi^+ = (273.2 \pm 0.1)\, m_e.$$

The mode of decay leading to emission of a muon is chiefly characteristic of the positively charged π mesons, as has been shown by experiments in which the sign of the charge was found by magnetic deflection. This is because negatively charged π mesons are readily captured by nuclei encountered in dense matter and they give rise to large-scale "star"

---

* Recent evidence indicates that the neutrinos emitted in pion decay differ from those produced by beta decay. Nevertheless the word "neutrino" will be retained as a generic term in this section.

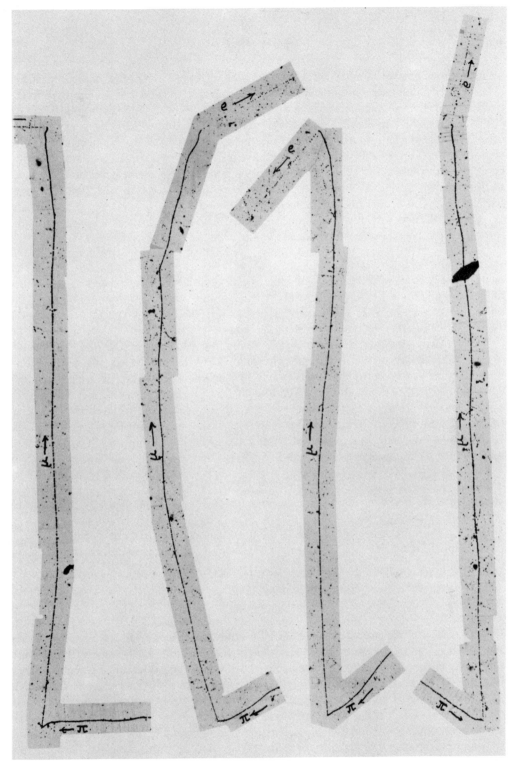

PLATE III. *Four separate examples of the successive decay of a pion into a muon and then into an electron, as recorded in Kodak NT 4 emulsion. In each case the pion (π) comes to rest in the emulsion, then emits a neutrino (which is not recorded) and a muon (μ) of range close to 600 microns. (See Fig. 10.6 for further details of the process.) (From The Study of Elementary Particles by the Photographic Method. C. F. Powell, P. H. Fowler, and D. H. Perkins. New York: Pergamon, 1959, p. 245.)*

465

disintegrations in photographic emulsion. The star is produced by many charged particles being emitted simultaneously in the high-energy disintegration, which effectively disrupts the nucleus. The effect is much more violent than the result of nuclear muon capture [Equation (10.1.1)] and its high probability shows that pions interact strongly with nucleons. This and other evidence suggests that the π meson is the meson predicted by Yukawa's theory of nuclear forces (Section 9.8), although a complete meson theory of strong interactions is still beset by mathematical difficulties. It should be emphasized that the negative pion produces nuclear "explosions" only because of the presence of nucleons. In free flight the same particle decays according to the scheme of Equation (10.3.1).

Although the decay mode of Equation (10.3.1) is dominant in π mesons, it appears possible for the alternative transition to an electron plus neutrino to take place, that is,

$$\pi \rightarrow e + \nu \qquad\qquad [10.3.2]$$

or a similar process with the extra emission of a photon. Calculations based on the theory of weak interactions show that these decay modes must be much less probable than the muon decay and experiments confirm this prediction. The electronic decay occurs, on the average, once in every 8000 pion decays detected.

The fact that π mesons are not commonly found in cosmic rays reaching sea level shows that their intrinsic mean lifetime (in the rest frame) is less than about 10^{-7} sec. A lower limit to the lifetime can be set by the observation that many pions come to rest in photographic emulsion before they decay, indicating that the lifetime is greater than 10^{-9} sec. At the same time, it is very rare for a π meson to be stopped in air or in the gas of an ion counter, so that in the atmosphere the chief result is muon decay for both positive and negative pions. Experiments with artificially produced pions have given an accurate result for the mean lifetime of the particles at rest (see Section 5.5.g)

$$\tau_0 = (2.55 \pm 0.03) \times 10^{-8} \text{ sec.}$$

In dense matter negative pions disappear at a faster rate than this figure would indicate, because of nuclear capture.

In addition to the strong interactions leading to the production of star disintegrations in photographic emulsion, simple pion-nucleon reactions have been studied, including the following:

$$\pi^- + p^+ \rightarrow n^0 + \gamma \qquad\qquad [10.3.3]$$
$$\pi^- + d^+ \rightarrow 2n^0 + \gamma \qquad\qquad [10.3.4]$$
$$\pi^+ + d^+ \rightarrow 2p^+. \qquad\qquad [10.3.5]$$

Examination of these equations, together with Equations (10.3.1) and (10.3.2) representing the pion decay modes, reveals that the spin of the pion must be zero or an integral multiple of $\hbar$; thus the particle is a boson, in agreement with the Yukawa theory of nuclear forces (Section 9.8). Several experiments have shown that the spin is in fact zero, so that in the Klein-Gordon equation [Equation (7.9.2)] the field function ψ may be either scalar (with parity even) or pseudoscalar (with parity odd). It has been mentioned that the pseudoscalar-meson theory of nuclear forces is basically successful in providing the correct types of spin-spin and tensor interactions to account for the ground-state properties of the deuteron. Although other features of the nucleon-nucleon interaction do not appear in the simple meson theory, the pseudoscalar-meson interaction is capable of accounting for many experimental data on pion-nucleon reactions as well as the nucleon-nucleon interaction.

So far we have considered only charged pions, the mesons most easily investigated in cosmic-ray experiments. Pions were produced artificially for the first time in the Berkeley synchro-cyclotron in 1948. Shortly afterwards an energetic gamma radiation was detected coming from the target of the machine. Investigation of this effect showed that pairs of high-energy photons were being emitted from points close to the target area struck by the beam. The estimated energy per photon was 70 MeV, showing that about 140 MeV was being released in the decay of some particle produced in the target. Careful experiments led to the conclusion that the particle travels a short distance before it breaks up into two photons. Accordingly the particle is supposed to be a highly unstable meson, of zero charge and mass close to that of the pions. The neutral pion is therefore characterized by the dominant decay mode

$$\pi^0 \to 2\gamma \qquad\qquad [10.3.6]$$

which accounts for over 98% of decay events, and there is an alternative breakup into a photon and an electron pair

$$\pi^0 \to \gamma + e^+ + e^-. \qquad\qquad [10.3.7]$$

Further experiments have shown that neutral pions are produced when negative pions are captured by protons

$$\pi^- + p^+ \to n^0 + \pi^0. \qquad\qquad [10.3.8]$$

This reaction occurs with slow pions, and the fact that the neutron rest mass is greater than that of the proton serves to prove that the neutral pion must be less massive than the negative pions. Later experiments yield the following result for the neutral pion's rest mass

$$m_{\pi^0} = (264.2 \pm 0.1)\, m_e$$

and the mean lifetime of the particle is

$$(1.8 \pm 0.3) \times 10^{-16} \text{ sec.}$$

Study of the properties of the neutral pions has led to the conclusion that these particles have spin zero, with *odd* intrinsic parity (that is, their Klein-Gordon function is pseudoscalar), and that they interact strongly with nucleons. Their general similarity to the charged pions, in all respects except their much shorter lifetime, indicates that the three particles are to be regarded as a group, in accordance with early views on the nature of nucleon-nucleon interactions (Section 9.8). Furthermore it is possible to extend the concept of isospin (Section 9.6.c) to describe some of the properties of the pions. It is conventional to allot the following *t* numbers to the different particles

$$t = +1 \qquad \text{for } \pi^+$$
$$t = 0 \qquad \text{for } \pi^0$$
$$t = -1 \qquad \text{for } \pi^-$$

the entire scheme forming a $T = 1$ isospin vector, in analogy with a quantized spin vector $J = 1$. This formalism is consistent with pion-nucleon interactions which are in agreement with experimental results.

(b) *K mesons or kaons*

The *K* mesons form a group of massive mesons which were identified first in studies of cosmic rays at high altitudes. Rochester and Butler discovered rare cases of neutral "*V* particles," which decayed in a cloud chamber to yield two charged particles per event, the product particles being identified as pions

$$K^0 \to \pi^+ + \pi^-. \qquad\qquad [10.3.9]$$

The neutral K particle must therefore possess a rest mass greater than 550 m_e, the measured energy release being such that the calculated mass is about 1000 m_e.

Shortly after the discovery of V particles in the meson mass range, photographic-emulsion studies revealed the occurrence of rare events in which a charged particle decays to give three charged pions (Plate IV), according to the scheme

$$K^\pm \to \pi^\pm + \pi^+ + \pi^-. \qquad\qquad [10.3.10]$$

This type of K particle was known as the τ *meson* for several years, its mass being estimated as 966 m_e and its mean lifetime as 1.2×10^{-8} sec. During this period much information was acquired concerning mesons in the K mass range, but the evidence appeared to be conflicting because the K particles possess many different decay modes of comparable probability and at the time each decay mode was assigned to a single type of particle. Moreover it was found that, if parity is conserved in all the different decay processes, opposite parities must be assigned to K mesons of very similar mass. The dilemma was not resolved until 1956 when Lee and Yang pointed out that parity may not be conserved in weak-interaction processes such as those represented by Equations (10.3.9) and (10.3.10). This hypothesis received support from experiments on beta decay (see Section 10.7) and later the nonconservation of parity was shown to be characteristic of all weak interactions. This result enables us to ascribe all K decays to a single group of mesons (positive, neutral, and negative) with masses

$$m_{K^0} = (974.5 \pm 0.4)m_e \qquad \text{Neutral}$$
$$m_K = (966.3 \pm 0.4)m_e \qquad \text{Charged.}$$

At this stage another acute problem is raised by the observed mean lifetimes of kaons, which are in the region of 10^{-10} to 10^{-8} sec, characteristic of weak-interaction decays. It is found that kaons are produced copiously in many high-energy reactions involving pions and nucleons, the yield being indicative of strong interactions between kaons and the other reacting particles. Why, therefore, does a kaon not decay very rapidly into pions? In fact the pion-yielding processes represented by Equations (10.3.9) and (10.3.10) are of comparable probability with K decays into muons and other leptons, which do not have any strong interactions at all. This dilemma resulted in kaons being classified, with the massive *hyperons*, as "strange" particles which are inhibited from rapid decay by a new type of selection rule (see Section 10.6).

Further complications arise when the decay rate of the neutral kaon is studied. Two-pion decay processes [Equation (10.3.9)] are characterized by a mean lifetime in the region of 10^{-10} sec. If, however, a beam of neutral kaons is allowed to travel more than a few centimeters from its point of origin, different modes of decay are observed. These modes include the production of three pions (two charged and one neutral or three neutral) and various mixtures of a pion with muons, electrons, and neutrinos. The mean lifetime for these slow processes is about 10^{-7} sec, or a thousand times longer than the two-pion decay lifetime. The reason for this double lifetime effect is found in the existence of an antiparticle ($\bar{K}^\circ$) distinct from the neutral kaon (K°). The particles K° and $\bar{K}^\circ$ have the same mass and their properties are similar except in the "strangeness" number (see Section 10.6). Moreover, they can be converted one into the other at a slow rate. The net result is that different mixtures of K° and $\bar{K}^\circ$ can form the short-lived neutral kaon (usually written K_1°) or the long-lived neutral kaon (usually written K_2°).

As stated above, the long-lived neutral component of a kaon beam is characterized by decay into three pions or into a pion plus leptons. Recently experiments have indicated a

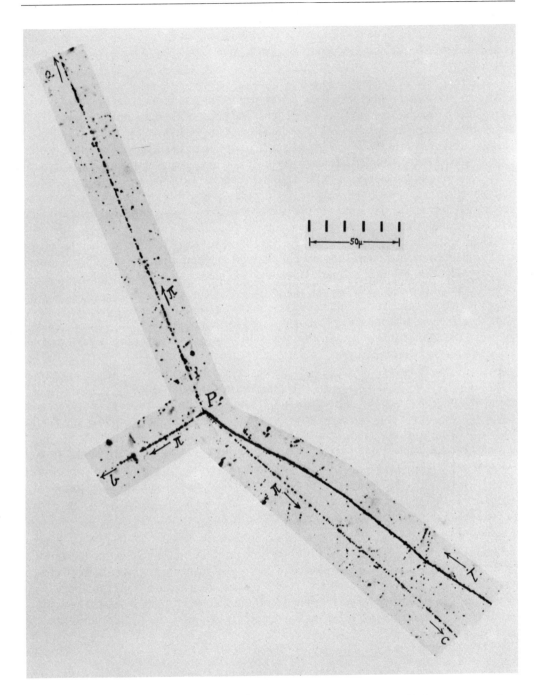

PLATE IV. *At the point P a slow charged kaon (marked τ in the photograph) decays to give three charged pions, all four tracks being recorded in (Ilford G 5 emulsion). Estimates of the energies of the emitted particles show that the rest mass of the kaon was close to 960 electron rest masses. (From The Study of Elementary Particles by the Photographic Method. C. F. Powell, P. H. Fowler, and D. H. Perkins. New York: Pergamon, 1959, p. 292.)*

rare mode of decay by K_2° into two pions, a process which is forbidden in current theories of weak interactions. The significance of such a mode of decay, now experimentally established, will be discussed briefly in Section 10.7.

(c) Highly unstable mesons

An immense amount of research work was devoted to establishing the existence of two major meson groups—the pions and the kaons. Members of these groups are bosons with zero spin and they interact strongly with nucleons. However the decay processes of these particles are comparatively slow, with the single exception of the disintegration of a neutral pion into two photons—an electromagnetic process. The experimental methods used in the early work were suitable only for detecting those particles with lifetimes exceeding 10^{-15} sec approximately. The question now arises whether there are further types of meson possessing very short lifetimes, of the order of 10^{-20} sec or less. Such highly unstable particles might well be produced in strong-interaction processes which lead eventually to pion or kaon production. If, however, their lifetimes are very short they will disintegrate before leaving an identifiable track in a bubble chamber or photographic emulsion. It is therefore necessary to apply statistical methods to find out whether the pions and kaons are produced singly or via some intermediate particle.

By 1960 a great deal of information had been acquired from the Berkeley bubble chambers and other instruments concerning the multiple production of pions, notably from processes involving the annihilation of antiprotons (Plate VII). In one investigation Alvarez and his collaborators* analyzed 800 events of the type

$$p + \bar{p} \rightarrow 2\pi^+ + 2\pi^- + \pi^\circ \qquad [10.3.11]$$

with particular reference to the production of pions in threes. Each event yields five pions and a group of three pions can be selected from these in 10 ways, of which four correspond to a net charge of zero (π^+, π^-, π°). If an uncharged intermediate meson produces such a triplet (Plate V), its mass should be calculable from the experimental data, specifically from the expression

$$M_3 c^2 = [(E_1 + E_2 + E_3)^2 - c^2(\mathbf{P}_1 + \mathbf{P}_2 + \mathbf{P}_3)^2]^{1/2},$$

where E_1, E_2, E_3 stand for the total energies of the pions, $\mathbf{P}_1, \mathbf{P}_2, \mathbf{P}_3$ are their respective linear momenta, and M_3 is the rest mass of the hypothetical intermediate meson. However, for every significant value of M_3 calculated from the experimental data, there must be three meaningless values of M_3 obtained by incorrect identification of the pions forming the triplet. When the values of M_3 are plotted in the form of histogram (Figure 10.3) it is found that the great majority of the points form a random distribution, corresponding to the dotted line. Superimposed on the random distribution, however, there is a sharp peak which is interpreted as evidence of a highly unstable uncharged meson, the ω° meson, breaking up according to the scheme

$$\omega^\circ \rightarrow \pi^+ + \pi^- + \pi^\circ. \qquad [10.3.12]$$

This result is confirmed by analysis of other processes in which pions are produced in groups, for example, the production of seven pions by antiproton annihilation (Figure 10.3)†. Again one finds evidence of a peak in the distribution of M_3 values and this peak agrees with the previous data. The ω° meson is now assigned a rest-mass energy of (783 ± 2) MeV and, since this is the only meson found in this region, the isospin number T is zero. The proper

* B. C. Majlic, L. W. Alvarez, A. H. Rosenfeld, and M. L. Stevenson, Phys. Rev. Letters, **7**, 178 (1961).
† N. H. Xuong and G. R. Lynch, Phys. Rev. Letters, **7**, 327 (1961).

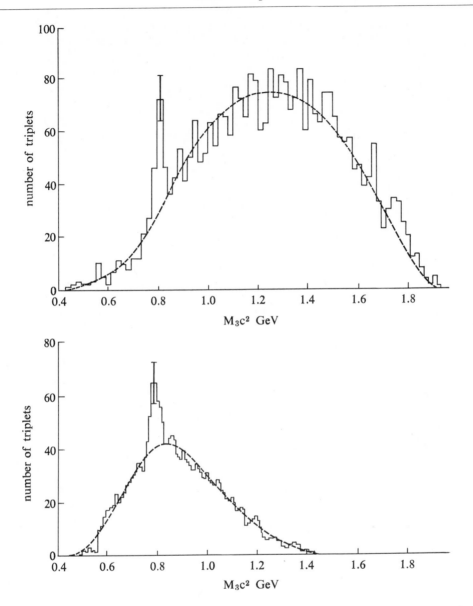

FIGURE 10.3 *Histograms showing the distribution of values of the triplet-pion mass energy (M_3c^2 in GeV) obtained when the results of pion-producing reactions are analyzed. The upper graph represents the data of Majlic, Alvarez, Rosenfeld, and Stevenson on events in which 5 pions are emitted; the lower graph shows the data of Xuong and Lynch on events producing 7 pions each. In both cases there is a random distribution, indicated by the dotted line, and a superimposed peak at 0.8 GeV. The peak is interpreted in terms of the ω° resonant state which breaks up very rapidly to yield three pions ($\pi^+ + \pi^- + \pi^\circ$).*

spin and parity of the ω° meson have to be determined by detailed study of the modes of disintegration. The spin number is 1 and the parity is odd, corresponding to a *vector* meson. The mean lifetime can be roughly estimated from the width of the peak in the observed distribution of M_3 values and is found to be greater than 5×10^{-23} sec.

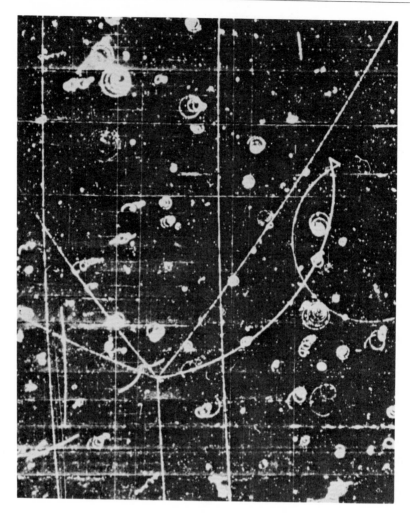

PLATE V.   *A bubble-chamber event characteristic of the ω° resonance state. An antiproton $(\bar{p})$ enters the field of view from the bottom and annihilates with a proton to form two pions plus an omega particle of very short lifetime. The omega particle decays rapidly into two charged pions and a neutral pion. Details of the process, as reconstructed from study of many such events, are shown in the facsimiles on the right. (From Ford, The World of Elementary Particles.*
New York: Blaisdell, 1963, pp. 182–183.)

The ω° meson is only one of numerous unstable "particles" which have now been discovered in reactions involving pions, kaons, and baryons.* Another unstable vector meson, the ρ meson, has been identified in two-pion processes; the rest-mass energy of the ρ meson is (757 ± 5) MeV and its isospin number is 1. In addition there are several K^* particles, breaking up into various combinations of kaons and pions. These "resonance" particles may play an important role in nucleon-nucleon interactions, certain features of which are not readily explained by the Yukawa theory (see Section 9.8). It is probable that a satisfactory theory of strong interactions must embrace the short-lived mesons as well as the better known pions and kaons.

* R. D. Hill, "Resonance Particles," *Scientific American*, **208**, No. 1, 39 (1963).

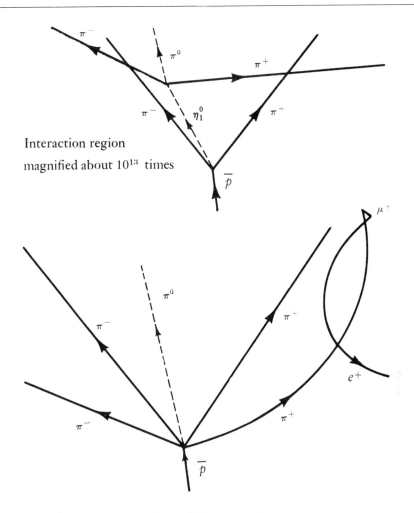

Interaction region
magnified about 10^{13} times

PLATE V (*continued.*)

10.4 Hyperons

The first hyperon to be identified was the neutral *lambda particle*, found among the "*V* particles" of Rochester and Butler. Some of their cloud-chamber photographs yielded evidence of a neutral particle decaying into a pion plus a proton, according to the equation

$$\Lambda^\circ \to \pi^- + p^+. \tag{10.4.1}$$

The rest mass of the lambda particle is found to be

$$m_\Lambda = (2182.8 \pm 0.2)m_e.$$

An alternative decay mode has been established

$$\Lambda^\circ \to \pi^\circ + n^\circ \tag{10.4.2}$$

with a frequency of occurrence (34 ± 3%) which is close to half of the frequency of the charged decay mode (66 ± 3%). Both modes of disintegration indicate that the lambda particle may be a fermion with spin $\frac{1}{2}\hbar$, as has been shown by more detailed analysis. If the baryon number (B) is to be conserved in these processes we must ascribe a baryon number +1 (like that of the neutron or proton) to the new particle.

The mean lifetime of the lambda particle at rest is estimated as (2.62 ± 0.02) × 10^{-10} sec, which is comparatively long on the nuclear scale. Indeed detailed comparison with other neutral-particle decays indicates that the lambda-particle disintegrations [Equations (10.4.1) and (10.4.2)] are due to weak interactions only. This feature is characteristic of nearly all the hyperons (unstable particles more massive than the nucleon) discussed in this section. At the same time, hyperons are produced copiously in many particle reactions above 1 GeV input energy. This observation raises the same kind of difficulty already encountered in connection with the kaons (Section 10.3.b) and introduces the concept of "strangeness" (see Section 10.6).

The most striking new property exhibited by the lambda particles is a capacity for being absorbed temporarily by a complex nucleus to form a "hyperfragment," which has a lifetime long enough for the whole nucleus to recoil from its point of origin in some high-energy reaction and to stop in matter before breaking up (Plate VI). For example, the nucleus H^3 can pick up a lambda particle and form the hyperfragment $_\Lambda$H^4 which has zero spin and finally disintegrates with an energy release corresponding to a binding energy of 1.8 MeV

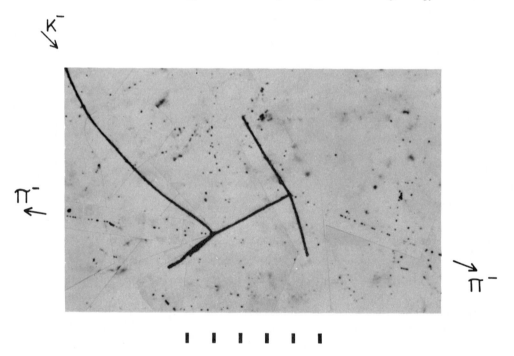

PLATE VI. *The capture of a slow K$^-$ particle by an oxygen nucleus in Ilford K 5 emulsion leading to the emission of a negative pion (to the left), several baryons (lower left) and a $_\Lambda$Li$_3^7$ hyperfragment. The hyperfragment traveled a short distance in the emulsion before disintegrating at rest to yield a second negative pion plus He^4 and He^3 nuclei emitted in nearly opposite directions. (The scale divisions are 10 microns apart.) (From The Study of Elementary Particles by the Photographic Method. C. F. Powell, P. H. Fowler, and D. H. Perkins. New York: Pergamon, 1959, p. 389.)*

for the lambda particle. The hyperfragment is similar in its properties to the nucleus He^4; thus the hyperon acts very much like a nucleon, except in its energy relations and its final disintegration into a pion plus nucleon. The hyperfragment evidence shows that the lambda particle is attracted by nuclei and that its rate of decay is not greatly affected by the near presence of nucleons, despite the fact that nucleon-nucleon collisions produce lambdas in large quantities. This fact again emphasizes the strange properties of the new particles.

Charged hyperons have been discovered both in cosmic rays and in the products of high-energy reactions in the laboratory. *Sigma particles* are found with decay modes yielding nucleons and pions. The negative sigma has a single mode of decay

$$\Sigma^- \to n^\circ + \pi^- \qquad [10.4.3]$$

with a mean lifetime of $(1.58 \pm 0.05) \times 10^{-10}$ sec and a rest mass

$$m_{\Sigma^-} = (2342.6 \pm 0.4)m_e.$$

The positively charged sigma exhibits two modes of decay with almost equal frequencies of occurrence

$$\Sigma^+ \to n^\circ + \pi^+ \qquad [10.4.4]$$
$$\Sigma^+ \to p^+ + \pi^\circ \qquad [10.4.5]$$

and possesses a mean lifetime of $(0.788 \pm 0.027) \times 10^{-10}$ sec. The rest mass is significantly lower than that of the negatively charged sigma particle, although the difference is not so great that their family resemblance is obscured

$$m_{\Sigma^+} = (2327.6 \pm 0.3)m_e.$$

This difference in mass is sufficient to show that the positive and negative sigmas are *not* antiparticles of each other, a conclusion which is supported by the observation that their decay modes lead to production of ordinary nucleons (not the antiparticles).

A neutral sigma particle has been identified by its decay into a photon plus a lambda particle

$$\Sigma^\circ \to \gamma + \Lambda^\circ \qquad [10.4.6]$$

which is a fast electromagnetic reaction with a very short lifetime (much less than 10^{-12} sec). The mass of Σ° falls into line between the masses of the other two sigma particles

$$m_{\Sigma^\circ} = (2333.2 \pm 0.6)m_e.$$

A negatively charged "cascade" hyperon or *xi particle* was found in cloud-chamber pictures showing a charged particle decaying into a neutral particle plus a pion, the neutral particle then giving two charged particles within a period of the order of 10^{-10} sec. The data were consistent with the neutral particle being a lambda particle, so the first decay is written

$$\Xi^- \to \pi^- + \Lambda^\circ. \qquad [10.4.7]$$

Like the other hyperons, the xi particle appears to be a baryon with spin $\frac{1}{2}\hbar$, and the mean lifetime is of the order of 10^{-10} sec. The rest mass of the charged Ξ is

$$m_{\Xi^-} = (2584.7 \pm 0.4)m_e$$

and there is also a neutral hyperon of similar mass, detected by the disintegration mode

$$\Xi^\circ \to \pi^\circ + \Lambda^\circ \qquad [10.4.8]$$

with a mean lifetime of approximately 4×10^{-15} sec.

Recently evidence has been found for the existence of anti-xi particles, in line with the Dirac theory of fermions (Section 7.9), according to which all such particles should have antiparticles which are distinct from the "proper" particles in some important respect. In terms of charge, the particle and antiparticle must be opposed, as in the electron case, but neutral particles require further analysis. In the case of the neutron, the magnetic moments are presumably opposed, in the sense that the neutron proper has moment antiparallel to the spin while the antineutron has moment and spin parallel. In the hyperon cases, particles and antiparticles are distinguished by different decay modes: thus whereas a lambda particle decays into a pion plus a proton [Equation (10.4.1)] the antilambda particle yields a pion plus an antiproton:

$$\overline{\Lambda}^\circ \rightarrow \pi^+ + (\bar{p})^-.$$ [10.4.9]

This result is required by baryon conservation, since, by definition of an antiparticle, the antiproton must have baryon number -1 and the antilambda likewise.

In addition to the hyperons described above, all with lifetimes in the measurable region around 10^{-10} sec, there are highly unstable pion-hyperon and pion-nucleon combinations which are identified by the methods used in studying highly unstable mesons (Section 10.3.c). It has been known for some years that a nucleon plus pion can form a short-lived resonance with spin $I = \frac{3}{2}$, isospin $T = \frac{3}{2}$, and total energy 1238 MeV. Many more high energy states of pions and kaons with nucleons and hyperons are now known, all possessing half-odd integral spins and very short lifetimes in the region of 10^{-20} sec. The problem of classifying these particle states is discussed in Section 10.6.

10.5 Antiparticles

The concept of an antiparticle arises from the basic relativistic relation between the total energy (E) and linear momentum (P) of any particle with rest mass m_0

$$E^2 = P^2c^2 + m_0^2c^4.$$ [Equation (5.6.5)]

This equation can be solved for E with either positive or negative results; moreover, if P is zero in some particular reference frame, we obtain the solutions $E = \pm m_0c^2$. We can picture the negative energy states as separated from the positive energy states by a gap of width $2m_0c^2$ (as in Figure 7.17) unless $m_0 = 0$, when the entire range of energies is accessible. In classical mechanics negative energy states are always inaccessible for particles of finite rest mass because energy changes are assumed to be continuous (in principle), so that discontinuous changes of large magnitude can be ruled out. Such discontinuous changes are possible in quantum mechanics and any relativistic scheme, such as that of Dirac (Section 7.9), has to take the negative energy states into account. Dirac's tentative solution to this problem was to assume that under normal circumstances all negative energy states are filled for the electron proper. When a "hole" is created in the band of filled negative energy states, this hole acts like an antiparticle, that is, a positron in Dirac's case. This type of theory can be regarded as a working model which makes calculations possible for fermion interactions involving antiparticles.

It is known that the Dirac theory cannot be applied rigorously to nucleons, since their magnetic moments are "anomalous" (see Section 9.7), presumably because of meson effects. Nevertheless the nucleons, being fermions, should have formal properties similar to those of the electron and should possess antiparticles. For many years these *antinucleons* remained undiscovered despite several attempts to detect them in cosmic rays and in nuclear experiments. It is clear that the conservation of baryon numbers would require that energy spent in creating an antiproton, for example, must produce a complete "proton pair," analogous to the emission of electron pairs by photons

$$\Delta E \to p^+ + (\bar{p})^-,$$ [10.5.1]

where ΔE is the energy lost by reacting particles. In this equation the baryon number is zero on the left and the sum of baryon numbers must therefore be zero on the right. The situation is entirely similar to the conversion of a photon into an electron pair

$$\gamma \to e^+ + e^-$$ [10.5.2]

in which the lepton number is conserved throughout.

If a proton pair is to be produced, the energy needed is 1880 MeV in the center-of-mass coordinates of reacting particles and this requires a still higher kinetic energy of proton

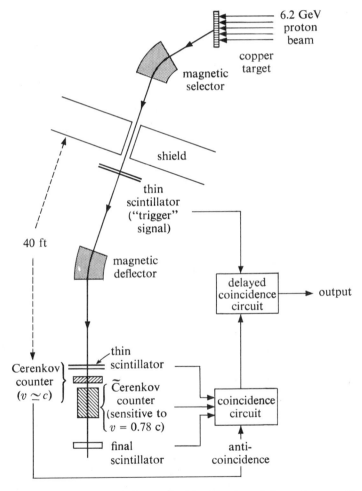

FIGURE 10.4 *Apparatus used at Berkeley in the identification of the antiproton. Negative protons emitted from the synchrotron target passed through an elaborate selection system to ensure their detection despite the presence of a heavy meson background.*

p?
500 µ   45 MeV π⁻   π 90 MeV

P
23 MeV

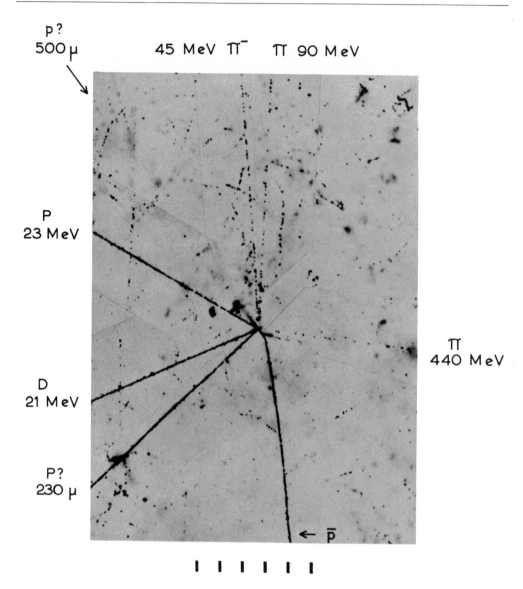

π
440 MeV

D
21 MeV

P?
230 µ

← p̄

PLATE VII. *An antiproton (p̄) generated by the Berkeley Bevatron stops in Ilford G 5 emulsion and is annihilated by a complex nucleus with the emission of at least 3 pions (marked π), probably 3 protons (p) and a deuteron (d). (The scale division are 10 microns apart.) (From The Study of Elementary Particles by the Photographic Method. C. F. Powell, P. H. Fowler, and D. H. Perkins. New York: Pergamon, 1959, p. 407.)*

bombardment if the pairs are to be made in nucleon-nucleon collisions. According to Equation (9.1.6) the proton energy in the laboratory system must be $6m_0c^2 = 5.6$ GeV before antiprotons can be created. The first accelerator to reach this level was the Bevatron at Berkeley and antiprotons were identified among the products of high-energy reactions at 6.2 GeV in 1956.* Experimental difficulties of a high order had to be overcome before the identification could be regarded as certain. Numerous negatively charged particles of

* E. Segré and C. E. Wiegand, "The Anti-Proton," *Sci. Am.*, **194**, No. 6, 37 (1956).

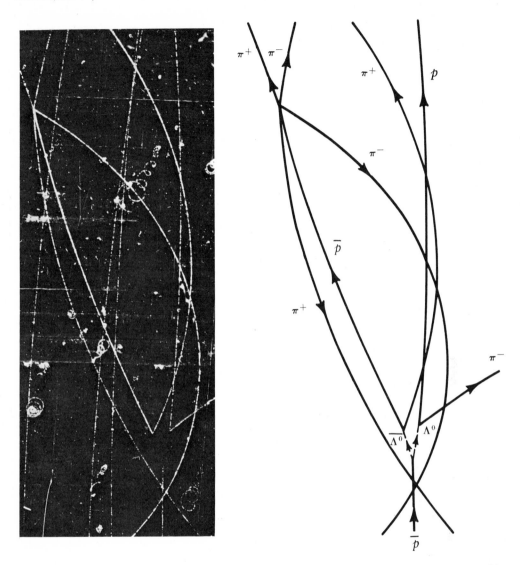

PLATE VIII. *An antiproton ($\bar{p}$) enters a bubble chamber and annihilates with a proton to yield a lambda particle and an antilambda particle. The lambda particle decays into a proton plus a negative pion while its antiparticle produces an antiproton plus a positive pion. The second antiproton travels a short way in the liquid before being annihilated to produce several pions. Details of the processes are shown in facsimile on the right. (From Ford, The World of Elementary Particles. New York: Blaisdell, 1963, pp. 20–21.)*

high momentum, for example, pions and kaons, are emitted from targets bombarded by 6.2 GeV protons and it was found that about 40,000 background particles were present for each antiproton detected.

The apparatus used in the first antiproton experiments is shown schematically in Figure 10.4. The proton beam struck a copper target and the negatively charged particles emitted were first passed through a magnetic-deflection system which selected the particles with the correct momentum, as estimated for antiprotons produced by the "proton-pair" process.

The selected particles were focused into a beam passing through a heavy shield and into a thin scintillation counter which acted as the "trigger" for a velocity-measuring system. The particles traveled a distance of 40 ft *in vacuo* and were deflected a second time before they reached the final counter assembly. Here scintillation counters working in delayed coincidence with the first "trigger" counter were able to sort out the particles with the correct velocity, calculated for antiprotons with the momentum already selected. This velocity was close to 0.78 c, whereas pions and kaons of the same momentum have velocities approaching the velocity of light (c). Although the scintillation-counter system was theoretically capable of identifying genuine antiprotons by itself, since the velocity and momentum were both measured, it was found that spurious events could still be recorded, owing to the very heavy background of unwanted particles. Accordingly, a Čerenkov counter (Section 9.2.c) was included in the final counter assembly and was arranged to be sensitive to particles with speed 0.78 c ($\pm 3\%$). This counter worked in coincidence with the scintillation counters whereas a second Čerenkov counter, insensitive to particles with speed 0.78 c, worked in anticoincidence with the other counters. In this way a very elaborate checking scheme was set up and the final counting rate, of about four events per hour of machine time, was definitely due to antiprotons. Other experiments led to the identification of antineutrons emitted from the target and showed that antinucleons produce characteristic disintegrations when stopped in matter. Whereas electron-pair annihilation always produces photons [Equation (4.9.9)], the annihilation of antinucleons with nucleons usually leads to multiple pion production, since a great deal of energy is available and strong interactions (involving mesons) are presumably favored (Plate VII).

The identification of antihyperons by their characteristic decay modes has already been mentioned (Section 10.4). On occasion the annihilation of an antiproton with a proton produces a pair of hyperons, for example, lambda plus antilambda (Plate VIII). All known fermions have been shown to possess antiparticles and are therefore described formally by Dirac's equation, with the possible exception of the neutrino and antineutrino which are discussed in Section 10.7.

The situation is quite different when bosons are considered, because the "hole" theory of antiparticles cannot be applied. Nevertheless positively charged particles (such as π^+ and K^+) can still be regarded as antiparticles to their negative counterparts (π^- and K^-). The uncharged photon and pion are taken to be identical with their antiparticles and this is borne out by decay modes of the known antihyperons. The neutral kaons form a special group in which the particle (K°) and its antiparticle ($\bar{K}^\circ$) can transform into each other, the net result being two different decay rates (ascribed to K_1° and K_2° "particles") for neutral kaons produced in high-energy reactions (see Section 10.3.b).

10.6 Particle Classification and "Strangeness"

During the years following the discovery of pi mesons and V particles, much experimental information was amassed about different particles and their decay modes. Some simplification was achieved in 1956 when it was realized that parity is not conserved in weak interactions, such as those responsible for beta decay and the decay of most mesons and hyperons. It then became possible for the various particles to be regrouped into "leptons" (neutrino, electron, muon), "mesons" (pion, kaon), and "baryons" (nucleon, hyperons), with the photon in a class apart. This type of grouping is shown in Appendix V, where the most important properties of each particle are listed. It should be emphasized that such listings are of temporary value only, because further developments, notably in the meson and neutrino fields, should add considerably to our knowledge of unstable particles.

When the properties of the known particles are studied, the chief regularities appear in the spin (which is zero for mesons of moderate stability, $\frac{1}{2}\hbar$ for leptons and baryons, and $\hbar$ for the photon), and in the charge. The fact that all charged particles carry the same elementary charge suggests that electromagnetic interactions, that is, photon-particle interactions, fall into a separate category. Electromagnetic interactions are known to be much stronger than the weak interactions detected in beta decay, but they are not so strong as the meson-nucleon interactions which are assumed to be responsible for nuclear forces. The difference emerges when the concept of isospin is studied (see Section 9.6.c). The isospin number T is conserved in strong interactions, and therefore has a partial validity in all nuclear processes, but it is not conserved in electromagnetic interactions. We see, therefore, that in this case, at least, the extent to which a conservation rule is obeyed depends on the strength of interactions. The only quantities which are absolutely conserved, in processes investigated so far, are the charge number (q), the lepton number (L), and baryon number (B), in addition to the mechanical properties measured as energy, linear momentum and angular momentum.

If we write the component of isospin (T) represented by a particular particle as the number t, we can assign $t = \frac{1}{2}$ to the proton, $t = -\frac{1}{2}$ to the neutron, and proceed to analyze nuclear states in terms of the "T multiplets" (see Section 9.9.d). The charge number of a nucleon (q) can therefore be written

$$q = \tfrac{1}{2} + t. \tag{10.6.1}$$

When antiparticles are considered, this equation must be generalized by the introduction of the baryon number B, which is $+1$ for nucleons proper and -1 for antinucleons. Then with $t = \frac{1}{2}$ for the antineutron and $t = -\frac{1}{2}$ for the antiproton, the equation

$$q = \tfrac{1}{2}B + t \tag{10.6.2}$$

will fit all cases involving nucleons.

It has been mentioned that isospin numbers (t) can be assigned to π mesons (see Section 10.3.a), for which the baryon number $B = 0$ so that we obtain $q = t$. This assignment has wide application in strong-interaction processes involving pions and nucleons, since the total isospin number (T) is conserved in such processes. However, the equation (10.6.2) cannot be applied to either kaons or hyperons, which are regarded as *strange* particles because they have properties appearing at first sight to be paradoxical.

The most remarkable experimental observation about strange particles is that they are produced in great abundance by high-energy reactions, but always *in pairs*, that is, if we get one strange particle of some kind there must be a simultaneous emission of a different strange particle. A typical reaction producing strange particles is

$$\pi^- + p^+ \rightarrow \Lambda^\circ + K^\circ \tag{10.6.3}$$

and the yield is so high that the reaction must be ascribed to a strong interaction. We should then expect the product particles to decay by strong interactions in a very short time, but this is not observed. Instead the decay rate of individual strange particles is very slow, except in the case of Σ° which can decay to a photon and a lambda particle [Equation (10.4.6)].

The rule of *associated production* of strange particles together with their slow rate of decay suggests that there is a conservation rule to be satisfied under conditions of strong interaction, in processes like that of Equation (10.6.3), but not in weak interactions. Such a rule should be able to explain slow rates of decay as due to "forbidden" transitions, analogous to the beta-decay processes which are not allowed by the Fermi and Gamow-Teller selection rules but are nevertheless observed with appreciable frequency. The new rule should also account for the *absence* of associated production reactions such as

$$n^0 + p^+ \not\rightarrow \Lambda^0 + \Sigma^+ \qquad [10.6.4]$$

which does not violate any of the rules previously mentioned, but is not observed.

A successful scheme for dealing with the problem of strange particles was introduced independently by Gell-Mann and Nishijima. A new quantum number S, called the *strangeness* number, is defined by the equation

$$S = 2(q - \tfrac{1}{2}B - t) \qquad [10.6.5]$$

and S is supposed to be conserved in all strong-interaction processes. The number S is automatically zero for all pions and nucleons, by virtue of Equation (10.6.2); therefore all strong-interaction transitions which conserve energy, charge, momentum, baryon number, and angular momentum are *allowed* for pions and nucleons in the new scheme.

The S values for hyperons are worked out as follows. The lambda particle has $B = 1$ and it appears to be a solitary particle in the grouping of particles by mass, so we surmise that $T = 0$ and obtain $S = -1$. The sigma particles also have $B = 1$, but there are three of them, close together in mass, so we assume that they form a $T = 1$ triad, with $t = +1$, 0, -1 for the charge numbers $q = +1$, 0, -1, and this indicates that $S = -1$ for any sigma particle. The xi particles are known in negatively charged and neutral forms, so we postulate that $t = -\tfrac{1}{2}$ for the particle with $q = -1$ and that $t = +\tfrac{1}{2}$ for the neutral particle, the pair forming a $T = \tfrac{1}{2}$ diad. This yields $S = -2$ for the xi particles and we see that the transition from a xi particle to a nucleon (with $S = 0$) is doubly forbidden, whereas the transition to a lambda particle plus pion [Equation (10.4.7)] is singly forbidden. This situation enables the xi particle to decay by weak interaction to a lambda particle, and thence to a nucleon, forming the "cascade" process; but direct transition to a nucleon has not been observed.

In the Gell-Mann classification of particles, the K mesons are split into two groups, of opposite strangeness. Thus the K^+ particle is supposed to have $t = \tfrac{1}{2}$, which, with $B = 0$, yields $S = +1$, while the negative kaon has $t = -\tfrac{1}{2}$ and $S = -1$. There are two forms of the neutral kaon, as previously mentioned, and these are written K^0 (with $S = +1$) and $\bar{K}^0$ (with $S = -1$). This scheme illustrates the general result that the strangeness number changes sign when we pass from a particle to its antiparticle, a rule which is observed in the hyperons as well as the kaons. The classification of particles according to their strangeness and isospin numbers can then be carried out, as shown in Table 10.1, where strangeness values from -2 to $+2$ and isospin numbers $T = 0$, $\tfrac{1}{2}$, and 1 are included. It is seen that many of the known particles fall into place with no overlapping, but there are still gaps in the scheme and it might be extended to higher values of S.

Although the fundamental basis of the strangeness classification is not understood, the scheme has been of great value in interpreting experimental results. Associated production of strange particles by strong interactions is required by the condition that the particles available for beam production are usually those with $S = 0$. Thus if we bombard nucleons with nucleons or pions, the strange particles must be produced in pairs with opposed strangeness, for example, $\Lambda^0 + K^0$, as in Equation (10.6.3). It is not possible to obtain a lambda plus a sigma particle [Equation (10.6.4)] without violating the conservation of strangeness number. The cascade decay of the xi particles has already been explained. In

TABLE 10.1
Gell-Mann Classification of Particles

Strangeness: $S =$		-2	-1	0	$+1$	$+2$
Isospin: T						
0	$t = 0$		Λ^0		$\overline{\Lambda}^0$	
$\frac{1}{2}$	$\begin{cases} t = +\frac{1}{2} \\ t = -\frac{1}{2} \end{cases}$	Ξ^0 Ξ^-	$\overline{K}^0$ K^-	$(p, \bar{n})$ $(n, \bar{p})$	K^+ K^0	$\overline{\Xi}^+$ Ξ°
1	$\begin{cases} t = +1 \\ t = 0 \\ t = -1 \end{cases}$		Σ^+ Σ^0 Σ^-	π^+ π^0 π^-	$\overline{\Sigma}^+$ $\overline{\Sigma}^0$ $\overline{\Sigma}^-$	

general, a strange particle does not decay rapidly unless it meets a particle of the opposite strangeness, which cannot occur in ordinary matter. It follows that all strange particles must decay by weak interactions unless an electromagnetic decay mode is available, for example Equation (10.4.6), and this is possible only when the strangeness is the same for both decaying and product particles.

Other reactions brought under the strangeness rules include the kaon-induced reactions. When K^- particles are used to induce disintegrations, hyperons are the most likely products since these have $S = -1$, like the K^- particle. Use of the K^+ particles as projectiles does not lead to many reactions unless the energy is so high that antihyperons can be made. This kind of difference between K^- and K^+ behavior appears also in reactions producing the kaons. Thus a K^+ is readily generated by pion-nucleon reactions, for example,

$$\pi^+ + n^0 \rightarrow \Lambda^0 + K^+, \qquad [10.6.6]$$

where the total S is zero on both sides. The similar process producing negative kaons

$$\pi^- + n^0 \rightarrow K^- + K^0 + n^0 \qquad [10.6.7]$$

requires more energy than the previous reaction, so in practice the positive kaons predominate in production by strong interactions.

So far we have considered only the classification of particles with fairly long lifetimes, much longer than 10^{-20} sec, which is the approximate lifetime of the highly unstable mesons and baryons discovered by resonance methods. Evidently a broader classification than the scheme of Table 10.1 is needed to embrace all the particles and particle states now known. If the weakly-interacting leptons and the solitary photon are ignored, it is possible to organize the remaining strongly interacting particles into two groups, described generically as the "boson" group (including all strongly interacting mesons) and the "baryon" group (including all hyperon and nucleon states).† In this scheme, states of the same strangeness number (S) are arranged in the same vertical column, in order of increasing total energy. Thus the nucleon ground state, of energy 938 MeV and represented by the neutron and proton, is succeeded by various N* states, including the pion-nucleon resonance with spin $I = \frac{3}{2}$ at 1238 MeV. The hyperon states of strangeness $S = -1$ commence with the sigma and lambda particles, which are succeeded by various Y* states. Transitions between the different energy levels are of two kinds: the rapid strangeness-conserving changes involving emission or absorption of a pion and the slower changes

† V. F. Weisskopf, *Physics Today*, **16**, No. 6, 26 (1963).

involving emission or absorption of a kaon, which requires S to change by one and is therefore allowed only in weak-interaction processes.

An alternative method of classifying meson and baryon states is the octet model or "eightfold way" of Ne'eman and Gell-Mann.* In this scheme, which is based on the properties of the SU3 group of transformations, states of the same spin and parity are arranged in multiplets of 8, 10, and possibly (at high excitations) 27. Thus the group of pseudoscalar mesons (written 0^-) consists of eight states—the three pions, four kaons, and one η meson. Vector mesons (written 1^-) also constitute an octet—the single ω meson, three ρ-meson states, and four K^* states. The long-lived baryon group, of spin $\frac{1}{2}$ and even parity (written $\frac{1}{2}^+$), form an octet of particles (neutron, proton, lambda, three sigmas, and two xis) and an octet of antiparticles. A group of ten baryon states of spin $\frac{3}{2}$ and even parity, called a decuplet, has recently been completed by the identification of a predicted particle of strangeness $S = -3$ and comparatively long lifetime—the Ω^- particle of total energy 1680 MeV.† The most important feature of the octet-decuplet model is its specification of numerical relations between the rest-mass energies of particles within one group and these relations have been verified by observation.

The comparative success of the octet model in correlating many experimental results concerning strongly interacting particles is probably significant in revealing the existence of fundamental order beneath the complexity of phenomena. Before this order can be traced, it is necessary to obtain more information about weak interactions and the role of the neutrino in these processes.

10.7 Neutrinos and Nonconservation of Parity‡

The various particle reactions and disintegrations described in this chapter have been assigned, on general grounds of probability and reaction rate, to strong, electromagnetic and weak interactions. In all processes, the conservation of energy, momentum, and charge has been regarded as axiomatic, and there is strong evidence to support the view that lepton and baryon numbers can be assigned to particles in the fermion groups in such a way that the total L and B numbers are always conserved in any process. At the same time, there are certain quantities, including the isospin number (T) and the strangeness number (S), which are conserved in strong interactions but not in weak interactions. A more fundamental property, the *parity* of a state formed by a group of particles, is known to be conserved, to a high degree of accuracy, in strong and electromagnetic interactions, that is, in ordinary nuclear and atomic transitions. In 1956 it was discovered that parity is *not* conserved in weak-interaction processes, for example in the emission of beta particles by nuclei, where a neutrino or antineutrino accompanies the emission. Since the neutrino, as a fermion of zero mass, possesses special properties relating to parity, the following discussion is largely based on neutrino behavior. At the same time, it should be emphasized that parity is not conserved in any of the weak-interaction changes studied to date, whether neutrinos are involved or not.

* G. F. Chew, M. Gell-Mann, and A. H. Rosenfeld, Scientific American, **210**, No. 2, 74. (1964).
† W. B. Fowler and N. P. Samios, "The Omega-Minus Experiment," Scientific American, **211**, No. 4, 36 (1964).
‡ P. Morrison, "The Overthrow of Parity," Scientific American, **196**, No. 4, 45 (1957); S. B. Treiman, "The Weak Interactions," Scientific American, **200**, No. 3, 72 (1959).

The neutrino is unique in being a fermion of zero rest mass, which must therefore travel at speed c relative to any reference frame and which possesses no interactions except the weak Fermi type described in the theory of beta decay (Section 9.11). An important question arising from this theory is whether or not there are two kinds of neutrino, the particle proper and its antiparticle, emitted in beta-decay processes. Several experiments were carried out to settle this question, but at first no conclusive results were obtained. Later on the neutrino-capture experiments of Reines and Cowan, compared with those of Davis, indicated that both kinds of neutrino exist. However, there remains a theoretical difficulty. In what ways can a neutrino differ from an antineutrino, since they have the same spin, also zero charge and mass? A possible answer to this question is provided by applying Dirac's equation [Equation (7.9.3)] to the neutrino problem.

In the Dirac theory of fermions, a Hamiltonian operator H is adopted of the form

$$H = c(\alpha \, \mathbf{P}) + \beta m_0 c^2, \qquad \text{[Equation (7.9.8)]}$$

where α_1, α_2, α_3, and β are four operators of unit magnitude anticommuting with each other. In the special case of a fermion with zero rest mass, the β term drops out and only three anticommuting operators are required. In 1929 Weyl pointed out that the Pauli 2×2 matrix operators σ_1, σ_2, and σ_3 (Section 7.8) can be used for this purpose, so that the Hamiltonian becomes

$$H = c(\sigma \, \mathbf{P}) \qquad \text{[10.7.1]}$$

and the state function ψ contains two components only, compared with four components in the Dirac theory. The eigenvalues of H for a free neutrino are necessarily

$$E = \pm cP \qquad \text{see Equation (5.6.5)}$$

so we can imagine the spin vector σ as being either parallel or antiparallel to the momentum vector $\mathbf{P}$. In other words, the neutrino and antineutrino can be distinguished, in principle, by their direction of spin, which is either left-handed or right-handed along the direction of motion.

The Hamiltonian expression [Equation (10.7.1)] is arbitrary with respect to sign, so we cannot say which particle is right-handed and which left-handed, but the principle of distinction is clear in the Weyl theory. In terms of the particle "helicity," defined as the quantity

$$\mathscr{H} = \frac{(\sigma \, \mathbf{P})}{|P|}, \qquad \text{[10.7.2]}$$

we have $\mathscr{H} = \pm 1$ for neutrinos. Experimental tests are then needed to find out the helicity of the neutrino and antineutrino separately.

The two-component theory of neutrinos was not adopted at first because it violates the principle of conservation of parity. This may be seen from Figure 10.5, where a nuclear process involving the emission of a neutrino is viewed directly and simultaneously in a mirror, the spatial reflection corresponding to a test for parity (Section 7.4). If parity is conserved in all processes, no over-all change can be introduced by mirror reflection, so that right-handed events are as probable as left-handed events. In the Weyl theory, on the other hand, a definite helicity is assigned to the neutrino. If this particle is left-handed, the mirror image is right-handed and so the image cannot correspond to the emission of a neutrino proper. On these grounds the Weyl theory was rejected, since parity was supposed to be conserved.

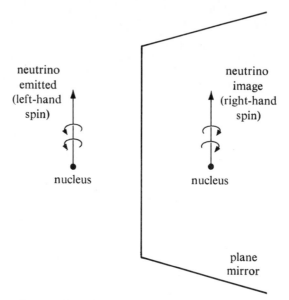

FIGURE 10.5   *The introduction of a definite helicity of the neutrino leads to violation of the conserva-tion of parity. If a left-handed neutrino is emitted in some nuclear process, its image in a mirror is right-handed. Weyl's theory assigns one direction of spin only to the neutrino, and is therefore inconsistent with parity conservation.*

The situation changed radically in 1956,[*] when Lee and Yang pointed out that conserva-tion of parity is apparently violated in the two-meson and three-meson decay modes of the K mesons [Equations (10.3.9) and (10.3.10)]. They suggested that this feature is character-istic of all weak interactions, including those responsible for beta decay, and immediately many experiments were carried out to test the idea. If parity is conserved, beta particles emitted from nuclei which have their spins aligned should travel with equal probability in all directions. This is not the case if neutrinos or antineutrinos of definite helicity are emitted simultaneously with the electrons. Wu and her collaborators[†] set up an apparatus with Co[60] nuclei aligned in a strong magnetic field at very low temperatures. They found that the emitted positrons had a nonisotropic angular distribution with respect to the nuclear spin direction; this result could only be explained as due to a failure in the parity-conservation rule. Many other experiments were performed in corroboration of this conclusion. In general the results are in agreement with the predictions of the two-component theory and with a dominant "$V - A$" interaction responsible for beta decay (see Section 9.11).

A particularly clear example of spatial asymmetry introduced by the helicity property of neutrinos is provided by the sequence of decays from pion via muon to electron, depicted in Figure 10.6. A positive pion at rest decays into a muon plus neutrino

$$\pi^+ \to \mu^+ + \nu,$$ [10.7.3]

where we have assumed that the lepton number is zero for the pion and that the neutrino has properties similar to the particle associated with *positron* emission by nuclei. The muon and neutrino must travel in opposite directions and the conservation of angular momentum

* T. D. Lee and C. N. Yang, Phys. Rev., **104**, 254 (1956).
† C. S. Wu, E. Ambler, R. Hayward, D. Hoppes, and R. Hudson, Phys. Rev., **105**, 1413 (1957).

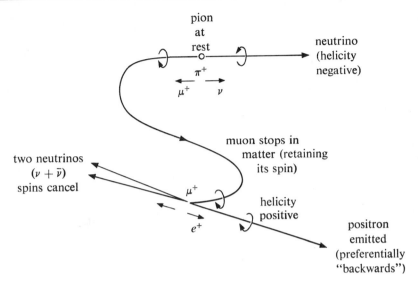

FIGURE 10.6   *The sequence of decays from pion through muon to electron. The muon and neutrino are given off in opposite directions with the same helicity. The muon retains its spin (under suitable conditions) until it stops, when two neutrinos (ν + ν̄) and a positron are emitted. The neutrinos travel in the same direction in most cases, and the positron is emitted preferentially in the backwards direction (relative to the muon direction). It follows that the positron has the opposite helicity to the original neutrino.*

requires that their spins be in the same sense relative to their direction of motion, that is, the muon adopts the same helicity as the neutrino. The muon retains this polarization, in the absence of strong magnetic fields or other interactions, until it comes to rest, when it decays to give a positron plus two neutrinos

$$\mu^+ \rightarrow e^+ + \nu + \bar{\nu}. \qquad [10.7.4]$$

Here it should be pointed out that the evidence of the electron energy spectrum obtained in muon decay (Figure 10.3) is consistent with the conservation of lepton number in Equation (10.7.4). Also we can see that, in the majority of cases, the electron energy is near the upper limit (55 MeV), so that the two neutrinos must be emitted nearly in the same direction. The helicity rule then predicts that their total spin must be zero in most cases. It follows that the muon spin, which was aligned parallel or antiparallel with the muon direction before decay, must be transferred to the positron.

Under these conditions, the helicity of the neutrinos causes an appreciable polarization of the positrons finally emitted. Moreover, by analogy with the beta decay of aligned nuclei, we might expect a spatial asymmetry in emission of the positrons, relative to the muon direction before decay. Such a spatial asymmetry was observed, both in photographic-emulsion studies and in counting experiments, the positrons being preferentially emitted in the "backwards" direction, that is, at 180° to the muon direction. This observation enables us to state that the positron helicity must be predominantly *opposite* to the muon helicity, which in turn was fixed by the helicity of the first neutrino emitted [Equation (10.7.2)]. Thus if the positron helicity can be found, that of the neutrino is known. Experimentally it is found that positrons emerging from the pion-muon decay sequence have positive helicity, which implies negative helicity for the muons, hence negative helicity for the neutrino first emitted. The experimental results on electrons derived from negative muons indicate that the antineutrino possesses positive helicity.

The adoption of the two-component theory of neutrinos means the abandonment of parity conservation in beta-decay and meson-decay processes, but simultaneously a new relation between matter and antimatter is introduced. Since the neutrino and antineutrino possess opposite helicities, the operation of mirror reflection (Figure 10.5) is linked to the transformation from matter to antimatter, or vice versa. Thus the spatial asymmetries observed in similar processes involving particles and antiparticles should always be of opposite sign. The experimental results show that the weak-interaction Hamiltonians, which are not invariant under spatial reflections alone, are nevertheless invariant when the reflection is combined with a transformation between matter and antimatter—the so-called "charge-conjugation" transformation.

This principle can also be expressed in operator form, if we introduce an operator C representing charge conjugation and an operator P (the parity operator) corresponding to mirror reflection. Then the combined operation CP (or PC instead, since the operators commute) applied to a given type of physical process results in a process which also is physically observable. In other words, such processes are "CP invariant." It is believed that strong-interaction processes are separately C invariant and P invariant, but, as we have seen, weak-interaction processes are not P invariant although they are probably CP invariant.

There is a very general theorem in quantum field theory to the effect that all processes must be invariant under the combined operation CPT, where T is a "time-reversal" operator corresponding to the substitution of $(-t)$ for $(+t)$ in all mathematical expressions describing the process. The property of CP invariance therefore implies T invariance, that is, invariance under time reversal. However, it is now a matter of investigation whether CP invariance is a general property of weak interactions. For example, the disintegration of the long-lived K_2^0 "particle" into two pions is forbidden under CP invariance (see Section 10.3.b). The process is certainly rare but some recent experiments suggest that it does occur. Further experiments are needed to decide whether time-reversal invariance is generally obeyed.

The theory of weak interactions was put on a firm basis by the introduction of a *universal Fermi interaction*, partly the work of Feynman and Gell-Mann.* This theory is based on the idea that all weak interactions can be traced to simple combinations of the Fermi-type four-particle interactions exemplified by Equation (9.11.11). With the aid of coupling constants derived from beta-decay data, it is possible to calculate the mean lifetime of the muon, also the rate of pion decay into an electron and neutrino [Equation (10.3.2)]—and both of these quantities are correctly given by the "$V - A$" interaction of beta decay (Section 9.11.d).

Certain difficulties remain, however, notably the question whether the neutrinos observed in nuclear processes are identical with those produced in meson decay. Reasons have been adduced for the existence of two types of neutrino, one type coupled to electrons and the other to muons. Experimental evidence on this point has been obtained at Brookhaven, where the 33 GeV proton synchrotron is a powerful source of energetic neutrinos produced by pion decay. The neutrino beam has been detected after passing through a great thickness of steel by the reactions induced in a large spark chamber (Plate II). Whereas beta-decay neutrinos normally emit electrons when they are captured by nucleons [Equation (9.11.10)] the high-energy neutrinos were found to produce muons instead. It is therefore supposed

* R. P. Feynman and M. Gell-Mann, *Phys. Rev.*, **109**, 193 (1957).

that the pion-produced neutrinos are coupled to muons and the positive pion decay process is written

$$\pi^+ \to \mu^+ + \nu_\mu. \qquad [10.7.5]$$

By way of contrast, the muon decays to produce one "muon-neutrino" (ν_μ) and one "electron-neutrino" (ν_e)

$$\mu^+ \to e^+ + \nu_\mu + \bar\nu_e. \qquad [10.7.6]$$

Both types of neutrinos possess antiparticles and their formal properties are similar throughout.

Further analysis of the conservation rules shows that many of them can be linked to symmetry principles based on the idea of invariance. In Section 7.4 we stated that parity is conserved if the Hamiltonian function is invariant under spatial reflections of the mirror-image type. The experimental results now show that this invariance is not exhibited by weak interactions, although all the evidence indicates that strong and electromagnetic interaction processes are reflection invariant. Certain types of invariance are almost self-evident in any system of equations describing particle behavior; for example, we can impose the condition that interaction potentials are invariant under changes of coordinate axes in space and time. This type of invariance leads to the conservation of energy and linear momentum. Similarly, invariance under rotation of the axes is linked to the conservation of angular momentum. Thus the basic principles of mechanics can be illustrated as symmetry principles in space and time. The situation becomes less clear in electromagnetic theory, where we have to consider transformations in "isospace," that is, the "space" in which the isospin number (T) represents the quantized magnitude of an axial vector. In isospace, invariance under a change of scale is linked to the conservation of electric charge, which applies in all physical processes yet investigated. Axis rotation in isospace should be linked to the conservation of isospin; that is, the quantum number T should be constant, but, as we have seen, this number is conserved in strong-interaction processes only. Some work has been done to extend the invariance principle to the conservation of lepton number (L) and baryon number (B), but more knowledge of the relations between particles is needed before these conservation rules can be fully understood.

FURTHER READING

Cosmic rays:
    J. E. HOOPER and M. SCHARFF, *The Cosmic Radiation* (Methuen Monographs, J. Wiley & Sons, New York, 1958).
    G. D. ROCHESTER and J. G. WILSON, *Cloud Chamber Photographs of the Cosmic Radiation* (Academic Press, Inc., New York, 1952).
Meson discoveries:
    C. F. POWELL, "Mesons," in *Reports on Progress in Physics* (Physical Society, London, 1950, Vol. XIII).
Elementary Particles:
    C. N. YANG, *Elementary Particles* (Princeton University Press, Princeton, New Jersey, 1962).
    K. W. FORD, *The World of Elementary Particles* (Blaisdell Publishing Co., New York, 1963).
    R. D. HILL, *Tracking Down Particles* (W. A. Benjamin, Inc., New York, 1963).

Particle interactions:

E. FERMI, *Elementary Particles* (Yale University Press, New Haven, Connecticut, 1951).
Parity Experiments:

C. S. WU, "The Neutrino" in *Theoretical Physics in the 20th Century*, editors, M. Fierz and V. F. Weisskopf (Interscience Publishers, New York, 1960).
Invariance principles:

N. KEMMER, J. C. POLKINGHORNE, and D. L. PURSEY, "Invariance in Elementary-particle Physics," in Reports on Progress in Physics, Vol. XXII, 1959, Physical Society, London.

PROBLEMS FOR CHAPTER 10

DATA REQUIRED:

Speed of light *in vacuo*:	$c = 3.0 \times 10^8$ m/sec
Elementary charge:	$e = 1.6 \times 10^{-19}$ C
Planck's constant:	$h = 6.6 \times 10^{-34}$ J sec
	$\hbar = 1.05 \times 10^{-34}$ J sec
Electronic rest mass:	$m_e = 9.1 \times 10^{-31}$ kg
	$m_e c^2 = 0.51$ MeV
Proton rest mass:	$m_p = 1.67 \times 10^{-27}$ kg
	$m_p c^2 = 938$ MeV

10.1. The "Crab" nebula is the remains of a supernova and it may possibly be a source of cosmic rays. If the observed magnetic field of strength $B = 10^{-7}$ weber/m² is spread over a region of diameter 6×10^{16} m, what is the maximum kinetic energy of singly charged particles retained in orbit within this region? What is the maximum kinetic energy of bare nuclei of atomic number $Z = 10$?

10.2. (a) Use the energy-loss formula of Equation (9.4.13), together with the data of Figure 9.27 to find the total range in standard air of a muon with initial kinetic energy 4 MeV.

(b) Given that the muons of this energy emitted in pion decay have a mean range of 600 microns in photographic emulsion, estimate the ratio of ranges in air and emulsion for these particles.

(c) Also show that, in this low-velocity region, the muons have a mean range about 5.5 times that of protons with the same initial kinetic energy.

10.3. Assuming that interplanetary space is permeated with magnetic fields of mean strength 10^{-8} weber/m², calculate the least energy of a proton which can travel from the Sun to the Earth (a distance of 1.5×10^8 km) without turning back toward the Sun.

10.4. Assuming that the effective radius of a nucleus is given by Equation (9.3.12) $(r = r_0 \sqrt[3]{A})$ with $r_0 = 1.3$ fermi and the Z, A relation is given by Equation (9.3.15)

$$Z = \frac{A}{2 + 0.015A^{2/3}},$$

estimate the value of the atomic mass number A at which the first Bohr radius $(n = 1)$ of a μ-mesic atom is equal to the nuclear radius. (Muon mass = $207\ m_e$).

10.5. If negatively charged pions can form "π-mesic atoms" what is the wavelength of radiation emitted when a pion, of mass $273\ m_e$, passes from the $n = 2$ to the $n = 1$ state in an atom of aluminum $(Z = 13)$?

10.6. In rare cases, a charged pion (of mass 273 m_e) decays to give an electron plus a neutrino. In such an event what is the kinetic energy of the electron emitted?

10.7. Pi mesons produced in a high-energy accelerator describe paths in the fringing magnetic field, of mean strength 0.1 weber/m², with radius of curvature 10 m. From these data find:

   (i) the kinetic energy per pion, if the rest mass is 273 m_e;

   (ii) the pion speed relative to the laboratory;

   (iii) the measured mean lifetime of the pions under these conditions if the mean lifetime at rest is 2.5 × 10⁻⁸ sec.

10.8. If a neutral pion decays in flight into two photons, show that the rest-mass energy of the pion is equal to

$$m_0 c^2 = 2(E_1 E_2)^{1/2} \sin \tfrac{1}{2}\theta,$$

where E_1 and E_2 are the photon energies and θ is the angle between the photon directions (in the laboratory frame of reference).

10.9. Calculate the rest mass and kinetic energy of a neutral kaon observed to decay into two charged particles as a "*V* event" if (i) the particles are identified as pions with tracks at right angles in the laboratory frame *and* (ii) the pion tracks have radii of curvature 0.8 m and 1.6 m, respectively, in a magnetic field of strength 0.85 weber/m². (Take pion rest mass = 273 m_e).

10.10. Find the least bombarding energy (K_0) for protons to produce a pair of xi particles in a nucleon-nucleon collision, given that each of these particles has a rest mass 1.4 times that of the proton.

10.11. Decide whether or not the strangeness number S is conserved in electromagnetic transitions by considering the following possible photonic decays of the strange particles:

$$K^0 \rightarrow \gamma + \pi^0 \qquad \text{NOT observed}$$
$$\Lambda^0 \rightarrow \gamma + n^0 \qquad \text{NOT observed}$$
$$\Sigma^+ \rightarrow \gamma + p^+ \qquad \text{NOT observed}$$
$$\Sigma^0 \rightarrow \gamma + \Lambda^0 \qquad \text{OBSERVED}$$
$$\Sigma^0 \rightarrow \gamma + K^0 \qquad \text{NOT observed}$$
$$\Xi^0 \rightarrow \gamma + \Lambda^0 \qquad \text{NOT observed.}$$

10.12. Apply the known conservation rules to predict whether the following reactions are possible, and, if so, what the reaction rate is likely to be. In each case, decide whether the process is (i) absolutely forbidden (on grounds of energy, angular momentum, baryon number, lepton number, or charge number) or (ii) observable in weak interactions only, or (iii) allowed for strong and electromagnetic interactions.

   (a) $\pi^- + p^+ \rightarrow n^0 + \gamma$

   (b) $\pi^- + d^+ \rightarrow 2n^0 + \pi^0$

   (c) $\pi^- + d^+ \rightarrow 2n^0$

   (d) $K^+ \rightarrow e^+ + \pi^0 + \nu_e$

   (e) $K^- + p^+ \rightarrow \Sigma^- + \pi^+$

   (f) $(\bar{p})^- + p^+ \rightarrow \Lambda^0 + \overline{\Lambda}^0$

   (g) $\Lambda^0 \rightarrow \pi^+ + \pi^-$.

APPENDIX I

Fundamental Physical Constants
(*NAS–NRC committee 1963.*)

Speed of light *in vacuo*:	$c = 2.99793 \times 10^8$ m/sec
Planck's constant:	$h = 6.6256 \times 10^{-34}$ J sec
	$\hbar = 1.0545 \times 10^{-34}$ J sec
Elementary charge:	$e = 1.6021 \times 10^{-19}$ C
Rest masses and energy equivalents:	
Electron: $m_e = 9.1091 \times 10^{-31}$ kg $= 0.000549$ u	
$m_e c^2 = 0.51101$ MeV	
Proton: $m_p = 1.6725 \times 10^{-27}$ kg $= 1.007277$ u	
$m_p c^2 = 938.26$ MeV	
Neutron: $m_n = 1.6748 \times 10^{-27}$ kg $= 1.008665$ u	
$m_n c^2 = 939.55$ MeV	
H^1 atom: $m_H = 1.6734 \times 10^{-27}$ kg $= 1.007825$ u	
$m_H c^2 = 938.77$ MeV	
Number of molecules per kilomole:	$N^* = 6.023 \times 10^{26}$
Boltzmann's constant:	$k = 1.381 \times 10^{-23}$ J/°K

APPENDIX II-A

Periodic Classification of the Elements
Based on Atomic Number (Z)

Group I	II	III	IV	V	VI	VII	0	Shells Complete
$_1$H							$_2$He	$1s$
$_3$Li	$_4$Be	$_5$B	$_6$C	$_7$N	$_8$O	$_9$F	$_{10}$Ne	$1; 2s, 2p$
$_{11}$Na	$_{12}$Mg	$_{13}$Al	$_{14}$Si	$_{15}$P	$_{16}$S	$_{17}$Cl	$_{18}$A	$1; 2; 3s, 3p$
$_{19}$K	$_{20}$Ca	$_{21}$Sc	(First Transition Series)					$1; 2; 3; 4s$
		$_{31}$Ga	$_{32}$Ge	$_{33}$As	$_{34}$Se	$_{35}$Br	$_{36}$Kr	plus $4p$
$_{37}$Rb	$_{38}$Sr	$_{39}$Y	(Second Transition Series)					$1; 2; 3; 4s, 4p, 4d; 5s$
		$_{49}$In	$_{50}$Sn	$_{51}$Sb	$_{52}$Te	$_{53}$I	$_{54}$Xe	plus $5p$
$_{55}$Cs	$_{56}$Ba	$_{57}$La	(Lanthanides) (Third Transition Series)					plus $4f, 5d, 6s$
		$_{81}$Tl	$_{82}$Pb	$_{83}$Bi	$_{84}$Po	$_{85}$At	$_{86}$Em	plus $6p$
$_{87}$Fr	$_{88}$Ra	$_{89}$Ac	(Actinides) ...					plus $7s, 5f$

Transition Series: completing subshell

1. $_{22}$Ti $\quad$ $_{23}$V $\quad$ $_{24}$Cr $\quad$ $_{25}$Mn $\quad$ $_{26}$Fe $\quad$ $_{27}$Co $\quad$ $_{28}$Ni $\quad$ $_{29}$Cu $\quad$ $_{30}$Zn $\qquad\qquad$ $3d$

2. $_{40}$Zr $\quad$ $_{41}$Nb $\quad$ $_{42}$Mo $\quad$ $_{43}$Tc $\quad$ $_{44}$Ru $\quad$ $_{45}$Rh $\quad$ $_{46}$Pd $\quad$ $_{47}$Ag $\quad$ $_{48}$Cd $\qquad\qquad$ $4d$

3. $_{72}$Hf $\quad$ $_{73}$Ta $\quad$ $_{74}$W $\quad$ $_{75}$Re $\quad$ $_{76}$Os $\quad$ $_{77}$Ir $\quad$ $_{78}$Pt $\quad$ $_{79}$Au $\quad$ $_{80}$Hg $\qquad\qquad$ $5d$

Lanthanides (Rare Earths):   completing subshell $4f$

$_{58}$Ce $\quad$ $_{59}$Pr $\quad$ $_{60}$Nd $\quad$ $_{61}$Pm $\quad$ $_{62}$Sm $\quad$ $_{63}$Eu $\quad$ $_{64}$Gd $\quad$ $_{65}$Tb $\quad$ $_{66}$Dy $\quad$ $_{67}$Ho $\quad$ $_{68}$Er $\quad$ $_{69}$Tm $\quad$ $_{70}$Yb $\quad$ $_{71}$Lu

Actinides: completing subshell $5f$

$_{90}$Th $\quad$ $_{91}$Pa $\quad$ $_{92}$U $\quad$ $_{93}$Np $\quad$ $_{94}$Pu $\quad$ $_{95}$Am $\quad$ $_{96}$Cm $\quad$ $_{97}$Bk $\quad$ $_{98}$Cf $\quad$ $_{99}$E $\quad$ $_{100}$Fm $\quad$ $_{101}$Mv $\quad$ $_{102}$(No) $\quad$ $_{103}$Lw

APPENDIX II-B

Mean Atomic Weights
(*on the C^{12} scale*)

Element	Symbol	Atomic Weight	Atomic Number	Element	Symbol	Atomic Weight	Atomic Number
Actinium	Ac	(227)	89	Germanium	Ge	72.59	32
Aluminum	Al	26.98	13	Gold	Au	196.97	79
Americium	Am	*	95	Hafnium	Hf	178.49	72
Antimony	Sb	121.75	51	Helium	He	4.00	2
Argon	A	39.95	18	Holmium	Ho	164.93	67
Arsenic	As	74.92	33	Hydrogen	H	1.008	1
Astatine	At	*	85	Indium	In	114.82	49
Barium	Ba	137.34	56	Iodine	I	126.90	53
Berkelium	Bk	*	97	Iridium	Ir	192.2	77
Beryllium	Be	9.01	4	Iron	Fe	55.85	26
Bismuth	Bi	208.98	83	Krypton	Kr	83.80	36
Boron	B	10.81	5	Lanthanum	La	138.91	57
Bromine	Br	79.91	35	Lawrencium	Lw	*	103
Cadmium	Cd	112.40	48	Lead	Pb	207.19	82
Calcium	Ca	40.08	20	Lithium	Li	6.94	3
Californium	Cf	*	98	Lutecium	Lu	174.97	71
Carbon	C	12.01	6	Magnesium	Mg	24.31	12
Cerium	Ce	140.12	58	Manganese	Mn	54.94	25
Cesium	Cs	132.91	55	Mendelevium	Mv	*	101
Chlorine	Cl	35.45	17	Mercury	Hg	200.59	80
Chromium	Cr	52.00	24	Molybdenum	Mo	95.94	42
Cobalt	Co	58.93	27	Neodymium	Nd	144.24	60
Copper	Cu	63.54	29	Neon	Ne	20.18	10
Curium	Cm	*	96	Neptunium	Np	*	93
Dysprosium	Dy	162.50	66	Nickel	Ni	58.71	28
Einsteinium	E	*	99	Niobium	Nb	92.91	41
Emanation	Em	*	86	Nitrogen	N	14.01	7
Erbium	Er	167.26	68	(Nobelium)	No	*	102
Europium	Eu	151.96	63	Osmium	Os	190.2	76
Fermium	Fm	*	100	Oxygen	O	16.00	8
Fluorine	F	19.00	9	Palladium	Pd	106.4	46
Francium	Fr	*	87	Phosphorus	P	30.97	15
Gadolinium	Gd	157.25	64	Platinum	Pt	195.09	78
Gallium	Ga	69.72	31	Plutonium	Pu	*	94

Mean Atomic Weights (*continued*)

Element	Symbol	Atomic Weight	Atomic Number	Element	Symbol	Atomic Weight	Atomic Number
Polonium	Po	(210)	84	Tantalum	Ta	180.95	73
Potassium	K	39.10	19	Technetium	Tc	*	43
Praseodymium	Pr	140.91	59	Tellurium	Te	127.60	52
Promethium	Pm	*	61	Terbium	Tb	158.92	65
Protoactinium	Pa	(231)	91	Thallium	Tl	204.37	81
Radium	Ra	(226)	88	Thorium	Th	(232)	90
Rhenium	Re	186.2	75	Thulium	Tm	*	69
Rhodium	Rh	102.91	45	Tin	Sn	118.69	50
Rubidium	Rb	85.47	37	Titanium	Ti	47.90	22
Ruthenium	Ru	101.07	44	Tungsten	W	183.85	74
Samarium	Sm	150.35	62	Uranium	U	(238)	92
Scandium	Sc	44.96	21	Vanadium	V	50.94	23
Selenium	Se	78.96	34	Xenon	Xe	131.30	54
Silicon	Si	28.09	14	Ytterbium	Yb	173.04	70
Silver	Ag	107.87	47	Yttrium	Y	88.91	39
Sodium	Na	22.99	11	Zinc	Zn	65.37	30
Strontium	Sr	87.62	38	Zirconium	Zr	91.22	40
Sulfur	S	32.06	16				

* Denotes elements which are made artificially or occur as short-lived members of radioactive series. The long-lived members of these series are represented by the most common isotope.

APPENDIX III-A

Table of Nuclides, Half-Lives, Rays Emitted, and
Energies of the Natural Radioactive Series

Nuclide	Identity	Half-Life	Max. Alpha Energy MeV	Max. Beta Energy MeV
Thorium	$_{90}Th^{232}$	1.4×10^{10} yr	4.0	
Mesothorium I	$_{88}Ra^{228}$	6.7 yr		0.055
Mesothorium II	$_{89}Ac^{228}$	6.1 hr		2.2
Radiothorium	$_{90}Th^{228}$	1.9 yr	5.4	
Thorium X	$_{88}Ra^{224}$	3.6 d	5.7	
Thoron	$_{86}Em^{220}$	56 sec	6.3	
Thorium A	$_{84}Po^{216}$	0.15 sec	6.8	
Thorium B	$_{82}Pb^{212}$	10.6 hr		0.58
Thorium C	$_{83}Bi^{212}$	61 min	6.1	2.25
Thorium C'	$_{84}Po^{212}$	3.0×10^{-7} sec	8.8	
Thorium C''	$_{81}Tl^{208}$	3.1 min		1.8
Uranium I	$_{92}U^{238}$	4.5×10^{9} yr	4.2	
Uranium X$_1$	$_{90}Th^{234}$	24 d		0.19
Uranium X$_2$	$_{91}Pa^{234}$	1.18 min		2.31
Uranium II	$_{92}U^{234}$	2.5×10^{5} yr	4.8	
Ionium	$_{90}Th^{230}$	7.6×10^{4} yr	4.7	
Radium	$_{88}Ra^{226}$	1620 yr	4.8	
Radon	$_{86}Em^{222}$	3.8 d	5.5	
Radium A	$_{84}Po^{218}$	3.05 min	6.0	
Radium B	$_{82}Pb^{214}$	27 min		1.03
Radium C	$_{83}Bi^{214}$	20 min	5.5	3.2
Radium C'	$_{84}Po^{214}$	1.6×10^{-4} sec	7.7	
Radium C''	$_{81}Tl^{210}$	1.3 min		2.3
Radium D	$_{82}Pb^{210}$	22 yr		0.06
Radium E	$_{83}Bi^{210}$	5.0 d		1.16
Radium F	$_{84}Po^{210}$	138 d	5.3	
Actinium U	$_{92}U^{235}$	7.1×10^{8} yr	4.6	
Uranium Y	$_{90}Th^{231}$	25.6 hr		0.30
Protoactinium	$_{91}Pa^{231}$	3.25×10^{4} yr	5.05	
Actinium	$_{89}Ac^{227}$	21.2 yr		0.043
Radioactinium	$_{90}Th^{227}$	18 d	6.0	
Actinium X	$_{88}Ra^{223}$	12 d	5.7	
Actinon	$_{86}Em^{219}$	4.0 sec	6.8	
Actinium A	$_{84}Po^{215}$	1.8×10^{-3} sec	7.4	
Actinium B	$_{82}Pb^{211}$	36 min		1.4
Actinium C	$_{83}Bi^{211}$	2.15 min	6.6	(0.6)
Actinium C'	$_{84}Po^{211}$	0.52 sec	7.4	
Actinium C''	$_{81}Tl^{207}$	4.8 min		1.44

APPENDIX III-B

Charts of the Natural Radioactive Series
1. *The "4n" series starting with Th^{232}.*

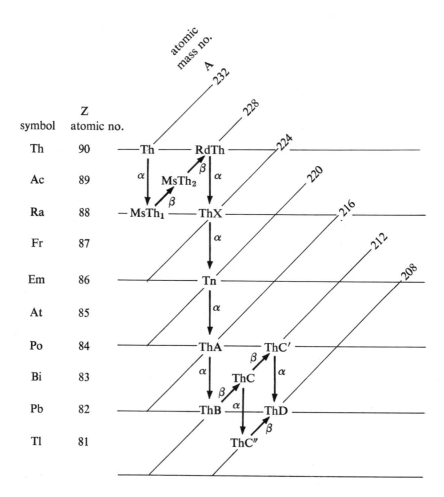

Symbols:

MsTh	Mesothorium	ThA	Thorium A
RdTh	Radiothorium	ThB	Thorium B
ThX	Thorium X	ThC	Thorium C
Tn	Thoron	ThD	Thorium D (Lead)

APPENDIX III-B

Charts of the Natural Radioactive Series
2. *The "4n + 2" series starting with U^{238}.*

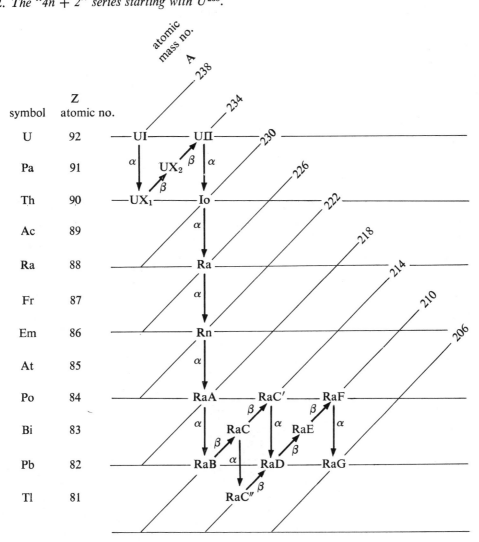

Symbols:

UI	Uranium I	Rn	Radon	RaE	Radium E
UX	Uranium X	RaA	Radium A	RaF	Radium F (Polonium)
UII	Uranium II	RaB	Radium B	RaG	Radium G (Lead)
Io	Ionium	RaC	Radium C		
Ra	Radium	RaD	Radium D		

499

APPENDIX III-B

Charts of the Natural Radioactive Series
3. *The "4n + 3" series starting with U²³⁵.*

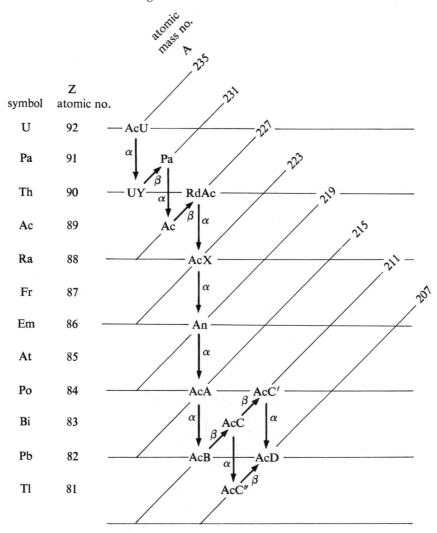

Symbols:

AcU	Actinium Uranium	An	Actinon
UY	Uranium Y	AcA	Actinium A
Pa	Protoactinium	AcB	Actinium B
Ac	Actinium	AcC	Actinium C
AcX	Actinium X	AcD	Actinium D (Lead)
RdAc	Radioactinium		

APPENDIX IV-A

Chart to Show the Relations of the Light
Nuclides from $Z = 0$ to $Z = 8$

*Stable nuclides are represented by solid squares,
beta-active nuclides by broken squares,
very unstable nuclides by double-broken lines.*

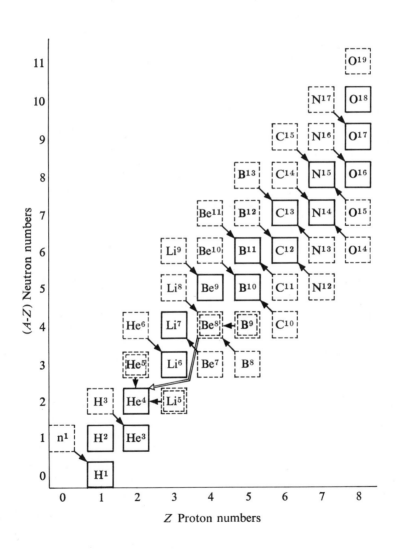

Z Proton numbers

APPENDIX IV-B

Table of Nuclear Data
for Light Nuclides

Atomic Number	Nuclide	(Stable) % in Natural Element	(Unstable) Mode of Decay	Half-Life	*Total Energy Release Q_0 in MeV
0	n^1		e^-	12 min	0.783
1	H^1	99.985			
	(D^2) H^2	0.015			
	(T^3) H^3		e^-	12.26 yr	0.0181
2	He^3	0.00013			
	He^4	99.99987			
	He^5		$n + He^4$	$\sim 2 \times 10^{-21}$ sec	
	He^6		e^-	0.81 sec	3.51
	He^7		e^-	$\sim 5 \times 10^{-5}$ sec	~ 10
3	Li^5		$p + He^4$	$\sim 10^{-21}$ sec	
	Li^6	7.42			
	Li^7	92.58			
	Li^8		e^-	0.85 sec	16.0
	Li^9		e^-	0.17 sec	14.1
4	Be^6		$p + Li^5$	$\sim 4 \times 10^{-21}$ sec	
	Be^7		EC	53 days	0.86
	Be^8		$2He^4$	$\sim 3 \times 10^{-16}$ sec	
	Be^9	100			
	Be^{10}		e^-	2.7×10^6 yr	0.56
	Be^{11}		e^-	13.6 sec	11.5
5	B^8		e^+	0.78 sec	18
	B^9		$p + Be^8$	3×10^{-19} sec	
	B^{10}	19.78			
	B^{11}	80.22			
	B^{12}		e^-	0.020 sec	13.4
	B^{13}		e^-	0.019 sec	13.4
6	C^{10}		e^+	19 sec	3.62
	C^{11}		e^+	20.5 min	1.98
	C^{12}	98.89			
	C^{13}	1.11			
	C^{14}		e^-	5730 yr	0.156
	C^{15}		e^-	2.25 sec	9.77
	C^{16}		e^-	0.74 sec	8.0

* Calculated from the nuclidic ground-state masses: thus Q_0 is the maximum energy release in negative beta decay or electron capture. Subtract 1.02 MeV for maximum positron energy.

Table of Nuclear Data for Light Nuclides (*continued*)

Atomic Number	Nuclide	(Stable) % in Natural Element	(Unstable) Mode of Decay	Half-Life	*Total Energy Release Q_0 in MeV
7	N^{12}		e^+	0.011 sec	17.6
	N^{13}		e^+	10.0 min	2.22
	N^{14}	99.64			
	N^{15}	0.36			
	N^{16}		e^-	7.35 sec	10.4
	N^{17}		e^-	4.14 sec	8.7
8	O^{14}		e^+	71 sec	5.15
	O^{15}		e^+	124 sec	2.76
	O^{16}	99.759			
	O^{17}	0.037			
	O^{18}	0.204			
	O^{19}		e^-	29 sec	4.81
	O^{20}		e^-	14 sec	3.8

* Calculated from the nuclidic ground-state masses: thus Q_0 is the maximum energy release in negative beta decay or electron capture. Subtract 1.02 MeV for maximum positron energy.

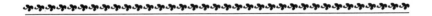

APPENDIX V-A

Classification of Particles

(*Excluding very unstable meson and hyperon states.*)

Main Groups	Particles		Antiparticles
Photon (spin $\hbar$)	Photon		
Leptons (spin $\frac{1}{2}\hbar$)	Neutrino (*e*)		Antineutrino (*e*)
	Neutrino (μ)		Antineutrino (μ)
	Electron		Positron
	Negative muon		Positive muon
Mesons (spin 0)	Positive pion	Neutral pion	Negative pion
	Positive kaon		Negative kaon
	Neutral kaon K^0		Neutral kaon $\bar{K}^0$
Baryons (spin $\frac{1}{2}\hbar$)	Proton		Antiproton
	Neutron		Antineutron
	Lambda hyperon		Antilambda
	Sigma hyperons $(+, 0, -)$		Antisigmas $(-, 0, +)$
	Xi hyperons $(-, 0)$		Antixis $(+, 0)$
(spin $\frac{3}{2}\hbar$)	Omega hyperon $(-)$		(?) Antiomega $(+)$

APPENDIX V-B

Particle Properties

Particle	Rest Mass (MeV)	Decay Schemes	Mean Lifetime (sec)
Photon γ	0	Stable	
Neutrino ν_e Antineutrino	0	Stable	
Neutrino ν_μ Antineutrino	≈ 0	Stable	
Electron e^- Positron e^+	0.51101	Stable	
Muon μ^- Muon μ^+	105.66	$e + \bar{\nu}_e + \nu_\mu$	2.200×10^{-6}
Pion π^+ Pion π^-	139.6	$\begin{Bmatrix} \mu + \nu_\mu \\ e + \nu_e \end{Bmatrix}$	2.55×10^{-8}
Pion π^0	135.0	$\begin{Bmatrix} 2\gamma \\ \gamma + e^- + e^+ \end{Bmatrix}$	1.8×10^{-16}
Kaon K^+ Kaon K^-	493.8	$\begin{Bmatrix} 2\pi \\ 3\pi \\ \mu + \nu_\mu \end{Bmatrix}$ and so forth	1.23×10^{-8}
Kaon K_1^0	498.0	2π	0.92×10^{-10}
Kaon K_2^0	498.0	$\begin{Bmatrix} 3\pi \\ \pi + \mu + \nu_\mu \\ \pi + e + \nu_e \end{Bmatrix}$	5.6×10^{-8}
Proton p^+ Antiproton	938.26	Stable	
Neutron n Antineutron	939.55	$p + e + \bar{\nu}_e$	1010
Lambda Λ^0 Antilambda	1115.4	$\begin{Bmatrix} p + \pi^- \\ n + \pi^0 \end{Bmatrix}$	2.62×10^{-10}
Sigma Σ^+ Antisigma	1189.4	$\begin{Bmatrix} p + \pi^0 \\ n + \pi^+ \end{Bmatrix}$	0.79×10^{-10}
Sigma Σ^0 Antisigma	1192.3	$\Lambda^0 + \gamma$	$< 1.0 \times 10^{-14}$
Sigma Σ^- Antisigma	1197.1	$n + \pi^-$	1.6×10^{-10}
Xi Ξ^0 Antixi	1314	$\Lambda^0 + \pi^0$	3.1×10^{-10}
Xi Ξ^- Antixi	1320.8	$\Lambda^0 + \pi^-$	1.74×10^{-10}
Omega	1680	$\begin{Bmatrix} \Xi + \pi \\ \Lambda + K \end{Bmatrix}$ and so forth	$\approx 10^{-10}$

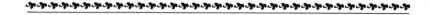

APPENDIX V-C

Resonant-State Properties

(1) *Meson States*

Symbol	Charges	Isospin	Spin	Parity	Energy (MeV)
η	0	0	0	−	549
ρ	$+0-$	1	1	−	763
ω	0	0	1	−	783
K^*	-0	$\frac{1}{2}$	1	−	891
φ	0	0	1	−	1020
f	0	0	2	+	1250

(2) *Baryon States*

Symbol	Isospin	Spin	Parity	Strangeness	Energy (MeV)
N^*_{33}	$\frac{3}{2}$	$\frac{3}{2}$	+	0	1238
N^*_{11}	$\frac{1}{2}$	$\frac{1}{2}$	+	0	1480
N^*_{13}	$\frac{1}{2}$	$\frac{3}{2}$	−	0	1520
N^*_{15}	$\frac{1}{2}$	$\frac{5}{2}$	+	0	1690
N^*_{37}	$\frac{3}{2}$	$\frac{7}{2}$	+	0	1920
Y^*_{13}	1	$\frac{3}{2}$	+	−1	1385
Y^*_{01}	0	$\frac{1}{2}$	−	−1	1405
Y^*_{03}	0	$\frac{3}{2}$	−	−1	1520
Ξ^*_{13}	$\frac{1}{2}$	$\frac{3}{2}$	+	−2	1530

* For a more complete account, see A. H. Rosenfeld, A. Barbaro-Galtieri, W. H. Barkas, P. L. Bastien, J. Kirz, and M. Roos, Rev. Mod. Phys., **36,** 977 (1964).

INDEX

ABCDEFGHIJ   7069876

ABOUT THE AUTHOR

DEREK LEONARD LIVESEY was born in Lancashire in 1923 and went from the local grammar school to St. John's College, Cambridge in 1940. After obtaining his B.A. degree, he spent three years on the British Atomic Energy project—at Liverpool University and at Cavendish Laboratory, Cambridge. He received his Ph.D. at Cambridge in 1947. Dr. Livesey spent the next ten years (apart from a year of research at Queen's University, Kingston, Ontario) teaching physics at two English boarding schools, Wellington and Oundle. Since 1957 he has been a member of the Department of Physics at the University of British Columbia, Vancouver.

Dr. Livesey's research work has been largely devoted to the application of the photographic emulsion method to problems in nuclear physics. In 1946 he was one of the originators of the concentrated emulsion technique, which led to important discoveries in several fields. Since 1960 he has been particularly interested in developing new methods of teaching physics in schools. After spending a year with Educational Services, Inc. in Massachusetts, he was partly responsible for preparing a two-year version of the P.S.S.C. program, which has been adopted for use in the schools of British Columbia.

THIS BOOK WAS SET IN
TIMES ROMAN AND BEMBO TYPES
BY THE UNIVERSITIES PRESS.
IT WAS DESIGNED BY THE STAFF OF
BLAISDELL PUBLISHING COMPANY.